FOOD, HOME
AND
SOCIETY
SECOND EDITION

Deirdre Madden

Gill and Macmillan

Published in Ireland by
Gill and Macmillan Ltd
Goldenbridge
Dublin 8
with associated companies throughout the world

© Deirdre Madden 1990
© Artwork, Gill and Macmillan Ltd 1990
Design and illustrations: Niche Ltd
Photo research: Anne Marie Ehrlich, Irish Press (Liam Flynn), The Irish Times
Cover design: Mark Loughran
Cover photos: The Slide File
Print origination in Ireland by
Seton Music Graphics Ltd, Cork
0 7171 1756 1

CONTENTS

To my parents

FOOD

1 NUTRITION

All human beings need food in order to survive. Food is necessary for growth, for supplying energy and for keeping us healthy.

In developing countries, food is often scarce and there is little choice in the foods which are available. In the western world, however, we have a wide variety of foods to choose from, making it easier to follow a healthy-eating pattern and lifestyle.

In spite of this, many people in the west choose to follow an unhealthy diet. This is due, perhaps, to a lack of understanding of nutrition or to lazy attitudes towards meal planning and good health. People are also influenced by high-powered advertising and marketing campaigns which encourage them to buy convenience foods, sweets and alcohol. These products are often high in kilocalories but low in nutritional value.

Bad food choices can result in a wide variety of nutritional disorders such as obesity, anaemia and vitamin deficiency. They can lead to even more serious diseases such as cancer and heart disease.

In order to ensure that we maximise our chances of a long and healthy life, it is necessary to increase our understanding of food and how it affects our bodies. We must learn to apply this knowledge to the choice, preparation and consumption of food throughout our lifetimes.

The western diet provides a wide variety of foods to choose from (Denis Hughes-Gilbey)

In developing countries scarcity of food leads to starvation (Hutchinson Library)

▶ UNDERSTANDING NUTRITION

CONSTITUENTS OF FOOD

All food is composed of complex chemical substances. Nutrition is the study of the chemical composition of foods and how the body utilises food. Each food is made up of one or more nutrients or constituents.

There are six groups of nutrients.

1. Proteins
2. Carbohydrates } macro-nutrients
3. Lipids

4. Vitamins
5. Mineral elements } micro-nutrients
6. Water

BASIC FUNCTIONS OF FOOD

1. For cell growth and repair.
2. To supply heat and energy (fuel) to the body.
3. To protect and regulate body processes, thus preventing disease.

Each type of body cell requires specific nutrients to build, repair and reproduce itself. For example, protein is required for the manufacture and maintenance of all cells. Energy foods such as carbohydrates and lipids are required to provide energy for the physical and chemical changes which take place in the cells. Calcium is needed for bone cells, iron for blood cells and so on.

Some facts about nutrients

- Each nutrient is made up of *molecules* which in turn are made up of complex arrangements of *elements*. For example, carbohydrates are made up of carbon, hydrogen and oxygen.

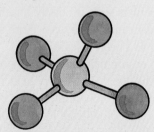

Fig 1.1 Model of a molecule

- *Organic nutrients* are those which contain carbon. They include proteins, carbohydrates, lipids and vitamins. *Inorganic nutrients* consist of the mineral elements such as iron, calcium and iodine.
- *The chemical formula* of a food molecule shows the total number of units (atoms) of each element in the molecule. For example, glucose is written:

$$C_6 H_{12} O_6$$

- *The basic structure* of organic nutrients usually consists of a chain which can be branched. In certain conditions, it forms a ring structure.

- Each nutrient has one or more functions in the body (*biological functions*).
- Nutrients are required by the body in amounts which vary according to a person's age, gender and activity. The estimated intake of nutrients required for good health is referred to as the *recommended daily allowance* (RDA).
- Nutrients which are required in large amounts are called *macro-nutrients*. They are measured in grams. Those needed in much smaller amounts, such as vitamins and minerals, are known as *micro-nutrients*. They are measured in milligrams (mg) or micrograms (μg).

$$1g = 1,000mg \qquad 1mg = 1,000μg$$

- Some foods such as milk contain several different nutrients. Others such as sugar may contain just one.
- Certain foods such as vegetables, fish and cheese are considered *nutritious*. But whether a food is nourishing or not really depends on the individual's requirements. For example, cow's milk is of little benefit to a person suffering from lactose intolerance, or wheat bread to a coeliac (a person with an intolerance to wheat).
- When essential nutrients are lacking in the diet, *deficiency symptoms* and/or diseases occur.
- *Cooking and processing* can affect nutrients.

Chain of Carbon atoms

$$-C-C-C-C-C-$$

Branched chain

$$-C-C-C-C-C-$$
$$-C-$$

Ring Structure

ENERGY AND FOOD

Energy can be defined as the capacity for doing work. When we eat food, its large, complex molecules must first be broken down by the digestive system into smaller, simpler molecules so that the food can be absorbed into the blood and used by the body.

Energy is released from food by a form of slow burning called *oxidation*. In this process, oxygen (taken in by the lungs) combines with the carbon in food to produce energy. The oxidation process can be written as a chemical formula as follows:

$$C_6H_{12}O_6 + 6O_2 \longrightarrow 6CO_2 + 6H_2O + energy$$

glucose + oxygen carbon dioxide + water + energy

Because this takes place within the cell, it is known as *cellular or internal respiration*.

ENZYMES

Enzymes are organic catalysts which control or accelerate chemical changes in living organisms without changing themselves. Enzymes are proteins which are secreted in solution by all living cells. They occur naturally in plants and animals. Thousands of chemical reactions are taking place in the body at any one time. Each stage is controlled by enzymes. They bring about many changes in digestion by breaking down large molecules into simpler substances. They play an important part in cellular respiration, excretion, fermentation and spoilage of foods, for example, browning and decay. Enzymes also control the natural cycle of food, that is — germination, growth, ripening and decomposition.

Fig 1.2 Enzymes break down large molecules into smaller ones

PROPERTIES OF ENZYMES
Every enzyme works under a specific set of conditions.
1. Each enzyme is involved in one reaction only and has no effect on any other. For example, a protein enzyme will not affect lipids.
2. pH: The pH environment is extremely important. Certain enzymes require a neutral environment, some an acid pH, while others require an alkaline pH.
   Example
   The enzyme pepsin will only work in an acid medium provided by hydrochloric acid in the stomach.
3. Temperature: Most enzymes work best at a moderate temperature.
   Animal enzymes — 37°C optimum temperature
   Plant enzymes — 25°C optimum temperature
   Low temperatures usually inhibit the activity of enzymes. High temperatures denature enzymes, which are proteins, in effect destroying them.
4. Co-enzymes: Some B-group vitamins act as co-enzymes without which certain enzymes could not function. For example, thiamine, riboflavin and B_6.
5. Hydrolysis: The chief reactions brought about by digestive enzymes involve the addition of water to a compound — the process known as *hydrolysis*.

$$C_{12}H_{22}O_{11} + H_2O \longrightarrow C_6H_{12}O_6 + C_6H_{12}O_6$$
(disaccharide)　　　　　(glucose)　+　(glucose)

Fig. 1.3 Hydrolysis Formula

METABOLISM
Metabolism is defined as the total of all the chemical reactions which take place in the body, in each living cell. Metabolic processes include the respiration, growth, excretion, nutrition and reproduction of each cell. Some metabolic processes involve the breakdown of chemical substances with the release of energy (as occurs in cellular respiration above). This is called *catabolism*. Others are involved

in building up new products — for example, cell walls — and require energy for the process (*anabolism*). (More on metabolism in Chapter 7.)

BASAL METABOLIC RATE
The speed at which a body uses up energy is known as its *metabolic rate*. This rises and falls as activity increases or decreases.

The basal metabolic rate (BMR) is the lowest level of energy required in order to keep the body warm and the internal organs functioning. It can be compared to the engine of a car when 'idling' or 'ticking over'. The basal metabolic rate is measured when an individual is lying down, fasting for at least twelve hours in a comfortable, warm room.

Fig 1.4 Some thin people can eat large amounts of food

Basal metabolism varies considerably between individuals, even those of similar age, size and gender. This accounts for the fact that some lean-type people can eat enormous amounts of food without getting fat while others put on weight in spite of a low kilocalorie/kilojoule intake. Basal metabolism accounts for almost two-thirds of a person's energy output. The remaining energy is used for muscle movement. The basal metabolic rate rises during periods of growth, such as in childhood and during pregnancy. As we grow older, our BMR decreases. Our kilocalorie/kilojoule intake should therefore reduce in proportion if we are to avoid gaining weight. The thyroid gland controls metabolism. An overactive or underactive thyroid results in an increased or decreased BMR.

Basal Metabolic Rate	per hour
Average man (70kg)	300kJ/70kcal
Average woman (60kg)	250kJ/60kcal
Child (1 year)	87kJ/21kcal
Average teenager	230-300kJ/55-70cal

The following activities will increase the metabolic rate:

Activity	kJ per hour	Kcal per hour
Sitting	360	85
Standing	368	90
Walking slowly	780	185
Light housework	840	200
Cycling	1,680	400
Dancing	1,790	450
Swimming	2,415	575
Walking upstairs	4,200	1,000

ENERGY BALANCE

To maintain a constant body weight, the energy intake of adults must equal energy output.

> Energy from food $=$ Energy for basal metabolism $+$ Energy for all activities

ENERGY INTAKE AND OBESITY

If more kilojoules/kilocalories are consumed than are necessary for the physical and chemical needs of the body, excess kJ/kc are converted into fat and stored under the skin as *adipose tissue*. When an excessive amount of fat is allowed to accumulate, it results in obesity.

The appetite is controlled by the *hypothalamus* in the brain. It is quite a reliable guide to the amount of food we need. However, appetite will not dictate the *choices* we make. These must be ruled by intelligent nutritional considerations.

ENERGY REQUIREMENTS

The amount of energy we need varies according to:
1. *Activity/occupation:* The greater the physical activity, the more kJ/kc are required. Active, manual jobs such as digging and sport require a greater energy intake than sedentary occupations such as studying or office work.
2. *Body size and composition:* Generally speaking, the larger the body, the greater the amount of energy required. On the other hand, a thin, nervous person may burn up more energy than a placid, fat person.
3. *Age:* From birth to adolescence, the amount of energy required increases. As the body ages, the energy requirement gradually reduces. During infancy and childhood, the amount of kJ/kc required per kilogram of body weight is greater than at any other time.

Running uses up large amounts of energy (S. and R. Greenhill)

4. *Pregnancy/lactation:* More energy is needed by women who are pregnant or breast feeding than they would normally require. This energy is needed for the healthy growth of the foetus and for milk production. Care must be taken, however, to avoid excessive weight gain during this time.
5. *Gender:* As the male body contains a higher rate of muscle to fat (which has a low metabolic rate) than that of women, it follows that men's energy requirements are higher (10-20%) than those of women of identical weight.
6. *Climate:* More kJ/kc are required in order to maintain body temperature in cold weather/climates than in warm weather/climates.

Daily Kilocalorie/Megajoule * requirements

	Female	Male
Child	1,400 kcal/5.9 mJ	1,400 kcal/5.9 mJ
Adolescent	2,300 kcal/9.6 mJ	2,800 kcal/11.7 mJ
Adult:		
active	2,200 kcal/9.2 mJ	3,500 kcal/14.7 mJ
sedentary	2,050 kcal/8.6 mJ	2,700 kcal/11.3 mJ
elderly	2,000 kcal/8.4 mJ	2,200 kcal/9.2 mJ
pregnant	2,700 kcal/10.0mJ	

* 1 megajoule = 1,000 kilojoules

Nutrients involved in the production/release of energy

Fats		Vitamin B group
Carbohydrates	+	Phosphates
Proteins		Iodine (thyroid gland)

MEASURING ENERGY

The energy obtained from food or used by the body may be measured in: (a) kilocalories (b) kilojoules.

A kilocalorie (kcal) is defined as the amount of heat required to raise the temperature of 1 litre of water by 1°C, that is from 21°C to 22°C.

A *kilojoule* (kJ) is the international unit of energy used by nutritionists today. *A joule is the work done in moving a force needed to accelerate a mass of 1 kilogram at the rate of 1 metre per second. A kilojoule is one thousand times greater.*

1 kilojoule (kJ) = 1,000 joules
1 megajoule (mJ) = 1,000 kJ

Both kilojoules and kilocalories are used in this book so that texts and food tables using either can be understood.

1 kilocalorie = 4.186 kilojoules (4.2 kJ, approx.)

To convert kilocalories to kilojoules, multiply by 4.2.

Example

100 ml milk = 65 kc x 4.2 = 273 kJ

ENERGY VALUE OF NUTRIENTS

The energy value of a food can be measured scientifically by calculating the amount of heat given off when it is burned. Food is oxidised under controlled conditions in a *calorimeter* and calculated in kJ/kc per gram.

When oxidised, it has been found that:

1g protein produces 4 kc/17 kJ
1g carbohydrate produces 4 kc/17 kJ
1g lipid produces 9 kc/38 kJ
1g alcohol produces 7 kc/29 kJ

Because most foods are a mixture of nutrients, more calculations must be made in order to arrive at the total energy value of a food. Luckily, such calculations have been worked out and listed in food tables*, usually in portions of 100g.

Example of calculation

100g milk contains 3.3 protein, 3.8 fat, 4.8 carbohydrate.

$$3.3 \times 4 = 13.2$$
$$3.8 \times 9 = 34.2$$
$$4.8 \times 4 = 19.2$$

Total = 66.6 kc
x 4.2
280 kilojoules

* See back of book.

▶PROTEIN

Life could not exist without proteins — they are the main molecules from which living cells are made. Proteins are the only nutrients which contain the element nitrogen. Nitrogen is vital for all cell manufacture and, therefore, for growth. For this reason, proteins are absolutely essential to the human diet.

ELEMENTAL COMPOSITION OF PROTEIN

Proteins are composed of carbon, hydrogen, oxygen and nitrogen (CHON). Some also contain small amounts of sulphur (S), phosphorus (P) and iron (Fe).

CHEMICAL STRUCTURE AND COMPOSITION

Proteins are large molecules with a complex chemical structure. Each protein is made up of smaller units called *amino acids* which are linked together in three-dimensional chains called *polypeptide chains*.

C = carbon atom
NH_2 = Amino group (alkaline)
COOH = carboxyl group (acid)
R is variable

In each amino acid, R represents a different combination of atoms linked into the carbon atom.

Example

Glycine: R = a hydrogen atom

Glycine

Methionine is an essential amino acid with a more complicated structure. Note that it contains sulphur.

Methionine

Basic structure of an Amino Acid

MORE ABOUT AMINO ACIDS

- They are relatively small molecules } For these reasons, amino acids can easily diffuse through the walls of the intestine.
- They are water-soluble.
- There are twenty common amino acids which can be arranged like beads in a necklace in a vast number of combinations to form proteins. One of the simplest proteins, *insulin*, contains about fifty amino acid units. Others like *haemoglobin* are made up of over five hundred. *Urease*, which is found in soya beans, contains 4,500 amino acids!

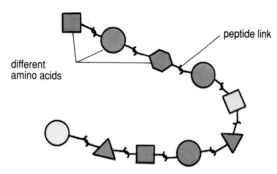

Proteins are formed from amino acid units

- Protein chains are formed when the alkaline amino group (NH₂) of one amino acid reacts with the acidic carboxyl (COOH) group of the next one. This joining is called a *peptide link* (CONH).

   The link takes place when the OH is removed from the carboxyl group and the H from the amino group to form one molecule of H₂O (water). This reaction is known as *condensation*. The large molecule formed from the two amino acids is called a *peptide* (or, more correctly, a dipeptide). When long chains of amino acids combine, they are known as a polypeptide chain.

Peptide link

- The reverse reaction — *hydrolysis* — occurs during digestion. The water components OH and H, which separated out when the link was formed, combine respectively with the carboxyl and amino groups of two amino acids, thus breaking the link and separating the larger peptide molecule into its two component amino acids.

THE ESSENTIAL AMINO ACIDS

The human body can manufacture or synthesise many of the amino acids it needs. These are known as the *non-essential amino acids*. However, there are eight amino acids which the human body cannot manufacture and which must be obtained ready-made from food. These are known as the *essential amino acids*. A further two essential amino acids are needed by children because they cannot make them fast enough for their own growing needs.

Essential amino acids	Some non-essential amino acids
Valine, Lysine	Glycine
Isoleucine	Cystine
Leucine	Cysteine
Methionine	Serine
Tryptophan	Tyrosine
Phenylalanine	Alanine
Threonine	Glutamic acid (used to make monosodium glutamate)
Arginine } children Histidine	

BIOLOGICAL VALUE OF PROTEIN

This is a measure of the quality of a protein. The biological value of a protein food is measured by the number of essential amino acids it contains in proportion to body needs. It is written as a percentage — %.

- Proteins which contain all the essential amino acids in the correct proportion have a *high biological value* (HBV) and are known as complete proteins. Most of these are from animal sources*.
- Proteins which are deficient in one or more of the essential amino acids are known as *low biological value* (LBV) or incomplete proteins. These are usually from vegetable sources*.

   Eggs have 100% biological value. This means that all the protein in eggs can be used by the body.

Food	Biological Value	Food	Biological Value
Eggs	100%	Rice	67%
Milk	95%	Wheat	53%
Meat/Fish	80-90%	Maize	40%
Soya bean	74%*	Gelatine	0%*

* Exceptions: Protein in soya bean, a vegetable food, has a relatively high biological value. Protein in gelatine, an animal food, has no biological value.

SUPPLEMENTARY/COMPLEMENTARY VALUE OF PROTEINS

Many proteins have the ability to make good the deficiency of another. For example, at one meal, a person might eat a food which is low in one amino acid along with another food which is a good source of this amino acid. The two foods combine to give all the essential amino acids. This is known as the *supplementary value of a protein*. For this reason, vegans can stay healthy on a totally vegetarian diet. Take the example of beans on toast. Wheat/bread is low in the essential amino acid, lysine, but high in methionine; pulses are high in lysine with reduced methionine. Other complementary proteins are maize and beans (often found together in Mexican cookery) and peanut butter sandwiches.

Some Important Proteins
Each protein has its own chemical name.

Animal		Vegetable	
myosin	– meat	gluten	– wheat
caseinogen	– cheese	glycine	– soya bean*
lactalbumin	– milk	excelsin	– nuts*
albumin	– egg	zein	– maize
gelatin	– bones	legumin	– pulses
haemoglobin	– blood		
collagen	– connective tissue		

* Good vegetable sources of essential amino acids.

CLASSIFICATION OF PROTEIN

Protein can be classified according to its structure or its biological value.

PROTEIN STRUCTURE

Although the protein molecule is basically a chain of amino acids, the chain formation can be arranged in various ways to make proteins with totally different properties.

1. GLOBULAR

These protein chains are formed into a roughly spherical shape, like a tangled ball of wool.

Example: albumin in egg white.

Globular

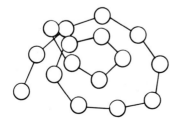

2. FIBROUS

These protein chains are straight or twisted into coils or zigzags.

Examples: collagen in connective tissue which is tough and non-elastic; elastin in arteries and gluten in flour have stretchy, elastic properties.

Fibrous

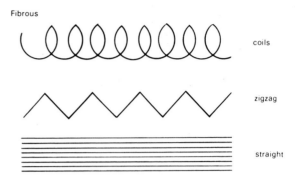

coils

zigzag

straight

3. CONJUGATED

These consist of a protein molecule chemically combined with a non-protein molecule, such as fat or pigment.

Examples: lipoproteins (lipid + protein); haemoglobin (pigment + protein); nucleoproteins (nucleic acid + protein = DNA).

Conjugated

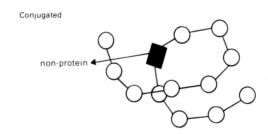

non-protein

SOURCES OF PROTEIN

Classification according to biological value:

- **HIGH BIOLOGICAL VALUE:**
  meat, fish, eggs, milk, cheese, yoghurt. Soya beans are a vegetable source.

- **LOW BIOLOGICAL VALUE:**
  nuts, pulse vegetables (including dried pulses such as lentils), whole cereals, bread. There are small amounts in some other vegetables such as potatoes.

Note: The main sources of high biological value proteins are animals. Rearing animals is a slow, expensive way of producing protein, compared with growing cereals, pulses etc. Bread and cereals are valuable sources of protein as they are eaten in relatively large quantities. New techniques have enabled artificial 'meats' to be manufactured from cheap sources such as soya beans (TVP/TSP) and from micro-organisms such as bacteria, yeasts and algae (page 52).

Foods high in protein

BIOLOGICAL FUNCTIONS OF PROTEIN
1. Essential for growth — very important in the diet of infants, children, adolescents, pregnant and nursing mothers.
2. Essential for repair of worn or damaged body cells, such as after injury or surgery.
3. It is a source of energy.
4. Protein forms enzymes, hormones and antibodies.

EFFECTS OF PROTEIN DEFICIENCY
1. Retarded growth in children.
2. Worn-out cells are not replaced. This prevents healing of wounds and delays recovery from illness.
3. In severe cases, as in underdeveloped countries, protein/calorie deficiency diseases such as kwashiorkor and marasmus may occur, particularly in children.
4. Malfunction of various organs due to hormone/enzyme deficiency.
5. Susceptibility to disease, due to lack of antibodies.

RECOMMENDED DAILY ALLOWANCE OF PROTEIN
One gram of protein is needed daily for each kilogram of body weight. More is required by children, adolescents, pregnant and nursing mothers. In western countries most people eat more protein than they need. At least one-third of protein intake should be of high biological value.

Child	30-50g
Average adult	55-70g
Pregnant female	90g

ENERGY VALUE OF PROTEIN
One gram of protein supplies 4 kcal/17 kJ of energy.

DEAMINATION (PROTEIN AS A SOURCE OF ENERGY)
Most of the protein we eat is broken down into amino acids and used by the body for structural and repair work. If more protein than necessary is consumed, the excess is broken down by the liver.
1. The amino group, NH_2, is removed from the molecule and converted into ammonia and then urea. This is excreted in the urine by the kidneys.
2. The carboxyl group, COOH, is oxidised to provide heat and energy or stored in the body as an energy reserve.

DENATURATION
Denaturation is a change in the nature of a protein — a breakdown of its structure. It generally occurs during food preparation, when a protein is heated, subjected to physical agitation or when chemicals are added to it.

During denaturation, the molecule unravels, losing its normal zigzag or globular structure and its elasticity so that it can no longer function as before. Denaturation is generally irreversible. It may be caused by:
1. *Heat:* The protein coagulates and shrinks. For example, egg yolk and white solidify, and milk forms a skin on top.
2. *Agitation such as whipping or shaking:* The egg white changes to foam. Cooking coagulates the foam in its expanded state. Examples include meringues and soufflés.
3. *Addition of chemicals:* Acids, alkalis, alcohol and enzymes (for example, rennin) may cause denaturation. For example lemon juice or vinegar will curdle milk. Rennin clots milk in cheese-making. Many poisons work by denaturing essential body proteins.

WHAT IS A PROPERTY?
A property of a material or object is a quality or physical characteristic which is part of it, such as density or strength.

Examples
Solid/liquid/gas
Hard/soft
High density/low density
Soluble/insoluble
Pliable/elastic/firm
Crystalline

Other questions to ask
What temperature does it boil/freeze/melt at?
Does it have an odour?
Does it evaporate easily? (volatile)
Is it thick and viscous?
Is it breakable?
What colour is it?
Is it shiny/matt?

PROPERTIES OF PROTEIN

1. Proteins are readily affected by heat.
- Heat causes *denaturation* — for example, coagulation and shrinkage.
- Some proteins change colour. For example, myoglobin in meat turns brown.
- Connective tissue dissolves in moist heat to form gelatine.
- Destruction of some amino acids, when food is overcooked, makes food indigestible.
2. *Solubility:* Most proteins are insoluble in water. Exception: (a) egg white; (b) connective tissue dissolves in *hot* water.
3. *Enzymes can cause coagulation* — for example, rennet in cheese-making.
4. *Elasticity:* Some fibrous proteins such as gluten are quite elastic.
5. *Maillard reaction:* This is a form of browning caused by the chemical interaction of carbohydrates and certain amino acids. Roast meat, potatoes and baked products such as cakes turn brown in this way.

Tests to show the presence of protein in food

1. Burning
Place a small amount of food such as egg white in a crucible. Place on a tripod over a bunsen burner. If the food contains protein, there is a distinctive smell of burning feathers.

2. Biuret Test
Put a small amount of egg white solution into a test tube. Add a few drops of potassium hydroxide and mix well. Add a few drops of 1% copper sulphate solution. Result: a violet colour appears if protein is present. A pale or rose-pink colour indicates the presence of simple proteins such as amino acids.

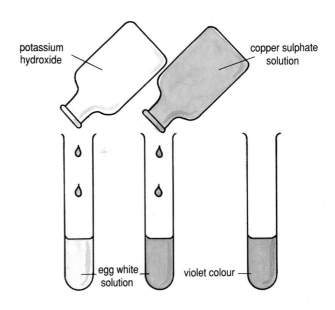

Biuret test

CARBOHYDRATES

Carbohydrates are the cheapest and most plentiful source of energy. They are chiefly found in plant foods where they are manufactured by photosynthesis.

PHOTOSYNTHESIS (MANUFACTURE BY LIGHT)

Plants use the sun's energy to convert water and carbon dioxide into glucose and oxygen.
- Plant roots absorb water (H_2O) from the soil.
- Leaves absorb carbon dioxide (CO_2) from the air.
- Chlorophyll, a green pigment in leaves, converts sunlight to energy.
- These combine to create monosaccharides such as glucose.
- Oxygen (O_2) is released into the atmosphere.

Glucose which is not required at once by the plant is converted into starch for storage or used to form the complex carbohydrate, cellulose, which forms the supporting framework of the plant.

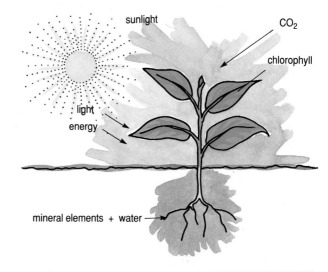

$$6CO_2 + 6H_2O + \text{sunlight} \rightarrow C_6H_{12}O_6 + 6O_2$$
carbon + water + energy → glucose + oxygen
dioxide

Photosynthesis

ELEMENTAL COMPOSITION OF CARBOHYDRATES

Carbohydrates are compounds made up of carbon, hydrogen and oxygen (CHO). The hydrogen and oxygen are present in the same ratio as water, 2:1.

CLASSIFICATION

Carbohydrates are classified according to their structure. All are based on a simple sugar unit known as a *monosaccharide* which may combine in pairs (*disaccharides*) or in long chains (*polysaccharides*).

Carbohydrate Classification		
Monosaccharide (simple sugar)	*Disaccharide* (double sugar)	*Polysaccharide* (complex sugars)
$C_6H_{12}O_6$	$C_{12}H_{22}O_{11}$	$(C_6H_{10}O_5)_n$
Glucose (fruit, for example grapes) Fructose (honey, sweet fruit) Galactose (digested milk)	Sucrose (cane and beet sugar) Lactose (milk sugar) Maltose (germinating barley, i.e. malt)	Starch (cereals, vegetables) Pectin (fruit) Cellulose (plant fibre) Glycogen (animal starch)

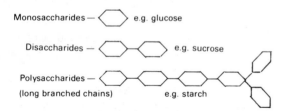

Monosaccharides — e.g. glucose

Disaccharides — e.g. sucrose

Polysaccharides — (long branched chains) e.g. starch

THE CHEMICAL STRUCTURE OF CARBOHYDRATES

The chemical structure of all carbohydrates is based on a simple sugar unit called a *monosaccharide*. The most common of these is glucose which occurs naturally in fruit and circulates in the blood. Glucose is sweet and soluble. It has a 'ring' structure.

Structure of Glucose

Monosaccharides, fructose and galactose, have the same number of carbon, hydrogen and oxygen atoms, $C_6H_{12}O_6$, but they are arranged differently.

- *Disaccharides* $C_{12}H_{22}O_{11}$. These occur when two monosaccharides chemically link together with the loss of one water molecule. As a result, the disaccharide molecule has only 22 hydrogen and 11 oxygen atoms. The water molecule H_2O has been removed.

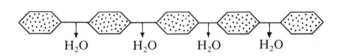

fructose	+	glucose	→	sucrose	+	water
$C_6H_{12}O_6$		$C_6H_{12}O_6$		$C_{12}H_{22}O_{11}$		H_2O

Formation of a disaccharide (sucrose)

Sucrose	=	1 glucose	+	1 fructose molecule
Lactose	=	1 glucose	+	1 galactose molecule
Maltose	=	1 glucose	+	1 glucose molecule

- *Polysaccharides*

  These consist of many (poly) monosaccharide units linked together chemically, each with the elimination of water (*condensation*).

  Formula: $(C_6H_{10}O_5)_n$

n varies according to the number of monosaccharide units present in the polysaccharide.

H_2O H_2O H_2O H_2O

Part of a long starch molecule

EXAMPLES OF POLYSACCHARIDES

STARCH

This is made up of long chains of glucose units. It occurs mainly in cereals and in vegetable foods such as root vegetables and potatoes. Grains of starch vary in size and structure, according to the plant in which they are found.

GLYCOGEN

This is a form of animal starch made up of branched chains of glucose units. It is stored by the body in the liver and muscles as an energy reserve. When energy is required quickly, it is easily converted back into glucose.

CELLULOSE

Cellulose consists of large, complex molecules which make up the structural framework and fibrous parts of plants.

It is plentiful in stems, seeds, leaves and the root, particularly on the outer layers, as in bran. Because of the complex structure of cellulose, digestive enzymes in humans cannot break it down. It therefore passes through the body without providing any energy. The principal function of cellulose is to act as roughage, thus stimulating the gut and preventing constipation (see pages 40–41).

PECTIN
This is a complex polysaccharide found in some ripe fruit and vegetables. It acts as a setting agent in jam-making due to its ability to form a 'gel'.

DEXTRIN
When starchy foods are heated, some of the very long starch chains are broken down into shorter chains called dextrins, with the loss of water. Toast is an example.

SOURCES OF CARBOHYDRATE

Foods high in carbohydrates

SUGAR
Natural sources include sugar-cane, sugar-beet, ripe and dried fruit, milk, honey and some vegetables such as carrots and onions. Other sources are table sugar, syrup, cakes, biscuits, sweets, jam, soft drinks, ice cream and canned fruit.

STARCH
Starch is found in cereals such as wheat and rice; in cereal products such as bread, cakes, pasta, breakfast cereals; and in root vegetables and potatoes.

CELLULOSE
Cellulose is found in cereals, vegetables and fruit, particularly in their skins and outer husks such as bran.

PECTIN
Pectin is present in the cell walls of some fruit and vegetables.

BIOLOGICAL FUNCTIONS OF CARBOHYDRATES
1. Carbohydrates are a cheap source of heat and energy.
2. Excess carbohydrate is converted into fat which is stored as adipose tissue, mainly beneath the skin. (While this helps to reduce heat loss, too much causes obesity.)
3. Some carbohydrate is stored as glycogen in the liver and muscles for immediate conversion to glucose/ energy.
4. Carbohydrates spare proteins, so that any protein eaten will not have to be used as a source of energy.
5. Cellulose stimulates peristalsis in the gut and helps to prevent constipation and other bowel disorders.

DIGESTION AND UTILISATION OF CARBOHYDRATES
Starch and sugar are broken down into monosaccharides during digestion. Digested glucose, sometimes called blood sugar, may be:
- used at once for the production of heat and energy
- stored as glycogen
- converted into fat for long-term storage.

Note: Cellulose and pectin are not digested.

DIETARY PROBLEMS RELATING TO CARBOHYDRATES
Deficiency symptoms resulting from the lack of carbohydrates are rare in western countries as it is the cheapest food available. Starvation, from lack of all food, is unfortunately all too common in famine-ridden, underdeveloped countries.

Our most frequent problems relate to:
- overindulgence in high-energy foods, leading to obesity.
- consumption of overprocessed foods, resulting in insufficient fibre in the diet which in turn leads to bowel problems, such as constipation.
- dental caries (decay) caused by eating too much sugar, combined with poor dental hygiene.

RECOMMENDED DAILY ALLOWANCE OF CARBOHYDRATES
There is no specific carbohydrate allowance recommended. Allowances in this area relate to total kilocalorie intake, that is from fat and protein as well as carbohydrate. The main recommendations made by nutritionists are to:
- reduce sugar intake.
- increase fibre intake — eat whole cereals rather than refined foods.
- avoid 'empty' kcal/kJ intake — foods which provide little or no nutrients except energy such as sugar and alcohol.

Too much carbohydrate may cause obesity
(Hutchison Library)

ENERGY VALUE OF CARBOHYDRATES
1 gram of carbohydrate supplies 4 kcal/17 kJ of energy.

PROPERTIES OF SUGAR
1. Sugars are sweet, crystalline solids.
2. Sugar is soluble in water, particularly in warm water, which enables it to be easily digested and transported in the body.
3. When boiled, sugar first dissolves, then becomes a syrup. As water evaporates it caramelises and eventually burns (carbonises). Dry heat causes caramelisation, then carbonisation.
4. Reducing sugars: Some sugars are capable of reduction. (*A reducing agent is a substance which can remove oxygen from a compound, thus 'reducing' it in mass.*) Fehling's solution can be used to identify reducing sugars such as glucose, fructose, maltose and lactose.
   Non-reducing sugar/carbohydrates: sucrose, starch.
5. Hydrolysis: Sugars have the ability to react with water and break down into simpler substances (hydrolysis).
- Sucrose + H_2O converts to its monosaccharides, glucose and fructose, (called *invert sugar*). This occurs in the production of sweets and in jam-making. Because invert sugar contains fructose, it is sweeter than sucrose.
- During digestion, disaccharides and starch are hydrolysed, breaking down into monosaccharides. This action is speeded up by enzymes and acids and occurs more readily when heat is applied.

PROPERTIES OF STARCH
1. Starch is insoluble in cold water.
2. Gelatinisation: When mixed with water, starch forms a sticky paste (careful blending and stirring are essential during cooking to prevent lumping of sauces etc.).
3. Starch dissolves, swells and bursts when heated, thus thickening liquids such as white sauce.
4. Dry heat causes starch cells to burst. Examples are baking pastry and popcorn. Overheating causes carbonisation.
5. Dextrins: When dry heat is applied to starch, shorter chain polysaccharides (dextrins) are formed.
6. Starch is hygroscopic — it absorbs water/water vapour. For example, starchy products are used to keep baking powder dry; biscuits soften when exposed to air.

PROPERTIES OF CELLULOSE
Although cellulose is particularly insoluble in water:
1. It absorbs large amounts of water, creating bulk in the diet.
2. It cannot be digested by the human body.
3. It stimulates peristaltic action in the gut.

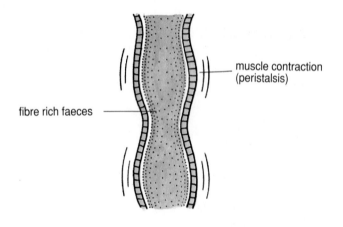

Fibre stimulates muscular contraction of the bowel

TESTS FOR CARBOHYDRATE
1. *Test to detect the presence of sugar (Fehling's test)*
   Place food (fruit or glucose) to be tested in a test tube. (Table sugar should not be used.) Mix together equal quantities (5cm³) Fehling's solution A and B. This gives a clear, blue colour. Add to the test tube, stir and heat gently. Result: a brick-red precipitate, indicating a reducing sugar such as glucose or fructose.
2. *To test for the presence of starch*
   Place small amounts of dry food on a clean white surface such as a tile. Using a dropper, place one drop of diluted iodine solution on each. A blue/black colour indicates the presence of starch.

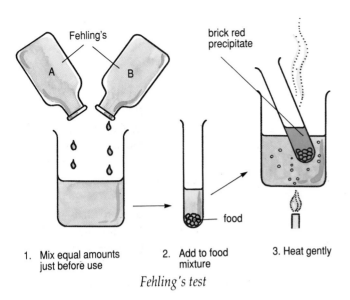

1. Mix equal amounts just before use
2. Add to food mixture
3. Heat gently

Fehling's test

FUNCTIONS OF ENERGY IN THE DIET
Carbohydrates and lipids are the principal sources of energy in the diet. Energy is required by the body for the following reasons:
1. Manufacture of cells (anabolism) e.g. growth.
2. Muscle movement, voluntary and involuntary.
3. Cell and nerve activity.
4. Maintenance of body temperature at 37°C.

► LIPIDS OR FATS

Lipids are greasy substances of plant or animal origin. Lipids are called oils when they are liquid at room temperature. They are called fats when they are solid at room temperature (20°C).

ELEMENTAL COMPOSITION OF LIPID
Lipids are composed of carbon, hydrogen and oxygen. Their large proportion of carbon makes them the most concentrated source of fuel in the diet.

CHEMICAL STRUCTURE OF A LIPID
Lipids are formed when three fatty acids combine with glycerol. This gives them the chemical name Triglycerides. Here is how it happens. Glycerol is a trihydric alcohol — it has three hydroxyl (OH) groups. To each of these OH groups, a fatty acid attaches itself, with the elimination of water.

CH$_2$	OH	+ fatty acid 1
CH	OH	+ fatty acid 2 → triglyceride + 3H$_2$O
CH$_2$	OH	+ fatty acid 3
glycerol		+ 3 fatty acids → triglyceride (lipid) + water

The reverse (hydrolysis) occurs during digestion when, speeded up by the enzyme lipase, water attaches itself to the triglyceride breaking it into its components, fatty acids and glycerol.

CLASSIFICATION OF FATTY ACIDS
Fatty acid molecules are made up of carbon chains of differing lengths. Such molecules can be written as CH$_3$ (CH$_2$)$_n$ COOH. There are two different types of fatty acids:

■ *Saturated fatty acids*
When every carbon atom in the fatty acid molecule has its full quota of hydrogen atoms, it is said to be saturated — it cannot hold any more hydrogen as every bond is complete.
Saturated fatty acids are:
1. hard at room temperature
2. usually found in animal sources such as meat fat and dairy produce.
   Examples: Butyric acid in butter
   Stearic acid in meat fat

Saturated
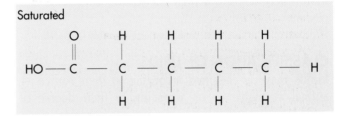

■ *Unsaturated fatty acids*
The carbon chains in these molecules are not saturated with hydrogen; when this occurs, a double bond forms between two carbon atoms. This can occur once or more often.

Unsaturated
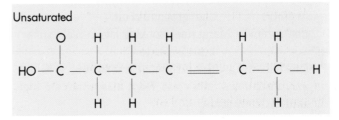

A monounsaturated fatty acid		1 double bond	e.g. oleic acid
Polyunsaturated fatty acids	2 or more double bonds	2 double bonds	linoleic acid
		3 double bonds	linolenic acid
		4 double bonds	arachidonic acid

Unsaturated fatty acids are:
1. usually soft or oily at room temperature.
2. found mainly in vegetable foods, oils and fish.

ESSENTIAL FATTY ACIDS

Polyunsaturated fatty acids — linoleic, linolenic and arachidonic acids — are essential to the efficient functioning of the body as they are required for building cell membranes. For this reason they are known as the *essential fatty acids*. They must be obtained from food (see sources above) as the body cannot synthesise them from other sources (although linoleic acid can be used to manufacture the other two). Essential fatty acids are also thought to counteract the hardening effect of cholesterol on arteries, whereas saturated fats tend to have the opposite effect.

CONSISTENCY OF LIPIDS

All lipids or fats contain an identical molecule of glycerol. It is the fatty acids which vary. The types of fatty acid in the lipid determine the taste, texture, colour and consistency of a fat. Most fats and oils contain both saturated and unsaturated fatty acids. Animal fats usually have a higher proportion of saturated fatty acids, whereas soft fats and oils (mainly from fish and plant* sources) are more likely to have a high polyunsaturated fatty acid content.

* Coconut oil is an exception, containing 76% saturated fatty acids.

CLASSIFICATION OF LIPIDS

Lipids may be classified according to their source — animal/vegetable — or according to their degree of saturation.

- *Animal* (mainly hard or saturated) Meat and meat fat—suet, lard, dripping
  Oily fish*, fish liver oils
  Butter, cream, some cheeses, full cream milk and egg yolk
- *Vegetable* (mainly unsaturated) Nuts; vegetable and nut oils, e.g. olive and groundnut oil
  Margarine*, cooking fats, cereals, soya bean, avocado

* Note: Oily fish, which is from an animal source, is high in polyunsaturated fatty acids. Hard margarines are high in saturated fatty acids.

Foods high in lipids

BIOLOGICAL FUNCTIONS OF LIPIDS

1. Supplies large amounts of heat and energy.
2. Excess fat, stored as adipose tissue, helps to insulate the body.
3. Protects delicate organs such as nerves and kidneys.
4. Lipids act as a source of fat-soluble vitamins — A, D, E, K.
5. Source of essential fatty acids.
6. Fats give a feeling of fullness and delay the onset of hunger.

EFFECTS OF LIPID DEFICIENCY

Deficiency is extremely unlikely, except in the case of starvation. There is the possibility of deficiency in fat-soluble vitamins and essential fatty acids.

RECOMMENDED DAILY ALLOWANCE OF LIPIDS

This is given as a percentage of total kJ/kcal intake. It is recommended that the average 42% fat eaten in the western diet be reduced to 33% of total kJ/kcal intake, half coming from animal and half from marine and vegetable sources.

This could be done by:
- cutting down on fried foods.
- reducing intake of cakes and pastries.
- reducing intake of cream, rich desserts and hard cheese.
- spreading fat thinly on bread etc.
- trimming excess fat from joints of meat.
- changing from butter to polyunsaturated spreads.

Note: Don't forget to cut down on the 'invisible' fats in egg yolk, milk and convenience foods.

ENERGY VALUE OF LIPIDS

1 gram lipid supplies 9 kcal/37 kJ of energy, more than twice as much as protein or carbohydrate.

PROPERTIES OF LIPIDS

1. *Insoluble in water*, but soluble in solvents such as ether and benzene.
2. Solid fats *melt when heated*, giving off any water at 100°C.
3. Lipids *boil at extremely high temperatures*.
4. *Plasticity*: Some lipids which contain a mixture of saturated and unsaturated fatty acids are soft, yet have shape and structure. This makes them ideal for cake-making (creaming) and pastry-making (rubbing in).
5. *Rancidity*: When lipids spoil, they are said to be rancid. There are two types of rancidity.
   Oxidative rancidity is the most common. It occurs when oxygen in the air combines with the carbon at the double bond of an unsaturated carbon chain.

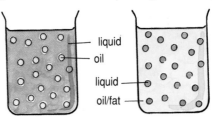

Rancidity

Hydrolytic rancidity is caused by enzymes or bacteria which break down the lipid into fatty acids and glycerol. This sometimes occurs in a freezer when enzymes survive and cause fatty food such as bacon to become rancid.

Rancidity causes an unpleasant taste and smell. Correct storage — covered in a cool, dark place — helps to prevent rancidity. Antioxidants are used to prevent rancidity and to prolong the shelf-life of foods containing lipids. They combine with any oxygen present in the food, preventing it from combining with the lipid.

6. Lipids *readily absorb flavours* and should be kept covered.
7. *Hydrogenation*: This is a chemical process whereby oils are converted into solid fats by forcing hydrogen through them, using nickel as a catalyst. The unsaturated carbon atoms take up the hydrogen, thus becoming saturated and hard. This process is used in the manufacture of margarine.

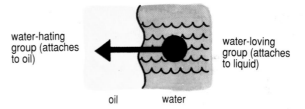

Hydrogenation

8. Lipids are capable of forming emulsions

EMULSIONS

When two liquids such as oil and water — which do not usually mix together — are forced to do so, the result is a colloidal solution called an *emulsion*.

A temporary emulsion is created by vigorously shaking oil and vinegar as in a French dressing, but these will separate before long into their components.

(a) oil in water (o/w) emulsion, e.g. milk

(b) water in oil (w/o) emulsion, e.g. butter, margarine

- liquid
- oil
- liquid
- oil/fat

OTHER EXAMPLES OF EMULSIONS

The cream in milk — an oil in water emulsion
Butter and margarine — water in fat/oil emulsion
Mayonnaise — oil in vinegar emulsion
A permanent emulsion can be formed by adding an *emulsifier.* Each molecule of the emulsifier has a hydrophillic (water-loving) head and a hydrophobic (water-hating) tail. The water-loving head attaches itself to the water/vinegar molecules. The water-hating tail attaches itself to the fat/oil molecule and holds them together.

water-hating group (attaches to oil)

water-loving group (attaches to liquid)

oil   water

EXAMPLES OF EMULSIFIERS

Lecithin — a phospholipid present in egg yolk, soya beans
Gluten — in flour
Casein — in milk
Gums, pectin — in plants
Glycerol monostearate (GMS) is a commercial emulsifier prepared from glycerol and fatty acids. Alginates are prepared from seaweed.

EFFECTS OF HEAT ON LIPIDS

- Solid fats melt when heated.
- At 100°C, any water present boils and evaporates.
- Each oil and fat has a different optimum temperature for frying (average 175°-195°C). After this, they start to decompose.

SMOKE POINT

When overheated, lipids start to decompose when the glycerol separates from the fatty acids. The glycerol changes to an acrid-smelling compound called acrolein and a blue haze rises. It occurs between 200°C (solids) and

16

250°C (oils); fats reach the smoke point at a lower temperature than oils. Impurities also lower the smoke point. A fat used several times will reach smoke point and burn sooner than fresh fat or oil.

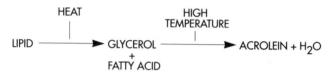

FLASH POINT

This occurs when lipids are greatly overheated. A vapour rises which can burst spontaneously into flames. The average flash point for fats is 310°C. For oils, it is 325°C.

TESTS FOR LIPID

1. Press a sample of food against brown or blotting paper. A greasy, translucent mark will remain if fat is present.
2. Break up a small sample of food in a dry test tube. Add a few drops of Sudan III dye. A pinky/red colour indicates the presence of oils. It may be necessary to heat some foods slightly to obtain a result.
3. To distinguish saturated from unsaturated lipids — Put 10g of finely chopped suet into one test tube and 10 ml sunflower oil into another. Add 10ml of ether to each and stir. Using a dropper, add iodine to each in turn until a good yellow colour is obtained. Count the number of drops added to each — the unsaturated fat will require more iodine.

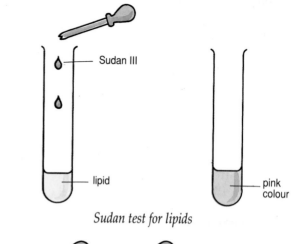

Sudan test for lipids

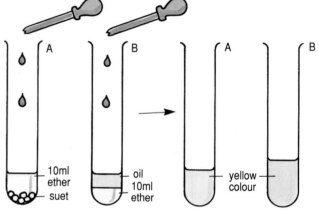

Test to distinguish between a saturated and an unsaturated fat

► VITAMINS

Vitamins are complex chemical substances required by the body in very small amounts. They are usually, but not always, obtained from food. Although vitamins do not produce energy, they are required for the normal functioning of the body. If they are not included in the diet, deficiency diseases such as scurvy and rickets may occur. These are rare in developed countries, although mild deficiency may occur among those on low incomes, the elderly and those with erratic eating habits. Symptoms of these vitamin deficiencies often include tiredness, mouth ulcers and poor condition of skin, hair, teeth and nails.

- Each vitamin is completely different from any other one.
- Each vitamin has a specific function and cannot take the place of another.
- Most vitamins cannot be synthesised by the body, except small amounts of the B group, vitamins D and K.

- Vitamins are identified by letter — for example, vitamins A, B, C. They are also known by a chemical name. For example, ascorbic acid is the chemical name for vitamin C.
- Many vitamins may now be made synthetically. They are available as vitamin supplements in the form of tonics and pills.
- A vitamin intake greater than recommended is of no benefit and may, in fact, be harmful.
- A good, mixed diet should provide all the vitamins necessary for complete health.

Vitamins which are required in minute quantities are measured in milligrams (mg) or micrograms (μg). In spite of recommended daily allowances, it is difficult to measure the amount of a vitamin absorbed by an individual as vitamins in food are so easily affected by a wide range of conditions. These include freshness, storage conditions, food preparation, cooking, preservation and so on.

Factors such as smoking and alcohol consumption can reduce the levels of vitamins C and B. Many drugs — even everyday drugs such as aspirin, antibiotics and the contraceptive pill — can also reduce vitamin levels in the body.

CLASSIFICATION OF VITAMINS

Vitamins are grouped according to solubility.
- Fat-soluble vitamins: A, D, E, K
- Water-soluble vitamins: B group, C

As vitamins are relatively small molecules, it is not necessary for them to be broken down by digestion before being absorbed into the bloodstream. Fat-soluble vitamins are absorbed with fatty foods through the walls of the intestine. Those not required are stored by the liver. Water-soluble vitamins are absorbed through the walls of the stomach and intestine. Excess is eliminated through the kidneys. As water soluble vitamins are not stored, care should be taken to obtain a regular supply.

► FAT SOLUBLE VITAMINS

VITAMIN A (RETINOL)

This is available to the body in two forms:
1. Retinol or pure vitamin A.
2. Carotene or provitamin A.

Retinol is so named because it is concerned with the retina of the eye. It is only found in animal foods.

Carotene in the form of beta carotene is present with chlorophyll in plants. It is a yellow pigment with a similar chemical structure to vitamin A and is found in carrots and many fruits. Carotene is converted to vitamin A in the gut wall. This conversion is not very efficient, as only about one-quarter of the carotene converts to vitamin A.

Sources of vitamin A (in order of importance)

Vitamin A (retinol)	Carotene
halibut liver oil	kale
cod liver oil	carrots
liver	spinach
butter and margarine	watercress
cheese, egg yolk	dried apricots, prunes
herrings	tomatoes
milk and cream (in summer)	cabbage, peas

PROPERTIES OF VITAMIN A
- A yellow, fat-soluble alcohol.
- Insoluble in water.
- Can be destroyed by oxygen, as when exposed to air and light.

- Heat-stable, therefore little affected by cooking or heat preserving. Prolonged high temperatures destroy it.
- Some loss when food is dried, as when raisins are dried in the sun.

FUNCTIONS OF VITAMIN A
1. It regulates growth.
2. It promotes healthy skin.
3. Maintenance of epithelial (lining) membranes such as the cornea and bronchial tubes.
4. Necessary for healthy eyes to manufacture rhodopsin, the pigment in the retina which helps the eye to adapt to dim light.

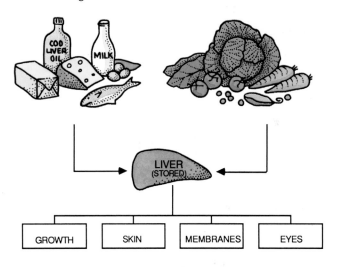

Sources and functions of Vitamin A

EFFECTS OF VITAMIN A DEFICIENCY
1. Retarded growth, malformed bones.
2. Roughening and dryness of skin (follicular keratosis).
3. Xerophthalmia: inflammation of the eye membranes leading to blindness (common in the Third World, where the diet consists mainly of cereals).
4. Night blindness, an inability to see in dim light.

Recommended daily allowance

Children	300-750 µg
Adults	750 µg
During pregnancy/nursing	1,200 µg

VITAMIN A CONTENT OF FOOD

100g liver	6,000 µg
100g herring	45 µg
100g cheddar cheese	420 µg
100g carrots	2,000 µg
100g cabbage	50 µg
100g tomatoes	117 µg

VITAMIN D (CALCIFEROLS)

There are two forms of vitamin D.

1. Cholecalciferol (D_3) which occurs in animals when the sun activates the provitamin 7-dehydrocholesterol which is present in the fat under the skin.
2. Ergocalciferol (D_2) obtained when the provitamin ergosterol found in yeasts and fungi is activated by ultraviolet light. It is manufactured for use as a vitamin supplement.

PROPERTIES OF VITAMIN D

Vitamin D is probably the most stable of the vitamins. It is:

1. Heat-stable: unaffected by cooking or preserving.
2. Unaffected by oxidation, acids or alkalis.
3. Insoluble in water: unaffected by steeping or moist cooking methods
4. Fat-soluble.

SOURCES OF VITAMIN D
(IN ORDER OF IMPORTANCE)

Only a few animal foods contain cholecalciferol. Most people obtain adequate supplies from the sunlight.

	amounts	μg
Sunlight		
Halibut liver oil	1 drop	600
Cod liver oil	1 5ml teasp.	830
Oily fish (e.g. herrings)	100g	22
Margarine	100g	8
Eggs	100g	1.5
Dairy produce (in summer)	100g	0.5

Sources of Vitamin D

RECOMMENDED DAILY ALLOWANCE OF VITAMIN D

Adults	2.5 μg cholecalciferol
Children/pregnant and nursing mothers	10 μg cholecalciferol

FUNCTIONS OF VITAMIN D

1. Necessary for the absorption and laying down of calcium and phosphorus in bones and teeth.

2. Regulates calcium balance between skeleton and blood.
3. Prevents rickets.

EFFECTS OF VITAMIN D DEFICIENCY

1. Rickets, a disease which causes malformation of bones in children, is caused by insufficient calcium/phosphorus/vitamin D.
2. Osteomalacia, a disease similar to rickets which occurs in adults. The bones lose calcium and become weak.
3. Dental decay.

Most people get enough Vitamin D from sunlight

Deficiency is rare in the western world, although it occurs occasionally among the elderly or in babies who are kept too well wrapped up. Rickets was common among children in the past, especially in smoky industrial cities in the UK where the sun's rays could not penetrate the thick blanket of smog over the cities. Cod liver oil helped to alleviate the problem. Eastern women such as Muslims are among those most at risk today. Their culture demands that they cover their bodies from head to foot when out of doors and their diet contains little animal fat.

Why might this woman need extra Vitamin D?
(Hutchison Library/Bernard Gerard)

HYPERVITAMINOSIS A AND D

As fat-soluble vitamins are not excreted in the urine, excess is stored in the body. If large amounts of vitamins A and D are taken over a long period, they reach toxic levels and can result in death. The most common occurrence of hypervitaminosis is in infants, where mothers overdose them with halibut oil (500 times stronger than cod liver oil) in the mistaken idea that, 'if a little is good, a lot is better'.

SYMPTOMS

- Hypervitaminosis A: Itching, headache, enlarged liver, painful swelling of bones.
- Hypervitaminosis D: Vomiting, thirst, weight loss and death.

VITAMIN E (TOCOPHEROLS)

It is now evident that vitamin E is far more important in the diet of animals than that of humans. It is present in many foods and no major deficiency disease is known.

PROPERTIES OF VITAMIN E

1. A yellow, fat-soluble alcohol.
2. Insoluble in water.
3. Stable to heat and acids.
4. Unstable to alkalis and ultra-violet light.
5. A powerful antioxidant — delays rancidity.

SOURCES OF VITAMIN E

Most foods contain a little vitamin E. The best sources are:
eggs, cereals, wheat-germ
vegetable and cereal oils such as corn oil
animal fats
pulse vegetable, especially soya beans

FUNCTIONS OF VITAMIN E (NOT ALL PROVEN)

1. Thought to be necessary for metabolism.
2. Acts as an antioxidant, both in cell membrane and commercially.
3. It is possible that its antioxidant properties prevent oxidation of polyunsaturated fatty acids within the body, thus enabling them to reduce susceptibility to coronary heart disease

EFFECTS OF VITAMIN E DEFICIENCY

While no major deficiency disease is known, this is not to say that vitamin E is not important. It seems likely that the average diet supplies all we need. Reserves are stored in the liver.
1. Muscular dystrophy (wasting).
2. Fragile red blood cells (but not anaemia).

Note: The idea that vitamin E prevents wrinkling, miscarriage and impotence has no basis in fact.

RECOMMENDED DAILY ALLOWANCE

Vitamins E and K: None, as they are present is almost all food and deficiency is almost unknown.

VITAMIN K (QUINONES)

This is sometimes called the coagulations vitamin. It is more important in the diet of animals than humans. As the human body can synthesise this vitamin in the gut, and since it occurs in many foods, deficiency symptoms are rare.

PROPERTIES OF VITAMIN K

1. Fat-soluble.
2. Insoluble in water.
3. Affected by irradiation.

SOURCES OF VITAMIN K

1. Liver, green vegetables, fish, fish liver oils.
2. Manufactured by bacteria in the intestine.

FUNCTIONS OF VITAMIN K

Necessary for blood clotting.
(Vitamin K is a component of prothrombin: Chapter 7).

EFFECTS OF VITAMIN K DEFICIENCY

Haemorrhages and failure of blood to clot due to reduced prothrombin level.

This is very rare. It does occasionally occur in new babies (whose gut hasn't started to manufacture the vitamin) and in those with liver disease (the absorbed vitamin is distributed by the liver).

▶ **WATER-SOLUBLE VITAMINS** ▬▬▬▬

VITAMIN B GROUP

This is a group of vitamins which share some functions and which are found in similar foods. There are six important vitamins in the group.

Thiamine (B_1)	Pyrodoxine (B_6)
Riboflavin (B_2)	Folic acid
Nicotinic Acid	Cyanocobalamin (B_{12})

The B numbers B_3 and B_4 etc. were found to be either unessential to the body or part of an existing B vitamin. Reference to them was therefore discontinued many years ago.

1. BERIBERI

This is caused by lack of thiamine. Thiamine forms part of an enzyme, phytase, which is concerned with the breakdown of pyruvic acid, a toxic byproduct of carbohydrate metabolism. It is the accumulation of this compound which causes beriberi. This disease affects transmission of impulses along the nerves, leading to

Vitamin B group

Properties/Stability	Sources (generally in order of importance)	RDA	Functions	Effects of deficiency
Thiamine (B_1) ■ Extremely water soluble ■ Unstable at high temperatures ■ Sensitive to alkalis such as bread soda ■ 70% loss in milling/processing	1. Unprocessed cereals, wheat germ 2. Yeast, breakfast cereals (fortified) 3. Heart, liver, kidney, carcase meat 4. Milk, eggs, vegetables	Relates to carbohydrate intake Average: 1mg per day	1. Essential for release of energy from carbohydrates 2. Essential for upkeep of nerves (prevents beriberi) 3. Necessary for appetite and good health	1. Fatigue, depression, irritability 2. Nervous disease, particularly beriberi[1] 3. Retarded growth 4. Due to poor diet, alcoholics may get alcoholic neuritis
Riboflavin (B_2) ■ Water soluble ■ Fairly stable to heat ■ Destroyed by alkalis ■ Affected by light, e.g. milk in bottles	1. Beef, liver, kidney, heart 2. Yeast, yeast extract 3. Milk, eggs, cheese 4. Green and sprouting vegetables and seeds	Relates to carbohydrate intake Average: 1.5 mg (some made in gut)	1. Involved in metabolism of proteins, lipids and carbohydrates 2. Essential for up-keep of tissues — e.g. skin, eyes, tongue 3. Necessary for growth and good health	1. Inflammation and itching of skin 2. Cracks around mouth, tongue, nose 3. Eye infection 4. Retarded growth
Nicotinic acid (Niacin in US) ■ Water soluble ■ Stable to heat ■ Fairly stable to acids and alkalis ■ 80-90% loss in milling	1. Meat, offal, meat extracts 2. Yeast, bran, wheat germ, flour 3. Fish, pulses, dried fruit 4. Some manufactured by bacteria in gut from tryptophan	Related to protein intake Average: 15-20mg (160g liver gives this)	1. Involved in energy release from food 2. Essential for healthy skin 3. Prevents pellagra[2]	Rare in western world Mild deficiency causes weakness, weight loss, depression. Severe deficiency causes pellagra (See note over)
Pyridoxine (B_6) ■ Water soluble ■ Reasonably heat stable ■ Affected by high temperatures ■ Sensitive to oxidation	Most foods: Liver, cereals, wheat germ, fish, yeast, seeds are good sources	2 mg; more when certain drugs are taken	1. Acts as a co-enzyme in the metabolism of proteins 2. Assists the formation of haemoglobin and structural proteins	1. Insomnia, dermatitis, irritability 2. Convulsions in infants born with deficiency 3. May cause a form of anaemia 4. Possible cause of premenstrual tension
Folic acid ■ Water soluble ■ Stable in an acid environment ■ Fairly heat stable ■ Sensitive to light and oxidation	1. Offal, wholegrain cereals 2. Dark green vegetables 3. Pulses 4. Some manufactured in gut	300 µg; more during pregnancy	Involved in the formation of red blood cells (works with vitamin B_{12})	Rare, due to gut synthesis Mild deficiency: fatigue Severe deficiency: anaemia, particularly during pregnancy.
(Cyano) cobalamin (B_{12}) ■ Water soluble ■ Stable in heat – up to 100°C ■ Affected by strong acids and alkalis ■ Affected by light	Plentiful in animal protein foods such as liver, kidney and other meat, fish, cheese. No B_{12} in plant foods. Therefore there is a high risk of deficiency among vegans and vegetarians.	3-4 µg	1. Essential for formation of red blood cells 2. Helps form protective myelein sheath around the nerves 3. Helps treat pernicious anaemia.	1. Anaemia caused by arrested development of red blood cells 2. Nerve degeneration, leading to lack of sensation and movement 3. While other factors cause pernicious anaemia, B_{12} cures it. N.B. High risk of deficiency in vegans and vegetarians.

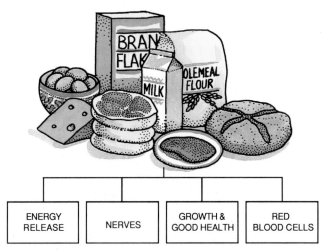

ENERGY RELEASE	NERVES	GROWTH & GOOD HEALTH	RED BLOOD CELLS

Sources and functions of Vitamin B

muscle wasting, paralysis and even death. Two forms are known: dry beriberi and wet beriberi.

2. PELLAGRA

This is caused by lack of nicotinic acid. It is rare today, but was a common cause of death in the past, particularly among the poor in maize-eating countries. This is because maize is very low in nicotinic acid and also because the maize protein, zein, is low in tryptophan, an amino acid which can be converted to nicotinic acid in the intestine. The symptoms of pellagra are a swollen red tongue and the '3Ds': diarrhoea, depression or dementia (madness), and dermatitis. Pellagra often caused death.

VITAMIN C (ASCORBIC ACID)

PROPERTIES OF VITAMIN C

1. It is an acid, crystalline substance with a sweet-sour taste.
2. It is water-soluble.
3. Ascorbic acid is a reducing agent, acting as an anti-oxidant.
4. Being water-soluble, it is not stored by the body. A regular supply is therefore essential for good health.

STABILITY/EFFECTS OF COOKING ON VITAMIN C

1. Vitamin C is the most unstable of vitamins. It is very easily destroyed.
2. It is very soluble in water. Avoid steeping and cooking food in water.
3. Fairly stable in dry conditions.
4. Unstable to heat and considerably reduced by cooking.
5. It is readily oxidised — oxygen in the air destroys it. It gradually decomposes when exposed to air and light for any length of time.

6. When vegetables are chopped or shredded, an oxidising enzyme (oxidase) present in the cell walls of plants destroys it (minimum loss: 50%). Blanching food when freezing destroys oxidase.
7. Destroyed by alkalis. Never use bread-soda when cooking green vegetables.
8. Processing. Freezing has little effect, as the damaging enzymes are destroyed by blanching. There is some loss on canning and considerable loss when food is dried.

SOURCES OF VITAMIN C

Most fresh fruit and vegetables. Rare in animal foods.

Best Fruit Sources	*Best Vegetable Sources*
rose-hip syrup	capsicums (peppers)
blackcurrants	parsley, watercress
citrus fruits	broccoli, cabbage and other greens
strawberries	tomatoes, potatoes (new)
	bean sprouts

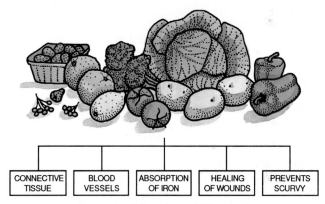

CONNECTIVE TISSUE	BLOOD VESSELS	ABSORPTION OF IRON	HEALING OF WOUNDS	PREVENTS SCURVY

Sources and functions of Vitamin C

FUNCTIONS OF VITAMIN C

1. Necessary for the formation of the connective tissue, collagen, which binds cells of skin, bones etc. together. It is therefore important for growth.
2. Essential for formation of strong blood vessels.
3. Helps wounds to heal.
4. Necessary for proper absorption of iron.
5. Necessary for proper cell metabolism.
6. Prevents scurvy (symptoms: sore, bleeding gums; loose teeth; fatigue; pains in the limbs).
7. Acts as an antioxidant.
8. It helps prevent infection. (Large amounts are said to prevent or reduce the severity of colds, but this has not been proved.)

RECOMMENDED DAILY ALLOWANCE

Daily	30mg
During pregnancy	80mg
USA	49mg
USSR	100mg

EFFECTS OF VITAMIN C DEFICIENCY
1. Weakening of body tissues, skin, gums, blood vessels, leading to bruising and bleeding.
2. Listlessness, weakness and susceptibility to infection.
3. Delayed healing of wounds.
4. Incomplete absorption of iron, leading to anaemia.
5. Scurvy in severe cases.

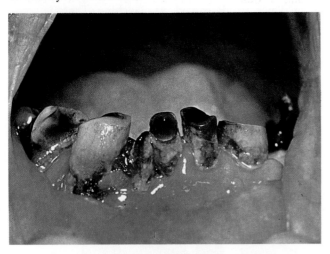

Scurvy — the result of Vitamin C deficiency
(C. James Webb)

TEST FOR VITAMIN C
1. Take 1 tablet of dichlorophenol indophenol (DC-PIP) and place in a test tube. Add 20cm³ water and stir. Solution will now be blue.
2. Add food to be tested (e.g. orange juice), drop by drop. This food will first turn pinkish and then become clear if ascorbic acid is present.

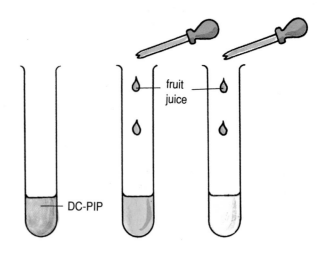

Test for Vitamin C (ascorbic acid)

TO RETAIN VITAMINS/MINERALS IN FOOD
POINTS TO REMEMBER

1. Eat raw, where possible
2. Avoid soaking in water. Avoid peeling.
3. Shred vegetables with a sharp knife. Do not tear.
4. Use as soon as possible after chopping or shredding.
5. Cook for the shortest possible time.
6. Use the minimum amount of cooking liquid.
7. Keep pans covered.
8. Never use bread-soda when cooking green vegetables.
9. Avoid keeping food warm for long periods of time.
10. Avoid reheating food.

► MINERAL ELEMENTS

The human body requires about twenty mineral elements. Each has a specific function and is found in certain foods. For this reason it is not possible to generalise when discussing minerals, except to say that they all help to protect the body from disease. A good, varied diet should supply all essential minerals. Minerals are lost into the water during cooking (see above).

Principal Mineral Elements

Calcium (Ca)	Iron (Fe)	Potassium (K)
Phosphorus (P)	Magnesium (Mg)	Sulphur (S)
Sodium (Na)	Iodine (I)	Chlorine (C1)

Trace Elements
(required in minute amounts)

Copper (Cu)	Fluorine (Fl)
Zinc (Zn)	Nickel (Ni)
Cobalt (Co)	

CALCIUM
The body contains a greater percentage of calcium than any other mineral. Most calcium is found in the bones (99%), with small amounts in the muscle and blood.

SOURCES OF CALCIUM
1. Milk, cheese
2. Tinned fish (of which bones are eaten)
3. Green vegetables, fortified flour (white)
4. Hard water

FUNCTIONS OF CALCIUM
1. Necessary for development of strong bones and teeth.
2. Necessary for normal clotting of blood.
3. Necessary for normal functioning of muscles and nerves.

EFFECTS OF CALCIUM DEFICIENCY
1. Rickets and osteomalacia, if deficiency is severe.
2. Poor quality, badly-formed teeth
3. Irritability and muscular spasm.
4. Osteoporosis, weakening of bones in old people.

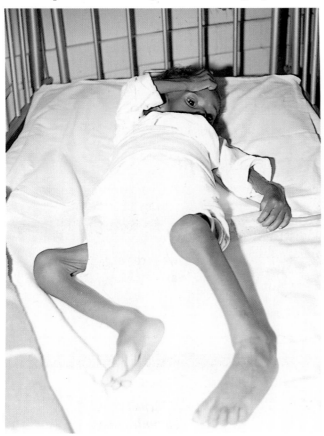

Child hospitalised with severe rickets
(Hutchison Library)

RECOMMENDED DAILY ALLOWANCE
Adults	500mg
Teenagers	1,000mg
Pregnant and nursing mothers	1,200mg

It is particularly important that pregnant and nursing mothers, children, teenagers, old people and those with fractured bones obtain a plentiful supply of calcium. If a pregnant mother takes insufficient calcium in her diet, it will be drawn from her bones to supply the foetus. Malnourished women who breast feed lose calcium through their milk. In both cases osteomalacia may occur, particularly in the case of repeated pregnancies.

CALCIFICATION
The bones of a foetus are composed of cartilege (the strong, flexible material of which the ear lobe is made). Bones and teeth are hardened by the absorption of a combination of calcium and phosphorus (calcium phosphate) which becomes enmeshed in the cartilage framework. This is called *calcification*.

(a) cartilage framework   (b) calcium phosphate laid down in bones

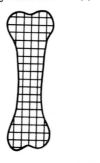

Calcification

When rickets occurs, calcification does not take place, with the result that the legs, ribs and pelvis become bent and misshapen, leaving the victim permanently deformed.

FACTORS WHICH HELP CALCIUM ABSORPTION
The absorption of calcium does not just depend on the amount in the diet. Less than 40% of the calcium we eat is absorbed, the remainder being excreted in the faeces and the urine. Many factors affect its absorption.
- Vitamin D: Ample supplies through diet and/or sunlight are essential. Children on diets with sufficient calcium can develop rickets if vitamin D is lacking.
- Phosphorus, an essential ingredient in calcium phosphate, must be present in the correct proportion.
- Parathormone: a hormone produced in the parathyroid gland in the neck controls the calcium balance in the blood.
- An acid environment improves solubility and therefore absorption of calcium. For this reason, vitamin C (ascorbic acid) is useful.
- Protein has a role in calcium absorption.

FACTORS WHICH REDUCE CALCIUM ABSORPTION
- Insufficient phosphorus (unlikely) or incorrect calcium/phosphorus ratio — 1:1.5.
- Phytic acid: A phosphorus-containing compound present in many cereals and pulses, especially in their outer husks. It combines with the calcium in food, making it unavailable to the body. This is why extra

Other Minerals

Sources	RDA	Functions	Effects of Deficiency
Phosphorus Good supply in most foods, in particular meat, fish, eggs, dairy produce, whole cereals, green vegetables	None	1. Necessary for bone and tooth formation. 2. Essential component of DNA which carries our heredity characteristics. 3. Essential component of cells, blood and many enzymes and hormones. 4. Necessary for all body metabolism. 5. Forms part of the compounds ATP and ADP which are involved in energy release in the cell.	None known  *Goitre causes swelling of the neck (Hutchinson Library)*
Iodine Amount in soil differs between one area and another. In soil with a high iodine content, it will be present in vegetables, cereals, milk. Also present in sea fish, seaweed and iodised salt.	150μg	Essential for manufacture of thyroxine — a hormone produced by the thyroid gland. This controls the rate of metabolism.	Goitre, which causes enlargement of the thyroid gland and swelling of the neck, lack of energy, obesity and mental backwardness (cretinism)
Sodium Present in all body fluids and is essential for life. 1. Common salt, added at cooking or at the table. 2. Bacon, smoked fish, cheese, snack foods.	In a temperate climate: 2g. Average consumption: 15g in West.	1. Essential for correct water balance of the body. 2. Keeps blood and body fluids alkaline. 3. Maintains osmotic pressure in body fluids.	Loss of appetite, apathy, vomiting, muscle cramps. Take extra salt when excessive water loss occurs, e.g. heavy perspiration, diarrhoea, vomiting.

Note: When extra salt is required, the body reduces the amount excreted in the urine

Sources	RDA	Functions	Effects of Deficiency
Fluorine Sea fish, tea, drinking water, either naturally or added.	2 mg (more for children)	Forms part of enamel coating of tooth. Prevents decay by strengthening teeth.	Impaired tooth development. Dental caries.
Potassium Most foods. Good sources — soya beans, nuts, fish, bacon, bread.	No RDA, as it is present in most foods.	Maintains optimum cell environment. Necessary for cell formation.	Rare except in cases of severe injury or illness, and severe prolonged diarrhoea, or starvation e.g. bulimia or anorexia nervosa. Symptoms: mental apathy, muscular weakness leading to paralysis, kidney damage, irregular heartbeat, epilepsy, seizures.

Copper	Helps form haemoglobin and enzymes.
Chlorine	Helps form hydrochloric acid in the stomach.
Magnesium	Necessary for protein synthesis, enzyme and muscle activity.

calcium (calcium carbonate) is added to flour (fortified flour). Ironically, it is not usually added to wholemeal flour which retains more bran, and hence more phytic acid. During yeast bread-making, the enzyme phytase breaks phytic acid into a harmless compound.

- Oxalic acid, present in rhubarb, spinach and strawberries, acts in a similar way to phytic acid.
- Excess fat: As the fatty acids break down during digestion, they can combine with calcium to inhibit its absorption.
- Large amounts of protein increase excretion of calcium in urine.

IRON
Most of the iron in the body is found in the blood. Iron is also present in the liver, spleen and bone marrow. Small amounts are lost through wear and tear, larger amounts through haemorrhaging and menstruation.

SOURCES OF IRON
Liver, kidney, red meat, whole cereals, brown bread, dark green vegetables.

RECOMMENDED DAILY ALLOWANCE
Men	10mg
Women	12mg
Teenagers	15mg
Pregnant /nursing mothers	15mg

A 150g portion of liver would supply these requirements.

FUNCTION OF IRON
Iron is necessary for the formation of haemoglobin in red blood cells. This is necessary to pick up oxygen in the lungs and transport it to the tissues for oxidation.

ABSORPTION OF IRON
The absorption of iron is greatly influenced by the body's need for it. When the need for iron is greater, the body will absorb more. On average, only about 10% of the iron in food is absorbed by the body. The following factors affect its absorption.

- Vitamin C, because it is a reducing agent, increases the absorption of iron by reducing it from the ferric state found in most foods to its absorbable ferrous state.

- Protein is also thought to assist iron absorption.
- Cellulose, phytic acid and oxalates (see Calcium) in some plant foods form insoluble compounds with iron thus inhibiting its absorption. In some countries, iron is added to flour to counteract this. In general the iron in vegetable foods is not as easily absorbed as that in meat.

EFFECTS OF IRON DEFICIENCY
1. Tiredness, feeling 'run down'.
2. In severe cases anaemia (page 38) occurs, particularly in women.

VITAMIN/MINERAL INTERRELATIONSHIPS
Many nutrients work together to maintain body functions.
- Vitamin B is required, for example, for correct metabolism of carbohydrates.
- Vitamin C is necessary for the proper absorption of iron.
- Vitamins B_6 and B_{12}, folic acid, as well as iron, also help in the formation of red blood cells.
- Calcium, phosphorus, magnesium and vitamin D work together to ensure correct absorption and laying down of calcium and phosphorus in the bones.

SUMMARY
Recommended daily allowance of nutrients (for adults)

Protein	1g per kilogram weight		
Carbohydrate	related to individual metabolism and physical activity		
Lipid	as for carbohydrate (half from animal, half from vegetable sources)		
Vitamin A	750μg	Calcium	500 mg
Vitamin D	2.5μg	Iron	12mg
Vitamin B_1		Iodine	150μg
(Thiamine)	1mg	Water	
Riboflavin	1.5mg	(liquid)	1.5 litres
Nicotinic acid	15-20mg	(food sources)	0.8 litre
Vitamin C	30mg		

Note: In the past, vitamins A and D were measured in International Units (IU). This form of measurement is now obsolete.

WATER

Water is absolutely essential to life. It makes up two-thirds of body weight, forming the main ingredient in blood, lymph, cell liquid, extracellular fluid and digestive secretions.

GENERAL PROPERTIES
1. Pure water has no colour, taste or smell.
2. Its pH value is neutral. It is neither acid nor alkaline.
3. It is a good solvent, being capable of dissolving many substances.
4. It readily absorbs and retains heat.
5. It freezes at 0°C and boils at 100°C.
6. At over 100°C, it converts to water vapour.
7. It evaporates easily.

Diseases of Malnutrition
Many of these are diseases which can be prevented.

Disease	Description	Symptoms/Effects	Prevention/Treatment
Anaemia (page 38)	Lack of haemoglobin in blood	Tiredness, lack of energy	Increase iron/vitamin C intake
Anorexia nervosa (page 37)	Psychosis causing self-starvation	Lack of energy, emaciation, death	Psychotherapy and diet
Beriberi (page 19)	Disease of nerves	Paralysis, death	Increase thiamine (B_1) intake
Bowel disorders (page 40)	Constipation, diverticulitis, cancer	Difficulty in defecation, abdominal pain	Increase fibre intake
Coronary heart disease (page 37)	Hardening and blockage of coronary arteries	Chest pain, lack of energy, heart attack, death	Substitute polyunsaturated oils for animal fats, reduce weight, stop smoking. Exercise
Dental caries	Bacteria/plaque form acids which destroy enamel	Cavities, loss of teeth	Increase calcium/vitamin D intake
Goitre	Reduction in thyroxine — hormone which controls metabolism	Lack of energy, obesity, swollen neck	Increase iodine intake
Kwashiorkor	Third World disease due to starvation	Apathy, retarded growth, odema causing swollen abdomen	Increase protein/energy intake
Marasmus	Disease of Third World children, due to total lack of nutrients	Lack of energy, fretfulness, emaciation, wizened appearance, death	Increase food, particularly kilocalorie intake
Obesity	Body is more than 20% overweight.	Tiredness, lack of energy. Strain on many organs, including heart.	Follow a low-energy diet. Increase exercise.
Pellagra	Common in Third World. Caused by lack of nicotinic acid (B group)	Diarrhoea, depression, dermatitis, dementia, death	Increase protein foods, particularly liver
Rickets/Osteomalacia	Bones of children do not harden. Calcium lost from adult bones.	Deformed bones	Increase calcium/vitamin D intake, for example, more exposure to sun.
Scurvy	Caused by lack of vitamin C	Lack of energy, wounds don't heel, sore bleeding gums, pains in limbs	Increase vitamin C intake
Starvation	Lack of several nutrients	See Marasmus/Kwashiorkor	Sufficient protein/energy in diet
Xeropthalmia	Third World disease of eyes due to lack of vitamin A	Eye infections leading to blindness, night blindness	Increase vitamin A intake

ELEMENTAL COMPOSITION

Water is composed of hydrogen and oxygen in the ratio of 2:1 (H_2O).

SOURCES OF WATER

Water is obtained from drinking water, milk and from beverages such as tea and alcoholic drinks. Foods with a high percentage of water include fruit and green vegetables.

FUNCTIONS OF WATER

1. Transport: Water (as blood) transports nutrients, oxygen, CO_2, blood cells, hormones and enzymes around the body.
2. Helps to control body temperature by evaporating perspiration from the skin.
3. Distributes heat generated by metabolism.
4. Dissolves food, aids digestion (hydrolysis) and absorption.
5. Assists in the removal of waste through the kidneys.
6. Essential ingredient of all body cells.
7. Water is often a source of minerals such as calcium and fluorine.
8. It quenches thirst.

DAILY REQUIREMENT

As 2-2.5 litres of water are lost daily by excretion, perspiration and breathing, an equal amount is required daily by the body to avoid dehydration — 1.5 litres in beverages, 0.8 litre in foods.

MALNUTRITION

Malnutrition is defined as a long term imbalance of nutrients in the diet. It may be caused by lack of a

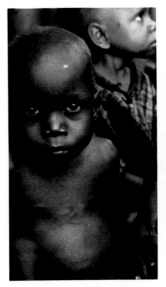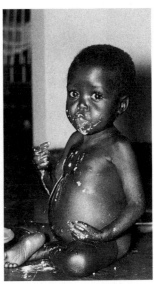

Child suffering from and recovering from marasmus
(S. and R. Greenhill [left] C. James Webb [right])

nutrient, such as protein or a vitamin, or by overeating, as in the case of obesity.

General symptoms of malnutrition include tiredness, feeling run down, dry skin and dull hair.

UNDERNUTRITION

This is an all-too-frequent part of life for the poor in Third World countries. It occurs when the total intake of nutrients is less than the body's requirements. Energy intake is inadequate and the diet is deficient in important nutrients, resulting in starvation in severe cases. Diseases of undernutrition often occur in young children, particularly after weaning. They include marasmus and kwashiorkor (see chart).

► THE COLOUR AND FLAVOUR OF FOOD

All food is composed of chemical substances. These are responsible for its colour, flavour, structure and nutritive value. Some colours occur naturally in food. Others are placed there by the manufacturer in order to make the food taste appealing and look more attractive. This, however, may have little to do with a food's nutritive value.

PHYSICAL ASPECTS OF COLOUR

- As colour is probably the first thing we notice in a shop or on a plate, it plays an important part in our choice of food.
- Bright greens, reds, oranges and the rich browns of roast meat and gravy tempt us to eat.
- Unappetising colours such as grey mashed potatoes put us off food.

Colour makes food more appealing
(Denis Hughes-Gilbey)

- Colour is a good guide to quality and freshness. A yellow, wilted cabbage or a bruised apple or orange shows us at once that it is inferior in taste and food value.
- Colour can show that a food is bad, as with slime and mould on food.
- Colours should be considered when menu planning in order to make the food look more attractive.

CHEMICAL ASPECTS OF COLOUR

- Colour pigments provide colour in foods such as tea, coffee, cocoa (tannin), green plants (chlorophyll). Carotene gives carrots, tomatoes and some shellfish their orange-red colour and cream its pale yellow colour. The pigment in red cabbage is retained by the use of vinegar.
- The colour of animal foods is often affected by their diet. This can be seen in the pale colour of milk-fed veal and the colour of egg shells and yolks.
- Oxidation: The reaction of oxygen with enzymes in foods causes discolouration, such as browning apples.
- Some colours are associated with flavours — yellow with lemon, red with strawberry.
- Cooking causes changes in colour.
  (a) Carbohydrates break down to short chain dextrins.
  (b) Maillard reaction — reaction of amino acids with carbohydrates, e.g. fried potatoes.
  (c) Myoglobin, the colour pigment in meat, is denatured to a brown pigment haemin. (Myoglobin also takes up oxygen to form the bright red oxyhaemoglobin of freshly cut meat.)
  (d) Caramelisation of sugar by heat.
  (e) Overcooking causes carbonisation or blackening.

THE PHYSICAL ASPECTS OF FLAVOUR

- The flavour of food depends on two factors: taste and smell.
- We can anticipate the flavour of a food by its aroma. One of the reasons why hot bread shops enticed us away from the sliced pan was their enticing aroma of freshly-baked bread.

- The appetising odour of food stimulates our digestive juices.
- We can detect when some foods have gone bad by their odour and flavour — eggs, sour milk, rancid fat.

HOW WE TASTE FOOD

1. The sight or aroma of food stimulates saliva production. This helps to dissolve food when we eat it.
2. Chemicals present in food stimulate the 9,000 or so sensory cells or taste buds on the surface of the tongue.
3. These are arranged in groups which are sensitive to four different kinds of taste: sweet, sour, salty and bitter.
4. Nerve endings in the nose are sensitive to the food chemicals which are dissolved in the air, which passes upward from the mouth. These interpret the more subtle differences of flavour. When the nose is blocked during a cold, we cannot taste the food because the nerve endings are covered with thick mucous.

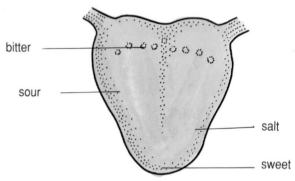

THE CHEMICAL ASPECTS OF FLAVOUR

- Essential oils are produced in the plant by oil glands. They are composed mainly of carbon and hydrogen, although sulphur is present in some pungent oils, causing the strong smell in garlic, horseradish, onions and mustard.
- The bark, seeds and roots of plants may be dried to produce spices or dissolved in alcohol to produce essences.
- Natural food flavourings include salt, sugar, acids — for example vinegar, herbs and spices.
- Cooking introduces new flavours either by the effect of heat (see above) or by the blending of various foods.
- Sourness is determined by the hydrogen ion concentration in the food.

Other physical factors which influence our evaluation and enjoyment of food are texture, shape, moistness and crispness. When these qualities are missing from food, it is considered unappetising. Many additives fool our eyes and tastebuds into thinking a food is better than it is — read on!

FOOD ADDITIVES

Additives are natural or artificial substances, not usually regarded as foods themselves, which are added to food to improve its appearance, taste, texture and keeping quality or to assist processing.

Food additives are not permitted when they:
1. disguise faulty processing
2. deceive the consumer
3. reduce the nutritive value of food.

Additives may be:
1. natural, for example, salt, sugar, spice
2. nature-identical (chemicals which are made synthetically but which are chemically identical to those found in nature)
3. synthetic (chemicals made artificially and not identical to natural substances).

SAFEGUARDS

Each country has legislation which controls the purity of food and the use of additives in food, stipulating the maximum levels of them which may be used (for example, our Health Regulation Act, 1973). A joint Food and Agricultural Organisation of the UN (FAO) and World Health Organisation (WHO) Committee (JECFA) monitors and sets out guidelines for the use of additives. They must:
- satisfy a technological need
- satisfy a consumer demand
- be toxicologically acceptable

(Toxicological studies must follow strict procedures — a minimum of six different wide-ranging tests is required.) Studies have their limits, however, and the safety of an additive cannot be definitely proven. As many different foods are eaten, containing hundreds of different additives, there is the danger that a 'cocktail' mixture of several additives could have ill effects. Some additives are known to cause allergies (see Synthetic Colours), others are suspected of having carcinogenic (cancer-producing) effects. The safest course is to avoid the more artificial or convenience foods and to eat natural, organically-grown foods as far as possible. Even natural foods can cause problems, though. The following foods sometimes produce allergic reaction: cows' milk, chocolate, citrus fruit, tomatoes. There is no doubt that additives are an important and, in most cases, necessary part of modern food production. Without them we would have a far more restricted choice of food, and food would be more susceptible to contamination, resulting in food poisoning.

E NUMBERS

EC regulations require each additive in processed food to be listed on the package with its *E number*. An E number is given to each additive (except flavours) which is generally considered safe to use in food. It is an extensive list containing both natural and synthetic substances.

It is continually under revision, since additives which are suspect are removed and replaced with safer ones.

CLASSIFICATION OF ADDITIVES
1. Colourings
2. Preservatives
3. Nutritive additives
4. Flavourings
5. Physical conditioning agents

Note: E numbers have been included for interest and to make additives in commercial products identifiable, but knowledge of numbers is not required for examinations.

COLOURINGS (E100–E180)

Colour in natural food is an indication of maturity, quality and freshness. Colourings are used in food:
1. to improve appearance of food.
2. to replace colour lost in preserving.
3. because of consumer demand.

Natural colours include:
- Annatto (E160B): yellow colour used in butter, cheese, margarine; obtained from seeds of a tropical tree.
- Caramel (E150): a brown colour obtained by heating carbohydrate.
- Chlorophyll (E140): green colour obtained from grass, nettles etc.
- Cochineal (E120): red colour obtained from a dried cactus insect.
- Saffron: yellow colour, oriental flavour; obtained from a crocus plant.

Synthetic Colours

These are cheaper, more permanent and have a greater range of colours. Many are derived from azo dyes (coal-tar dyes). About 10% of users, usually those with sensitivity to aspirin, may show allergic reactions such as itching, rashes, hay fever, asthma and migraine.

Examples of synthetic colours
- Riboflavin (E101) yellow
- Tartrazine (E102) yellow*
- Red (E128) used in cooked meats and currently under investigation.

* Tartrazine (E102): This and many other azo dyes can cause various unpleasant symptoms in certain susceptible people, for example those sensitive to aspirin. Symptoms include itching, hay fever, rashes, hyperactivity in children and sleeplessness.

Bleaching agents such as potassium bromate (E924) are used to whiten flour artificially. They destroy some nutrients, including vitamin E.

Colourings are used in many convenience foods, including soft drinks, sweets, jelly, jam, ice cream, smoked fish and canned vegetables. They are not permitted in fresh meat, fish, poultry, milk, milk products, fresh fruit and vegetables.

PRESERVATIVES (E200–E290)
Preservatives are used to:
1. prevent or retard growth of micro-organisms such as bacteria.
2. prevent action of enzymes.
3. prevent oxidation.
4. make food safer to eat.
5. prolong shelf life.
6. reduce waste.

Natural preservatives include sugar, salt, alcohol, spices, wood smoke, vinegar (acetic acid, E260).

Permitted chemical preservatives include:
■ Sorbic acid (E200) used in flour, cakes, processed foods.
■ Benzoic acid (E210) used in coffee.
■ Sulphur dioxide (E220) used in many convenience foods, bacon products, sausages.
■ Sodium and potassium nitrates (saltpetre) used in cured meats. They prevent botulism but may have side effects.

Preservatives are used in a wide range of foods — yoghurt, cakes, pickles, convenience foods, fruit juice. There are strict limits on the amounts permitted. Most preservatives are banned in baby foods.

Antioxidants (E300–E321)
These are substances which react with the oxygen in the air, delaying or preventing oxidation which causes rancidity in lipid foods such as cooking oils, crisps, biscuits etc. Anti-oxidants also prevent discolouration in fruit and vegetables.

Natural antioxidants: Vitamin C (E300), Vitamin E (E306).
Synthetic antioxidants: BHA (butylated hydroxyanisole, E320), BHT (butylated hydroxytoluene, E321).

These antioxidants are used in many packaged foods and in strictly controlled quantities.

NUTRITIVE ADDITIVES (DIETARY SUPPLEMENTS)
These are used to:
1. replace nutrients lost in processing or
2. increase the food value of a product, usually with the object of increasing sales.

Margarine must have A and D vitamins added. (They occur naturally in butter.)

Flour: Iron and some B vitamins are added to white flour. Extra calcium is added to white flour to counteract the effect of phytic acid (pages 23, 25).

Breakfast cereals may have added B vitamins and iron. Fruit drinks and instant mashed potato often have added vitamin C.

Baby milks have nutrients added to make them similar to breast milk.

Fluoride is added to water to reduce dental caries.

Most convenience foods contain additives

FLAVOURINGS
These do not come under the rulings controlling E prefixes, but are controlled by normal food laws relating to food quality. Flavourings improve the flavour of food which may deteriorate during processing or storage.

1. *Natural Flavourings*
Herbs, spices, sugar, salt, citric acid.
Essences are obtained by dissolving strongly-flavoured plants etc. in a solvent, such as alcohol. Vanilla pod treated in this way produces vanilla essence.

2. *Synthetic Flavourings*
These are made by imitating the complex chemical structure of natural flavourings and synthesising them from chemicals.
Examples:
(a) Compounds prepared from natural substances, for example, maltol (E636) from tree bark which gives a 'freshly-baked' odour to bread and cakes.
(b) Esters: Amyl acetate (pear flavour), ethyl acetate (rum flavour).
(c) Aldehydes: Benzaldehyde (almond/cherry flavour).

3. *Flavour Enhancers*
These intensify the natural flavours in food by stimulating the taste buds. They do not have a flavour of their own.

Monosodium glutamate (E621) is derived from an amino acid. Excessive use causes nausea, headache and palpitations. It is used in many packet and snack foods such as crisps, soups and flavoured noodles.

Flavour enhancers are not permitted in baby foods.

4. *Synthetic Sweeteners*

These are substances, other than sugar, which produce a sweet taste. Some, such as sorbitol (E420), are half as sweet as sugar and, like sugar, produce energy. Others are non-caloric, including saccharine and Nutrasweet (page 76).

PHYSICAL CONDITIONING AGENTS (E222–E494)

These maintain or alter the condition/consistency of food.

1. *Emulsifiers*

Function in food:

- to force oil and water to mix without separating
- to maintain consistency of many foods

Emulsifiers include: lecithin (E322) from soya or egg yolk; alginates (E400) from seaweed; plant gums (E410–E416); pectin (E440); carrageen (E407); GMS glyceryl monostearate (E471), a synthetic emulsifier/stabiliser used in salad dressings, desserts, ice cream.

2. *Stabilisers*

Stabilisers prevent droplets in emulsions from coalescing by thickening the product or increasing viscosity. Many also thicken foods and increase the antioxidant effect.

Stabilisers include citric acid (E330), alginates (see Emulsifiers) and polyphosphates (E450). Polyphosphates are used in theory to tenderise meat (ham, chicken). But they have the effect of making meat spongy, so that it absorbs water when meat is tumbled in the polyphosphates during processing. Sometimes, up to 50% by weight is added so that one pays meat prices for water!

3. *Thickeners*

These add to the viscosity of food. Most are obtained from plants or seaweed (see Emulsifiers).

OTHER PHYSICAL CONDITIONING AGENTS

- *Anti-caking agents:* Used in foods such as salt and icing sugar to prevent lumping and to help them to flow freely. Examples: Stearic acid (E570), kaolin (E559), calcium silicate (E552).
- *Anti-foaming agents:* Prevent scum and froth on boiling.
- *Anti-spattering agents:* Stabilisers such as lecithin are used in cooking fats and oils to keep water droplets apart.
- *Buffers:* Bases/alkalis used to maintain pH at required level.
- *Bulking agent:* Used to increase the bulk of food such as slimming foods, or to replace more expensive ingredients, making food cheaper to produce.

- *Firming agents:* Prevent fruit and vegetables from softening during processing, for example calcium and magnesium salts.
- *Gelling agents:* Substances such as stabilisers which also form a gel.
- *Glazing agents:* Agents such as mineral hydrocarbons (E905–E907) put a shine on food and prevent it from drying out. Used in dried fruit, sweets and chewing gum.
- *Humectants:* These absorb water vapour from the air and prevent food from drying out. Examples: sorbitol (E420), mannitol (E421), glycerol (E422), all of which are also sweeteners. They are used in confectionery, sweets and ice cream.
- *Modified starch:* Used to thicken and bulk out foods, (E1400-E1442). Numbered before EC rules used E prefixes.
- *Packaging gas:* Inert gas sealed into sachet foods to replace air and to prevent oxidation.
- *Release agents:* Coatings on food which prevent them from sticking during processing.
- *Sequestrants:* These combine with trace metals in food such as calcium, iron and copper to inhibit the oxidising effect these have on food.

FOOD ADDITIVES

ADVANTAGES

1. They make it possible to provide large numbers of people with a wide choice of food.
2. They improve colour and flavour of less attractive or bland foods.
3. They ensure a consistent quality of food.
4. Preservatives help to prevent food poisoning.
5. They preserve food, thus increasing shelf life and reducing waste.

DISADVANTAGES

1. Many have side effects including hyperactivity in children and allergies in adults.
2. Some may have a cumulative effect, eventually reaching toxic level.
3. Many, including polyphosphates and bulking agents, deceive the consumer and produce a cheaper, less wholesome product.

CONTAMINANTS

Contaminants are substances which are present in food unintentionally or illegally. They are generally harmful to the body. These may include: antibiotics; hormones; insecticides remaining in food due to bad farming practices; mercury; radioactivity sometimes found in fish; lubricants; dissolved metals and foreign bodies which may find their way into food during manufacture.

2 PLANNING THE DIET

From childhood we adopt the eating patterns of our parents and absorb many of their attitudes about food. So it is important that parents set a healthy example by purchasing nutritious foods and planning well-balanced meals for their family. Our choice of food affects how we feel and how we look. Choose wisely! Remember: you are what you eat!

Healthy eating habits start in childhood
(S. and R. Greenhill)

► A BALANCED DIET

A well balanced diet will contain all the necessary nutrients in the correct proportion for the weight and needs of the individual. It is generally accepted that a balanced diet will contain approximately:

> 1/6 protein — half animal, half vegetable ⎱ ratio of
> 2/6 fat — half animal, half vegetable ⎬ energy
> 3/6 carbohydrate — including dietary fibre ⎰ foods

Essential vitamins and minerals must also be present. The best way to ensure a healthy diet is to eat a varied selection of fresh foods, including whole cereals, fresh vegetables and fruit, some of which should be eaten raw. An unbalanced diet will fail to provide all the essential nutrients. As a result, deficiency diseases may occur.

DIETARY REQUIREMENTS

All humans need the same basic nutrients in order to stay healthy, but they need them in different amounts. Whoever is responsible for family meals must be aware of the type and amount of food required by each family member.

Reminder: Food requirements vary according to the rate of growth, age, body size/build, gender, activity and state of health.

1. BABIES

Breast feeding, if it is possible, gives babies a better start in life for a number of reasons.

- The nutrients in breast milk are in the right proportion and at the correct temperature for the needs of a baby, unlike cow's milk.
- Breast milk contains much more vitamin C and vitamin D.

Breast feeding is better for baby (S. and R. Greenhill)

- Antibodies pass from mother to child through breast milk. This helps the baby resist infections.
- Such close contact between mother and baby provides close psychological bonding.
- Breast milk is more hygienic. This is particularly important in Third World countries where sterilising facilities may be limited.
- There is danger of overdiluting or underdiluting formula preparations. Feeds which are too concentrated can cause dehydration, a condition which may be fatal in infants.

Strict hygiene must be observed when making up bottle feeds. Cow's milk must be diluted in water. Never make up more than one day's supply of feeds. Be sure to store these in a refrigerator until required. When using a dried milk formula, follow the manufacturer's instructions exactly. Never give an extra scoop and do not heap the scoop when measuring.

A baby's growth rate is very rapid indeed. New-born babies feed at three-hourly to four-hourly intervals. As they grow, larger feeds are given at longer intervals. Milk feeds should be supplemented after a few weeks with vitamin C (orange juice) and vitamins A and D (cod and liver oil). Later, iron should be added to the diet by giving the baby egg yolk and strained green vegetables. (A baby is born with enough iron to last six months.)

These additional foods also prepare the baby for weaning — changing to a mixed diet when solids and other new foods are introduced at 4-6 months. Weaning should be done gradually, with one food introduced at a time. The foods should be puréed or sieved. Do not add salt or sugar. Use fresh foods which are concentrated sources of nutrients, such as liver, white fish, fruit, vegetables and egg yolk (egg white is indigestible by infants). Limit the amount of sugar, cereals and fruit squashes.

2. CHILDREN
Food for children should be highly nutritious and attractively presented in small, easy-to-manage helpings. Introduce new foods gradually, and keep seasonings and spices to a minimum.
Special Needs
- Concentrated (animal) protein. Children are growing rapidly.
- Calcium for strong bones and teeth.
- Energy foods. Children are very active. (Make sure that energy sources are nourishing, high-fibre foods, not sugary products and snack foods.)

Avoid feeding sugary and snack foods to children

- Vitamins and minerals will be provided by fresh fruit, vegetables and sunshine.
- Fibre and B vitamins which are obtained from high-fibre cereals and brown bread. Encourage children to eat raw vegetables and fruit.

They should avoid:
- Eating between meals
- Faddy habits
- Sweet, sugary foods and drinks
- Over-processed foods
- Fried and salted foods

3. ADOLESCENTS
The teenage years are also a period of rapid growth. Adolescents have greater nutritional needs than any other group.
- Plenty of animal and vegetable protein is required.
- Energy foods will depend on activity. An inactive teenager can become obese. On the other hand, too great an emphasis on slimness may result in anorexia nervosa.
- Iron and vitamin C are important, especially for girls. Anaemia is not uncommon among adolescent females.
- While acne is due to hormone activity, a reduction in fatty foods can help to reduce its severity.
- A good, mixed diet is important. Avoid too many snack foods. This is a dangerous time for slimming. Many teenagers try crank diets, but only diets supervised by a doctor or dietician should be undertaken.

4. ADULTS
The average adult also requires a well-balanced diet.
- Protein is mainly required for cell replacement and repair. 2 x 100g portions of animal protein and 2 x 100g portions of vegetable protein will fulfil daily needs. Energy intake will depend on how active the lifestyle.
- Fruit and vegetables, preferably raw or lightly cooked, will provide vitamins, minerals and fibre.
- Sedentary workers should restrict high-energy foods, particularly animal fat and sugar. They should get as much exercise as possible.

5. MANUAL WORKERS
This group uses a great deal of energy. They should concentrate on energy sources which also supply other nutrients, particularly the vitamin B group which is involved in the release of energy from food.
Suitable foods are:
- Whole cereals, pulse vegetables, oily fish, meat, cheese.
- Vegetable fats are preferable to animal fats.

6. PREGNANT/NURSING MOTHERS

The diet of a woman during pregnancy and lactation is extremely important, as the health of both the mother and her baby depends on it. This does not mean that she 'eats for two'. It is the quality of the food rather than the quantity which is important. A pregnant woman requires a more concentrated diet of nutritious foods. Energy requirements are only slightly higher during pregnancy. Maximum weight gain should be 12 kg (about 28 lbs). Women who put on too much weight at this time risk hypertension (high blood pressure), difficulties at birth, varicose veins etc. They may also experience difficulty losing weight after the birth.

A poor diet during pregnancy often results in an undersized baby which has a greater likelihood of peri-natal death.

Pregnant and nursing mothers require:
- Calcium and vitamin D for bone formation.
- Protein for the developing foetus, placenta and milk production.
- Iron (and vitamin C) for the manufacture of red blood cells. If the blood count is low, a doctor may prescribe supplements of iron or folic acid, a B group vitamin essential for the formation of blood cells.
- Fibre rich foods, to avoid constipation.
- Vitamins A and B for general health, eyes, nerves etc.

Note: Take no medication unless instructed to do so by your doctor. Avoid alcohol and cigarettes — they are very bad for the baby.

7. THE ELDERLY

Most elderly people can continue to follow a normal, well-balanced diet. But kilocalorie intake should be reduced because both metabolism and the level of physical activity usually slow down as people get older. They must take care to avoid getting overweight.

Reduced income, difficulty in getting to the shops, problems such as arthritis and rheumatism which make it difficult to cook, and mental confusion can be responsible for inadequate diets among the elderly. Many are apathetic and exist on nutritionally unsound staples such as white bread and may have difficulty in chewing due to loss of teeth.

Meals-on-Wheels is a social service which does much to improve the diet of the housebound elderly.

Dietary and Other Problems of Elderly	Cause/Cure
Anaemia	Insufficient iron
Arthritis	Controlled diet may help
Atherosclerosis (heart disease)	Life style and diet — reduce animal fat
Blood pressure (high)	Reduce salt
Brittle bones	Calcium deficiency
Constipation	Due to insufficient fibre
Diverticulitis (inflamed pockets in intestine)	Increase fibre intake
Hypothermia	Lack of warmth
Susceptibility to infection	Protective nutrients, especially vitamin C

Suitable Foods for the Elderly

- Protein is needed for cell replacement and repair. Good digestible sources are liver, white fish, chicken and eggs (although too many eggs will raise cholesterol level).
- Anaemia may be a problem. Liver is a cheap, iron-rich food.
- Calcium and vitamin D are required in order to prevent bone degeneration (osteoporosis). Cheese will provide both calcium and protein, although it may be indigestible and high in cholesterol unless low fat cheeses are used. Sunlight is important for the elderly.
- Vitamin A is essential for healthy eyes, skin and membranes.
- Vitamin C is important for blood vessels, healing and iron absorption. (Many elderly people take insufficient vitamin C and suffer from a mild form of scurvy.)
- Vitamin B: whole wheat cereals, bread, porridge Fibre: pulse vegetables and fruit
- Minerals: Reduce salt intake to avoid high blood pressure.
- Avoid animal fats, sugar and snack foods.
- Healthy convenience foods such as tinned beans and frozen vegetables can be a boon to the elderly because they are easy to prepare and cook, and are available in small quantities.

8. INVALIDS

Food for an invalid and convalescent should provide the maximum amount of nourishment in the least amount of bulk.

A patient usually passes through three stages: illness, recovery and convalescence.

- *Illness/fever:* The patient has little inclination to eat. Provide plenty of liquids — fruit drinks, water, watered milk and broths — to prevent dehydration.

- *Recovery:* The patient starts to improve and is able to eat small amounts of easily digested solids such as milk, lightly cooked eggs and breast of chicken. Avoid fats as they are indigestible and energy needs are low at this time. Cooking methods include steaming, stewing and poaching.

- *Convalescence:* The appetite is returning to normal and activity is increasing. Ensure a concentrated supply of protein, vitamins and minerals.

Essential Foods
- Protein: To repair diseased, damaged and wasted tissue.
- Vitamin C: Helps to heal tissues and wounds; prevents bed sores.

- Vitamin A: Prevents various infections; necessary for membranes.
- Iron: Prevents anaemia, common in illness.
- Roughage: Prevents constipation which is common after operations and when patients are bedridden.
- Energy foods: Reduce these and concentrate on easily digested, nutritious food.

Rules
1. Follow doctor's orders.
2. Use best quality fresh food. Avoid leftovers and convenience foods.
3. Observe strictest hygiene in the kitchen and sick room.
4. Choose light, easily digested foods which are high in nutrients.
5. Avoid fried foods, fatty meats, rich puddings and highly seasoned foods.
6. Serve small portions. A few small meals are better than one or two larger ones.
7. Serve meals regularly on a clean, attractively set tray.

► SPECIAL DIETS

CONDITIONS REQUIRING DIETARY RESTRICTIONS

It is essential that anyone embarking on a specialised diet has a sound knowledge of nutrition. It is a wise precaution to obtain a doctor's permission before starting any diet, particularly for pregnant women or for those who are still growing — children and teenagers.

1. OBESITY

Obesity is a condition in which the body accumulates an excessive amount of fat. A person is considered to be obese if body weight is 20% above the normal weight for a person's height.

About one-third of adults in the western world are obese. It is more common in the lower socio-economic groups, probably due to the fact that many cheaper foods are high in kilocalories. Obesity is much more common in children today than was the case in the past. The condition is not necessarily hereditary. It is more often found among children within a family because they follow the same eating patterns as those of their overweight parents, causing extra fat cells to form.

Causes of Obesity
1. The most frequent cause is the consumption of more energy (in the form of food and drink) than the body uses up. Energy is required by the body for:

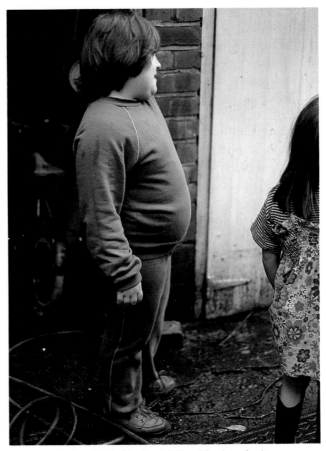

Bad eating habits in childhood lead to obesity
(S. and R. Greenhill)

- basal metabolism
- physical activity
- maintenance of body temperature

Once these needs have been met, any excess is stored as fat.

2. Obesity is more common among people who lead sedentary lives. Work and leisure patterns have become more passive. For example, television watching takes up more leisure time today than more active pastimes.

3. Psychological problems may be behind many cases of obesity. Emotional factors such as depression and boredom may trigger off the urge to eat. *Bulimia nervosa*, or binge eating, is such a case where large quantities of high-calorie foods are eaten at one time.

4. Hormone imbalance is usually caused by deficiency of the thyroid hormone, thyroxine, which controls metabolism. This slows down metabolism, causing overweight.

5. Fluid retention (oedema)

Problems associated with, or aggravated by, obesity

- Low self image
- Accidents are more common
- Diabetes
- Gall bladder problems
- Respiratory problems
- Heart disease
- High blood pressure
- Infertility in woman
- Osteoarthritis
- Toxaemia and difficulty in childbirth
- Varicose veins
- Shorter life expectancy

Prevention of Obesity

Prevention of obesity is much simpler than its cure. Learn to stop eating before you feel really full. Health and nutrition education are particularly essential. It is important that parents ensure that healthy eating is encouraged in the home and that 'junk', sugary foods discouraged. The best way to do this is to *avoid buying this type of food*.

Dietary Changes

Permanent weight reduction involves reducing kilocalorie intake, increasing physical activity, or both. When a diet provides less energy than required, the body will use up its fat stores to supply the energy needed, thus causing a reduction in weight.

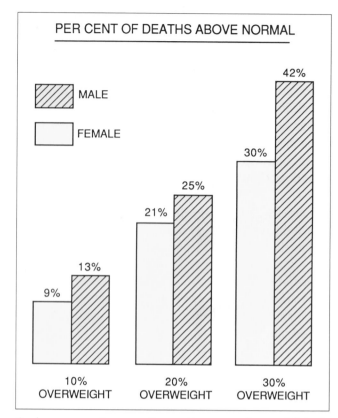

PER CENT OF DEATHS ABOVE NORMAL

MALE
FEMALE

42%
30%
25%
21%
13%
9%

10% OVERWEIGHT
20% OVERWEIGHT
30% OVERWEIGHT

1. A permanent new eating pattern must be established, consisting of a well balanced diet of low calorie foods — but not based on kilocalories alone. Eat three nutritious meals a day.

2. Restrict carbohydrates such as sugar, sweets and biscuits which have little nutritional value. Concentrate instead on high-fibre carbohydrates which give a feeling of fullness with fewer kilocalories.

3. Reduction of carbohydrates helps to reduce fat intake — less bread means less butter. Do not cook food in fat.

4. Protein intake should be maintained, but choose low calorie proteins such as white fish, lean meat, offal, chicken and skimmed milk.

5. Eat plenty of green and fruit-type vegetables such as tomatoes and cucumbers. Use them raw, as in undressed salads. Fruit is also beneficial and reasonably low in energy.

6. Remember: No food is slimming. No food burns up energy quickly. Slimming tablets, crash diets etc. have little lasting effect and may be dangerous.

7. Avoid alcohol. Drink plenty of water.

8. Exercise is excellent for toning up muscles and gives a feeling of well being. A considerable amount of exercise must be taken to produce weight loss.

9. Motivation is essential if one is to stay on a diet. Joining a slimming club provides support and motivation.

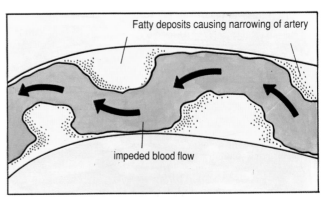

ANOREXIA NERVOSA

A discussion on slimming is not complete without mentioning the 'slimmer's disease'. *Anorexia nervosa* is a complex psychological condition which usually affects adolescent girls in which they drastically reduce weight by excessive dieting. It is a neurosis — an inability to see oneself as one really is. Patients develop an obsessive aversion to food, often due to emotional stress or a fear of growing up. They become emaciated and may eventually die unless treated by psychotherapy and a special dietary regime.

*Adolescent girls who diet excessively may become anorexic
(S. and R. Greenhill)*

Artherosclerosis

The chances of developing heart disease increase with age, particularly for males with a history of the disease in the family. However, there are other factors which can be improved by a change of diet and lifestyle. Coronary heart disease is a major cause of death in the western world, almost certainly because of our stressful and inactive lifestyle and our tendency to smoke and drink too much.

The main causes of heart disease are:

- incorrect diet
- high alcohol consumption
- cigarette smoking
- lack of exercise
- obesity
- stress
- heredity

2. HEART DISEASE

Coronary heart disease is a reduction of the flow of blood through the coronary arteries which supply blood to the heart muscle. This is caused by atherosclerosis, an accumulation of fatty substances including cholesterol, on the walls of the arteries, and a gradual hardening of the arteries themselves. This causes the diameter of the arteries to become smaller, slowing down circulation and causing the blood pressure to increase. As a result, the heart has to work harder to pump the blood around the body. Coronary thrombosis (heart attack) occurs when a clot blocks one of the narrow arteries.

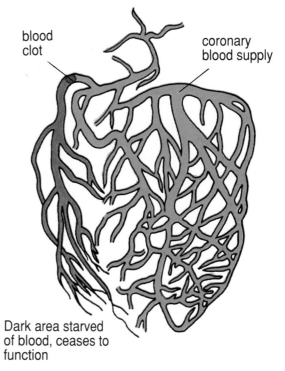

How a heart attack occurs

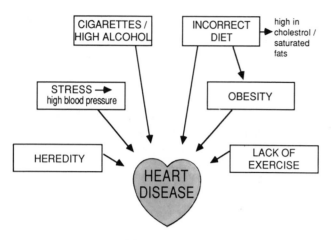

Factors which contribute to heart disease

Cholesterol

This is a fatty substance (steroid) in the blood which helps to convey fat through the body. It occurs naturally in the body, being synthesised by the liver. Cholesterol is also taken in foods, particularly those containing animal fat. Excess is deposited on the walls of the arteries, although this is thought to be less likely if plenty of exercise is taken. Over 260mg cholesterol per millilitre of blood is high risk.

To reduce the possibility of heart disease

1. Reduce intake of foods rich in saturated fats and cholesterol such as butter and animal fats.
2. Replace these foods with those containing unsaturated fats (see below).
3. Keep body at the correct weight for height. Reduce weight, if necessary.
4. Take regular exercise.
5. Do not smoke, and keep alcohol to a minimum.
6. Avoid worry and stress. Develop a more relaxed attitude to life.

Diet for those with heart disease

- Avoid: egg yolk, shellfish, too much red meat, fat meat and offal, fried foods, butter, cream, sugar, dripping.
- Eat plenty of: fruit ,vegetables, fish (oily and white); whole cereals and other fibre foods.

Sources of cholesterol, saturated and polyunsaturated fats

Cholesterol	Saturated fat	Polyunsaturated oils
Egg yolk	Suet, lard, dripping	Sunflower seed oil
Offal	Butter, cream	Corn, peanut, soya oil
Shellfish	Hard cheese	Soft margarines, (labelled so)
Dairy products	Hard margarine	Most nuts, oily fish

- Substitute skim milk for whole milk. Substitute skimmed milk cheese, such as cottage cheese or quark, for full milk cheeses such as cheddar.
- Substitute fish and chicken for red meats. Eat vegetable protein foods such as pulses and cereals instead of animal protein.
- Substitute polyunsaturated spreads for butter

3. ANAEMIA

Anaemia is the name given to a shortage of haemoglobin, or red cells, in the blood. Its symptoms are tiredness, breathlessness, lack of energy, headaches.

Anaemia may be caused by:
- Shortage of iron in the diet. This is corrected simply by increasing intake of iron-rich foods, particularly liver, kidney, red meat, whole cereals, brown bread, pulse and green vegetables, parsley, or by iron supplements.
- Defective absorption of iron. This may be due to a deficiency of vitamin C, B_{12} or folic acid, all of which are required for proper absorption of iron.
- Frequent or heavy blood loss. Anaemia is very common among women (due to menstruation) and care should be taken during pregnancy that sufficient iron is taken. Iron or folic acid supplements may be prescribed.
- Pernicious anaemia is a more severe form. It is caused by a lack of a chemical in the gastric juice called the intrinsic factor which is necessary for the absorption of vitamin B_{12}. Pernicious anaemia is easily treated by the consumption of liver or vitamin B_{12} supplements.

4. DIABETES

The most frequent form of diabetes is *diabetes mellitus*. Insulin is a hormone secreted by the pancreas. It controls the level of sugar in the blood. Diabetes is a disease in which little or no insulin is produced so that excess glucose accumulates in the blood and is excreted by the kidneys, leaving little in the tissues for energy production.

The usual symptoms of diabetes are considerable increase in the amount of urine excreted (due to osmosis) and excessive thirst. Diabetes tends to be hereditary and is more common in people who are overweight.

The condition is controlled by:
- insulin injections
- diet (in milder cases)

Diet for diabetics

A diet must be worked out for each individual patient. It is basically a low-sugar diet. In the past, all carbohydrates were restricted but today this is rarely considered to be necessary. It is essential that a diabetic keeps strictly to the prescribed diet. Meals must be eaten at frequent intervals. Failure to comply with such directions can lead to coma.

Sorbitol: This is a natural sweetener made from glucose which is used in diabetic foodstuffs such as jam, chocolate and canned fruit. As it breaks down slowly, it does not raise blood sugar level significantly and less insulin is required.

Note: Sorbitol's calorie level remains the same as sugar. Saccharine, a synthetic sweetener, may also be used.

5. COELIAC DISEASE

This is a condition in which the patient is incapable of absorbing gluten. It is thought to be caused by the deficiency of an enzyme in the intestine which breaks down gluten. This causes gluten to be absorbed into the bloodstream as large peptide molecules instead of amino acids. This damages the sensitive mucous lining of the intestine and also interferes with the absorption of fat and some other nutrients. Those suffering for coeliac disease, usually children, fail to thrive. They lose weight and may show dietary deficiency symptoms such as anaemia.

Dietary treatment for coeliacs

All foods containing gluten must be omitted from the diet. These include all wheat products such as bread, cakes, biscuits, pastry, many breakfast cereals and pasta. A wide range of convenience foods such as sausages must also be avoided. Many of these are thickened with flour or cooked in breadcrumbs. Some snack foods, foods containing rye and, in some cases, oats and barley may also be forbidden.

Suitable foods for coeliacs include the following.
- Gluten-free flour is available and products such as bread are made from it.
- Cereals such as maize (cornflakes), rice etc. may be eaten.
- Cornflour may be used for thickening purposes.

6. GASTRIC AND DUODENAL ULCERS

An ulcer begins as an inflammation of the mucous membrane which gradually becomes an open sore and may eventually perforate the wall of an organ so that the contents escape. The action of pepsin and hydrochloric acid on the ulcer causes pain and discomfort. Gastric ulcers occur in the stomach, while duodenal ulcers are found at the start of the small intestine. Both are known as peptic ulcers.

Ulcers tend to be: (a) hereditary; (b) aggravated by smoking, alcohol and aspirin; (c) common in people who lead stressful lives.

Symptoms
- Severe pain, either before a meal (gastric), or two to three hours after a meal (duodenal ulcers).
- Internal bleeding, leading to anaemia.

- In severe cases, a perforated ulcer can result in peritonitis (inflammation of the abdominal membranes) and death.

Diet for ulcers
Irregular and rushed meals can help to cause ulcers.
- Eat small, frequent meals in a relaxed atmosphere.
- Avoid fried and spicy foods, alcohol and caffeine, as these irritate the mucous membrane.
- Follow a light diet of easily digested milky foods.
- Avoid tension and stress.
- Avoid smoking and alcohol.

7. GALL STONES

Gall stones are caused by an accumulation of cholesterol, bile salts and, occasionally, calcium salts in the gall bladder which stores bile. In many patients, they cause no problems as there are several small stones. Occasionally, one large stone occurs and when this blocks the bile duct, severe pain is felt. The gall bladder may become inflamed and jaundice may occur due to an accumulation of bile pigments. The usual treatment is to remove the stones surgically, although laser treatment is now being used to break them up.

A low cholesterol diet (see Heart Disease) helps to prevent gall stones. A low fat diet must be followed for any gall bladder problem in order to reduce the production of bile and to rest the gall bladder.

Gall stones are more common in females and those who are overweight.

8. LOW SALT DIET

The daily requirement of sodium in temperate climates is 1-2g per day. In situations which lead to a great deal of perspiration — living in hot climates, strenuous work or sport — more sodium will be required. Rarely, however, would it reach the average consumption in western countries which is 15g per day.

There is strong evidence to suppose that high salt consumption increases the risk of hypertension (high blood pressure, kidney failure and strokes). A reduction in salt intake reduces hypertension.

Dietary treatment
- Avoid adding salt at table.
- Reduce amounts of salt added to cooked dishes.
- Avoid bacon, tinned meat, salted and tinned fish, cheese.
- Avoid manufactured sauces, soups, cakes and biscuits.
- Avoid snack foods such as crisps and peanuts.
- In very severe cases, salt-free bread and milk may be required. Salt substitutes such as potassium chloride may be used.

9. ACNE

Acne vulgaris is a skin infection which is particularly common in adolescents due to increased production of sebum. It consists of an outbreak of blackheads which block the hair follicles. The blackhead consists of hardened sebum from the sebaceous glands. It is often surrounded by a circle of inflamed skin. If the area becomes badly infected, it may leave scars. It usually clears up after puberty.

Although not caused by diet, it is usually recommended that acne sufferers cut down on fats, such as fried foods and snack foods, increase their intake of fresh raw fruit and vegetables, and drink lots of water.

10. GASTROENTERITIS AND DIARRHOEA

Gastroenteritis (often called food poisoning) occurs when the gastrointestinal tract becomes inflamed. This is usually caused by bacteria and results in symptoms such as cramp-like pains, nausea, vomiting and diarrhoea. In the latter case, the bowel infection prevents the reabsorption of digestive liquids so that they pass out of the body with the undigested food. Dehydration is likely unless the intake of liquids is increased (particularly important in the case of infants).

Treatment
- Avoid all food for 24 hours.
- Drink lots of water.
- Gradually introduce easily digested low fat/low fibre foods such as dry toast, skimmed milk, steamed white fish and poached egg on toast.

Note: Be particularly scrupulous about personal and household hygiene, as such infections are especially contagious.

11. DIETARY FIBRE

Dietary fibre is made up of several complex chemicals, not all carbohydrates, which include cellulose, pectin and lignin. Dietary fibre forms the structural framework of plants and is present in the stem, seeds, leaves and roots of plants, particularly in the outer layers or the skin. It is most plentiful in whole cereals (and their products), nuts and pulse vegetables. Hard fruit and potatoes are also good sources, particularly when eaten with their skins. Wheat bran is a very important source as it contains 44% fibre.

In the past, dietary fibre, then called roughage, was considered to be an impurity in food. For this reason manufacturers and millers removed it from their products, resulting in white flour and bread which were considered to be superior to the wholemeal variety. Today, fibre is considered to be an essential part of a healthy diet.

The function of fibre

Dietary fibre can absorb large amounts of water (up to six times its own weight). As a result, it makes the waste food in the bowel soft and bulky. The muscular movements (peristalsis) of the intestinal wall are stimulated by the large mass so that the residue passes through more quickly.

When there is insufficient fibre in the diet, the faeces (residue of food) does not absorb water and becomes hard and difficult to propel forward and out of the body. This causes discomfort and constipation, and may cause painful distended pockets called diverticula to form in the wall of the intestine.

(a) High fibre diet
Faeces pass readily through the bowel

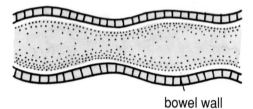

bowel wall

(b) Low fibre diet
Faeces more concentrated and hard

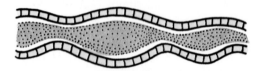

(c) Diverticulitis

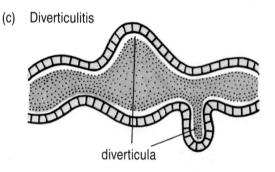

diverticula

Effects of fibre on bowel

Some scientists believe that the slow passage of residue through the bowel encourages the development of toxic products such as *carcinogenic* (cancer-forming) chemicals. Although this is difficult to prove, there is little doubt that cancer of the colon or bowel is becoming a common western disease which is almost unheard of in countries where a high-fibre diet is the norm.

The average western diet contains only half the recommended intake of dietary fibre, which is 30g.

Fibre-rich foods	(per 100g)	
Wheat bran (100g)	62.0g	dietary fibre
1 tablesp.	3.0g	
All Bran	27.5g	
Fresh/frozen peas	9.0g	
Wholemeal bread*	8.75g	
Muesli	8.0g	
Peanuts	8.0g	
Baked beans	7.3g	
Canned kidney beans	6.8g	
Sweetcorn	5.7g	
Brown rice (dry)	4.8g	
Brown bread*	4.5g	
White rice (dry)	2.8g	
Baked potato (skin eaten)	2.5g	
White bread*	2.5g	
Banana	2.3g	
Orange	1.0g	

* Compare the fibre content of different types of bread.

HIGH-FIBRE DIET

This is advantageous to all, particularly those suffering from obesity, constipation and other bowel disorders.

Advantages
1. A high-fibre diet reduces incidences of constipation and bowel disease by helping bowel movement.
2. Fibre produces no energy, therefore does not put on weight. When fibre-rich products replace high energy nutrients, fewer kJ/kc are eaten.
3. By absorbing water in the stomach, fibre produces a feeling of fullness so that less food is eaten.
4. Fibre is generally believed to reduce possibility of bowel cancer, heart disease, gall stones and appendicitis.
5. Fibre-rich foods are plentiful and often cheaper than other foods.

Disadvantages
1. Very large amounts of fibre tend to reduce the absorption of minerals such as zinc and iron, leading to anaemia.
2. Flatulence and increased bowel movements may be caused.

To follow a high fibre diet
- Choose whole wheat bread instead of white.
- Replace processed rice and pasta with the whole grain variety.
- Choose unprocessed, whole grain breakfast cereals instead of processed, high sugar brands.
- Eat lots of pulse vegetables such as peas, beans and lentils.
- Add a tablespoon of bran to your breakfast cereal.
- Choose nuts or prunes for a snack instead of sweets etc.
- Eat plenty of fruit, including dried fruit.
- Reduce sugar intake, including brown sugar which is almost as high in kJ/kc.

12. VEGETARIAN DIETS

Vegetarianism is the practice of living on vegetable foods. This is usually because an individual has a religious, humane or aesthetic reason for doing so. There are two types of vegetarian:
1. Lacto-vegetarians do not eat animal flesh or sometimes fish. They will eat animal products such as milk, eggs and cheese.
2. Strict vegetarians or vegans eat no animal food whatsoever and live entirely on plant foods.

Diet for vegetarians

Lacto-vegetarians present no problems as they can obtain all the nutrients they require. Vegans, on the other hand, run the risk of lack of iron, calcium and vitamin B_{12}. The latter can now be taken as a supplement. (It is made by the fermentation of micro-organisms.) A knowledge of plant sources of iron (green vegetables, cereals, pulses, dried fruit) should ensure that it is not deficient in the diet.

The supplementary value of proteins is important in the vegetarian diet so that vegetable foods deficient in one essential amino acid can be compensated for by eating a food rich in that amino acid.

There are four main groups for vegetarians.
1. Beans and nuts
2. Grains
3. Dairy produce (unsuitable for vegans)
4. Fruit and vegetables

To ensure that they get all the necessary nutrients, vegetarians must eat something every day from each food group.

Many orientals eat a largely vegetarian diet
(S. and R. Greenhill)

Vegetarians are rarely obese. They are also unlikely to suffer from high-cholesterol problems or those resulting from lack of fibre, such as diverticulitis, as their diet is traditionally low in saturated fat and high in fibre.

Points on vegetarian meals

1. Take extra care to ensure that the diet is well balanced. Provide a good variety of plant foods.
2. Good sources of vegetable proteins: pulse vegetables, cereals, dried pulses such as haricot beans, nuts.
3. Choose whole cereals for their extra fibre and vitamin B content.
4. Use vegetable fats such as margarine and oils only.
5. Use vegetable stock only.
6. Soya protein (TVP) may be used as a meat substitute. Soya milk may be used as a milk substitute.
7. Soya flour may be used to enrich dishes as it is a good source of protein, but it does not thicken as does wheat flour.

Suitable dishes for vegetarians

- Lactovegetarians: omelettes, quiches, pizza, curried eggs, macaroni cheese, in addition to the following.
- Vegans: vegetable casseroles and pies, salads, vegetable soups, fried rice, nut cutlets, soya protein (TVP) dishes, stuffed vegetables, wholemeal pastas such as vegetarian lasagne, many eastern dishes.

MACROBIOTIC DIET

This is based on the dietary practices of Japanese Buddhists. It is largely vegetarian and foods are organically grown without artificial fertilisers. Most preserved foods, sugar and chemicals are avoided.

HEALTH FOODS

The term 'health food' has evolved in the past couple of decades and its meaning is far from clear. The term seems to imply that 'normal' food is neither healthy nor 'organic',

which of course it is! There is little evidence that 'health foods' are more or less wholesome than normal food.

Many health food advocates are environmental groups who worry about the effect on our health of pesticides, herbicides, hormones, additives, and overprocessing on our food. While we must be conscious of these factors and careful of what we eat, the fact is that strict legislation controls such products and how they are used in foods (often to a greater degree than with organic foods). If controls are adhered to, things such as pesticides should present little danger. The main promoters of 'health foods' seem to be the producers and shop chains who play on one's fear of illness to sell their products.

Here are some of the products sold in health food stores.

- *'Natural' food* — free-range eggs, chickens, goat's milk, wholemeal bread.
- *Tonic foods* — which claim to have health-giving properties such as honey, yoghurt, royal jelly, ginsing.
- *Supplements* — vitamin and mineral preparations (all of which are unnecessary in a normal healthy diet), herb tea, yeast preparations, lecithin, protein powder.
- *'Organic' foods* — all foods are organic! This term generally suggest that inorganic (chemical) fertilisers have not been used when growing them. Chemical fertilisers and natural fertilisers such as manure are chemically much the same.
- *Wholefoods* — these are probably the only true health foods. They consist of high-fibre foods which have undergone little processing — wholemeal flour, whole grain rice and pasta, dried pulses such as lentils and kidney beans, nuts, seeds, grains such as buck wheat, and made-up products such as muesli.
- *Vegetarian and oriental products* such as soya oil, flour, milk, tofu, (soya bean curd), TVP/TSP, (page 53), water chestnuts, bamboo shoots, mung beans.

► MEAL PLANNING

When planning meals, consider the following points.

1. NUTRITIONAL VALUE

The meal should be nutritionally well balanced (see page 32). It should supply:

- Protein
- Sufficient energy foods (fats and carbohydrates) for body size, age and activity.
- All essential nutrients, including vitamins, minerals and fibre.

2. TIME AVAILABLE

Careful planning will avoid a last-minute rush. When time is short, use salads which need little or no cooking and quick-cooking methods such as grilling. Do not be tempted to use too many convenience foods.

3. MONEY AVAILABLE

The cost of food and fuel should be considered. Cheap foods like eggs and stewing meat are just as nourishing as expensive foods if money is scarce. Ready prepared

What influences our choice of food?

foods such as snack food, ready-made salads and pizzas usually work out quite expensive, as you are paying someone else to do the preparation.

4. THE TIME OF YEAR
- Serve more hot meals in winter, light cool meals in summer.
- Choose foods in season as they are cheaper and tastier.

5. NUMBER OF PEOPLE
The number of people eating and their ages will influence the amount and type of food you buy and the way you present it. This prevents waste.

6. VARIETY
Provide a variety of colour, flavour, texture and appearance between one course and the next. Alternate hot with cold courses, crisp with soft textures, one method of cooking with another.

7. DIETARY RESTRICTIONS
Be aware of any foods which must be avoided for religious or dietary reasons, for example, salt, gluten, sugar, meat (if serving vegetarians). Consider individual tastes, within reason. Other factors which influence the planning of meals include:
- Resources available such as cooking and storage facilities.
- Ease of access to shops.
- Ability of cook.
- Type of meal — whether formal or informal.
- Family routine — for example, shift work and overtime may affect meal times.

Provide a pleasant setting for each meal. A clean table/cloth/mats, clean, attractive table appointments such as glasses, china and cutlery and a relaxed, easy atmosphere in which to enjoy the meal are almost as important as the food itself.

WEEKLY MENU PLAN
Plan the main meals of the week in advance.
- In this way it is easier to check whether each day's food is nutritionally well balanced.
- It serves as a guide for the weekly shopping.
- It reduces waste and caters for left-overs.
- Such organisation will avoid fuss and allow time for preparation.
- It should ensure variety and avoid monotonous menus.
- Double amounts of some foods can be cooked one day. This saves fuel and gives the cook an easy time the following day.
- There is less likelihood of falling back on impulse buying and convenience foods due to 'emergencies'.

TIME PLAN (meal served at 1 pm)

Egg mayonnaise

Chicken casserole
Baked potatoes

Swiss apple pudding
Cream

11.15	Turn on oven. Prepare ingredients for casserole.
11.25	Start casserole and put to cook.
11.35	Prepare potatoes and place in oven.
11.40	Set table.
11.50	Prepare salad and vegetables for egg mayonnaise. Chill.
12.00	Hard-boil eggs.
12.10	Prepare Swiss apple pudding.
12.25	Put to cook.
12.30	Assemble egg mayonnaise. Chill.
12.40	Put water, rolls, butter on table.
12.45	Whip cream and put in bowl.
12.50	Tidy up and turn off oven.
12.55	Slit potatoes and finish off.
1.00	Serve egg mayonnaise, followed by casserole and potatoes.

Note: All cooking is done in the oven — a major saving in fuel.

PLANNING YOUR COOKING

1. Set out all the equipment you need before you start.
2. Weigh out the ingredients accurately.
3. Clear up work surfaces and wash up as you go.
4. Make the most of modern equipment, e.g. processors, freezers.
5. Make full use of the oven when it is being used, e.g. bake potatoes with a casserole; bake a few items, e.g. cakes, tarts etc. at one time.
6. Allow plenty of time for preparation and cooking. The dish which takes longest should be cooked first.
7. A time plan ensures that all parts of the meal are ready at the correct time. It ensures that the nutritional value of foods is not lost by keeping foods warm.
8. Try to serve meals at regular times each day.

COSTING A RECIPE OR MEAL

In order to work out the cost of a meal, it is necessary to know the approximate size of portions.

Average portions:

Meat/fish — 150g (without bone)

Vegetables — 100-200g

Rice/pasta— 50g (uncooked)

Most recipes such as soup and puddings provide for four portions.

When asked to 'cost' a recipe, itemise the main ingredients, allow a few pence for fuel and give a total.

Costing a quiche lorraine	Complete
150g (6 oz) plain flour	
75g (3 oz) margarine	
Squeeze lemon juice	
Filling:	
2 eggs	
200ml (⅓ pt) creamy milk	
25g (1 oz) margarine	
3-4 streaky rashers	
100g (4 oz) cheddar cheese	
Fuel	
Total for 4	£

ENTERTAINING

The most important ingredient for successful entertaining is a friendly atmosphere and a good mixture of people. However, some of the following points will help things to run smoothly.

1. Prepare as much as possible beforehand — cleaning, advance cooking etc. Make a shopping list of all you need and shop early.
2. Collect linen, tableware and cutlery. Everything should be spotlessly clean. Set the table in plenty of time.

3. Plan the menu so that as much as possible can be prepared in advance — a cold first and last course, e.g. pâté and fruit salad, allow the cook time to sit down and to relax without any last-minute preparation.
4. A simple meal is usually the best choice. It is often tastier, more nutritious and digestible than a rich, elaborate one.
5. Avoid risky dishes, such as soufflés or those which need to be served the moment they are cooked.
6. Try out recipes on family and close friends first. Do not use guests as guinea pigs!
7. Avoid dishes which are an acquired taste, curry for example unless you are sure everyone likes them, or you can provide a choice.
8. Make use of labour-saving equipment. A freezer is useful for advance cooking. A hostess trolley keeps food piping hot.
9. Cover food when prepared and add garnishes at the last minute.

An elaborate meal would have some or all of these courses.

Menu

Hors-d'œuvre

Soup (potage)

Entrée

Remove
(Main course with vegetables)

Pudding or sweet

Coffee

BUFFETS

A buffet is the easiest way to feed a large number of people.

- Dishes should be chosen which are tasty and attractive and which can be prepared in advance.
- Arrange food, plates, cutlery etc. so that guests can help themselves. Allow plenty of napkins. Disposable dishes save washing up, but they can easily unbalance.
- Food should be easy to manage so that it can be eaten with a fork or the fingers.
- Arrange plenty of seats and small tables around the room.
- Serve bowls of nuts or crisps at the beginning so that people can help themselves.
- Drinks should be served from a separate table.
- Suitable foods:

  Hot: curry, risotto, vol au vent, pizza, casseroles, sausage rolls.

  Cold*:   salads, quiches, cold meats, kedgeree.

*Keep under refrigeration until just before the meal to avoid contamination by bacteria.

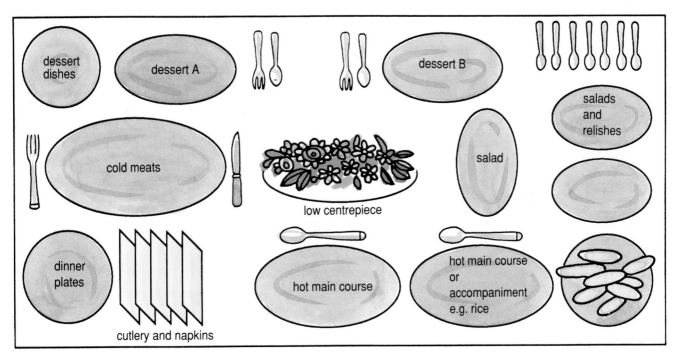

A buffet table

A table setting for dinner

PRESENTATION OF FOOD

1. Serve hot foods on hot plates as soon as they are cooked. Served cold foods, chilled, on cold plates.
2. Arrange food attractively on plates. Wipe off spills with kitchen paper.
3. Garnish food attractively with a garnish which complements the food such as thin slices of fruit or vegetable and herbs.
4. Sauces provide colour and moisture and increase the food value. It is now considered more attractive to arrange food neatly *on* a thin layer of sauce rather than disguise food with a coating of sauce.
5. Table appointments (china, glass, cutlery) should be attractive and sparkling clean.
6. An attractive low centrepiece of flowers or fruit will provide a focal point on the table.

a soup spoon	g dessert fork
b fish knife	h dessert knife
c dinner knife	i condiments
d dinner fork	j drinking glass
e fish fork	k butter rolls
f dessert spoon	l side plate and napkin

THE SCIENCE OF FOOD

► MEAT

Meat may be classified as follows
- *Carcase meat:* the flesh of animals such as cattle (beef), sheep (mutton, lamb) and pigs (pork, bacon, ham).
- *Poultry:* tame fowl such as turkeys, chickens, ducks and geese.
- *Game:* wild animals and birds protected by law and killed for sport at specified times of the year: rabbit, hare, deer (venison), pheasant, grouse.
- *Offal:* edible internal organs such as liver, kidney, heart and tongue, as well as oxtail and feet.

Average composition of carcase meat (cooked)					
Protein 20-25%	Fat 10-30%	Carbo-hydrate 0%	Vitamins B Group (B_1, B_2, B_{12})	Minerals 0.7% iron phos	Water 50-60%

NUTRITIVE VALUE OF MEAT

PROTEIN
Meat is rich in high biological-value protein. Myosin, albumin and globulin are present in meat fibres. Collagen and elastin are found in connective tissues.

LIPID
The amount of fat varies with the type of animal and the cut of meat. For example, chicken contains little fat while pork and lamb contain a considerable amount.

CARBOHYDRATE
Carcase meat contains no carbohydrate. Liver may have small amounts of glycogen.

VITAMINS
Meat is a good source of B group vitamins, particularly niacin. Liver also contains vitamins A and D.

MINERALS
Red meat is a good source of easily-absorbed iron, particularly in liver and kidney. Phosphorus, potassium and sulphur are present in varying amounts. Tripe is a good source of calcium.

WATER
Raw, lean meat contains about 70% water. Cooked meat and fatty cuts contain considerably less.

EXTRACTIVES
This is the name given to the soluble flavourings present in meat fibres which are drawn out during cooking. They include salts of potassium, phosphates and amino acids. They give each meat its characteristic flavour, but may be lost during moist cooking and thawing.

PIGMENTS
Myoglobin, a compound similar to haemoglobin, is found in the muscle of red meat.

DIETETIC VALUE
Meat is a good source of high biological-value protein, iron and B group vitamins, all of which are particularly important for children and pregnant women. In spite of this, however, meat is not essential in the diet. Vegetarians can live perfectly healthy lives without it. It is important to keep this in mind when one considers that it is the most expensive form of food that we eat. As meat lacks carbohydrate and vitamin C, it should be served with food rich in these nutrients, such as potatoes and salad. The method of cooking affects the food value of meat. Fried meat, for example, has more fat.

STRUCTURE OF MEAT
Lean mat is composed of bundles of long muscle fibres. Each fibre has a wall of elastin and is filled with water in which are dissolved protein, minerals and extractives. The bundles of fibres are held together with collagen which dissolves into gelatine during moist cooking.

Fat is present: (a) between the fibres as invisible fat (marbling); (b) on the outer surfaces as adipose tissue; and (c) around organs such as the kidney where it acts as a protective layer. Older animals contain a greater amount of fat.

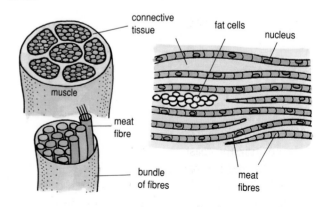

Structure of meat

TOUGHNESS

The meat of young animals consists of short, fine fibres. Meat becomes tough due to:

- *Age*
  Meat from older animals contains longer, thicker fibres and more connective tissue.
- *Activity*
  The more active the muscle — for example the legs and neck — the longer and thicker the fibres become, and the greater the build up of connective tissue. Such meat also has a darker colour and a stronger flavour.

Tenderising meat

This may be done:

1. *Before slaughter*, by injecting the live animals with tenderising enzymes.
2. *Hanging:* Before slaughter, animals are rested in order to allow glycogen to build up in their muscles. After slaughter, the muscles stiffen in rigor mortis, making the meat tough. During hanging, the glycogen gradually changes to lactic acid. This helps to tenderise the meat, improving its flavour and its keeping qualities. Proteolytic enzymes present in meat also help to break down fibres.
3. *Mechanically*, by piercing the meat with thin knives or needles or by pounding it with a heavy object such as a steak hammer. This not only breaks the fibres but also releases juices, nutrients and flavour. Mincing also has this effect.
4. *Chemically*, by sprinkling meat with tenderising chemicals. These contain proteolytic enzymes which, like digestive enzymes, break down meat fibres. Examples of tenderising agents include papain from the pawpaw fruit and bromelin from pineapples.
5. *Marinating:* Meat is steeped in a marinade of acid such as lemon juice and flavourings. These break down the protein and connective tissue, thus making the meat tender.
6. *Moist, gentle methods of cooking:* Cooking methods such as stewing also tenderise meat fibres by converting connective tissue to gelatine.

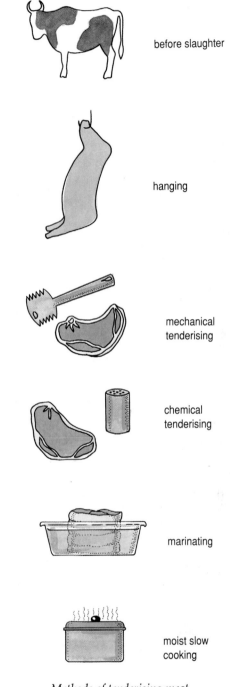

before slaughter

hanging

mechanical tenderising

chemical tenderising

marinating

moist slow cooking

Methods of tenderising meat

PROCESSING MEAT

At the abattoir, the beast is stunned, slaughtered and bled quickly (to reduce bacterial contamination). Offal is removed, after which the carcase is inspected and graded by meat inspectors. It is split in two (beef in four) and chilled quickly to 5°C. Strict hygiene must be observed at all stages of meat production. EC legislation ensures that veterinary checks are carried out at each stage.

The meat is hung at 5°C for the required time: beef for 10 days and lamb for 4 days. It is cut and jointed according to the bone structure of the animal. The meat may then be processed by one of the following methods.

1. *Vacuum Packing*

   Boned meat such as bacon and rashers is packed into strong polythene and all air is removed. Vacuum-packed meat must be kept under refrigeration until required. Storage time is 3-4 weeks.

2. *Freezing*

   Meat freezes well. Commercially it is boned, trimmed of fat and blast frozen (-30°C) or made into ready-prepared meals. Quick-frozen meat retains the most nutrients. There is a slight reduction of B vitamins and extractives with drip loss — more so if carelessly frozen. Fat may go rancid if badly stored. Salt meat may not be stored for long.

3. *Canning*

   Corned beef, tongue and meat stews are available in cans. There is some loss of B vitamins, particularly thiamine, due to the high temperatures used in processing.

4. *Dehydration*

   Today, the most acceptable method of dehydration is freeze drying (page 128). There is some loss of vitamin B_1 (thiamine). Dehydration is only suitable for small pieces of meat such as minced meat.

5. *Curing (salting)*

   In the past, strong (dry) salting was necessary to preserve meat. With the use of refrigeration, milder cures are now considered sufficient. The carcase is halved and then injected with a solution of preserving salts such as sodium chloride (salt) and potassium nitrate (saltpetre). It is then immersed in tanks of brine for 3-4 days and hung to mature at 5°C for six days. During this time, the pale myoglobin of the pork muscle changes to the pink nitrosomyoglobin of cured meat. *Smoked meat* is subjected to smoke fumes for some of this time. The best hind legs are removed and subjected to a separate, longer curing process to produce *ham*.

6. *Mechanically-recovered meat*

   Machines have now been developed to remove every particle of meat, including marrow and tendons, from bones by centrifugal force. These particles are then minced into a slurry and thickened by the use of additives to form products such as sausages, hamburgers and meat pies.

7. *Meat extracts* like Oxo and Bovril are made from the fluid which is expelled from meat during cooking. The fluid is dried and salt is added to preserve it. Such products are of little nutritive value.

BUYING MEAT

As meat is particularly susceptible to bacterial contamination, hygiene is essential at each stage of production.

- Buy from a clean, well-ventilated shop. Assistants should be clean and money should be handled separately.
- Buy in small amounts, as meat deteriorates quickly.
- Buy a cut suitable for the cooking method you plan to use. Tender cuts — grill, fry or roast; tough cuts — stew, braise.
- Meat should be well hung, moist and firm. It should have a good colour and there should be no unpleasant smell.
- It should be lean, with the minimum of fat, gristle and bone.
- Short muscle fibres and a little marbling between meat fibres are signs of good-quality, tender meat.
- As frozen meat is difficult to judge by appearance, make sure to buy it from a reliable source.

  Note: Colour is determined by the pigment myoglobin, a protein present in meat. The amount of myoglobin increases with age, so meat from older animals is darker. When meat is cut, the myoglobin takes on oxygen and becomes brighter. But on continued exposure, it turns brown which, although unattractive, does not alter the quality of the meat.

EFFECTS OF COOKING ON MEAT

1. Protein coagulates. The meat becomes firmer, but toughens if cooked too quickly.
2. Elastin surrounding the meat fibres contracts, squeezing juices out. The water evaporates and the meat shrinks, causing on average 20% loss of weight.
3. Moist cooking causes collagen to change to gelatine, allowing the meat fibres to loosen and become tender.
4. Denaturation of myoglobin and haemoglobin causes meat to turn brown.
5. Fat decomposes and melts, keeping meat moist.
6. Bacteria are destroyed.
7. Extractives are released, forming a tasty coating on the surface of the meat and appetising odours.

COOKING METHODS, (PAGE 85).

OFFAL

This term is used to describe the edible internal organs of meat as well as items such as oxtail and feet. Internal offal should be absolutely fresh. It is not hung, as it has little muscle. Offal is a good source of protein, iron and B group vitamins. It contains little fat, is cheap and there is little waste. The flesh should be firm, with no unpleasant smell. Offal from young animals such as lambs and calves is more tender and less strong flavoured, but it is more expensive than beef offal.

BEEF

Beef should have a fresh, moist appearance. The lean should be firm, smooth and bright red in colour with some marbling. The fat should be firm and dry without any discolouration. Its colour varies from cream to yellow depending on the breed and diet of the animal. Old animals have more fat and gristle. Beef forequarter contains more connective tissue, and is therefore tougher and cheaper than the hindquarter.

1. *Neck, shoulder: lean — often minced. Use for soups and stews.*

2. *Ribsteak (chuck): trim, dice, use for stewing, braising.*

3. *Top rib (housekeeper's cut): slow roast or braise.*

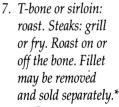

6. *Rib roast: buy on* or off the bone. Roast.*

7. *T-bone or sirloin: roast. Steaks: grill or fry. Roast on or off the bone. Fillet may be removed and sold separately.**

8. *Sirloin (rump) steak: very tender. Grill, fry.*

10. *Round*

10 (a) *Topside: inside leg therefore most tender round cut. Slow roast, braise or cut in strips and stir fry.*

10 (b) *Eye of round: pot roast, braise.*

10 (c) *Silverside: fresh; pot roast Corned or spiced beef — boil.*

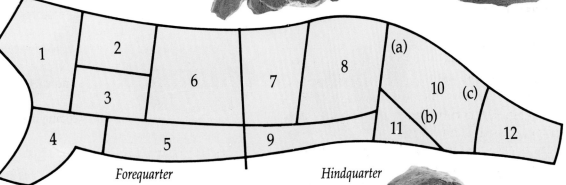

Forequarter　　　*Hindquarter*

4. *Shin: lean, tough, but well flavoured. Use for stock, soups, stews.*

5. *Brisket: boned and rolled — potroast. Also salted, sold as corned beef and boiled.*

9. *Flank: mince or cut in cubes and stew.*

11. *Round (ball of): slice and stew or braise.*

12. *Shin: as for 4; soups and stews*

*Roast beef — traditionally served with Yorkshire pudding and horseradish sauce.

(photos: CBF, Irish Livestock and Meat Board)

LAMB AND MUTTON

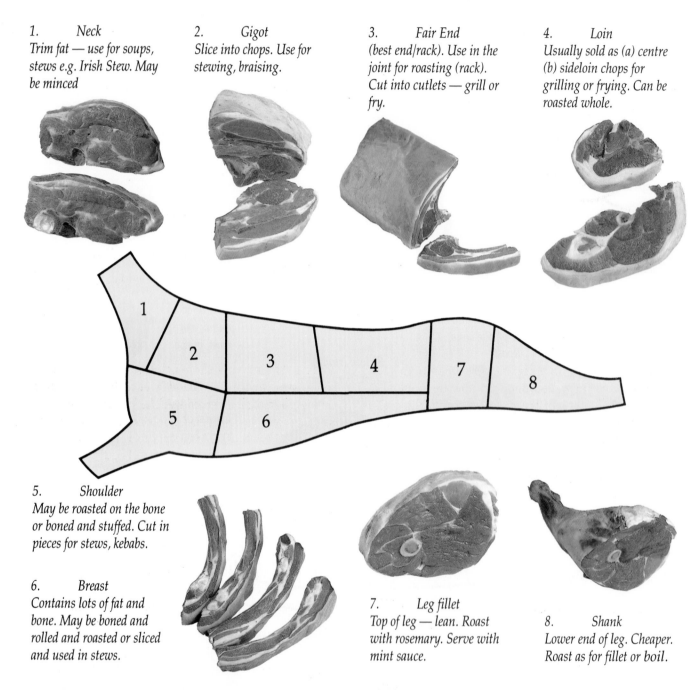

1.   Neck
Trim fat — use for soups, stews e.g. Irish Stew. May be minced

2.   Gigot
Slice into chops. Use for stewing, braising.

3.   Fair End
(best end/rack). Use in the joint for roasting (rack). Cut into cutlets — grill or fry.

4.   Loin
Usually sold as (a) centre (b) sideloin chops for grilling or frying. Can be roasted whole.

5.   Shoulder
May be roasted on the bone or boned and stuffed. Cut in pieces for stews, kebabs.

6.   Breast
Contains lots of fat and bone. May be boned and rolled and roasted or sliced and used in stews.

7.   Leg fillet
Top of leg — lean. Roast with rosemary. Serve with mint sauce.

8.   Shank
Lower end of leg. Cheaper. Roast as for fillet or boil.

LAMB

New season's lamb is available in Spring. Expensive at first, it becomes cheaper during summer months. Lamb is approximately six months old. The lean should be fine grained and light pink in colour; the fat, pearly white. Lamb is more tender, tasty and less strongly flavoured than mutton.

Roast lamb: Serve with mint sauce.

MUTTON

Mutton is obtained from a sheep, over one year old. The lean is a brownish red colour, not blood red like beef. The fibres of lamb and mutton are shorter than beef and there is less connective tissue, making them more digestible than beef. The fat is hard and white.

Roast mutton: Serve with redcurrant jelly.

(photos: CBF)

CUTS OF PORK

1. *Head — boil, brawn.*

2. *Shoulder* (hand and spring). Roast, stuffed, or cut up and stew.*

3. *Gigot* (spare rib). Roast slowly, braise, stew.*

4. *Loin — tender Piece — roast. Chops — grill or fry.*

5. *Belly — stew; salted — boil.*

6. *Leg (fillet) — roast.*

7. *Leg* (shank): roast (boned, stuffed).*

8. *Feet — boil.*

* May be cut in strips, pieces for kebabs, stir fries etc.

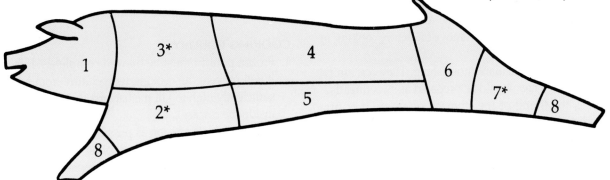

Pork is fresh meat from a pig; the best comes from young pigs. Due to refrigeration pork can now be eaten all the year round. Because of the pig's feeding habits and its tendency to harbour parasites, pork must be thoroughly cooked. The lean of pork should be fairly moist and pink in colour with some marbling. Fibres should be fine and closely packed. The fat should be white and firm without discolouration.

Bacon is the flesh of a pig which has been salted and, in some cases, smoked. It should have a thin rind; a thick rind is a sign of an older animal. The lean of bacon should be bright pink in colour and the fat a pinkish white, free from discolouration. Mild cured bacon will have a paler flesh, smoked bacon a darker flesh and rind.

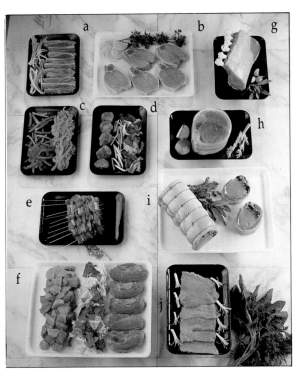

(a) Belly (see 5 above)

(b) Butterfly chops — double chops cut across the backbone

(c) Pork strips for stir fries*

(d) Medallion steaks cut from pork steak

(e) Pork kebabs (grill)

(f) Pork pieces for stewing*

(g) Rack of pork (roast) (4 above)

(h) Boned leg fillet (6 above)

(i) Rolled loin (4 above)

(j) Escallops of pork: flattened strips of leg fillet or porksteak — dip in breadcrumbs and fry.

(photos: CBF)

To prepare offal for cooking

Wash well in tepid water. Cut away blood vessels and remove membranes. Cook gently. Most pieces take a short time to cook due to lack of connective tissue.

- *Liver* is rich in iron, protein and vitamins A and B. It is the only meat which contains some vitamin C.
- *Kidney* should be firm, plump and surrounded by suet.
- *Heart:* Lamb and pork hearts are most acceptable. It must be gently cooked, for example stewed or pot-roasted.
- *Tongue* contains protein, fat, calcium and vitamin B.
- *Sweetbreads* are pancreas and thymus glands. They are easy to digest and useful in the diet of invalids. Soak in cold water, blanch and remove fat before cooking as required.
- *Brains* are not particularly nourishing. They contain fat and protein. They should be prepared as sweetbreads.
- *Tripe* is the lining of the stomach of an ox. It is prepared and partly cooked by the butcher and requires further cooking at home. It is easy to digest and rich in calcium.

    There are two types of tripe: honeycomb and blanket tripe.
- *Oxtail* is very bony. It is used in soups and stews.
- *Feet:* Calves' and pigs' feet are also bony. They are usually boiled.

OTHER MEAT PRODUCTS

- *Brawn* is chopped, cooked meat set in gelled stock.
- *Pâté* is a purée of liver, flavourings and fat.
- *Gelatine* is extracted from the collagen in the bones and hooves of animals and then purified. It is transparent, tasteless and odourless and sets liquid to form a gel. It is an animal protein of low biological value.

    Types of gelatine: powdered, leaf and aspic. Agar is a setting agent made from seaweed.

    How to use gelatine: Soak 15g gelatine in 2-4 tablespoons of cold liquid. Dissolve by stirring in a bowl over gently-simmering water. Do not boil. Pour a thin stream of the liquid onto prepared ingredients (15g: 500ml), stirring all the time. When beginning to thicken, pour mixture into a wet mould and place in the refrigerator. (Acids restrict setting.)

POULTRY

Chicken and turkey contain easily-digested forms of protein. They have little fat or connective tissue.

Ducks and geese contain a higher percentage of fat. Poultry provides B group vitamins and calcium, but less iron than red meat. (See food tables, end of book.)

TYPES OF POULTRY

- *Poussin:* A very small chicken, suitable for one portion.
- *Broiler:* A quickly-fattened young chicken, suitable for roasting and grilling (broiling). May be sold in portions.
- *Roasting chickens:* Large chicken, 1.0-2.5kg in weight.
- *Boiling fowl:* Tough, older birds suitable for casseroles.

POULTRY PREPARATION

Poultry is a very common source of food poisoning as it frequently harbours salmonella bacteria. Strict hygiene must be observed when handling poultry. Equipment used for raw and cooked poultry must be separate or else be thoroughly washed after dealing with the raw product.

COOKING POULTRY

1. Frozen poultry must be thawed completely. If it is not, it will prevent the cooking temperature from becoming sufficiently high to kill the bacteria (65°F for 15 minutes inside the carcase).
2. Remove giblets as soon as possible after purchase.
3. Separate raw poultry from all other foods.
4. Utensils and surfaces used for preparation should be washed afterwards in hot, soapy water.
5. Avoid stuffing birds. This prevents them from heating up sufficiently. Instead, place herbs and seasoning in cavity and cook the stuffing separately.
6. Ensure that all poultry/game is thoroughly cooked.
7. Do not recontaminate cooked fowl by placing it on any preparation surface used for raw meat.
8. Cool leftovers quickly. Store in a cool place, and use up as soon as possible. Do not reheat poultry on the bone.

MEAT SUBSTITUTES OR NOVEL PROTEIN FOODS

Research of protein alternatives to meat has been taking place for some time. The most successful of the meat substitutes is soya protein, called textured vegetable protein (TVP). Other meat substitutes include protein extracted from micro-organisms such as bacteria and yeast, and from algae.

MANUFACTURE OF SOYA PROTEIN

- Oil is extracted from the soya bean.
- The bean is ground into flour.
- Carbohydrate is removed. What remains is protein.
- Vegetable oils, seasonings and flavourings such as chicken or beef flavour are added.
- The mixture is then pulped and extruded, like a synthetic fibre. It is then woven, chopped or minced, according to the type of product required. It is then dehydrated and packed.

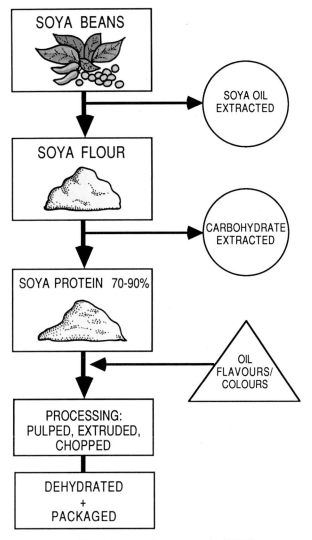

Manufacture of soya protein (TVP)

DIRECTIONS FOR USE

Soya protein is usually sold dried or canned. Its shelf life is one year. Once it is reconstituted, soya protein must be treated as fresh meat.

Steep it in twice its volume of cold water for 30 minutes, or in hot water for 10-15 minutes. Prepare dish in the usual way. Add soya protein pieces and simmer gently for about 15 minutes to heat through.

NUTRITIVE VALUE OF SOYA PROTEIN

Soya beans have the highest biological value of any vegetable protein food (74%), but they lack one essential amino acid — methionine. Many manufacturers add this during processing and B group vitamins and iron are also added. Soya protein is a richer source of calcium than meat and contains little fat; any fat present is polyunsaturated.

Advantages	Disadvantages
1. Slightly cheaper than meat.	1. Taste is inferior to meat.
2. Keeps well.	2. Many people dislike its smell and texture.
3. It is a nutritionally sound meat substitute.	3. Size of pieces is restricted to small pieces to resemble mince or stewing chunks.
4. Little preparation needed.	
5. No shrinkage or waste.	4. Requires extra ingredients and ingenuity in cooking to make it acceptable.
6. Ideal for vegetarians.	
7. A useful source of dietary fibre.	
8. Helps to reduce world food shortage.	

Other soya products: soya milk for vegans; soy sauce; soya bean curd such as tofu, (used in Asian cookery); soya flour, soya oil.

USE OF SOYA PROTEIN

- Soya protein may be used as a meat extender — mixed with meat to make it go further. It is most acceptable if the ratio is 75:25 meat to soya.
- It is used as a meat substitute in well flavoured dishes such as curry.

▶ FISH

Average Composition of Fish						
Type	Protein	Fat	Carbohydrate	Vitamins	Minerals 1.5%	Water
White	17%	0.5%	0%	B	iodine/phos.	80%
Oily	18%	10-20%*	0%	A, B, D	iodine/phos.	65%
Shell	20%	2.5%	0%	B	iron/cal./iodine	75%

* Depending on season

SOURCES

Saltwater fish: These include cod, haddock, herring and most shellfish. They may swim at the bottom of the sea (*demersal*) or, like most oily fish, near the surface (*pelagic*).
Freshwater fish: These swim in rivers and lakes. Examples are trout, perch and eels.

CLASSIFICATION OF FISH

Fish may be classified according to shape, that is whether it is round or flat. But the most usual method of classifying fish is by its appearance and nutritive value.

White Fish	Oily Fish	Shellfish
Cod, haddock, whiting, plaice, sole, turbot, skate (ray) monkfish	Herring, mackerel trout, salmon, sardines, whitebait	*Crustaceans:* have legs and claws, e.g. shrimp, lobster, crab *Molluscs:* no legs, scallops, mussels

NUTRITIVE VALUE OF FISH

PROTEIN

All fish is a good source of high biological-value protein, although slightly less than that of meat.

LIPID

The oil in white fish is stored in the liver which is removed during cleaning. Only traces remain in the flesh. Oily fish has its lipid distributed throughout the flesh. Unlike meats, the oil present in fish is high in polyunsaturated fatty acids. Shellfish contains cholesterol.

CARBOHYDRATE

This is lacking in all fish.

VITAMINS

All fish contain B group vitamins. Fish liver oils and oily fish are excellent sources of vitamins A and D.

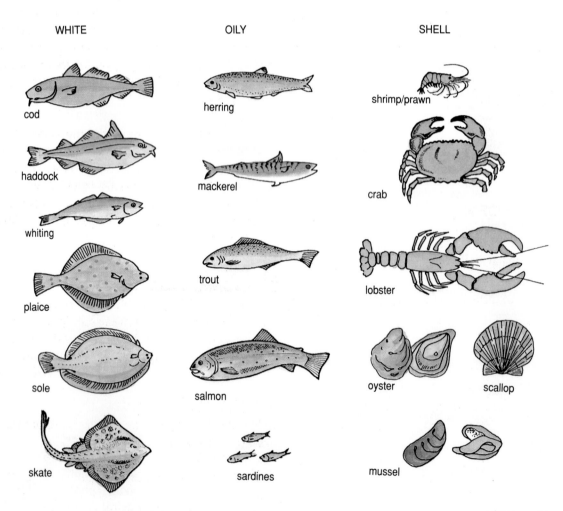

WHITE OILY SHELL

cod
haddock
whiting
plaice
sole
skate

herring
mackerel
trout
salmon
sardines

shrimp/prawn
crab
lobster
oyster
scallop
mussel

(not to scale)

Classification of fish

MINERALS

Fish is a good source of phosphorus and potassium. Iodine and fluorine are present in sea fish. Calcium is available by eating fish whose bones are softened by canning such as sardines and salmon. Fish is not a good source of iron.

WATER

White fish and shellfish contain up to 80% water. Oily fish has an average of 65% water.

DIETETIC VALUE OF FISH

Fish is a nutritious food for all and an excellent substitute for meat. As white fish contains little or no fat, it is low in kilocalories and very digestible. Oily fish such as herring is valuable for the extra vitamins and energy it provides cheaply. The oil in fish contains polyunsaturated fatty acids, so it is useful in low cholesterol diets.

Shellfish — nutritious but expensive (Denis Hughes–Gilbey)

THE STRUCTURE OF FISH FLESH

Fish is composed of bundles of short fibres known as *myomeres* which are held together with thin bands of *collagen* (connective tissue). This readily converts to gelatine on cooking, causing the fish to break apart easily. The fibres in shellfish are inclined to be coarse, making them more difficult to digest.

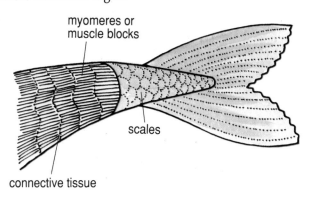

Structure of fish

SPOILAGE OF FISH

Fish is very perishable. Shellfish particularly can cause food poisoning. Like animals, fish store glycogen (animal starch) in their muscle. Unlike animals, however, they struggle violently when caught and use up the stored glycogen. As a result, little or no lactic acid is formed which would help to preserve the fish. Decay sets in quickly as bacteria break down the flesh and a strong-smelling nitrogen compound, trimethylamine, is formed.

PROCESSING FISH

Fish must be processed as soon as possible after catching.

1. *Freezing*
   Fish is kept on ice for short-term storage. It freezes very well when filleted or when processed into fish fingers, fish cakes and dishes such as fish in sauces. It should be blast-frozen at -30°C. There is a slight loss of water, minerals and B group vitamins on thawing.

2. *Canning*
   Salmon, sardines, tuna, herrings, crab and many other fish are suitable for canning. Fish may be canned in oil, in brine or in a sauce. There is some loss of thiamine during canning. The canning process softens bones, so such fish are a good source of calcium. As oily fish is the type most often canned, it is a source of vitamins A and D.

3. *Smoking fish*
   Fish is first salted to draw out the water. It is then smoked in kilns over oak chips for about four hours. It may be hot-smoked (110°C) or cold-smoked (30°C). Today, much fish is artificially 'smoked' by soaking in dyes and flavourings. Examples of smoked fish are kippers (smoked herrings), smoked mackerel, haddock, cod, trout and salmon.

ECONOMIC VALUE OF FISH

There is up to 70% waste in fish, as the head and bones are usually removed. The price of fish varies according to the weather, the season, the type of fish and its availability. The cheapest type of fish are gurnard, herring, mackerel and whiting. Shellfish are usually expensive.

BUYING FISH

1. Fish should be as fresh as possible. Signs of freshness:
   - No unpleasant odour.
   - Flesh is firm, with a close grain (if cut).
   - Eyes are bright and prominent.
   - Gills are red.
   - Skin is slimy and unbroken.
   - Scales are plentiful and firmly attached.

2. Buy fish in season — cheapest and best flavour.
3. Buy medium-sized fish. Small and large fish can be tasteless.
4. A whole fish should be plump, with a stiff tail.
5. Smoked fish should be glossy, the flesh firm but not sticky.
6. Always buy fish from a hygienic source.
7. Frozen fish should be rock-hard, with wrappings intact.

CUTS OF FISH
Fish are sold whole, gutted, filleted or in cutlets or steaks.

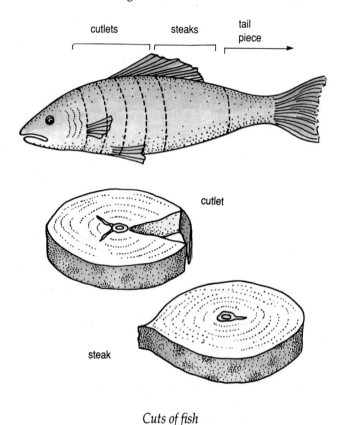

Cuts of fish

STORING FISH, page 83.

EFFECTS OF COOKING ON FISH
1. Protein coagulates. The fish shrinks slightly and becomes opaque.
2. Connective tissue changes to gelatine, making fish flake easily. Overcooking makes fish break up.
3. Bacteria and parasites are destroyed.
4. Some loss of B group vitamins. Vitamins A and D are unchanged.
5. Minerals, vitamins and extractives dissolve into the cooking liquid. This should be retained for sauces etc.

METHODS OF COOKING FISH
Fish has a delicate flavour. Use moderate heat for cooking all fish and time it carefully.

■ *Poaching:* Gentle cooking in a little liquid. It is suitable for whole fish or thick pieces. There is some loss of nutrients into the cooking liquid.
■ *Steaming:* This method is slower than poaching but there is less danger of overcooking and less nutrient loss. It is ideal for thin pieces of fish.
■ *Stewing:* This method is only suitable for more solid fish such as monkfish and shellfish, as most other fish tend to break up.
■ *Baking:* This is probably the ideal method for cooking whole fish or fillets which may be stuffed or masked with a sauce.
■ *Frying and grilling:* These are quick and simple methods of cooking thin and medium cuts of fish. Grilling is preferable, as it is less greasy and lower in kilocalories.
■ *Microwave cooking* is ideal for fish because of its high water content and the fact that browning is not necessary.

▶ DAIRY PRODUCE

MILK
Milk is nature's most perfect food. It contains all the nutrient groups required by humans, but little vitamin C or iron. Infants can live on milk alone for the first six months of life. After that, their diets must be supplemented with foods rich in these nutrients.

While milk from cows is the most frequent source, goats, mares, ewes, buffalos and camels also provide milk for human use in various cultures.

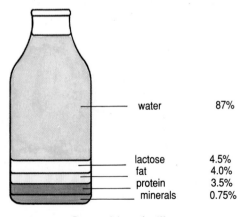

water	87%
lactose	4.5%
fat	4.0%
protein	3.5%
minerals	0.75%

Composition of milk

Average composition of milk

	Protein	Fat	Carbohydrate	Vitamins	Minerals	Water
Full cream milk	3.5%	4%	4.5%	A, B, D	0.7%	87%
Skimmed milk	3.5%	0.2%	5.0%	B	0.6%	90%
Human milk	2.25%	3.5%	6.5%	A, B, C, D	0.3%	87.4%

COMPOSITION OF MILK

This varies according to the breed from which the milk comes, length of time since calving and the animal's diet.

500ml whole milk contains 379 kcal/1,585 kJ;
500ml skimmed milk: 193 kcal/807 kJ

NUTRITIVE VALUE OF COW'S MILK

PROTEIN

Milk contains high biological-value protein, caseinogen, lactoglobulin and lactalbumin in an easily-digested form. During digestion, the enzyme rennin acts on the casein, causing it to clot.

LIPID

Fat is present in a fine emulsion, making it easy to digest. Lecithin helps to stabilise this emulsion. Cholesterol is also present. As fat molecules are less dense than water, they rise to the top of the milk to form cream.

CARBOHYDRATE

Milk contains lactose (milk sugar) which gives it a sweetish taste. Souring occurs when the lactose is changed to lactic acid by the lactic acid bacteria present in milk. As bacteria are more active in warm conditions, milk keeps longer when stored in a cold place.

VITAMINS

Milk contains varying amounts of vitamins A and D, having more in summer when cattle are out on grass. Carotene (provitamin A) gives cream its colour. Milk is rich in vitamin B_2 and has smaller amounts of vitamin B_1 (thiamine) and nicotinic acid. Traces of vitamin C are present in fresh, unprocessed milk.

Note: water-soluble vitamins are reduced when bottles of milk are left standing in sunlight.

MINERALS

Milk is rich in calcium and phosphorus, both essential for bone formation. It is therefore important in the diet of growing children and pregnant women. Milk contains potassium and magnesium, but little iron.

WATER

As milk has 87% water, it is a rather bulky food.

DIETETIC VALUE OF MILK

Milk is a cheap, nourishing food. Milk contains several of the nutrients concerned with growth — protein in an easily-digested form, calcium and vitamins A, B and D. For this reason, milk is an important food for pregnant and nursing mothers, infants, children and adolescents. These people should take milk daily. Skimmed milk is suitable for low kilocalorie, low cholesterol diets. As milk lacks starch and fibre, it makes good nutritional sense to combine it with cereals (as in rice pudding or breakfast cereals).

SKIMMED MILK

Most of the fat and fat-soluble vitamins, A and D, are removed when cream is separated from milk. The remaining liquid contains protein, lactose, all the minerals and B group vitamins. It has less flavour, however. Skimmed milk, sometimes sold as 'slim milk', is ideal for low-calorie and low-cholesterol diets. Due to its reduced vitamin content, it is unsuitable for babies. 'Light milk' is partly skimmed milk, containing about 1.7% fat.

SPOILAGE

As milk is a liquid food, it is an ideal breeding ground for bacteria. Milk may be contaminated with *pathogenic* bacteria, such as those causing diphtheria, tuberculosis (TB), brucellosis and gastroenteritis. It also contains *non-pathogenic* lactic acid bacteria which cause souring. To prevent growth of bacteria, keep milk cool, clean and covered. Heat treatments are used to destroy disease-bearing bacteria.

PREVENTING SPOILAGE

High standards of quality control and hygiene are necessary in milk production in order to avoid the spread of disease. Legislation such as Milk and Dairy Acts and the Food and Drugs Acts helps to ensure both quality and hygiene by:

- enforcing inspection of herds by veterinary surgeons.
- tuberculin testing.
- registration of farms; licensing of dairies.
- recommended procedure for milking, storing and transporting milk.
- pasteurisation and bottling of milk under strict control.

PROCESSING MILK

Milk is processed to:

- improve flavour (homogenisation)
- make milk safer and increase its shelf life (heat treatments).

1. *Homogenisation*

Milk is pumped through a tiny valve so that the fat globules are reduced. This makes the milk creamier and more digestible. Homogenisation is used before milk is processed in other ways such as pasteurising. The nutrients remain unchanged.

HEAT TREATMENTS

2. *Pasteurisation*

Milk is heated to 72°C for 15 seconds. It is then cooled rapidly to 10°C or below and sealed at once into sterilised bottles.

- Pathogenic and some souring bacteria are destroyed.
- There is a loss of any vitamin C and some B_1.
- A slight flavour change.
- Milk keeps longer.

3. *Ultra-Heat Treatment (UHT)*

Also known as long-life milk, this process is also used on cream. Milk is heated to 132°C for one second. It is rapidly cooled to 10°C or lower, then packed and sealed at once.

- Destroys all bacteria.
- Loss of vitamin C and some B_1.
- Noticeable change in flavour.
- Milk keeps for several months without refrigeration.
- Once opened, use as fresh milk.

4. *Sterilisation*

Milk is homogenised, bottled and sealed, then heated to 110°C for 30 minutes.

- All bacteria are destroyed.
- All vitamin C and greater amounts of B group vitamins are destroyed than by other heat treatments.
- Taste is altered considerably; less digestible.
- Milk keeps for several months.

5. *Evaporated and condensed milk*

These may be produced from whole or skimmed milk.

- *Evaporated milk* is pasteurised and evaporated to half its volume in low pressure vacuum pans. It is homogenised, then sterilised at 115°C for 20 minutes in sealed cans.
- *Condensed milk* is a more concentrated, sweetened version of evaporated milk. 15% sugar is added before evaporation to one-third its volume. The high concentration of sugar makes prolonged sterilisation unnecessary.
- Loss of vitamin C and B group (more so in evaporated milk).

- Taste is considerably altered, even when reconstituted.
- Sugar content of condensed milk is unacceptably high.
- Destroys bacteria.
- Keeps well indefinitely.
- Not suitable for infants.

6. *Dehydrated milk*

Both whole and skimmed milk may be dried. Skimmed milk keeps longer. The milk is first homogenised, then evaporated to 60% of its original volume. It is then spray or roller-dried. Extra vitamins may be added. *Coffee creamers* are not milk. They are made from glucose products and vegetable fat and are used to replace milk.

(a) *Spray drying*: Milk is sprayed into the top of a hot air chamber. As droplets fall they dry to a fine powder.

- Reconstitutes easily.
- Good flavour.
- Less lumpy than roller-dried milk.

(b) *Roller-dried milk*: Milk is run over heated, revolving rollers and scraped off as it dries.

- High temperature sterilises milk but destroys some vitamins and amino acids.
- Flavour is inferior to spray-dried milk.

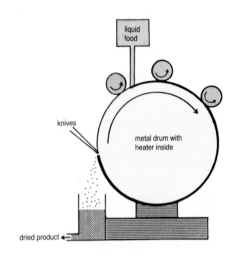

Roller drying

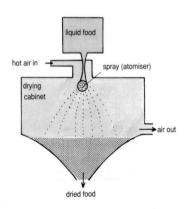

Spray drying

EFFECTS OF HEAT ON MILK
1. Considerable loss of vitamins C and B group.
2. Flavour altered.
3. Disease-bearing bacteria destroyed.
4. Protein coagulates, forming a skin on the surface of the milk. This rises on boiling, causing milk to boil over.

CURDLING
Curdling occurs when the protein separates from the liquid part of the milk. It can be caused by:
1. *Heat,* as when milk is added to very hot coffee.
2. *Acids:* This occurs in souring. Untreated milk sours naturally when its lactic acid bacteria feed on the lactose in milk, producing the waste product lactic acid. This acid causes the caseinogen to coagulate into lumps of casein, giving sour milk its lumpy appearance. Similar effects occur in cooking as when lemon juice is added to milk.
3. *Enzymes:* Rennin (an enzyme in the stomach) coagulates or clots caseinogen during digestion. Rennet (prepared from animal rennin) has the same effect during cheese-making.

STORING MILK
- Avoid leaving bottles on the doorstep, as sunlight destroys vitamins C and B_2 (riboflavin).
- Keep milk sealed in bottles in a cold, dark place such as a refrigerator for up to 2-4 days.

► MILK PRODUCTS

1. BUTTER
Butter is an emulsion of water in fat which is manufactured from pasteurised cream. As it is churned in a revolving drum, the fat globules join together in lumps and the liquid (butter-milk) is drained off. Salt may be added to flavour the butter. Water-soluble nutrients of milk — protein, lactose, minerals and B group vitamins — pass into the buttermilk.

NUTRITIVE VALUE OF BUTTER

PROTEIN
Butter is not considered to be a useful source of protein (casein), as very little remains after churning.

LIPID
Butter is a concentrated source of fat. It contains the saturated fatty acid known as butyric acid. It also contains cholesterol.

CARBOHYDRATE
Only traces of lactose remain after churning.

VITAMINS
Butter is a good source of vitamin A, with traces of vitamins D and E, depending on the diet of the animal.

MINERALS
Most are lost into the buttermilk. Only traces of calcium remain. If salt is added, butter is a source of sodium chloride.

WATER
By law, butter must not contain more than 16% water.

2. BUTTERMILK
Some butter is made from 'ripened' cream — cream which is slightly soured by lactic acid bacteria. The resulting liquid, buttermilk, is quite acid and useful for making soda bread.

3. DAIRY SPREADS AND SPREADABLE BUTTERS
Current research is coming up with a wide variety of butter products.
- *Spreadable butter*
  After churning, butter passes through an agitator which breaks down the hard fats and makes it spreadable.
- *Dairy spreads*
  These contain approximately 50% butter and 50% soya oils. They are spreadable straight from the refrigerator.
- *Low-calorie butter spreads*
  These contain half the fat of butter or margarine. Some have air and emulsifiers whipped into them. Others are made from buttermilk, milk protein and butter.

Note: By law, no product may be called butter if it has less than 80% butter fat present.
- *Concentrated butter* (96% fat) is butter that has had its water and salt content reduced. It is useful for cooking and frying. It is sold cheaply, but is extremely high in saturated fat and kilocalories.

Average composition of butter

Protein	Fat	Carbohydrate	Vitamins	Minerals	Water	kcal/kJ (100g)
1.0%	83%	0.5%	A, traces of D and E	Sodium chloride traces cal/phos	13-15%	795/3339

4. CREAM

The fat which rises to the top of milk may be skimmed off or separated by a centrifugal separator. All fresh cream is pasteurised. Irish cream contains about 30% fat (minimum fat content — 25%). Double cream contains 48% fat. Single cream has a minimum of 18% fat; contains useful amounts of vitamin A.

UHT (LONG-LIFE) CREAM

This is single cream which has been heat-treated in the same way as UHT milk. It keeps, unopened, for several weeks.

SOURED CREAM (12% FAT)

This is single cream which has been treated with a lactic acid culture to thicken it and to give it a pleasantly sour taste. It may be used in casseroles, in curries and as salad dressing. Never use cream which has soured naturally, as it has an unpleasant flavour. In an emergency, add lemon juice to fresh cream, or use natural yoghurt.

COMMERCIAL ICE CREAM

This is made from skimmed milk and vegetable fat.

5. YOGHURT

Yoghurt is a form of milk which has been fermented and thickened by lactic acid bacteria. It can be made from whole milk, but is more usually made from skimmed milk, with dried milk added to thicken it. Yoghurt is first pasteurised, then homogenised. It is warmed to 90°C to destroy bacteria, cooled to 37°C, then inoculated with a culture such as *Lactobacillus bulgaricus*. This ferments the lactose into lactic acid, thickening the yoghurt and giving it its characteristic acid flavour. After further cooling, extra ingredients such as fruit or nuts may be added.

FOOD VALUE OF YOGHURT

Yoghurt is very easy to digest. The food value of yoghurt is similar to the milk from which it is made, for example skimmed milk. Yoghurt has little fat. Extra ingredients such as sugar and fruit will alter its food value. Yoghurt is a good source of calcium. Vitamins A and D and milk protein may be added. It is a nutritious convenience food, ideal for children, invalids and the elderly. (For composition of yoghurt, see food tables, end of book.)

HOW TO USE YOGHURT

Use as a sweet directly from the carton. Natural yoghurt may be used in chilled soups, in stews such as stroganoff, in savoury dishes and as a salad dressing. When used in hot dishes, stir in at the end of the cooking time.

STORING YOGHURT

Warm temperatures will activate bacteria and make the yoghurt unpleasantly acid. Store in a refrigerator.

TO MAKE YOUR OWN YOGHURT

Bring 500ml pasteurised milk to the boil, then cool to 42°C. Add 15ml natural yoghurt and stir. Then place in a vacuum flask to incubate for eight hours.

6. CHEESE

Cheese is a form of concentrated milk. It is not only made from cow's milk, but from goat, sheep (Roquefort) and buffalo milk.

COMPOSITION OF CHEESE

This varies considerably — according to the type of animal, whether milk is whole or skimmed, and whether the finished cheese is to be hard or soft.

NUTRITIVE VALUE OF CHEESE (HARD)

Protein
Cheese is the best source of protein in the diet. It consists mainly of casein and is of high biological value.

Lipid
The high percentage of fat makes cheese a good source of energy, but it also makes it difficult to digest.

Carbohydrate
None. The lactose present is converted to lactic acid and drains away with the whey.

Vitamins
Cheese is an excellent source of vitamin A, and contains some B_2 (riboflavin).

Minerals
Cheese is an excellent source of calcium.

Water
The water content of cheese varies between 30% (Parmesan) and 77% (cottage cheese).

Average composition of cheese

	Protein	Fat	Carbohydrate	Vitamins	Minerals	Water	kcal/kJ(100g)
Cheddar	27%	33%	0%	A, B_2, niacin	6% (cal/phos)	34%	405/1700
Cottage	15%	4%	4%	A, B_2 (trace)	cal (trace)	77%	114/480

DIETETIC VALUE OF CHEESE

Cheese is a valuable food. It is extremely versatile and is available in a wide variety of forms. It is important in the diet of children, adolescents and pregnant and nursing mothers as it contains essential nutrients for growth (protein) and bone formation (calcium). Cheese is a concentrated and very nourishing energy source, unlike some sources of energy such as sugar. Because of its concentration and small bulk, it is ideal for packed meals. It is also reasonably cheap, with little waste. No cooking is required.

Since most cheeses are high in kilocalories/kJ, they can be fattening unless eaten in moderation. They are also high in saturated fats and cholesterol. Exceptions to this include cottage cheese, quark and other low fat cheeses. Those on low energy diets should keep to the latter.

Cheesemaking — chopping curds (Denis Hughes–Gilbey)

MANUFACTURE OF CHEESE

1. Various cultures or starters are used to give each cheese its characteristic colour, texture and flavour.
2. A *starter* of lactic acid bacteria is added to fresh pasteurised milk. This changes the lactose to lactic acid.
3. Milk is warmed to 30°C and *rennet* is added to coagulate the casein into *curds*. Most of the fat, vitamins and minerals remain in the curd.
4. The *whey* is drained off. The curds are chopped, then heated to shrink the protein and squeeze out more whey.
5. Salt is added and more whey is drained off. (If the process is stopped at this stage, cottage cheese is produced.)
6. The curd is pressed into moulds and sprayed with hot water to help form a skin. It is pressed for varying lengths of time, according to the type of cheese required.
7. The whole cheeses are removed and left to ripen or mature in carefully controlled conditions at 10°C from two months to two years.

Soft cheeses are not pressed after placing in moulds, so more whey is retained.

- *Blue-veined cheeses* are lightly-pressed, open-textured cheeses. They are pierced with needles containing a harmless mould during ripening.
- *Camembert and Brie:* A mould is put on the surface of these cheeses in order to obtain the characteristic powdery finish.
- *Cottage cheese:* A white curd-like cheese made from whole or skimmed milk. A starter such as rennet is used, the whey is drained off and salt added.
- *Cream cheese* is made like cottage cheese, but from a mixture of fresh milk and cream.

Classification of cheese

Hard (pressed)	Semi-hard	Soft	
I Parmesan	D Edam – skimmed milk	I Mozzarella	Ripened to produce strong flavours
E Cheddar	D Gouda	F Brie	
E Cheshire	F Port Salut	F Camembert	
E Double gloucester	F Roquefort	F Pont l'Évêque	
E Wensleydale	E Caerphilly	I Ricotta	
E Leicester	I Gorgonzola	Cottage cheese	Unripened, mild. Must be eaten fresh. Soft cheeses are more digestible.
S Emmenthal } holes	E Stilton } blue-veined	Cream cheese	
S Gruyère	Ir Irish Blue	Quark	
Ir Wexford			

I: Italian; E: English; S: Swiss; Ir: Irish; F: French; D: Dutch

Note: A wide variety of farmhouse cheeses is now available.

- *Quark* is a smooth, white unripened cheese made from skimmed milk. It contains only traces of fat.
- *Processed cheese:* A wide variety is available, including smoked cheese, herb cheeses, foil-wrapped mild cheese etc. Many processed cheeses are a mixture of grated fresh (unripened) cheeses and mature cheeses. Various ingredients are added, such as dried milk, emulsifiers, flavourings and preservatives. Processed cheeses have less nourishment than natural cheese and are unsuitable for cooking as they have little flavour.
- *Low fat versions* of many cheeses are available, including low fat cheddar.

EFFECTS OF COOKING ON CHEESE

It is preferable to eat cheese uncooked. Cook for the shortest possible time and at a low temperature.
1. Fat melts and separates after a short time.
2. Protein coagulates. With prolonged cooking, cheese denatures and becomes stringy, then hard and indigestible.
3. Little loss of food value.
4. Cheese carbonises and therefore browns well. It is useful for topping savoury dishes.
5. Add cheese towards the end of any cooking or sauce-making to avoid overcooking.

BUYING AND STORING CHEESE

1. Buy in small amounts. Vacuum-packed cheese keeps for several weeks, if unopened. Use by the date on the packet.
2. Fresh or soft cheeses should be used up quickly.
3. Store cheese in a refrigerator, loosely wrapped in polythene or foil.
4. Bring to room temperature by removing from the fridge one hour before use in order to bring out its flavour.

EGGS

Eggs are one of the most basic and versatile ingredients used in cookery. They are a cheap source of many important nutrients. The eggs most commonly eaten in this country are hen's eggs.

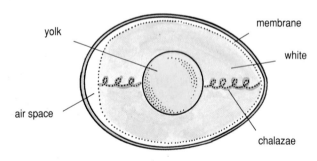

Egg structure

STRUCTURE OF EGGS

Eggs have three parts: the shell, yolk and white.

1. *Shell (10%)*
The egg shell is made of *calcium carbonate*. It contains numerous tiny pores which allow air, bacteria and moisture to pass through it. The shell is lined with a strong membrane. It has an air space at its round end which increases as the egg becomes more stale due to the evaporation of moisture from the egg. For this reason, stale eggs float.

2. *White (60%)*
This consists mainly of water with some protein, minerals and water-soluble vitamin B dissolved in it. The jelly-like white becomes thin and runny as it becomes stale.

3. *Yolk (30%)*
The yolk contains all the fat. It is held in the centre of the white by the chalazae. If these break, as happens when eggs are incorrectly stored (the pointed end should point down), the yolk rises towards the air space and goes stale quickly. Proteins break down when an egg is very stale, releasing foul-smelling hydrogen sulphide gas.

NUTRITIVE VALUE OF EGGS

An egg contains all the nutrients required by a developing chick.

PROTEIN

Eggs are a good source of protein which has a 100% biological value. Albumin is present in egg white. Vitellin and livetin are found in egg yolk.

LIPID

Eggs are a source of easily-digested fat. This is present in the yolk as a fine emulsion brought about by lecithin — a natural emulsifier. Cholesterol is also present in a greater proportion than in any other food.

CARBOHYDRATE

There is none present.

VITAMINS

Eggs contain fat-soluble vitamins A, D, E and K in useful amounts. Most of the B group vitamins are present, but not vitamin C. Carotene gives the yolk its yellow colour.

MINERALS
Iron, calcium and sulphur are present.

WATER
Most of the water present is in the egg white.

DIETETIC VALUE OF EGGS
Eggs are a cheap and extremely versatile food. They are easily digested, so are therefore important in the diets of children, invalids and the elderly. They are also useful in vegetarian and low kilocalorie diets (a large egg has about 150kc). Because eggs contain both saturated fat and cholesterol, their use should be restricted by those prone to heart disease. They contain useful amounts of iron, but vitamin C is needed for its absorption. Because they lack carbohydrates, eggs are usually served with carbohydrate foods, as in omelette and chips or egg on toast.

Note: Due to the slight possibility of contamination by salmonella, it is now thought advisable for vulnerable people such as children, invalids, and the elderly to cook eggs until the yolk is hard — particularly during salmonella outbreaks.
Never eat raw eggs.

CULINARY USES (see chart over)
1. As a protein alternative to meat and fish.
2. To thicken sauces and set ingredients such as custard and quiche.
3. To bind: Eggs hold food together, including hamburgers and fishcakes.
4. To coat: Eggs can be used as a batter or with breadcrumbs to coat fish, fritters etc.
5. To glaze: Food brushed with egg develops an attractive shine when cooked.
6. To aerate: When whisked or beaten, eggs entrap air and hold it until set by heat or by gelatine, as in soufflés.
7. To emulsify: Egg yolk contains an emulsifier, lecithin. This helps to hold the oil and vinegar together in mayonnaise and the fat and sugar together in creamed cakes.
8. To add extra nourishment to dishes as in baking.

EFFECTS OF HEAT ON EGGS
1. Proteins coagulate — the white at 60°C and the yolk at 68°C. For this reason eggs must be cooked at a low temperature.
2. Curdling: Too much heat causes the protein to shrink and squeeze out water, causing lumping or curdling.
3. Overcooking makes the white tough and rubbery and the yolk dry and crumbly. After prolonged cooking, a greenish rim forms around the yolk as the iron present reacts with the sulphur in the white (ferrous sulphide).
4. Egg albumin, which is fairly soluble in cold water, becomes insoluble when heated.
5. Slight loss of B group vitamins.

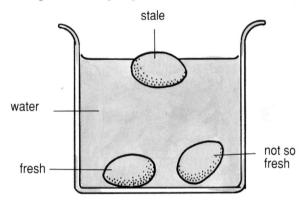

To test eggs for freshness

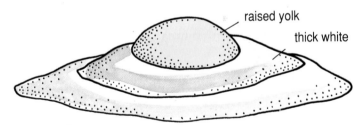

Fresh egg: well-rounded yolk, jelly-like white

FRESHNESS
Fresh eggs should have a rough shell and feel heavy for their size. They will sink if placed in salted water. Shelled eggs should have a well-rounded yolk surrounded by a jelly-like white. Stale eggs are flat with a watery white. Very stale eggs will smell strongly of hydrogen sulphide. Eggs keep for several weeks in ideal conditions.

Average composition of eggs

	Protein	Lipid	Carbohydrate	Vitamins	Minerals	Water	kcal/kJ(100g)
White	12%	0.25%	0	B	0.75%	87%	45/188
Yolk	16%	32%	0	A, D, B	2%	50%	350/1470
Whole egg (shelled)	13%	12%	0	A, D, B	1%	74%	195/662

Properties of Eggs

Eggs have certain properties which make them very useful in cookery.

- Egg proteins *coagulate* on heating.
- They can *entrap air*.
- They are good *emulsifiers*.

Principle	Application — culinary uses
Coagulation This occurs when the protein is heated. The egg solidifies and the white becomes opaque. Egg white coagulates at 60°C. Egg yolk coagulates at 68°C. When overheated — above coagulation temperature — the egg protein is denatured. It gets too hard, tough and indigestible. This causes curdling in dishes such as scrambled egg, custard and quiche. N.B. Always cook eggs using a gentle heat.	• *Fried, boiled and poached eggs* are obvious examples of coagulation. • *Thickening:* When eggs are mixed with a liquid such as milk and then heated, the egg protein coagulates around the liquid, forming a gel. Examples are egg custard and quiche. • *Binding:* When beaten egg is mixed with other dry ingredients and heated, it coagulates and holds them together. Examples: hamburgers, fish cakes. • *Coating:* Beaten egg holds breadcrumbs in place. When cooked, this coagulates to form a crisp coating. Example: fried fish. • *Clarifying:* Egg white is whisked into some clear soups and jellies etc. When heated, the white coagulates, trapping the impurities in a thick scum which is strained away leaving a clear liquid. • *Glazing:* Coagulated protein forms a glossy brown surface.

Entrapping air
Egg protein has the property of creating a foam. When egg white is beaten, air bubbles are formed. The beating generates sufficient heat to slightly coagulate the albumin which forms a thin layer around the air bubbles. The mixture becomes opaque, white and stiff. As the foam collapses in time, heat or gelatine are used to set the foam.
	• *Aerating cakes etc.* Beating encloses air in the mixture which is held in place by egg protein. The air expands and rises in the heat of the oven until the protein sets.
	• *Aerating using egg white, e.g. meringues, soufflés.*
	  • Use egg whites at room temperature to reach maximum volume.
	  • Overbeating results in loss of volume.
	  • Add sugar towards end of beating (never at the beginning) as sugar inhibits formation of foam.
	  • Fat inhibits formation of foam. Use a clean bowl and whisk. Make sure no specks of egg yolk fall in.
	  • Quality of aeration depends on freshness of eggs, temperature, length of time beaten and whether anything is added.

Emulsifying Egg yolk contains an important emulsifier, lecithin. It enables two immiscible liquids to combine. The egg yolk surrounds the droplets of oil/fat, preventing them from coalescing.	**Examples:** The fat/sugar in cakes forms an emulsion. Oil/vinegar in mayonnaise. Butter/vinegar in Hollandaise sauce.

GRADING EGGS

According to EC regulations, eggs are divided by weight into seven grades, size 1 being the largest.

weight in grams	
size 1	grams 70+
size 2	65-70
size 3	60-65
size 4	55-60
size 5	50-55
size 6	45-50
size 7	under 45g

Egg boxes must display the registered number and address of packer and the date of packing.

Eggs are also placed in classes, according to quality and freshness.

Class A: Top-quality, fresh eggs.
Class B: Fair quality. May be dirty, washed or refrigerated.
Class C: May be cracked or shelled. Used in food manufacture.
Extra: A label is placed on very fresh eggs which is removed one week after packing.

FATS AND OILS

Edible fats and oils are known as lipids. Fats, which usually come from animal sources, are solid at room temperature. Oils are liquid at room temperature and are usually obtained from plants. All lipids have a high energy value, are insoluble in water and slow to digest.

Classification of lipid foods

Animal (mainly saturated fats)*	Meat fat, suet, lard, dripping, cheese, cream, eggs, milk, butter. Marine oils (in fish) come from an animal source but contain polyunsaturated oils.
Vegetable (mainly poly-unsaturated oils)	Margarine, cooking fat, peanut butter. Nut oils, e.g. ground nut, walnut, almond, olive oil, soya and corn oils. Cotton seed and sunflower seed oils.

* Lipids may be chemically classified into saturated and unsaturated oils. (See chapter 1: Lipids)

- *Visible fats*
  These are fats clearly visible in food. They include fat on meat, butter, margarine, oil, suet and dripping.
- *Invisible fats*
  These are fats which are combined with other nutrients in a food. Examples are fats in milk, egg yolk, cheese, oily fish and nuts.

FAT FROM ANIMALS

Most fat occurs on animals as adipose tissue. On carcase meat, it is known as suet. When this is *rendered* (melted down), it becomes dripping (beef fat) or lard (pork fat).

All have a very high fat content — over 90%. Meat fats are suitable for roasting, frying and making meat casseroles, as they have a good meaty flavour. All have a high proportion of saturated fats and all contain cholesterol.

COOKING FATS

These are generally made from vegetable oils which have been *hydrogenated* (hardened) artificially by forcing hydrogen into them. They have little flavour. As they do not decompose at normal cooking temperatures, they are suitable for frying and roasting. Some such as Cookeen and Shortex are specially recommended for pastry making. Polyunsaturated cooking fat is available under the brand name Flora.

VEGETABLE OILS

Particular plants have large amounts of oil stored in their tissues. Nuts, soya beans, olives, rape seed and maize are typical examples. These are used to produce cooking fats and oils.

The plants are cleaned, crushed and heated slightly, then pressed to remove the oils. They are then refined to remove impurities, colour and flavours. Blends of cheaper oils are used to make cooking oils, but these may be high in saturated fats.

Oils are particularly suitable for cooking as they have a high smoking point. Additives may be used to prevent rancidity (antioxidants) and spattering (anti-spattering agents). Oils have an important function as a basic ingredient of salad dressings.

Most pure vegetable oils such as soya, corn and sunflower oils are low in saturated fats.

MARGARINE

Margarine is a butter substitute. By law, it may not contain more than 16% water. Vitamins A and D are added during manufacture.

Protein	Lipid	Carbohydrate
0.2%	81%	0%

Vitamins	Minerals	Water	kcal/kJ(100g)
A, D	trace cal.	16%	730/3,000

MANUFACTURE OF MARGARINE

1. *Oil extraction:* Oils are extracted from plant sources and refined to remove impurities and strong flavours.
2. *Hydrogenation:* Hydrogen gas is forced through the oil in the presence of a nickel catalyst to speed up hardening. This changes the unsaturated oils into saturated fats.
3. *Other ingredients* are blended in: skimmed milk, colourings, salt, vitamins A and D and emulsifiers.
4. *A votator* machine churns the ingredients until they reach the correct consistency.
5. *Temperature* is lowered. The margarine is then shaped and packed.

TYPES OF MARGARINE

Modern technology can create a margarine to suit every purpose.

- *All-purpose (block) margarines* such as Stork are made from vegetable oils (for example, groundnut), fish or animal oils, or a mixture of these. Generally high in saturated fats (730-740 kcal per 100g). Good for creaming.
- *Soft 'luxury' margarines* such as Blueband have a medium saturated fat content. They spread and cream easily. Useful for quick 'all-in-one' recipes. Bought in tubs.
- *Low-fat spreads* such as Outline contain about half the fat (therefore half the kilocalories) of butter or margarine. Most consist of margarine blended with water or skimmed milk. For this reason, the fat content is too low for it to be called margarine (360-400 kcal per 100g). It spreads easily, but is not suitable for normal baking recipes or for frying (the high moisture content causes spattering).

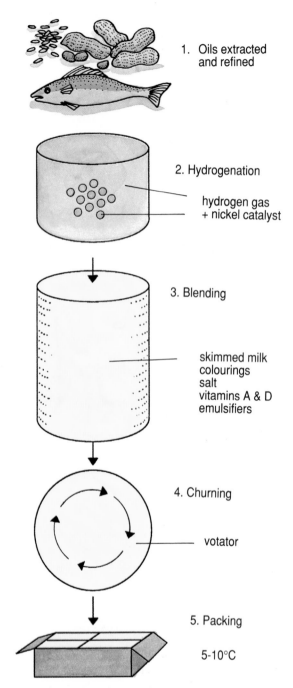

1. Oils extracted and refined

2. Hydrogenation

hydrogen gas + nickel catalyst

3. Blending

skimmed milk colourings salt vitamins A & D emulsifiers

4. Churning

votator

5. Packing

5-10°C

Manufacture of margarine

- *Polyunsaturated margarines* such as Flora are usually made from sunflower oil. They contain a high proportion of polyunsaturated oils (minimum 45%) and are recommended for low cholesterol diets, as the saturated fat content is less than 25%.

Note: All margarines contain a high proportion of saturated fats unless the label states that they are high in polyunsaturates.

USES OF FAT

Fats improve the flavour, appearance, nutritional and energy value and the keeping qualities of food.

Uses of fat	Fat used	Uses of fat	Fat used
1. Spreading — for flavour.	Butter, margarine	6. Anti-staling — fats improve keeping qualities of bread and cakes.	Butter, margarine
2. Frying — to flavour and prevent food sticking.	Oil, cooking fat, butter		
3. Shortening — to give a crumbly texture to pastry and flavour to rubbed in mixtures.	Butter, margarine, lard	7. Source of fat soluble vitamins A and D.	Butter, margarine
4. Creaming, as in Madeira cakes.	Block margarine	8. Sauces, such as roux sauces, Hollandaise	Butter, margarine
5. Flavouring as in baking, mashed potatoes.	Butter, margarine	9. Emulsions such as mayonnaise, Hollandaise	Oil, butter

VEGETABLES, NUTS AND FRUIT

Most vegetables can be grouped as follows:

Leafy Greens	Roots and Tubers	Pulse vegetables	Fruits	Bulbs
Cabbage	Carrots	Peas	Tomato	Onion
Kale	Parsnips	Broad beans	Cucumber	Shallot
Spinach	Swedes	Runner beans	Courgette	Garlic
Lettuce	Turnips	French beans	Marrow	Leeks
Brussels sprouts	Beetroots	Dried pulses	Capsicums	
Broccoli } flowers	Potatoes } tubers	(e.g. kidney beans haricot beans)	(green and red peppers)	
Cauliflower	Jerusalem artichokes		Aubergines	

Vegetables not included above are: *stems* such as asparagus and celery; *fungi* such as mushrooms; and *nuts* which are a good source of oil. *Sprouting seeds* like bean sprouts and alfalfa are rich in vitamin C and low in kilocalories.

NUTRITIVE VALUE OF VEGETABLES

PROTEIN
Protein is low in most vegetables, with the exception of pulses which are a good source. Soya beans and nuts are excellent sources. Protein in vegetables is of low biological value, with the exception of soya beans.

FAT
Fat is deficient in almost all vegetables except soya beans, nuts, olives. Certain seeds such as rape seed and cotton seed are good sources. Fats from vegetable sources are usually polyunsaturated fats.

CARBOHYDRATE
Carbohydrate may be present in the form of starch, as in root vegetables, or in the form of sugar, as in onions, carrots and beetroot.

CELLULOSE
This carbohydrate forms the structural framework of vegetables. It is most plentiful on the skin and outer husks. If possible, vegetables should be cooked and eaten without peeling.

VITAMINS
Most vegetables are a good source of pro-vitamin A (carotene), which is plentiful in carrots, dark leafy greens, peppers and tomatoes. Thiamine is plentiful in pulses. Vegetables are an excellent source of ascorbic acid (vitamin C), particularly when served raw. Green vegetables, peppers and watercress are good sources. Although only small amounts of vitamin C are present in potatoes, they are a useful source as we eat them in large quantities. Care must be taken when cooking vegetables to retain vitamin C.

MINERALS
Vegetables are useful sources of many minerals and trace elements. Calcium, potassium, iodine and iron are present in many vegetables, iron in particular being present in dark greens and pulses.

Note: The oxalates in spinach prevent its iron from being absorbed.

Average composition of vegetables (per 100g)						
Vegetables	Protein	Fats	Carbohydrates	Vitamins	Minerals	Water
Greens	1-3%	0%	2-3%	A, C	cal./iron	90%
Roots	1%	0%	5-20%	A, C	cal./iron	70-90%
Pulses	2-5%	0%	5-10%	A, C	cal./ir./potass.	75-90%
Fruits	1%	0%	2%	A, C	iron	90-95%
Bulbs	1%	0%	5%	C, B (trace)	cal.	93%

*For more detailed information, see food tables, end of book.

WATER
Most vegetables contain large quantities of water, many having over 90%.

*Vegetables add colour and nutrients to the diet
(Denis Hughes–Gilbey)*

EFFECT OF HEAT ON VEGETABLES
1. Cell walls are softened and broken, making them more digestible.
2. Starch grains burst, releasing starch.
3. Water-soluble vitamins and minerals dissolve into the cooking water.
4. About 50% vitamin C and B group vitamins are destroyed.
5. Loss of colour, flavour and texture, particularly when over-cooked.

TO RETAIN THE NUTRIENTS IN VEGETABLES
Both vitamin C and B group are unstable when heated. These water-soluble vitamins and any mineral elements present are likely to leach into the cooking liquid, so this should be used up in soups or sauces instead of being thrown away.
1. Only use fresh, good quality vegetables — raw, if possible.
2. Using a sharp knife, trim sparingly and wash under running water. Avoid steeping.
3. Avoid chopping and peeling, if possible. This liberates oxidase from the cell walls which destroys vitamin C.
4. Prepare vegetables just before cooking them.
5. Cook quickly in the minimum amount of boiling water. Use a saucepan with a tightly-fitting lid. Open saucepans encourage oxidation.
6. Never use bread-soda. It destroys vitamin C. Copper and brass pans have the same effect.
7. Cook until barely tender, drain well and serve at once.
8. Avoid keeping vegetables warm or reheating them.
9. Retain cooking water for sauces, soups and casseroles.
10. Cooking methods such as the 'conservative' method, steaming and pressure cooking reduce nutrient loss as there is little or no contact with water.

EFFECT OF PROCESSING ON VEGETABLES
- *Drying* results in loss of vitamins B_1 and C.
- *Sulphur dioxide* destroys vitamin B_1.
- *Freeze-drying:* some loss of vitamin C.
- *Canning* is very convenient as vegetables need no further cooking. There is a loss of texture and sometimes of colour. Heat processing causes loss of vitamins B_1 and C. There is further loss of these vitamins and minerals into canning liquid.
- *Freezing:* Vegetables retain colour, flavour and texture. As there is little loss of nutrients, freezing is the best method of processing vegetables. It is also the most expensive. There is no waste, and cooking time is short. Vegetables must be blanched before processing to destroy oxidising enzymes.

GRADING VEGETABLES AND FRUIT
EC grading requires that vegetables sold should be clean and free from soil and any contaminants such as pesticides. Each pack should have produce of uniform quality and size. It should be labelled clearly to show quality, origin and, where appropriate, variety. Classes are:

Extra — best quality produce.
Class 1 — good quality.
Class 2 — marketable but defects of shape, blemishes etc.
Class 3 — marketable but inferior.

ADVANTAGES OF FRUIT AND VEGETABLES IN THE DIET

- Rich in vitamins A and C.
- Good source of minerals, especially iron.
- Good source of cellulose or dietary fibre.
- Most are low in kilocalories.
- Low in fat, therefore good for low-cholesterol and low-kilocalorie diets.
- Should be eaten raw, as in salads.
- Wide variety of fruit and vegetables available.

Note: Wash fruit and vegetables thoroughly to clean them and remove any traces of insecticide.

PULSES

Pulse vegetables are the seeds of leguminous (pod-bearing) plants. Pulses are the dried seeds of such plants.

NUTRITIVE/DIETETIC VALUE OF PULSES

They are a good economical source of low biological value protein. Soya beans have the highest biological value. Pulses are a good source of energy and fibre. They also provide calcium, iron and B vitamins. They are easy to store and are an important vegetarian food.

TYPES OF PULSES

Peas — both green and split.
Chick peas — grown and used extensively in India.
Lentils — a wide variety, for example Egyptian (orange), French (greenish yellow).
Beans — a wide variety — black, red, white kidney beans, Haricot (used for baked beans) and butter beans.
Mung beans — used to grow bean sprouts (rich in vitamin C).
Soya beans — an important source of cheap protein. While they have a relatively high biological value for a plant food, they are deficient in some amino acids.

USE OF PULSES

Large pulses are soaked for several hours (sometimes overnight) before cooking to rehydrate them and shorten cooking time. Rinse well. Bring to boil and *boil rapidly for 10 minutes*. This destroys toxins present on the outside skin of many beans. Then simmer until soft.

Buy fruit and vegetables in season
(S. and R. Greenhill)

BUYING VEGETABLES AND FRUIT

Fruit and vegetables deteriorate rapidly. Buy only what you need and use as soon as possible.

1. Buy in season when they are plentiful, cheap and at their best.
2. Fruit and vegetables should look fresh, unbruised and insect free, with a good bright colour.
3. Buy loose or netted produce — plastic encourages mould growth.
4. Select your own choice rather than having them picked for you.
5. Roots and tubers should be heavy for size and hard, not pliable or discoloured. Avoid washed vegetables — they deteriorate more rapidly.
6. Greens should be crisp and fruits should be brightly-coloured and heavy for size.
7. Medium-sized fruit and vegetables are a good choice. Small vegetables are tasty but expensive. Some large vegetables lack flavour.

NUTS

Nuts are useful in the diet, particularly that of vegetarians, due to their relatively high protein content (25%). They are also high in fat (50%), with carbohydrate in the form of cellulose, small amounts of B vitamins and some iron.

Nuts keep well, adding texture and variety to the diet. They can be used whole, chopped or ground in a variety of dishes, both savoury and sweet. Nuts are used in biscuits, cakes, sweets such as marzipan, salads and as a main course like nut loaf or nut cutlets. Peanuts and mixed nuts are useful as nutritious snacks, for packed lunches etc. But don't forget their energy value is very high — nearly 600 kilocalories in a normal 100g packet.

► FRUIT

Classification of fruit		
Type of Fruits	*Example*	*Season Starts*
Citrus fruits	Oranges, lemon, grapefruit	January
Hard fruits } drupes Stone fruits	Apples, pears, plums, damsons, peaches, cherries, avocado	September, summer/autumn
Berries	Strawberries, raspberries, blackberries, gooseberries, red and black currants	Summer
Dried Fruit	Raisins, sultanas, prunes	Imported
Others	Rhubarb, grapes, bananas	Summer, September, imported

COMPOSITION OF FRUIT

(See food tables, end of book.)

NUTRITIVE VALUE OF FRUIT

PROTEIN

Only traces present.

FAT

None present except in avocados and olives.

CARBOHYDRATES

These may be in the form of sugar, starch, cellulose or pectin which is essential for the setting of jam. All fruits contain sugar as sucrose, fructose and glucose. Unripe fruit has a greater proportion of starch. Cellulose forms the skin and cell framework and helps peristalsis in the bowel. Dried fruit has a very high proportion of sugar.

VITAMINS

Fruit is valued for its vitamin C (ascorbic acid) content. Apricots, peaches and black currants are also rich in carotene (pro-vitamin A). Best fruit sources of vitamin C in order of importance are rose-hips, black currants, citrus fruits, strawberries, raspberries and apples.

MINERALS

Most fruits contain varying amounts of calcium and iron.

WATER

Most fruits have a high water content — over 80%. Dried fruit has approximately 20% water.

CHANGES IN FRUIT WHICH OCCUR ON RIPENING

Fruit goes through a cycle of growth, ripening and decay. This is controlled by enzymes within the fruit.

1. Starch in unripe fruit changes to sugar (fructose).
2. Pectose changes to pectin. When over-ripe it becomes pectic acid.*

* *Unripe*	*Ripe*	*Over-ripe*
Pectose	Pectin	Pectic Acid

3. Enzymes bring about changes in colour and flavour. These continue to work even after harvesting.
4. Enzymes, together with yeasts and mould, eventually decompose fruit. To delay decomposition, fruit may be packed in wrapping paper which is impregnated with preservatives, stored in an environment with a low level of oxygen to prevent oxidation, or sprayed with preservatives (citrus).
5. Ethylene gas* is given off during ripening.

* Ethylene gas is used commercially to hasten the ripening of fruits during storage.

EFFECTS OF HEAT ON FRUIT

It is preferable to eat fruit raw, as fruit is affected by cooking in a similar way to vegetables (see page 68). Due to acidity, vitamin C loss is less but may still be up to 75%.

- Cell walls are softened. Fruit disintegrates when over-cooked.
- Some water is absorbed.
- Some loss of colour and flavour.
- Water-soluble vitamins and minerals are released into the cooking liquid, which should be used up.

EFFECT OF PREPARATION AND PROCESSING

- Discolouration of fruits such as apples is due to enzymic action and oxidation.

- Metals react with fruit. Carbon steel utensils discolour fruit. Brass and copper containers reduce vitamin C content. Lead, zinc and aluminium may be dissolved by acids present in fruit.
- In the drying of fruit, substantial amounts of vitamins A, B group and C are lost.

- In canning, many fruits soften. Vitamin C is reduced. Added sugar increases kilocalorie content. Lacquered tins are essential to prevent discolouration by acid.
- Freezing: Food value changes little, although the texture may soften.

GRADING OF FRUIT
As for vegetables, (pages 68-69).

► CEREALS AND CARBOHYDRATE FOOD

CEREALS
The cereal grain is the fruit of cultivated grasses. Cereals are the staple food of most of the human race, as they are cheap and easy to grow in almost every climate. The main cereals eaten by humans, in order of world production, are wheat, rice, maize, barley, millet, oats and rye.

NUTRITIVE VALUE OF CEREALS

PROTEIN
Cereals contain useful amounts of low biological value protein. Several essential amino acids such as lysine are deficient. Gluten is the principal protein in wheat and rye.

LIPID
Small amounts are present in the germ.

CARBOHYDRATE
The main constituent of cereal foods is carbohydrate — up to 75% is in the form of starch. All unprocessed cereals are a good source of fibre.

VITAMINS
Cereals are an excellent source of B group vitamins, although these may be reduced by processing. Vitamin E is also present.

MINERALS
Calcium, iron and phosphorus are present, but the phytic acid in wheat bran reduces absorption of calcium and iron.

WATER
The low water content of cereals makes them easy to store.

DIETETIC VALUE OF CEREALS
Cereals are a staple food for much of the human race. They are a nutritious form of energy, particularly when unprocessed. However, some factors can cause problems in the diet.
1. Gluten in wheat cannot be absorbed by those with coeliac disease.
2. Phytic acid inhibits the absorption of iron and calcium. This rarely causes problems, unless the general diet is inadequate. In any case, it is common practice to add supplements of these minerals to white bread.
3. Pellagra, caused by lack of niacin, occurs in maize-eating populations, as maize is deficient in tryptophan from which the body manufactures niacin.
4. Beriberi, caused by lack of vitamin B_1 (thiamine), is common among those whose staple diet is 'polished' rice — rice from which the bran has been removed.

STRUCTURE OF WHEAT GRAIN
(other cereals have similar structure.)
The wheat grain is oval in shape with a tuft of hairs growing from the top. The grain has three main parts:

1. THE HUSK OF BRAN (13%)
This consists of layers of cellulose which are indigestible by humans but are important in the diet as they provide roughage in the intestine. Bran consists of cellulose and is rich in B group vitamins, particularly niacin. It also contains useful amounts of calcium, iron and phosphorus.

2. THE ENDOSPERM (85%)
This is the food reserve of the plant. It consists of an outer aleurone layer which is rich in protein. The remainder is

Average composition of wheat and wholemeal flour							
Protein	*Fat*	*Carbohydrate*	*Fibre*	*Vitamins*	*Minerals*	*Water*	*kcal/kJ(100g)*
12.0%	2%	65%	9%	B group	calcium	13%	318/1351

74%

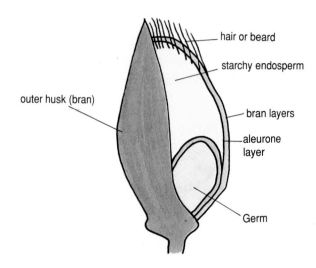

Structure of a wheat grain

mostly starch. It also contains protein (gluten) and B group vitamins.

3. THE GERM (2%)
This is attached to the stalk and contains all the nutrients necessary for the young plant to germinate and grow. It is rich in protein, B group vitamins and vitamin E. The germ contains the fat of the plant and mineral salts.

MILLING WHEAT
In order to make wheat more digestible, it must be crushed to release the nutrients. This is known as *milling*.
1. *Cleaning the grain:* Foreign substances are removed. The grain is washed, dried and conditioned — that is, given the moisture content suitable for the rollers.
2. *Blending:* Various types of wheat are mixed to make up the particular 'grist' or mixture required.
3. *Break rolling:* The wheat is passed through metal rollers which split open the grain. The processing of whole-meal flour is completed at this stage.
4. *Sieving:* Crushed grain is sieved to remove germ and bran.
5. *Rolling and sieving:* This is done repeatedly until the flour reaches the correct texture.
6. *Air-classifying:* Air is introduced to prevent lumps and to lighten the flour.
7. Additives such as calcium carbonate, bleaching agents and improvers such as vitamin C are usually added — the latter to speed up maturing.
8. Bran and germ are used in the manufacture of breakfast cereals, health foods etc.

EFFECTS OF HEAT ON CEREALS
1. *Moist heat:* Starch grains burst and gelatinise. Any liquid present is absorbed and thickened.

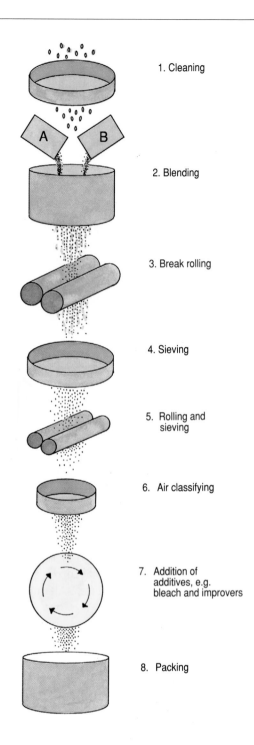

1. Cleaning
2. Blending
3. Break rolling
4. Sieving
5. Rolling and sieving
6. Air classifying
7. Addition of additives, e.g. bleach and improvers
8. Packing

Milling of flour

2. *Dry heat:* Starch grains burst, releasing starch cells which absorb fat or moisture — for example fat in pastry, eggs/milk in cakes and bread, oil in popcorn.
3. Protein coagulates and sets baked products such as bread.
4. Cellulose softens and absorbs water.
5. Starch becomes digestible.
6. Some B group vitamins are destroyed, particularly thiamine.
7. Surface starch changes to dextrin, causing browning.

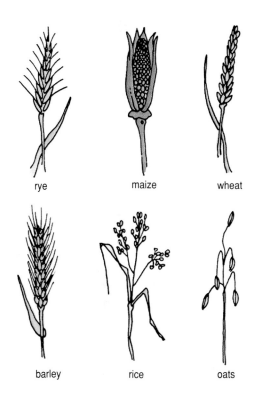

rye   maize   wheat

barley   rice   oats

COOKING RICE

Allow 50-75 g per portion.

COOKING TIME

White rice — 12 minutes   } Immerse in boiling,
Brown rice — 30-40 minutes } salted water.

PASTA

This is a staple food in Italy and is also extensively used in China. Good-quality pasta is made from the semolina (rough endosperm) of durum wheat — flour which has a high protein content. The flour is mixed with water, oil and sometimes with eggs. It is then rolled out or extruded in shapes such as spaghetti, macaroni.

Commercial pasta is dried and stores well. It can also be made at home and used fresh. Wholemeal pasta and spinach-flavoured green pasta are also available. Portions are the same as those for rice (cooking time — 12 minutes).

spaghetti   vermicelli

macaroni   lasagne

tagliatelle (wide noodles)

conchiglie

cannelloni (large tubes)

ravioli (packets of pasta, stuffed with filling)

OTHER CEREALS

- *Barley:* Used in the production of alcohol and vinegar. Pearl barley is used to thicken soups and stews.
- *Maize:* This is commonly known as corn. It is almost 100% starch. Used as a vegetable and to make breakfast cereals such as cornflakes, cornflour, corn oil and popcorn (dried grains).
- *Rye:* Grown extensively in northeastern Europe as it is resistant to cold. Used to make rye bread and crisp breads.
- *Oats:* This is a very nourishing cereal, as humans have not found it possible to remove the germ and bran! It is used for porridge and biscuits.
- *Rice:* The outer bran layers are traditionally rubbed off (polished) to improve its keeping qualities. This, unfortunately, removes most of its fibre and vitamin B.
- Brown rice, which is more nutritious than others, is now readily available.
- Long grain rice (Patna) is used for savoury dishes.
- Short grain rice (Carolina) has round grains and is suitable for puddings.
- Medium grain rice (Italian) has round grains. It is suitable for savoury dishes and risotto.
- Easycook rice has been steam-treated to make it less sticky.
- Ground rice is used for milk puddings, baking and biscuits.
- Rice flour is used in biscuits to give a 'short' texture.

OTHER CEREAL PRODUCTS

- *Breakfast cereals* — may or may not have fibre removed. They may be rolled, puffed, flaked or shredded. Most are fortified with vitamins and iron. Served with milk, they make a very nutritious food.
- *Non-cereal starchy products* — arrowroot, sago, tapioca are obtained from roots/stems of tropical plants. Used for thickening and in milk puddings.

FLOUR

Most flour is made from milled wheat but flour is also made from the following plants:

- rice
- maize (cornflour)
- barley
- rye
- soya

Wheat flour is an important commodity in the kitchen because:

1. It is the basis of most baked products.
2. It can thicken liquids such as soups and sauces.

WINTER/SPRING WHEAT

The climate in which wheat is grown determines its use in baking. Countries such as Canada which have hard winters will sow wheat in spring for harvesting in the autumn. This quick growth produces a high gluten flour known as strong flour or baker's flour (12% gluten).

Wheat sown in winter in milder climates grows more slowly, producing a flour with a lower gluten content (9% gluten). Plain flour is usually a mixture of the two.

CLASSIFICATION

1. *Wholemeal flour — 100% extraction*

   This contains the whole grain which is cleaned and crushed. Nothing is added or taken away. It is rich in B group vitamins, protein and fibre. Stone-ground flour has a rougher texture and is said to be higher in B group vitamins than is wholemeal flour.

2. *Wheaten meal or brown flour — 85% extraction*

   This flour contains less germ, B group vitamins and fibre than wholemeal flour but has more than that of white. Bran or caramel may be added to improve the colour.

   Note: Wholemeal flour does not keep as well as white flour because the presence of fat causes rancidity. Use within three months of purchase.

3. *White flour — 73% extraction*

   Sold as plain or cream flour, this has the germ and bran removed. The resulting product is composed chiefly of endosperm — starch and gluten. The vitamin B group and fibre are considerably reduced. No fat is present so that white flour keeps longer than does brown flour. Calcium and iron are added.

   Self-raising flour: This is plain, soft flour with a raising agent (sodium bicarbonate and cream of tartar) added. It is not suitable for pastry-making or baking with yeast.

4. *Strong flour*

   This is white flour containing a high proportion of gluten.* It is recommended for use when making pastry — particularly rich pastry such as puff pastry, and for yeast baking.

   * Gluten. Two proteins in wheat, gliadin and glutenin, convert to gluten when moistened. Gluten has elastic properties which enables it to stretch and rise as the CO_2 expands the dough. When the temperature of the dough rises sufficiently, the strands of gluten coagulate to form an aerated structure. Gluten is present in wheat and rye but not in other cereals which are therefore unsuitable for baking, but useful in the diet of coeliacs.

5. *Gluten-free flour*

   This is suitable for those suffering from coeliac disease. It is made by washing the starch out of the flour, then dehydrating the resulting liquid. The sticky gluten remains behind. Soya flour is added to improve its nutritive value.

Nutritive value of flour		
	Wholemeal	*White*
Protein	Higher in low biological protein	Some loss due to milling
Lipid	Present in germ and wholemeal flours	Deficient in fat
Carbohydrate	Large proportion present as starch	Very high percentage of starch
Cellulose	Good source of dietary fibre	$1/3$ of the fibre of wholemeal flour
Minerals	Calcium, iron, phosphorus	Extra calcium/iron/phosphorus (these are added during manufacture)
Vitamins	Very good source of B group vitamins; vitamin E present in germ	Reduced vitamin B due to milling. Some may be replaced commercially.
Water	14%	14.5%
Kilocalories (per 100g)	Wholemeal flour: 318 kcal/1351 kJ Less difference than is often thought.	White flour: 350 kcal/1493 kJ

6. *Starch-reduced flour*
This is made like gluten-free flour by washing some of the starch out of the flour, leaving behind a high protein, low-kilocalorie flour.

7. *High-ratio flour*
A very 'soft' flour used for confectionery. Only available commercially. (Adding some cornflour to flour has the same effect.)

SUGAR
The sugar which we use for cooking and at the table is the disaccharide sucrose — made up of fructose and glucose. Sugar is a sweet crystalline substance obtained from sugar cane or sugar beet. When refined, both are identical in composition — $C_{12}H_{22}O_{11}$.

DIETETIC VALUE OF SUGAR
Sugar is a cheap, concentrated and easily-digested form of energy. Sugar is a highly-refined food containing 99.9% carbohydrate, and therefore no other nutrients. In fact, sugar needs B group vitamins for its metabolism. Brown sugar is almost identical — it contains traces of minerals too small to be significant.

As we need fewer energy-giving foods today, due to less strenuous occupations and lifestyles, refined sugar is superfluous in most diets. In any case, all the starch we eat is converted to sugar in the body. Too much sugar in the diet takes the place of more nutritious foods and results in obesity and plaque formation on teeth, leading to decay. Refined sugar and sugar products should be replaced in the diet by less refined carbohydrates such as starch and fibre. Nutritious foods which contain sugar include fruit, milk and carrots.

VARIETIES OF SUGAR
Granulated — large white crystals. Used at table, in cooking, preserving, sweet making.

Caster — fine, white sugar crystals. Used in baking. Creams well.

Icing — powdered sugar. Used for icings, fillings and for sweetening cold dishes as it dissolves easily.

Sugar lumps — cubed sugar made from moistened, granulated sugar.

Preserving — very large crystals. Some varieties such as Sureset have pectin added.

Brown sugar — there are two types, natural and refined.

Natural — crystallised from unrefined sugar. Includes Demerara, with large sticky crystals, and Barbados, a dark brown strong-flavoured sugar with fine crystals (all made in country of origin).

Refined — made from white sugar which has been coloured and flavoured with molasses, for example 'soft brown sugar'.

OTHER SWEETENERS
Golden syrup, treacle — by-products of sugar refining. Contain minerals such as iron.

Glucose — produced commercially by hydrolysing starch with hydrochloric acid. It has no real advantage in the diet except as a quick source of energy — for athletes or Third World food aid.

Honey — made by bees from nectar. It is usually pasteurised to preserve it and destroy bacteria. 18% water. Contains glucose and fructose. It has no proven nutritional advantage over sugar in the diet.

Sorbitol — a natural sweetener made from glucose. It is less sweet than sugar and is useful in the diet of diabetics as it is absorbed more slowly.

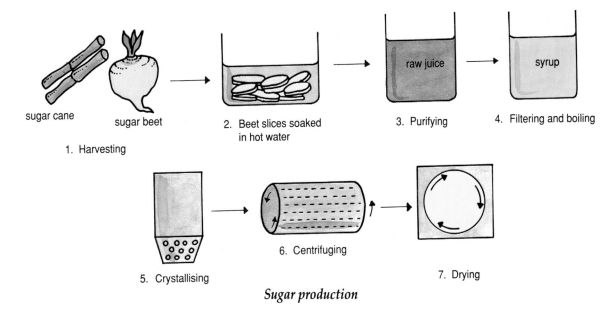

sugar cane   sugar beet   2. Beet slices soaked in hot water   3. Purifying   4. Filtering and boiling

1. Harvesting

raw juice   syrup

5. Crystallising   6. Centrifuging   7. Drying

Sugar production

ARTIFICIAL SWEETENERS

Although these taste sweet, they contain no sugar and little or no kilocalories. They are useful in the diet of diabetics and slimmers.

Saccharin — a synthetic sweetener produced from coal tar. It is 500 times sweeter than sugar, with a bitter aftertaste.

Aspartame (brand names Nutrasweet, Canderel) — a protein 200 times sweeter than sugar with no bitter aftertaste. Approved in several countries. Used in low kilocalorie products such as soft drinks. Dangerous for people with phenylketonuria (PKU), a protein disease.

SUGAR PRODUCTION

Sugar beet is washed, crushed and soaked in hot water to extract the sugar by osmosis. The resulting sugar syrup is dark in colour due to impurities. Lime and CO_2 are used to precipitate the impurities which are filtered off. The syrup is passed through a charcoal filter to remove colour. It is then boiled to concentrate the solution. The sugar is crystallised in vacuum pans, then centrifuged to separate the crystals from the liquid and dried.

USES OF SUGAR IN COOKING

1. As a sweetener.
2. As a preservative — in concentrations of over 65%, it inhibits the growth of micro-organisms.
3. It provides food for yeast in bread-making.
4. In cake making, it helps the fat to entrap air, making cakes light.
5. It colours food — caramel is produced by boiling a sugar solution to a high temperature.
6. Confectionery and sweets — the above principle is also used.
7. Cake decorating, icings, fillings.
8. It softens gluten in cake-making, creating a lighter product.
9. Syrups and glazes.
10. Meringues — it strengthens the protein in egg white, helping the mixture to retain air.

► HOME BAKING

Top-quality, wholesome ingredients are essential for good results.

Fat: Fat adds 'shortness', flavour and colour. The type of fat used varies according to the product being baked. Butter has the best flavour, but is difficult to cream. Margarine is useful for most baked products as it is easy to cream and to rub in. Luxury margarines are useful for 'all-in-one' recipes. Hard fats give best results in pastry-making. Fats improve the keeping quality of cakes.

Sugar: Caster sugar is the most suitable for baking as it creams and blends in well. Granulated sugar results in a 'grainy' texture and appearance. Brown sugar — Barbados or Demerara — introduces colour and extra flavour, but is unsuitable for some recipes.

Flour: See page 74.

CLASSIFICATION OF CAKES

Home-made cakes are classified according to the initial mixing process used when making the cake.

1. *Rubbing-in method*
   This is used for yeast breads, plain cakes and scones. The fat is rubbed into the flour with the fingertips.
2. *Creaming method*
   This method is used for Madeira mixture and fruit cakes. The fat and sugar are creamed together with an electric mixer or a wooden spoon.
3. *The whisking method*
   This method is used for fatless sponges and meringues. The eggs and sugar are whisked together.
4. *The melting method*
   This method is used for gingerbread and 'boiled' fruit cakes. Ingredients such as fat, syrups and sugar are melted in a saucepan before being added to the dry ingredients.
5. *All-in-one method*
   This method is used for Madeira, sponges and plain cakes. All ingredients are placed in a bowl together and beaten with a wooden spoon for 2-3 minutes (or an electric mixer for 1 minute). Soft luxury or easy-creaming margarines must be used for this method.

   Extra baking powder is required to make up for the lack of aeration provided by creaming. This is a quick and easy method of cake-making, but the texture is closer and the volume smaller than when making cakes by conventional methods.

RAISING AGENTS

Baked products are aerated by introducing air or gas into the mixture. This has the effect of lightening them and improving their texture and palatability.

The principle on which raising agents are based is *that gases expand and rise when heated*. Once the gas is intro-

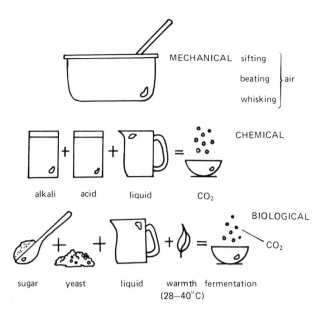

MECHANICAL   sifting

beating   air

whisking

CHEMICAL

alkali   acid   liquid CO_2

BIOLOGICAL

CO_2

sugar   yeast   liquid   warmth   fermentation
(28–40°C)

duced into the dough, it forms air bubbles which expand and push the dough upwards until the heat of the oven sets the gluten. The protein in flour (gluten) is elastic and enables the dough to stretch.

CARBON DIOXIDE MAY BE INTRODUCED:
■ **CHEMICALLY**

Chemical raising agents are based on the reaction of an acid and an alkali which produce CO_2 when moistened.

Bread soda + cream of tartar/sour milk = carbon dioxide + water
  (alkali)   (acid) CO_2 H_2O

Baking powder: the bread soda (sodium bicarbonate) and cream of tartar (potassium hydrogen tartarate) are already mixed (with rice flour, to prevent premature reaction). Once moistened, as with milk or egg, the reaction takes place, so baking should be placed in the oven as soon as possible.

Bread-soda used alone also produces CO_2. It decomposes in the dry heat of the oven, producing CO_2 and Na_2CO_3 (washing soda). It is only suitable for recipes using strongly-flavoured ingredients (such as treacle), to disguise the bitter soda taste in products such as gingerbread.

■ **BIOLOGICALLY**

Carbon dioxide may be introduced into the dough by fermentation. This occurs when yeast feeds on glucose, producing alcohol and CO_2. It may be shown as an equation:

$C_6H_{12}O_6$ + yeast   = $2C_2H_5OH$ + $2CO_2$ + energy
 glucose   Fermentation   alcohol   carbon dioxide

Yeast must have certain conditions if this reaction is to take place:

■ *Food:* Carbohydrates are present in flour. Sugar is added to the recipe.
■ *Warmth:* A temperature of 26-28°C provides the ideal environment. Too much heat (over 55°C) will kill yeast. Too cool a temperature will retard its growth.
■ *Moisture:* This is provided by the liquid ingredients, such as water, milk, eggs etc.
Fermentation occurs in stages.
1. Diastase (an enzyme present in flour) changes some starch to maltose when moistened.
2. Yeast enzymes (maltase and invertase) change disaccharides to monosaccharides, for example glucose.
3. Zymase changes monosaccharides to CO_2 and alcohol.

The carbon dioxide thus introduced into the dough expands and rises in a warm atmosphere outside the oven, pushing the dough upwards. At the same time, the gluten matures and becomes elastic. The yeast is killed in the high temperature of the oven. The alcohol evaporates and rising stops. The gluten sets, leaving the bread spongy and well risen. A crust forms on the loaf (dextrin).

(For more about yeast, see Microbiology, page 111)

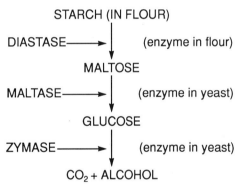

STARCH (IN FLOUR)

DIASTASE ⟶   (enzyme in flour)

MALTOSE

MALTASE ⟶   (enzyme in yeast)

GLUCOSE

ZYMASE ⟶   (enzyme in yeast)

CO_2 + ALCOHOL

TYPES OF YEAST

Baker's yeast (saccharomyces cerevisiae) is grown in a nutrient culture containing molasses in warm, well-aerated vats. It is then centrifuged to remove moisture.

1. *Fresh yeast*
This is known as baker's or compressed yeast. Beige in colour, it has a 'beery' smell. It crumbles easily and keeps for about 4-7 days in a refrigerator. It must be used fresh. Stale yeast is darker in colour and has a strong smell.
2. *Dried yeast*
This is dehydrated active yeast. It is available in granulated form. It keeps for up to six months when stored in an air-tight container.
3. *Fast-action dried yeast*
This is a blend of dried yeast and improvers, such as enzymes and ascorbic acid (vitamin C). These speed up fermentation and reduce the rising time. It is mixed directly into the flour.

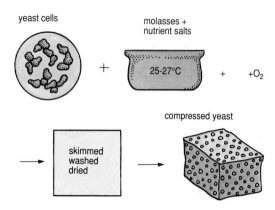

Cultivation of yeast

PROPORTIONS

Fresh yeast: 15g (1/2 oz) raises up to 450g flour. Blend with warmed liquid and one teaspoon of sugar and leave in a warm place until frothy. Then mix into dry ingredients.

Dried yeast (2 and 3 above): Use half of the amount of dried yeast to that required of fresh, that is 7-8g. Blend (2) as for fresh yeast; add (3) directly to flour.

RULES FOR BAKING WITH YEAST

1. Use good-quality fresh or active dried yeast in the correct *proportion*.
2. Use *strong flour* with a high gluten content.
3. *Avoid* using *too much salt* as it retards fermentation. Add just sufficient for flavouring.
4. *Sugar* is necessary for fermentation. Too much prevents it.
5. *Fat inhibits growth of yeast.* Extra yeast will be required in richer recipes containing ingredients such as fat and eggs.
6. *Liquid proportions:* 300ml to 450g flour. Blend yeast to a paste with a little of the tepid liquid before adding remaining liquid.
7. All ingredients and *utensils should be warm* (about 30°C) but not hot.
8. *Kneading:* helps the gluten to develop.
9. *Rising:* the dough must be risen slowly in a warm, moist atmosphere outside the oven until double its size. Place dough in a greased bowl in a large plastic bag. Depending on temperature, rising may take one hour in a warm atmosphere, two hours at room temperature or twelve hours in a refrigerator — a long, slow rise gives best results.
10. *Knocking back:* This is a second kneading which breaks up large air bubbles and introduces more oxygen.
11. *Proving:* The dough is now shaped, placed in tins and given a second rising — until double its size.
12. Yeast must be baked in a *hot oven* 220°C/425°F/gas 7 to kill yeast and cook bread.

USE OF ASCORBIC ACID
(THE CHORLEYWOOD PROCESS)

The addition of vitamin C helps to speed up the fermentation process of yeast. This is because the vitamin C acts as an oxidising agent or improver, thus 'strengthening' the gluten in the flour (making it more elastic).

Dissolve one crushed tablet in the liquid and beat well. A little extra yeast will be required. Proving time is reduced by one-third when this method is used. (The first rising is often omitted.)

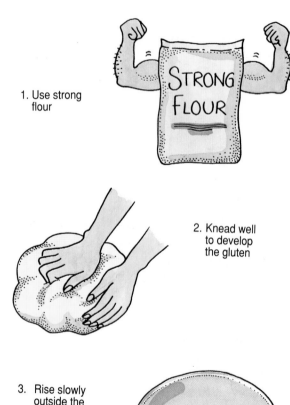

1. Use strong flour

2. Knead well to develop the gluten

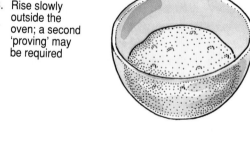

3. Rise slowly outside the oven; a second 'proving' may be required

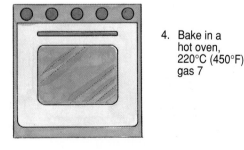

4. Bake in a hot oven, 220°C (450°F) gas 7

Baking with yeast

PASTRY

Pastry is a mixture of flour and fat which is moistened with water. Plain flour should always be used. Raising agents are not used except in suet pastry. The type of shortening and method of introducing it will depend on the type of pastry. For example, in shortcrust pastry, the fat is rubbed in. In flaky pastry, the fat is 'flaked' and folded. For puff pastry, the fat is rolled and folded in. Richer pastry may have extra ingredients such as sugar, eggs and lemon juice added.

RULES FOR MAKING PASTRY

1. All utensils and ingredients should be cold, except for hot pastry (see box).
2. Use the correct proportions of fresh ingredients.
3. Introduce as much air as possible, by sieving, rubbing in etc.
4. Mix with a knife and handle as little as possible.
5. Roll lightly and evenly.
6. Refrigerate. Allow pastry to relax in the fridge between rollings, after shaping and before baking. This prevents shrinking.
7. High temperatures are necessary when baking pastry in order to burst the starch grains of the flour so that they can absorb the fat. If the oven is too cool, the pastry will be tough and greasy. If necessary, the oven temperature may be reduced to moderate after 15 minutes to cook the filling.

Types of pastry

- Shortcrust — plain, rich, biscuit or flan, cheese, all-in-one (fork mix)
- Suet
- Rich (more fat) — rough puff, flaky, puff
- Hot — choux, hot water crust

Summary

Methods of raising baking

Air and steam	Carbon dioxide
1. Air-introduced mechanically by:	1. Produced chemically by using:
■ sieving — flour	■ baking powder
■ beating — batters	■ bicarbonate of soda + cream of tartar
■ rubbing in — scones	■ bicarbonate of soda alone
■ creaming — Madeira	
■ whisking — sponges, soufflés	
■ rolling/folding — rich pastries	
2. Steam-produced by liquids	2. Produced biologically by using yeast
water — choux pastry	
milk — batters	
eggs — most cakes	
Air and steam expand upon heating, become lighter and rise, pushing up the mixture.	CO_2 produced by above means expands and rises, thereby lifting the mixture.

► CONVENIENCE FOODS

Convenience foods are foods which have been prepared or processed by the manufacturer in order to save work and/or be easily stored. The majority of foods sold in a supermarket — with the obvious exceptions of fresh meat, fish, fruit and vegetables — could be classified as convenience foods.

Convenience foods

REASONS FOR INCREASED USE OF CONVENIENCE FOODS

Social changes in the last decades have altered many of our eating habits and increased the demand for convenience foods.

- More women have jobs outside the home.
- More people now live on their own. Young people live in bedsitters, and more elderly people in flats, often with limited cooking facilities.
- Fewer people work near home.
- People have more hobbies and interests outside the home.
- Families are less inclined to have meals together — they often work and eat in 'shifts'.
- Take-away foods are more readily available.
- Advertising tempts us to buy such foods.
- Technological developments have improved the quality and nutritive value of convenience foods.
- It is easier to transport and store food on a large scale when it is processed and packaged.

CLASSIFICATION OF CONVENIENCE FOODS

1. *Frozen foods:* A wide range is available: meat, fish, fruit, vegetables, complete meals, cakes and desserts. Although these are the most expensive form, they are superior in taste, texture and food value to other convenience foods. A deep freeze or at least a frozen-food section of a refrigerator is required in which to store them.
2. *Dehydrated foods:* These foods are cheap and easy to store. They come in sachets and packets — cereals, dried milk, soups and cake mixes. The flavour and colour are less appetising than other convenience foods and many additives are used. Many must be rehydrated before use.
3. *Canned and bottled foods:* These are heat-processed and keep well for up to two years. The texture is soft and many additives such as colourings are used. They are cheap and only need to be reheated before use. Examples include soups, fruits, vegetables, baby foods, meat, fish, jam, pickles and ketchup.
4. *Synthetic foods* which have been developed as a substitute for others, such as TVP and margarine.
5. *Instant foods:* These need no cooking and include cook-chill foods*, cooked meats, processed cheese, yoghurt, ice cream, instant desserts and snack foods such as potato crisps and peanuts.

---

* Cook/chill foods: These are dishes which are fully cooked and ready to eat. They are stored in sealed cartons in refrigerated display cabinets in supermarkets and delicatessens. Examples: breaded chicken pieces, spare ribs, lasagna, fish pie.

If these are not heated to a sufficiently high temperature at the initial cooking stage, and/or if they are not stored continuously at a temperature of below 4°C, serious food poisoning may result. Salmonella or listeriosis may result, leading to the death of vulnerable people such as invalids or the elderly. It is advisable to reheat cook/chill foods to high temperatures before eating in order to kill micro-organisms.

NUTRITIVE VALUE OF CONVENIENCE FOODS

In the past, convenience foods compared badly with fresh foods in terms of nutrients, particularly vitamins and minerals. Research and technology have improved the standard of these foods considerably.

1. Frozen foods are generally equal in food value to fresh foods.
2. Protein, carbohydrate and fat content of convenience foods remain more or less unchanged.
3. There is some loss of vitamin A, particularly in dried foods. The vitamin B group, especially thiamine, and vitamin C are reduced in heat-processed foods.
4. Vitamins and minerals leach into canning liquid which should be used for sauces etc.
5. Colour, flavour and texture may alter during processing — additives may be introduced to counteract this.
6. Many convenience foods, particularly dried and canned foods, contain a considerable amount of chemical additives.
7. Many snack foods have a high proportion of sugar, fat and refined starch, all of which are high in kilocalories.

Advantages	Disadvantages
1. Time-saving.	1. Usually more expensive than fresh foods.
2. Labour-saving.	2. Flavour rarely as good as home-cooked food.
3. No waste.	3. Texture and colour are often inferior.
4. Wide choice available.	4. Reduction in vitamins and minerals, particularly vitamins C, B_1.
5. Useful in emergencies or when time is limited.	5. Portions often small.
6. Handy for beginners, the elderly and the handicapped	6. Much money is wasted on advertising and packaging.
7. Useful when facilities are limited.	7. Many contain artificial additives.
8. Little fuel required to heat them.	8. Many are high in sugar, salt and saturated fat.
9. Easy to store, with a long shelf life.	

USING CONVENIENCE FOODS

BUYING
- Read the label for weight portions and contents.
- Avoid bulging, rusted or dented cans.
- Make sure frozen foods are sealed and frozen solid. Transfer quickly to home freezer.
- Check for expiry date, if any.
- Dehydrated foods should be sealed.
- Buy cook-chill foods from a reliable source. Use quickly.
- Follow directions for reconstituting, preparing, reheating.

USING
- Once opened, use up quickly.
- Thaw most frozen food in a refrigerator. Some food is cooked from frozen.

- Never refreeze thawed frozen produce.
- Serve with salads to increase the vitamin/mineral content lost in processing.

STORING

- Most are stored in a cool, dark, dry, well-ventilated cupboard. Perishables should be stored in a refrigerator.
- Frozen food must be stored below -18°C.
- Transfer leftovers to clean containers, cover and keep in the refrigerator. Use up quickly.
- Keep can opener clean and sharp.
- Use preserved food in rotation.

Avoid becoming dependent on convenience foods. Homemade food is more wholesome, has a better flavour and is usually cheaper. Keep a few packets and tins for emergency use only. Avoid using more than one type of convenience food in a meal.

PACKAGING FOOD

The purpose of packaging is: (1) to protect food from contamination by dust, flies or bacteria; (2) to prevent air drying out food; or (3) to prevent moisture making foods soft; and (4) to facilitate the handling, transport and distribution of food.

Packaging materials should be:

- non-toxic
- suitable for their purpose
- lightweight, but strong
- easy to open and, in some cases, to reseal
- moisture-proof to prevent food drying out or moisture in air making food soft, such as biscuits, crisps.

TYPES OF PACKAGING

1. *Paper:* Plain or waxed papers are not particularly suitable for many foods, except as an outside wrapping.
2. *Cardboard:* Used for egg cartons, breakfast cereals and much outer packing.
3. *Plastics:* PVC, polyethylene and polypropylene are ideal packaging materials as they fulfil the requirements above. Various thicknesses are available, for example boil-in-bag, vacuum packs, yoghurt cartons. Some plastics are suitable for microwave use (see pages 88-89).

4. *Cellulose film* or cling film is useful for wrapping foods for the refrigerator.
5. *Aluminium foil* (not made from tin) is used to cover stock cubes, biscuits etc. Thicker versions are used for foil-freezer dishes.
6. *Cans:* These may be made from aluminium (as are soft-drink cans), or tin (for canned foods).
7. *Glass* is still popular as it is see-through, hygienic and can be recycled. Unfortunately, it is also breakable.
8. *Aerosols:* These are pressurised cans containing a propellant gas such as fluorocarbon and the product itself. When the nozzle is pressed, the propellant gas forces the product downwards and up the tube from where it is emitted in a fine spray.

- Aerosols should always be used upright to prevent the escape of propellant and subsequent waste of product.
- They are highly inflammable and must never be used or stored near heat or naked flames. Dispose of empty cans carefully.
- Aerosols are an expensive form of packaging.
- Certain propellant gases affect the protective ozone layer in the stratosphere and their use is restricted in certain countries. Most people now look for the 'ozone friendly' label on aerosol cans.

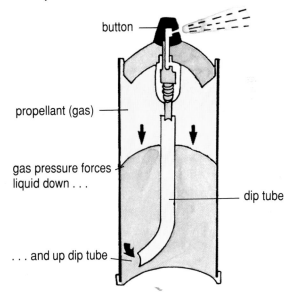

button

propellant (gas)

gas pressure forces liquid down . . .

dip tube

. . . and up dip tube

Structure of an aerosol spray

4 PREPARING FOOD

▶ BUDGETING FOR FOOD

The average budget allocates 25% of income for food, although a wealthy family might spend less than this. No matter how much is spent, however, a balanced diet must be followed. Over-economising on food can result in deficiency symptoms. Particular attention should be paid to the diets of children, pregnant women and the elderly. Make sure to allow sufficient protein foods for growth, and calcium-rich foods for healthy bones and teeth.

SHOPPING FOR FOOD
Those who shop have a major influence on the health of the family. Careless shopping can result in a malnourished family. Extravagant shopping can result in a constant struggle to make ends meet.
1. Work out a weekly menu and do major shopping once a week. This saves time, effort and travel costs (see Chapter 2).
2. Check food in stock, then make a list, grouping foods according to kind — meat, vegetables.
3. Stick to your list, within reason. Avoid impulse buying.
4. Buy good-quality food only. Many food bargains are a false economy.
5. Examine perishables such as fruit carefully and buy in usable quantities.
6. Know current food prices and shop around for best value.
7. Buy fruit and vegetables in season, or grow you own.
8. Read labels carefully. Look out for date stamp.
9. Shop in a clean, hygienic shop which has a good turnover.
10. See also Chapter 3: Buying Meat (page 48), Buying Fish (page 55), Buying Fruit and Vegetables, (page 69).

SHOPPING AND COOKING ON A LOW BUDGET
Poverty limits the availability and choice of food. Following a few simple rules can still allow for healthy eating on a low budget.
- *Avoid waste* of any kind.
- *Be economical* with fuel. Make full use of the oven when it is on (see page 84).
- *Supermarkets* are cheaper than local grocers for everyday groceries, but not usually for meat and vegetables.

Shopping for food
(Denis Hughes–Gilbey)

- *Cheap cuts* of meat are just as nourishing as expensive ones. Practise some interesting mince dishes and casseroles.
- *Own-brand* products such as 'Thrift' or 'Yellow Pack' goods are usually good value and cheap.
- *Avoid convenience foods.* You pay for all the packaging and advertising.
- *Bulk-buying* is sometimes cheaper, but not always.
- *Use up leftovers* — food wasted is wasted money.

CHEAP, NOURISHING FOODS
Some people spend a lot of money on nutritionally unbalanced meals. It should be remembered that many cheap foods are very nutritious.
- *Meat*: mince, stewing beef, streaky bacon, chicken, offal such as liver.
- *Fish*: smoked cod, whiting, gurnet, herrings, mackerel.
- *Other protein foods*: eggs, milk, hard cheeses, cottage cheese, yoghurt, (you can make this yourself).
- *Carbohydrate foods*: brown and white bread, pasta, rice, potatoes, root vegetables, onions.
- *Fat*: margarine (easy-spread margarines work out very economically).
- *Fruit*: Grow your own. Choose fruits in season.
- *Stuffing* foods makes them go farther.
- *Home baking and preserves* are cheaper than buying — more so when done in bulk.

FOOD STORAGE
Ideally, food should be eaten when it is perfectly fresh. But when this is not possible, it must be stored in conditions that will not speed up its deterioration in any way.

UNDERLYING PRINCIPLES OF FOOD STORAGE

Food storage should:
1. Inactivate or *reduce the enzyme action* in food which leads to decomposition and decay.
2. Prevent contamination and multiplication of *micro-organisms*. These cause deterioration of food and may cause food poisoning.
3. *Maintain the nutritive* value/colour/taste and texture of food.
4. *Prevent loss of moisture* from food such as meat, fruit and vegetables.
5. *Prevent* the effects of *oxidation* such as rancidity of fats.

The three main food storage areas in the home are:
- *the food freezer* — for long-term storage of perishable food.
- *the refrigerator* — for short-term storage of perishable food.
- *the store cupboard* — for dry and preserved food such as cans and packets.

In order to maintain fresh food in good condition for as long as possible, store in the following ways:
1. *At low temperatures* — in a refrigerator or a cool, ventilated cupboard to reduce the activity of micro-organisms and enzymes.
2. *In hygienic conditions*: Food containers and storage areas should be cleaned thoroughly and regularly.
3. Food storage areas should be *dry*. Damp storage encourages growth of micro-organisms, particularly moulds.
4. Food should be *cleaned* before storing, e.g. placing in a refrigerator.
5. Food should be *covered* to prevent contamination, moisture loss and oxidation such as rancidity.
6. Food should be stored *away from light*. This prevents the damaging effects of ultraviolet rays from sunlight which cause loss of flavour and nutrients such as vitamin B_1 and C.
7. Use food in *rotation*.

For storage of frozen food, see page 121.

Good storage — clean and covered

Uncovered food leads to contamination

- *Meat*: This should be loosely covered and placed in the coldest part of the refrigerator. Remove poultry from its plastic bag before storing in the refrigerator. Use within 2-3 days.

Note: Keep raw meat and fish separate from all other foods.

- *Fish*: Wash and dry. Store on ice, loosely covered in the refrigerator. Use within 1 day.
- *Eggs*: Place pointed side down on the egg rack of a refrigerator, and away from strong-smelling foods. Remove for 1 hour before use.
- *Milk/cream:* Store in covered bottles/cartons in the refrigerator. Once opened, use up within 2 or 3 days, and sooner in hot weather.
- *Butter and fats:* Store, tightly wrapped, in a refrigerator to prevent oxidation.
- *Cheese:* Wrap loosely in a polythene bag and store in the refrigerator. Use vacuum-packed cheese before expiry date. Some cheeses, including cream cheese, keep for several weeks. Others must be used within 2-3 days.
- *Oils:* Keep in a cool, dark place, but not in a refrigerator.
- *Vegetables:* Wash leafy vegetables and store in a plastic bag in the salad drawer of a refrigerator. Roots, bulbs, and tubers should be stored loosely — remove plastic bags — in a cool, dry, dark place and not in a warm, steamy kitchen (darkness delays sprouting).
- *Fruit*: Store in a cool, dry, dark place. First remove any damaged fruit as mould will spread readily to other fruit.
- *Cereals*: Store in a cool, dry, dark place in rigid, moisture-proof containers. Wholemeal flour must be used up within 2 months.
- *Pulses*: Use within 6 months.
- *Canned foods*: Dry storage. Use in rotation — within 1-2 years.

➤ FOOD PREPARATION

Food must be washed or wiped, trimmed and, in some cases, cut up before cooking. Modern machines such as food processors reduce preparation time considerably. Accurate weighing and measuring is essential to the success of a recipe.

- *Meat:* Remove from refrigerator 30 minutes before use. Wipe with damp kitchen paper. Wash offal and poultry. Trim excess fat, gristle and bone, if required. Joints are skewered into shape and weighed to calculate the cooking time. Meat for stewing is cut into cubes. Thaw frozen meat fully, then cook thoroughly.
- *Salt meat* may need to be steeped.
- *Fish:* Cut off the head, remove entrails, fins, and trim tail. Wash well and dry. Skin and fillet, if wished.
- *Vegetables:* Prepare just before use. Trim outer leaves and separate leaves. Wash thoroughly, using a vegetable brush, if necessary. Cut into even pieces, if required. Shell pulse vegetables.
- *Fruit* should be just ripe. Wash well. Avoid peeling, if possible (for example, apples and pears). To prevent discolouration if peeled, place in water or toss in lemon juice. Remove pips, stones or seeds (for example, melon). Use a stainless steel knife when preparing fruit to avoid discolouration. Some metal containers such as copper saucepans may reduce vitamin C content.

COOKING ECONOMY

1. Serve foods raw where possible — salads, cheese. This saves fuel.
2. Never switch on the oven for one item. Make full use of it when it is on. If the main course is cooked in the oven, choose vegetable dishes and a pudding which can be oven cooked at the same time and temperature. While the oven is on, consider doing some baking as well.
3. Use rising heat for casseroles. Retained electric heat will finish the baking when the oven is switched off.
4. Use steamers, pressure cookers, electric slow cookers etc. to cook complete meals. They are economical on fuel.
5. Use the minimum of liquid to boil foods. Keep the lid on.

6. Bake in bulk and freeze.
7. Plan menus so that double amounts can be cooked on one day and the remainder utilised the following day. This saves time and fuel. For example:

Monday	Tuesday
Boiled ham	Pork chops, grilled
Buttered broccoli	Peas
Boiled potatoes (double)	Sauté potatoes (remainder)
Stewed apple (double)	Apple sauce (remainder)
Custard sauce (double)	Trifle (using remaining custard)

COOKING FOOD

Many foods have a better colour, flavour and nutritive value when eaten raw. Others are cooked to make them safe and to introduce variety.

The reasons for cooking are:
1. It improves the appearance and flavour.
2. It stimulates the digestive juices.
3. It makes food more digestible by softening cellulose and connective tissue.
4. It destroys micro-organisms, making it safe.
5. It helps to preserve food.
6. New flavours are created by mixing and combining foods.

Cooking is affected by various factors:
- Size of food
- Composition
- Thickness
- Finished results required

Food is cooked by:
1. *Conduction* — from one particle of food to the next.
2. *Convection* — liquid boiling, for example; hot air in the oven.
3. *Radiation* — grilling, for example. Heat rays pass straight onto the food and it continues cooking by conduction.

Heat brings about physical and chemical changes in food.
- *Physical:* Food changes colour, size or structure.
- *Chemical:* When a new substance is formed; for example dextrin is formed from the breakdown of starch in bread.

Principles of heat transfer in cooking

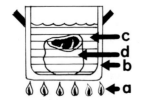

CONDUCTION
Heat conducted from heat source (a) to container (b) to liquid (c) to food (d)

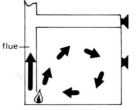

CONVECTION
convection of heat in a gas oven

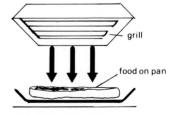

RADIATION
Heat rays pass directly to food

COOKING METHODS

1. COOKING BY DRY HEAT

▪ *Baking*

This means cooking food in dry heat in an oven. The oven is heated by radiation and convection — the hot air rises from the burners, or elements, and falls as it cools. This means that the top of the oven is hottest and the lowest shelf is the coolest, except in the case of fan ovens where the temperature is even throughout.

Baked foods dry out due to evaporation. To prevent this, cover the cooking dish or pour 1-2 tablespoons of liquid over food which should remain moist, like fish.

Foods suitable for baking are bread, cakes, puddings, meat, fish, fruit and vegetables.

▪ *Roasting*

This involves cooking food in hot fat in the oven, or on a spit or rotisserie. The fat with which the food is basted helps to prevent it from drying out.

- Food may be roasted in an *open tin* for better colour and flavour. It may also be *covered*, which reduces shrinkage. This takes longer, however, and the food does not brown as well.
- Meat may be *quick-roasted* — at 230°C/450°F/Gas 8 for 20 minutes — then reduced to moderate or *slow-roasted* at 190°C/375°F/Gas 5. Slow-roasting is more suited to less tender cuts; the meat shrinks less but does not develop a good 'roasted' flavour.
- A meat thermometer indicates when centre of meat is cooked.

Rules for roasting meat
1. Meat should be at room temperature before roasting.
2. Preheat the oven to the correct temperature. Place dripping in the pan to heat up.
3. Prepare, trim and wipe meat. Weigh to calculate cooking time.
4. Place meat onto tin or on a grid over the tin. Baste well and cook for the required time.
5. Allow meat to 'stand' for 10 minutes. This makes it easier to carve. Gravy can be made during this time.

---

1. Quick roasting meat — 230°C/450°F/Gas 8
Beef — about 20 mins. per 450 g (1 lb) and 20 mins. over
Lamb — about 23 mins. per 450 g (1 lb) and 23 mins. over
Pork — about 25-30 mins. per 450g (1 lb) and 25 mins. over
2. Reduce to moderate after 30 mins.

Foods suitable for quick roasting
- Beef — sirloin, rib roast
- Lamb — loin, best end, leg
- Pork — loin, leg

- Poultry — chicken, duck, goose, turkey
- Vegetables — potatoes, root vegetables

Pot-roasting

This is an economical method of roasting a small, less tender joint. The meat is cooked in 50g of fat in a tightly-covered, heavy saucepan. Prepare meat as for roasting above. Brown all over in hot fat. Cover and cook on a low heat for normal roasting time. Turn occasionally.

Vegetables may be pot-roasted with the joint.

Foods suitable for pot roasting
- Small chickens, individual roasts, sheep's heart.

▪ *Grilling/Barbecuing*

Grilling is cooking food under or over radiant heat. The high temperature used seals the surfaces, retaining moisture, nutrients and flavour. The grill must be preheated for best results and food should be brushed with melted fat or oil to prevent drying out.

Food suitable for grilling
- Best-quality tender cuts of meat. Only thin cuts are suitable, such as bacon rashers, lamb and pork chops, steak, sausages. Fish: small whole fish, thin cutlets and fillets. Mushrooms, tomatoes, toast.

2. FRYING

Frying is cooking by conduction or convection in hot fat or oil. Fat should be sufficiently hot to seal the surface of the food and crisp up the outside without burning it. Low frying temperatures result in greasy, sodden foods.

▪ *Shallow frying*

This method is used for cooking thin pieces of food in a little fat or oil.

▪ *Dry frying*

This method is used for cooking fatty foods such as rashers without fat in a non-stick pan.

▪ *Deep-fat frying*

This method is used for cooking thicker pieces of food by complete immersion in hot oil. Most foods are coated with egg and breadcrumbs or batter before frying. This protects the surface of the food from the hot fat and prevents the oil from absorbing flavours from food.

3. COOKING BY MOIST HEAT

Heat is transferred by liquid or steam.

▪ *Boiling*

This is cooking food in boiling (100°C) or simmering (90°C) liquid. The food may be covered with the liquid, but today there is greater emphasis on using the minimum amount of water in a tightly-covered saucepan in order to reduce nutrient loss. The food should be boiled first in order to coagulate the surface protein, and then simmered until cooked. As minerals and vitamins (B group and C) leach into the water, it is important to retain the drained liquid and use it for sauces, soups, etc.

Foods Suitable for Boiling

Salt meat	Joints of ham, bacon and corned beef — start cooking in *cold* water
Fresh meat	Chicken, leg of mutton — immerse in *boiling* water
Vegetables	Almost all vegetables may be boiled. Colour is retained and vegetables remain moist.
Rice and pasta	Cook in boiling water.

■ Poaching
Poaching involves cooking food very gently in liquid at 85°-90°C. This slow cooking prevents the food from breaking up and is used to cook fish and eggs.

■ Stewing
Stewing is a method of cooking food very gently in a small amount of liquid in a tightly-covered cooking vessel. It is a slow method (meat stews take about 1½ - 2 hours) and it is essential that the temperature remains well below boiling point at about 85°-90°C. Food may be stewed: (a) in a tightly-covered saucepan on the hob or (b) in a casserole in the oven. The latter takes 20-30 minutes longer.

Stewing is ideal for cooking tougher cuts of meat, as the low temperature and moist heat soften the connective tissue, changing it to gelatine. This separates the meat fibres, making it tender. High temperatures will cause meat to fall apart and liquid to evaporate so that the food is likely to stick and burn. Meat is usually cut up in order to expose a greater surface area to the liquid.

Types of Stew

Simple stews	Ingredients are layered in the cooking pot and water added. *Example:* Irish stew.
Brown stews	Ingredients (meat and onions) are browned first. A thickener such as flour may be added and then stock. *Examples:* ragout, goulash.
Rich stews	The meat is usually blanched first. The stew is thickened with egg yolk and cream. *Examples:* fricassée, blanquette.

Pressure cookers speed up the cooking of stews. Slow cookers cook stews at very low temperatures for several hours.

■ Braising
This is a combination of stewing, roasting and steaming. The food, usually a whole joint, is cooked slowly by moist heat in a tightly-covered saucepan or casserole.

The meat/vegetables are first browned in hot fat to seal in the juices and the meat is then placed on a bed of the diced vegetables (mirepoix). Sufficient brown stock is added to just cover the mirepoix. The meat is cooked for 35 minutes per 450g (1 lb) and 35 minutes over. The joint is basted frequently with the stock, which is thickened and used as a sauce.

Foods suitable for braising
Lean cuts of meat which are not so tender, e.g. top side of beef, fresh brisket of beef; breast or leg of lamb; pork or ham.
Vegetables: celery, onions, root vegetables.

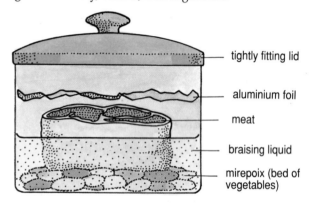

- tightly fitting lid
- aluminium foil
- meat
- braising liquid
- mirepoix (bed of vegetables)

■ Steaming
This is cooking food in the moist heat rising from boiling water. Because food is not immersed in water, there is less loss of nutrients. Food is easy to digest, making it an ideal method of cooking for invalids. This method is slow, taking one and a half times as long as boiling foods, although this may vary depending on how fast the water is boiling. It requires little attention.

Steaming may be carried out:
1. In a steamer over boiling water, as with vegetables.
2. Between two greased plates over a saucepan of boiling water. Good for fish.
3. In a covered bowl sitting in a saucepan, half-filled with boiling water. Used for steak and kidney puddings, plum pudding.
4. In a pressure cooker (see page 87)

■ 'Conservative' cooking
This is a tasty and nutritious method of cooking vegetables which conserves vitamins and minerals. To every 500g (1 lb) of sliced vegetables, allow 150 ml boiling water, 25g margarine and a little salt and pepper.

Cook gently in a tightly-covered saucepan for 20-30 minutes or in a covered casserole in a low oven (180°C/350°F/Gas 4) for 40-50 minutes.

PRESSURE COOKING

PRINCIPLE

The normal boiling point of water is 100°C. If the pressure is increased, water will boil at a higher temperature. This is achieved by placing a weight over the escape vent of a tightly-sealed saucepan called a *pressure cooker*. As steam is only allowed to escape at a controlled rate, pressure and temperature build up to the required level. Steam is forced through food so that it cooks very quickly.

Note: Air under pressure has a lower temperature than steam under pressure. For this reason, all the air must be driven out of the pressure cooker by allowing it to steam rapidly for a few minutes before applying weight and reducing the temperature.

The temperature within the cooker depends on the pressure/weight* used:

At 5 lb pressure (low) water boils at 108°C.
At 10 lb pressure (medium) water boils at 115°C.
At 15 lb pressure (high) water boils at 122° C.
(At normal atmospheric pressure, water boils at 100°C).

* Note: Some pressure cookers such as the Tefal brand have in-between pressures — for example 8 lb/12 lb. Use only according to instructions.

STRUCTURE OF A PRESSURE COOKER

A pressure cooker is a large saucepan of heavy-gauge aluminium with a high or low domed locking lid and a rubber gasket* or ring to make an airtight seal. There is a central vent on which are placed the weight or weights and through which steam escapes with a gentle hiss during cooking. A safety valve*, consisting of a rubber plug with a metal centre, ensures that if steam builds up to dangerous levels or the cooker boils dry, the valve will release the steam.

A perforated metal tray (trivet) is used to keep food out of the water. A separator (metal basket) enables different foods to be cooked together. An automatic pressure cooker has a timer which is set for the required time. It releases pressure automatically when the time is up.

* These may have to be replaced occasionally.

Valve weights:

5 lb (low) for bottling fruit and for puddings etc. containing a raising agent.
10 lb (medium) for certain preserves.
15 lb (high) for most pressure cooking.

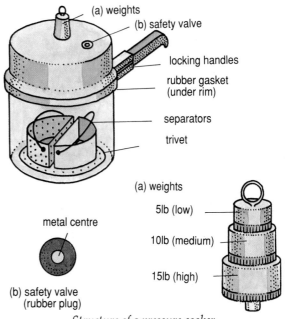

Structure of a pressure cooker

USING A PRESSURE COOKER

1. Pressure cookers may be used to steam, braise, boil or stew food and to make soups, jam and preserves.
2. Follow the manufacturer's instructions exactly.
3. Use the correct amount of water. The cooker must never be filled more than half full of liquids or two-thirds full of solids.
4. Place locking lid and weight in position correctly.
5. Place cooker on high heat, bring to boil and boil until a continuous loud hiss and jet of steam are emitted from cooker. Time cooking from now. Reduce heat so that a gentle hiss remains for the duration of cooking.
6. Never attempt to force lid open. Reduce pressure according to recipe instructions by:
   (a) standing at room temperature for about 15 minutes. Food continues to cook during this time. This is used for items with a large amount of liquid such as soups.
   (b) running cold water down side of cooker.
   (c) turning release control (on newer models).
   (d) Automatic cookers have automatic depressurising.
7. Time food accurately, as it is easy to overcook it.

Stew	—	20 minutes	
Carrots	—	4 minutes	
Potatoes	—	5 minutes	} depending on size
Stock	—	30 minutes	
Fish	—	3-5 minutes	

ADVANTAGES

- A complete meal can be cooked in one pot, saving time, fuel and washing up.
- Flavour and nutrients retained.

► MICROWAVE COOKERY

In a conventional oven, air is heated by electric elements or gas burners. It circulates around the oven by convection and the food cooks by conduction from the outside in. The outer surfaces become dry, crisp and brown during cooking.

WORKING PRINCIPLE OF MICROWAVE COOKERS

Microwave cookers use invisible electromagnetic waves, similar to radio or light waves, which move at a very high frequency. These reflect off the metal walls within the cooker and penetrate the food from all directions to a depth of 2-4 cm. The waves make the molecules in this part of the food vibrate rapidly, at a speed of over two thousand million a second, and create friction which produces an intense heat. This spreads to the centre of the food by conduction, thus cooking the food.

During microwave cooking, water is driven to the surface of food, which prevents it from becoming brown and crisp as in normal cooking. As the microwaves are not hot, the inside of the cooker remains cool.

Microwaves can be reflected, transmitted or absorbed.

- *Reflection:* Microwaves bounce off metal. They cannot pass through it and for this reason metal utensils may not be used in the cooker.
- *Transmission:* Microwaves pass readily through most materials including glass, china, paper and most plastics without heating them. For this reason these materials are used when cooking foods. They are only warmed by the heated food in them.
- *Absorption:* Microwaves are absorbed by food molecules such as water, fat and sugar.

Reflection

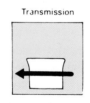
Transmission

Absorption

STRUCTURE OF MICROWAVE OVENS

The microwave oven consists of:
- a metal-lined cabinet connected to a 13 amp socket.
- an air vent to release steam (at the back).
- a door lined with perforated metal to prevent waves from escaping. It has a safety seal and lock to ensure that microwaves are confined to the cooker cavity. The cooker cannot function when the door is open.

- A transformer increases domestic voltage from 220V to a high frequency.
- A magnetron which converts electrical energy into microwave energy.
- A wave guide which conducts waves into the cabinet.
- A wave stirrer to make sure that waves continually change direction so that all parts of the oven receive waves.
- Controls: On/off switch. Time control. Cooking (power) control, which adjusts the amount of energy released into the oven. Usually five settings: Low, Defrost*, Medium, High, Full up to 750W depending on the cooker.

* Defrost works by pulsing the energy on and off so that food defrosts without cooking.

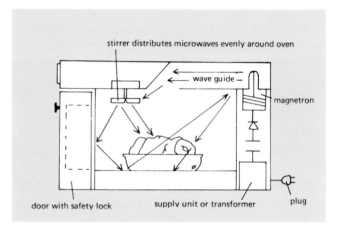

Microwave structure (side view)

Microwave cookers may also have a fan, a clock, a memory for programming cooking, a browning element — like a grill — a temperature probe and a turntable.

SUITABLE COOKING MATERIALS FOR MICROWAVES

Glass such as Pyrex; earthenware, china; kitchen paper; certain plastics; cling film (for covering); roasting bags; microwave cookware.

Note: Recent reports suggest that plasticisers from cling film may contaminate food when heated in a microwave. For this reason, ensure that special heat-resistant cling film is used, or better still, use a non-metal lid or plate to cover food.

Browning dishes: these consist of a ceramic dish with a special coating of tin-oxide which absorbs microwave energy.

MATERIALS UNSUITABLE FOR MICROWAVE COOKERY

Metal containers, aluminium foil, metal-trimmed dishes, melamine and polystyrene, very thick dishes (as these absorb too much energy, requiring extra cooking time).

SUITABLE FOODS/PROCESSES FOR MICROWAVES

- Thaws frozen food; reheats cooked food.
- Cooks most fresh food.
- Boils, poaches, steams, stews, dry-roasts, bakes.
- Makes jams and preserves quickly.
- Sauces (not more quickly).
- Melts chocolate

UNSUITABLE FOODS/PROCESSES FOR MICROWAVES

- Cooking in fat, frying. Large amounts of fat are dangerous.
- Batters: They become soggy.
- Many cakes: Recipes must be specially developed for microwaves.
- There is little advantage in cooking large quantities of food such as large joints in a microwave as they take quite a long time.

Microwaves cook food three times more quickly

COOKING IN A MICROWAVE

1. *Follow instruction book*/recipe exactly.
2. *The density, thickness, shape* and temperature of food can affect the timing of cooking with microwaves.
3. *Large amounts* of food, even separate foods like baked potatoes, take longer than small amounts — usually half as much time again.
4. *Arrange food in circles*, with thickest part outwards.
5. *Prod any food with a skin* to prevent bursting — potatoes, tomatoes, egg yolk, sausages, fish.
6. *Irregular shapes cook unevenly*. Protect thin parts of a food (for example, fish tail) by wrapping in a small amount of foil if there is a possibility that it will overcook. This is the only time metal is permitted in a microwave cooker.
7. *Cover most foods* to speed up cooking and to prevent soiling the oven:
   (a) with a non-metal lid or plate.
   (b) with cling film (see note above), but puncture to prevent bursting and do not allow it to touch the food.

(c) Cover greasy foods such as rashers with kitchen paper.

8. *Composition of food*: This affects the cooking time. Foods containing a high percentage of sugar and fat, for example, will cook very quickly. Plum pudding takes 10 minutes! Porous foods also cook/reheat quickly.
9. *Turn food regularly* from top to bottom and from side to side. Move food in dishes, such as casseroles, from outside to inside to ensure even cooking. Stir moist foods from outside to inside also.
10. *Standing time*: 'Standing time' is a part of the microwave cookery process. Food continues to cook in its own residual heat after it has been taken from the oven. Foods are removed when underdone and cooking finishes during standing time. Foods should be covered, usually with foil, until ready to be served.
Note: Failure to allow 'standing time' can result in the food being insufficiently cooked. Food poisoning may result.
11. *Microwave cooking is fast*, so it is easy to overcook foods. Remove when underdone and allow specified standing time. Check for 'doneness', especially that food is really hot in centre. Return for further cooking if necessary.

CARE AND CLEANING OF MICROWAVE COOKERS

1. *Never* operate the cooker when it is empty as it may damage the magnetron.
2. Pay particular attention to the door seal and keep it clear of food and grease.
3. Remove plug before cleaning.
4. Wipe up spills and splashes as they occur. A dirty oven absorbs microwave energy.
5. Remove any removable parts. Wash, rinse and dry.
6. Wipe inside of the oven after use with a cloth wrung out in hot, soapy water. Rinse and dry.
7. Avoid abrasives.
8. Do not attempt to use the cooker if it has been damaged in any way. Get a qualified service engineer to carry out safety checks before re-use.
9. Move as little as possible. It may damage the magnetron.

ADVANTAGES OF MICROWAVE COOKERS

1. *Speed*: Food cooks in half to one-third of normal time.
2. *Economy*: Shorter cooking times mean less energy is used.
3. *Colour, flavour and nutrients* are retained due to speed of cooking.

4. *Versatile*: Microwave ovens boil, bake, roast and stew.
5. *They reheat food* well without drying it out or altering the taste.
6. *Defrosting*: Food can be thawed quickly without cooking it.
7. *Safe*: Easy for children, elderly and handicapped to use as cooker does not become hot.
8. *Less washing up*: The same container can be used for freezing, cooking and serving.
9. *Easy to keep clean*: Splashes do not bake onto cooker surface.
10. *Ideal for a family* with flexible hours.
11. *Does not need* heavy-duty cable. Can simply be plugged into a 13 amp socket.

DISADVANTAGES
1. Not suitable for large items such as joints or turkeys.
2. Danger of food poisoning if instructions are not followed.
3. Does not normally brown meat or soften tough meat.
4. Not suitable for certain items including batters, some cakes and frying.

COMBINATION COOKERS
These combine normal cookers with microwave ovens. Some simply have a microwave fitted above or below a conventional oven. In others, the same cooker has microwave and normal convection facilities which may be used separately or together.

Soup — a nourishing start to a meal (Denis Hughes–Gilbey)

RECIPES

Note: All spoon measurements are level measuring spoons unless otherwise stated.

STARTERS

HORS-D'OEUVRE VARIÉS

This may consist of a mixture of raw or cooked vegetables, meat and/or fish. Arrange food on a specially sectioned dish or on individual plates.

Vegetables are usually dressed, e.g. with French dressing, to add extra flavour.

Choose from the following:

BEETROOT

Cooked, cut in fingers, or diced and tossed in French dressing.

CARROTS

Cooked and cut in strips, or raw, grated and tossed in French dressing.

TOMATO

Arranged in overlapping slices with French dressing or soured cream poured over it. Garnish with chopped chives or parsley.

CUCUMBER

Wipe and peel, if wished. Slice thinly or cut in 1.5 cm dice. Dress with natural yoghurt or soured cream dressing.

CELERY AND APPLE

Wash and dice. Do not peel apple. Dress with mayonnaise.

SARDINES

Remove carefully from tin and arrange overlapping on dish. Sprinkle with lemon juice. Garnish with lemon slices.

TUNA OR SALMON

Flake cooked or tinned fish roughly. Dress with mayonnaise or French dressing.

SHELLFISH

Remove cooked fish from shell. Toss in mayonnaise.

SALAMI OR OTHER SAUSAGE

Slice thinly and roll up, or arrange flat in overlapping slices.

SALAMI OR SMOKED SALMON

Roll into a coronet shape and fill with lemon-flavoured cream cheese or Quark (a low-fat cheese).

WEDGE OF AVOCADO PEAR

Dip in lemon juice, sprinkle with curry powder or cayenne and wrap in smoked salmon.

ONE-HALF PINEAPPLE SLICE

Wrap in a paper-thin slice of Parma ham.

Note: The latter three items can be secured with cocktail sticks, if necessary.

SCALLOPED FISH

A tasty dish using smoked fish in a cheese sauce. Serve fish in scallop shells, and brown under grill. Useful as a starter. For a main course, double ingredients and bake in pie dish for 25 min.

250 g fresh or smoked cod or haddock
200 ml milk and 100 ml water, flavoured with 1 slice onion, 2 cloves, pinch mace
300 ml Béchamel sauce made from poaching liquid (see page 103)
1 dessertsp. chopped parsley
Salt and pepper
1 teasp. anchovy essence (optional)
75 g grated Cheddar cheese
2 tablesp. white breadcrumbs
25 g butter
To garnish
Piped creamed potato (3)
Lemon twists
Parsley

1. *Put potatoes for garnish to cook in boiling salted water.*
2. *Infuse flavourings in milk for 10 minutes. Strain. Then use to poach fish for 10 minutes — until cooked. (Omit salt if using smoked fish.)*
3. *Drain poaching liquid into jug. Keep fish warm.*
4. *Make Béchamel sauce following recipe (page 102). Add parsley, essence, 50 g Cheddar cheese and stir well. Flake fish and add to sauce.*
5. *Drain and cream potatoes, and pipe around 4 scallop shells. Spoon fish mixture into centre.*
6. *Sprinkle with a mixture of breadcrumbs and the remaining cheese. Dot with butter.*
7. *Bake in hot oven for 10 minutes to heat through or brown under grill until bubbling.*

▶ SOUPS

BASIC MEAT PURÉE, e.g. OXTAIL SOUP

1 oxtail (jointed) or 300 g stewing beef
25 g dripping
1-2 streaky rashers
1 large onion   2 sticks celery
1 large carrot   1 leek (optional)
25 g flour   1.5 litres brown stock
1 teasp. tomato purée (or 1 skinned, chopped tomato)
Bouquet garni
Salt and pepper

1. *Wipe meat thoroughly with dampened kitchen paper. Cut beef in small pieces.*
2. *Melt dripping in a large heavy saucepan and sauté chopped bacon for 2-4 minutes. Add meat pieces, and fry until browned. Remove meat.*
3. *Prepare and dice vegetables, and sauté for 5 minutes, stirring all the time.*
4. *Add flour. Cook for 1 minute over a low heat, then gradually add stock, stirring all the time. Return meat.*
5. *Add tomato (purée), bouquet garni and seasoning, and slowly bring to the boil.*
6. *Reduce heat, cover and simmer gently for 2 hours. It will be necessary to skim soup now and then during cooking in order to remove grease.*
7. *Remove oxtail, and cut meat away from bone. Chop meat finely and return to soup (process soup in blender/processor, if wished).*
8. *Reheat soup, correct for seasoning and serve in a hot soup tureen. A little port or sherry may be added, if wished.*

■ This soup may be cooked in a pressure cooker for 40 minutes.

BASIC VEGETABLE PURÉE (TOMATO)

1 litre stock
225 g flavouring vegetable, e.g. onion, celery, leek
500 g main ingredient, e.g. tomatoes for tomato soup
½ teasp. salt
Freshly ground black pepper
25 g butter or margarine
25 g flour
Bouquet garni
Appropriate flavourings, e.g. basil with tomatoes
Milk (optional)
Garnish
Chopped parsley or chives

1. *Wash, peel and chop vegetables according to kind.*
2. *Heat fat and sauté vegetables for five minutes without browning. Reduce heat.*
3. *Stir in flour, cook on a low heat for 1–2 minutes, stirring briskly to avoid burning.*
4. *Gradually add stock, stirring all the time. Add seasonings and flavourings.*
5. *Bring to boil, cover and then simmer gently until vegetables are soft (30-45 minutes).*
6. *Sieve or process soup to a purée.*
7. *Return to rinsed saucepan. Add milk to correct consistency. Reheat, correct seasoning, and serve in a heated soup tureen or individual soup dishes.*

Variations		
Name of Soup	*Main ingredient*	*Special point*
Asparagus	450g tin asparagus	Green colouring may be necessary. Retain asparagus tops for garnish
Carrot (potage Crécy)	500g carrots, 1 potato, ½ teasp. sugar	To garnish — chopped mint
Cauliflower (crème Dubarry)	1 small cauliflower	Cream to serve
Celery	350g celery, pinch mace	Cream to serve
Leek and potato	250g each leeks and potatoes	Sauté covered for 10 minutes at stage 2 over low heat
Leek and tomato	250g each leeks and tomatoes	Stir in plain yoghurt to serve
Mushroom	250g mushrooms, pinch nutmeg, squeeze lemon juice	150ml cream to serve
Tomato	500g tomatoes or 1 tin; ½ teasp. sugar, pinch basil	Cream to serve

▶ MEAT

LASAGNE

2 tablesp. olive oil
l large onion, chopped
1 clove garlic, crushed
2 sticks celery (optional)
50 g streaky rashers
450 g lean minced beef
1 can tomatoes (400 g)
150 ml beef stock
1 dessertsp. tomato purée
¼ teasp. sugar
1 teasp. oregano or marjoram
Salt and freshly ground black pepper
200 g (9 sheets) ready-to-use lasagne
Cheese sauce
25 g margarine/butter
25 g flour
400 ml milk
Salt and pepper
175 g Cheddar or Parmesan cheese

1. *Heat 2 tablespoonfuls oil in large saucepan. Add onion, chopped celery and garlic. Fry over medium heat until golden.*
2. *Add rashers and fry until crisp. Stir in beef and continue frying until browned, stirring regularly.*
3. *Stir in tomatoes and their juice, stock, purée, sugar, herbs and seasoning. Bring to the boil, stirring all the time. Then reduce heat, cover and simmer gently for about 20 minutes, stirring occasionally until sauce is thick.*
4. *Cheese sauce: Melt margarine, add flour, cook for 1 minute. Gradually stir in milk, stirring between each addition. Season well. Bring slowly to the boil, stirring frequently. Then simmer for 3 minutes. Stir in cheese, keeping a little back.*
5. *Arrange on a greased oblong ovenproof dish. Start with a layer of meat sauce, then lasagne. Repeat, then add cheese sauce. Continue until used up, finishing with cheese sauce.*
6. *Sprinkle remaining cheese on top. Then bake in a moderate oven, 190°C (375°F)/Gas 5, for about 30 minutes until golden brown and bubbling.*
7. *Serve with wholemeal or French bread and green salad.*

MEAT (STEAK AND KIDNEY) PIE

225 g rough puff or flaky pastry (page 103)
400 g stewing steak ⎱ or other raw meat
100 g beef kidney ⎰
1 tablesp. flour
1 carrot, sliced thinly

A tasty meat pie
(Denis Hughes–Gilbey)

1 onion, finely chopped
3 or 4 mushrooms, sliced (optional)
1 or 2 sticks celery, chopped
2 tomatoes, skinned, sliced
Salt and pepper
Chopped parsley
150-300 ml stock
Beaten egg to glaze

1. *Make pastry and place in refrigerator while preparing filling.*
2. *Trim and wipe steak, cut in 3 cm cubes. Skin and core kidney, rinse and cut in 1.5 cm cubes. Toss both in flour.*
3. *Arrange meat and prepared vegetables in layers in 1-litre pie dish. Sprinkle seasoning and parsley between layers.*
4. *Add sufficient stock to come half-way up ingredients.*
5. *Roll out pastry a little larger than top of pie dish. Trim off strip, dampen rim of dish and stick pastry strip around it. Dampen pastry strip and lay pastry lid on top, pressing edges well to seal. Flake and decorate.*
6. *Cut a hole in the centre of pastry to enable steam to escape and use pastry trimmings to make leaves to decorate top. Glaze with beaten egg.*
7. *Bake in hot oven, 230°C(450°F)/Gas 8, for 20 minutes. Reduce heat to 180°C(350°F/Gas 4 and cook for 1-1¼ hours more. (Cover pie with a sheet of paper if it appears to be getting too brown.)*
8. *Garnish with parsley. Serve with baked potatoes and a green salad.*

LIVER STROGANOFF

450 g lamb's liver
2 tablesp. seasoned flour
1 tablesp. paprika
1 large onion
2 or 3 streaky rashers
50 g butter/margarine
100 g button mushrooms
Salt and pepper
4 or 5 tablesp. stock
4 or 5 tablesp. soured cream
To garnish
Chopped parsley
To serve
225 g rice

1. Rinse liver in warm water. Dry, trim away any blood-vessels, cut in strips and toss in flour and paprika.
2. Peel and slice onion, remove rind from rashers and cut in strips.
3. Melt half the butter in a heavy frying pan. Add liver and fry until well browned. Remove with slotted spoon.
4. Add remaining fat, and fry onion and bacon until lightly browned. Then add wiped sliced mushrooms and cook for 1 minute. Return liver to the pan.
5. Add stock and seasoning. Bring to boil and simmer for 2-3 minutes, stirring all the time.
6. Stir in soured cream and heat slightly. Serve on a bed of rice and garnish with chopped parsley.

CHICKEN MARENGO

(This recipe for chicken casserole was invented by Napoleon's chef from local ingredients, just before the battle of Marengo.)
1 chicken or 4 chicken joints
50 g flour
2 tablesp. cooking oil
25 g butter
2 carrots
2 sticks celery
1 large onion
1 or 2 cloves garlic, crushed
50 g streaky bacon
300 ml chicken stock
400 g can tomatoes
2 tablesp. sherry
Salt and black pepper
100 g mushrooms, sliced
1-2 tablesp. finely chopped parsley

1. Cut chicken into 4 or 8 joints. Wipe with damp kitchen paper and dry well. Toss in flour.

2. Heat oil and butter in large flameproof casserole. Fry chicken for 5-6 minutes until golden brown. Remove and set aside.
3. Prepare and slice vegetables. De-rind and chop bacon. Add both to oil and fry until golden brown. Drain well and set aside with chicken.
4. Stir remaining flour into fat and cook for 1 minute. Gradually stir in chicken stock, bring to the boil and simmer for 3-4 minutes. Stir in tomatoes (and juice), sherry, mushrooms and seasoning, and add cooked chicken and vegetables. Stir well; cover, and cook at 180°C(350°F)/Gas 4 for 50-60 minutes until chicken is cooked.
5. Serve in casserole, sprinked with chopped parsley. Baked potatoes or noodles would go well with this dish.

PORK/CHICKEN RISOTTO

3 tablesp. cooking oil
4 streaky rashers
2 medium onions
1 or 2 cloves garlic, crushed
1 red pepper
1 green pepper
350-400 g raw lean pork (for example, pork steak), or 2 large chicken breasts
375 g long grain rice
600 ml chicken stock
Pepper, salt
2 or 3 tomatoes
75 g mushrooms

1. Skin rashers and cut each in 5 pieces. Peel and chop onion.
2. Heat 1 tablespoon oil in large saucepan or casserole.
3. Fry rashers until beginning to brown. Add onion and garlic and cook gently for 3-4 minutes.
4. Meanwhile, wipe, de-seed and slice peppers. Add to onion and garlic mixture and cook for approximately 2 minutes more. Transfer all to plate.
5. Trim and cut meat into 2 cm cubes. Heat 1 tablespoon oil in saucepan, add meat, and cook until beginning to brown.
6. Stir in washed rice, then stock and seasoning. Bring to the boil. Return vegetables. Reduce heat, cover and simmer gently for 30 minutes, stirring frequently.
7. Meanwhile skin and slice tomatoes. Wipe and slice mushrooms. Heat remaining tablespoon of oil in a small saucepan and sauté mushrooms for 1 minute.
8. Add tomato and mushrooms to risotto five minutes before end of cooking time. Risotto is cooked when rice is soft, meat is tender, and all stock has been absorbed.
9. Serve in casserole sprinkled with finely chopped parsley. A crisp green salad proves a tasty accompaniment.
Note: casserole may be cooked in a moderate oven, 190°C(375°F)/Gas 5, for about 45-50 minutes.

FISH

STEAMED STUFFED ROLLS OF PLAICE

8 fillets of plaice
1 tablesp. milk
A little melted margarine (optional)
Stuffing
25 g margarine
1 small onion, finely chopped
50 g mushrooms, chopped
75 g breadcrumbs
Salt and pepper
1 teasp. chopped parsley
To garnish
Lemon slices or tomato halves
Parsley

1. Skin and wash fillets.
2. Make stuffing as follows. Melt margarine, sauté onion for 1 minute without browning, add mushrooms and sauté for 1 minute. Add remaining ingredients and mix well.
3. Spread stuffing on each fillet and roll up. Secure each with a skewer or cocktail stick.
4. Place on greased plate, brush with melted margarine and pour milk between fish. Cover with a lid or second plate.
5. Steam over boiling water for about 20 minutes until cooked. (Potatoes or another vegetable could be cooked in water beneath at the same time.)
6. Remove skewers/sticks. Serve on a warmed dish garnished with grilled tomato or lemon slices and parsley. If wished, potatoes could be piped around edge of dish, and tomato or cheese sauce poured over or between rolls of fish.

RUSSIAN FISH PIE

This may be made using raw, cooked, smoked or canned fish. Add 50 g Cheddar cheese, if wished, when using smoked cod or fresh white fish.
200 g rough puff pastry (page 103)
225 g raw fish (e.g. cod)
1 hard-boiled egg
2 tomatoes, skinned
1 tablesp. lemon juice
1 tablesp. capers (optional)
1 tablesp. chopped parsley
Béchamel Sauce (page 102)
25 g margarine
25 g flour
150 ml milk flavoured with a slice of onion, cloves
Salt and pepper
To glaze
Beaten egg

To garnish
Parsley
Lemon

1. Sauce: Infuse milk with flavouring for 20 minutes. Strain.
2. Skin and bone fish, if necessary. Wash, dry and cut in cubes.
3. Melt margarine. Add flour, and cook for 1 minute. Gradually add strained milk, stirring constantly. Bring to the boil and simmer for 3 minutes. Stir in lemon juice, capers, parsley, fish and seasoning.
4. Roll chilled pastry into a 25-30 cm square. Straighten edges.
5. Place fish mixture on centre of pastry in a diamond shape. Place sliced egg and tomato over top.
6. Dampen edges of pastry and bring four corners carefully together, sealing well and crimping to decorate. Use trimmings to make 4 leaves.
7. Using 2 fish slices, place on greased tin, brush with beaten egg. Bake in a hot oven, 225°C (440°F)/Gas 7-8, for 15-20 minutes until pastry has browned.
8. Reduce heat to 190°C (375°F)/Gas 5 and continue cooking for a further 30 minutes.
9. Serve on hot dish, garnish with lemon and parsley.
   Note: If using cooked or tinned fish, reduce cooking time by 10 minutes.

VEGETABLES

BRAISED CELERY

1 large head celery
1 medium onion (chopped)
1 medium carrot (diced)
25 g dripping or cooking fat
13 g flour
1 dessertsp. tomato purée or 2 tomatoes, skinned and chopped
400 ml stock
Salt and pepper
Pinch mixed herbs or bouquet garni

1. Heat fat in flameproof casserole. Add onion and fry until beginning to brown.
2. Add flour and stir over a gentle heat for 1 minute. Stir in tomatoes or purée and carrots.
3. Gradually blend in stock, add seasoning and herbs. Bring to boil and simmer gently for 30 minutes.
4. Meanwhile, prepare celery. Cut into 5 cm strips.
5. Liquidise sauce, if a smooth sauce is required, but this is not necessary.
6. Put celery and sauce into casserole and cook for about 1 hour at 180°C (350°F)/Gas 4 until tender.
7. Serve in casserole garnished with chopped parsley.

STUFFED PEPPERS

4 even-sized green or red peppers
Stuffing
1 tablesp. cooking oil
1 small onion, finely chopped
100 g minced beef
1 tablesp. tomato purée
2 tomatoes, skinned, chopped
¼ teasp. oregano
1 dessertsp. chopped parsley
Salt and pepper
100 g brown or white rice, cooked and drained

1. *Heat oil, add onion and fry until soft. Add beef and fry until brown.*
2. *Stir in purée, tomatoes, oregano, parsley, seasoning. Cook for 5 minutes.*
3. *Stir in rice.*
4. *Cut tops from peppers and remove core and seeds carefully with a scissors. Rinse out and dry.*
5. *Blanch peppers by covering in boiling water and allowing to stand for 5 minutes.*
6. *Drain peppers and stand in a greased ovenproof dish. Spoon in filling, brush lids with oil and cover. Add enough water to cover base of dish.*
7. *Cover dish with foil or a lid and bake at 190°C (375°F/Gas 5 for approximately 35 minutes until cooked.*
8. *Serve with a green salad.*

▶ **VEGETARIAN COOKERY**

VEGETABLE CURRY

3 tablesp. oil
2 medium onions
1 clove garlic, crushed
1 tablesp. curry powder
1 dessertsp. wholewheat flour
1 teasp. turmeric
50 g lentils
250 ml vegetable stock
4 carrots
4 potatoes
1 small cauliflower
2 tomatoes (skinned)
100 g French beans or peas
1 tablesp. tomato purée
Salt, pepper
1 carton natural yoghurt
1 tablesp. chopped parsley
To serve
Brown rice

1. *Peel and roughly chop onions.*
2. *Heat oil. Toss onion and garlic for 5 minutes. Add curry powder, flour and turmeric. Cook on a low heat for 2 minutes, stirring to prevent sticking.*
3. *Gradually stir in stock and lentils and leave aside.*
4. *Prepare vegetables. Wash, peel or scrape, if necessary, and cut in large dice. Break cauliflower into florets. Add carrots to sauce and simmer for 15 minutes.*
5. *Add remaining vegetables to saucepan (except beans) and bring to boil, stirring all the time. Add tomato purée and seasoning. Simmer gently until vegetables are almost soft.*

Add French beans and cook for 8 minutes more.
6. *Stir in yoghurt to create a marbled effect. Reheat gently.*
7. *Serve in a warmed dish surrounded with brown rice. Sprinkle with parsley.*

VEGETABLE AND NUT RISOTTO

3 tablesp. oil
550 ml boiling stock or water
225 g brown rice
2 medium onions
1 small green pepper
100 g cashew or peanuts
125 g mushrooms
2 firm tomatoes
50 g raisins
Freshly ground black pepper
Salt
Parsley

1. *Heat 2 tablespoonfuls of oil in a saucepan. Add rice and sauté for 4 minutes. Cover with boiling water and simmer for 30-40 minutes.*
2. *Peel and roughly chop onion. Wipe, de-seed and chop pepper. Wash and slice mushrooms. Skin and chop tomatoes.*
3. *Heat remaining oil in a frying pan. Add onions and sauté until soft.*
4. *Add pepper, nuts and mushrooms and cook for 7-8 minutes.*
5. *Add well-drained cooked rice, tomatoes, raisins and seasoning. Toss over a gentle heat, using a fork, until well mixed and heated through — about 4-5 minutes.*
6. *Serve in heated vegetable dish, garnished with parsley.*

STIR-FRIED VEGETABLES

Most vegetables may be stir-fried — cooked in a little oil, stirring all the time. Prepare all vegetables before starting to cook. Start by cooking the vegetable that takes longest first, working through the vegetables to those that need the least cooking.

225 g broccoli   225 g spring onions
225 g mushrooms   1 small red or yellow pepper
2-3 tablesp. oil, preferably sunflower
1 teasp. fresh root ginger, grated
1 tablesp. soy sauce
2 tablesp. medium sherry

1. Prepare all vegetables, cutting in different shapes for variety. Broccoli: choose thin stems, or split thick stems lengthwise. Wash well. Wash and trim spring onions, leave whole or split large onions in two. Wipe, trim stems and quarter mushrooms. Wipe pepper, remove core and seeds and cut in strips.

2. Heat oil to a high temperature in a wok or large frying pan and fry ginger for a couple of seconds. Add broccoli, stir-fry for 2 minutes. Add onions, stir-frying for 2 minutes.
3. Add remaining vegetables and cook for 3-4 minutes, stirring all the time.
4. Stir in sherry and soy sauce and stir-fry for 1-2 minutes more. Serve at once.

VARIATIONS
- Stir in a drained can of sweetcorn for last 2 minutes.
- Omit sherry and sprinkle finished dish with sesame oil.
- Other vegetables suitable for stir-frying: French beans, leeks, cauliflower, thin julienne strips of carrot.
- Meat stir-fries are made by cutting tender cuts of lean meat into thin strips and stir-frying before vegetables for 5 minutes.

VEGETARIAN LASAGNE
See page 368.

► SALADS

SALAD NIÇOISE
1 head lettuce
4 medium tomatoes
¼ cucumber
100 g French beans or 1 green or red pepper
1 small onion or 4 or 5 spring onions (chopped)
200 g tin tuna
2 hard-boiled eggs
50 g tin anchovies, drained
50 g black olives
125 ml French dressing

1. Wash lettuce and crisp in refrigerator. Quarter tomatoes and remove seeds. Prepare and cube cucumber. Core and remove seeds from pepper, if using, and slice.
2. Arrange lettuce in base of salad bowl. Lay beans, tomato and cucumber on top and sprinkle with chopped onion.
3. Top with tuna and garnish with quartered eggs and olives, with anchovies criss-crossed over top.
4. Sprinkle French dressing over salad just before serving.

WALDORF SALAD
2 red apples
1 green apple
1 small or ½ large head celery
50 g chopped walnuts
Dressing
4 tablesp. mayonnaise
2-3 tablesp. lemon juice
½ teasp. caster sugar

To serve
Lettuce leaves, parsley

1. Wash apples. Core, slice green apple, dice red apples. Toss well in lemon juice to prevent browning. Mix in caster sugar.
2. Trim and wash celery. Slice and add to apple mixture with mayonnaise.
3. Stir in walnuts. Chill.
4. Serve on bed of lettuce, sprinkled with chopped parsley, if wished.

VARIATIONS
1. Add cubed chicken breast for a more substantial salad.

2. Raisin and Nut Salad
4 dessert apples
3 tablesp. lemon juice
½ teasp. caster sugar
100 g walnuts, chopped
100 g seedless raisins
Watercress
Prepare as above and serve garnished with watercress.

3. Carrot and Orange Salad
275 g carrots, roughly grated
3 oranges, peeled and cut in segments
75 g raisins
4 tablesp. mayonnaise
Grate rind from one orange and mix with mayonnaise. Mix ingredients together and stir in mayonnaise.

► SALAD DRESSINGS

FRENCH DRESSING

Good pinch salt
Good shake pepper
Good pinch mustard
Good pinch caster sugar (optional)
2 tablesp. wine vinegar*
4 tablesp. olive oil*

* These are standard proportions. If a more oily dressing is required, 5, 6 or 7 tablespoonfuls of oil may be used.

1. *Put salt, pepper, mustard and sugar in a bowl. Grind well together with a wooden spoon.*
2. *Add vinegar and stir well.*
3. *Gradually add oil, stirring vigorously. Stir again just before serving. Use within 2 days. If wished, particularly when larger amounts are to be made, shake all ingredients together in a screw-topped jar or use a blender/processor for 2-3 seconds. Do not overblend.*

VARIATIONS

Vinaigrette
Add some finely chopped onion or chives, and parsley.

Garlic
Soak cut clove of garlic in oil 1 hour before use.

Mint
Add 1-2 teasp. chopped mint. Good with orange and lamb salads.

EGG MAYONNAISE

1 egg yolk
¼ teasp. salt
¼ teasp. mustard
¼ teasp. caster sugar
Freshly ground black pepper

150 ml olive/groundnut oil
1 tablesp. wine/cider vinegar or, if preferred, lemon juice

1. *Place egg yolk in small bowl with seasonings and sugar. Blend well with wooden spoon or electric hand whisk.*
2. *Add oil, which should be at room temperature, drop by drop — a medicine dropper is excellent for this — making sure you do not add the oil too quickly or the mixture will become thin instead of thick and buttery. Beat well after every drop, adding a little vinegar if it gets too thick.*
3. *When all oil has been added, gradually mix in vinegar. Taste and correct seasoning, if necessary.*
   Note: If the mayonnaise begins to curdle, put a fresh egg yolk into another bowl and add the curdled mixture very gradually, beating well after each addition. Then continue with the remaining oil.

VARIATIONS
Using one of the two recipes above as a base, add one of the following:

Green (Herb-Flavoured) Mayonnaise
Bunch of washed, chopped parsley or watercress.

Tartare Sauce
1 teaspoonful chopped gherkin, 1 teaspoonful capers, 1 teaspoonful very finely chopped onion. Serve with fish dishes.

Garlic Mayonnaise
(called aïoli and served with crudités)
Blend in 1-3 peeled crushed cloves of garlic (depending on how much you like it) with the seasonings at the beginning, and continue in usual way.

Curry Mayonnaise
Blend in 1 teaspoonful curry paste with seasonings.
If curry paste is not available, use ½ teasp. curry powder.

► EGGS AND CHEESE

OMELETTES

An omelette is one of the most useful egg dishes as it is so quick and easy to make. Unlike other egg dishes, omelettes are cooked at a relatively high temperature. They may be served plain or filled.
   There are basically two types of omelette:
1. *The plain or French omelette* — usually savoury.
2. *The soufflé omelette*, which may be sweet or savoury.

POINTS TO REMEMBER WHEN MAKING OMELETTES
1. *Use really fresh eggs.*
2. *Use an omelette pan kept solely for that purpose or a non-stick pan.*

3. ***Do not*** *overbeat eggs. Beat slightly, using a fork. A whisk is not recommended, as it breaks down the egg too much, giving the omelette an overcooked taste.*
4. *Use a palette knife to stir and fold omelette.*
5. *Prepare all fillings beforehand in a separate pan and preheat serving dish* **before** *starting to cook. The omelette should be eaten the moment it is cooked.*

   It should be creamy in the centre and slightly browned on the outside. Overcooking or slow cooking produces a tough, leathery omelette.

Omelette — a tasty alternative to meat dishes
(Denis Hughes–Gilbey)

PLAIN OR FRENCH OMELETTE

2 eggs (per person)
Salt, pepper
1 tablesp. water
1 level teasp. butter/margarine

1. Beat eggs just enough to mix yolks and whites. Add water and seasoning.
2. Place pan over a medium heat until hot, then add butter/margarine. (A non-stick pan should not be heated when empty.)
3. When it froths, pour in the beaten egg, and tilt pan until it covers its base. Use palette knife to draw cooked egg to centre, allowing liquid egg to run in underneath until egg has set but is still creamy on top.
4. Tilting pan away, fold one third of omelette to the centre, then opposite third. Turn pan, allowing omelette to fall onto warmed dish with folded sides underneath.
5. Serve at once, sprinkled with chopped parsley.

VARIATIONS
Fines herbes: Add 1 tablespoonful chopped, mixed fresh herbs, e.g. parsley, chives, thyme, just before cooking.
Cheese: Sprinkle 1-2 tablespoonfuls grated Cheddar or Gruyère over omelette in pan, just before folding. The heat of the omelette will melt the cheese.

FILLINGS
Make up the following in a small saucepan before starting omelette. Keep warm. Place in centre of omelette before folding.

1. Tomato
2 tomatoes, skinned and sliced
1 small onion, roughly chopped
13 g butter/margarine
Chopped basil
Sauté onion in melted fat until soft and beginning to colour. Add tomato and basil and cook for 1 minute.

2. Mushroom
50-75 g mushrooms
13 g butter/margarine
Sauté mushrooms in melted fat until beginning to soften. Do not overcook. A squeeze of lemon juice adds extra flavour.

3. Fish
Flake a little cooked fresh, smoked or canned fish, e.g. tuna, and mix in a little cheese or Béchamel sauce.

SOUFFLÉ OMELETTE

2 eggs (per person)
1 dessertsp. caster sugar
1 tablesp. cream or top of milk
15 g butter
Vanilla essence
1 tablesp. jam
Icing sugar

1. Separate yolks from whites of eggs.
2. Preheat grill, and put jam underneath it in a heatproof dish to warm slightly.
3. Cream yolks and sugar together; stir in cream and vanilla essence.
4. Stiffly beat egg whites and fold into yolk mixture.
5. Heat pan over medium heat. Add mixture and cook for almost 1 minute until brown underneath.
6. Remove jam. Place omelette under grill to cook upper side until cooked through.
7. Spread jam over half omelette, fold in two and slip onto warmed plate. Dredge with icing sugar. Serve at once.

Cheese soufflé (National Dairy Council)

CHEESE SOUFFLÉ

4 large eggs (separated)
50 g butter
40 g flour
Pinch mustard powder
Pinch cayenne and salt
300 ml milk
150 g Cheddar cheese, grated
1 tablesp. snipped chives (optional)
1 tablesp. browned crumbs

1. *Preheat oven to 180°C (350°F)/Gas 4. Grease soufflé dish and sprinkle with browned crumbs.*
2. *Melt butter in a small saucepan. Add flour, mustard and seasoning and stir over a gentle heat for 1-2 minutes.*
3. *Remove from heat and gradually stir in milk. Return to heat, bring to boil and simmer gently for 1 minute, stirring frequently.*
4. *Remove from heat and stir in cheese until melted. Beat in egg yolks one at a time and chives, if using.*
5. *Whisk egg whites until stiff, and fold lightly into sauce, using a metal spoon.*
6. *Pour the mixture into prepared soufflé dish.*
7. *Bake in the centre of the oven for 45-50 minutes until soufflé is well risen and golden brown. (Give it a shake if you think it is done. It should wobble slightly; if it moves a lot, leave it for another few minutes.)*

PANCAKES

300 ml batter-(thin) ──────▶
Cooking fat for frying
Caster sugar
Lemon wedges

100 g flour	
pinch salt	whisked in blender
1 egg	
300 ml milk	

1. *Pour batter into a jug.*
2. *Heat a little fat (just enough to grease base of pan) in an omelette pan.*

3. *When hot, pour in sufficient batter to barely coat the base of pan. Tilt pan around to coat it evenly.*
4. *Cook over a medium heat until golden brown underneath.*
5. *Turn with palette knife or toss, and cook the other side. Turn onto a plate kept warm over a saucepan of simmering water.*
6. *Repeat process for each pancake. Keep pancakes warm by covering plate with a lid.*
7. *To serve: Sprinkle each pancake with lemon juice, roll up and serve at once with caster sugar and extra lemon wedges. Note: Cooked pancakes freeze well. Store flat with a circle of greaseproof paper between pancakes. Place in plastic bag, seal and freeze (store for 2-3 months). Reheat by placing in a warm, greased pan, turn once; or use for stuffed pancakes or crêpes Suzette.*

STUFFED PANCAKES

Sweet Fillings
1. Stewed apples and cinnamon.
2. Jam or marmalade.
3. Banana, sliced, raw or sautéed.
4. Melt 25 g margarine, mix in 1 tablespoonful of brown sugar, 4 tablespoonfuls of raisins or sultanas, chopped dates and chopped walnuts.
5. Fresh raspberries (slightly crushed) with cream.
6. Butterscotch sauce, sprinkled with flaked almonds.

Savoury Fillings
Make up 300 ml Béchamel coating sauce. Stir in one of the following:
1. 175 g chopped cooked chicken.
2. 175 g smoked haddock and 75 g grated cheese.
3. Small tin salmon or tuna, mashed with 1 teaspoonful tomato purée.
4. 225 g mushrooms sliced and sautéed in 25 g butter/margarine.
5. Ham and tomato filling: Sauté 1 small, chopped onion in 25 g butter/margarine for 1-2 minutes. Add 2 tomatoes, skinned and chopped. Lay 1 slice of ham on each pancake, place filling in centre, season and roll up. Brush with melted butter. Reheat, covered, in oven 180°C (350°F)/Gas 4 for 10-15 minutes.

QUICHE LORRAINE (CHEESE AND BACON QUICHE)

Pastry
150 g plain flour
1/8 teasp. salt; 1/2 teasp. icing sugar
75 g margarine/butter
Squeeze lemon juice
Cold water

Quiche Lorraine (National Dairy Council)

Filling
2 eggs (or 4 egg yolks)
200 ml creamy milk (or cream)
Salt and pepper; pinch nutmeg
25 g butter/margarine
75 g streaky bacon
100 g cheese (Cheddar or Gruyère)

1. Make pastry by sieving plain flour, sugar and salt into bowl. Rub in margarine until it resembles fine breadcrumbs. Add lemon juice and sufficient water to make a stiff dough. Chill in refrigerator for 20 minutes.
2. Roll out pastry, to fit in 20 cm flan tin. Return to refrigerator while making filling.
3. Sauté de-rinded bacon in 25 g butter/margarine until soft and beginning to brown. Cut in strips.
4. Beat eggs, stir in milk (cream), nutmeg and seasoning.
5. Grate cheese and sprinkle over flan. Place bacon on top.
6. Pour egg mixture over and bake in a moderate oven 190°C (375°F)/Gas 5, for 30-40 minutes until mixture is set and golden brown on top.
7. Remove flan ring, serve on hot plate, cut in wedges, with a green salad. Garnish with tomato or cucumber slices.

Note: To ensure thorough cooking of pastry base, place a baking tray in oven while it is heating up and put the quiche on this to cook.

VARIATIONS

Leek or onion quiche: Substitute 2 large chopped sautéed onions or leeks for bacon: a vegetarian quiche.
Fish quiche: Substitute 100-200 g crab meat, prawns, fresh or smoked white fish for bacon.
Mushroom quiche: Substitute 150 g sliced sautéed mushrooms for bacon. Many other vegetables may also be used.

QUICK PIZZA

Scone Base
225 g flour
½ teasp. salt
1 teasp. baking powder
50 g margarine
Approximately 125 ml milk or water
Filling
25 g margarine or 1 tablesp. oil
1 medium onion, peeled
300 g tomatoes or 1 tin tomatoes
Salt and pepper
Pinch oregano or mixed herbs
100 g grated cheese

1. Start with the filling. Chop onion and sauté for 5 minutes in hot oil or fat in saucepan. Add peeled tomatoes or tinned tomatoes and their juice, herbs and seasoning.
2. Simmer gently while making dough, until mixture is thick and pulpy (break up tomatoes with a wooden spoon if necessary).
3. Base: Sieve flour, salt and baking powder into a bowl. Rub in margarine until it resembles fine breadcrumbs.
4. Moisten with liquid and mix to a fairly stiff dough. Roll into a large round 1 cm thick.
5. Place on greased baking tray, sprinkle cheese over (keeping back 1 tablespoonful) then spoon tomato mixture over cheese, covering it completely. Sprinkle remaining cheese on top.
6. Bake in a fairly hot oven, 200°C (400°F)/Gas 6, for about 30 minutes. Serve at once with a green salad for lunch or supper. It may also be eaten cold.

Pizza with mushrooms and salami (W. and C. MacDonnell/Paula Daly)

VARIATIONS

- Add 1 crushed clove garlic with onion.
- Sauté 50-75 g sliced mushrooms with onion.
- Add 50 g chopped ham, crisply fried bacon, chopped cooked sausage or salami to tomato mixture before placing on cheese.
- Add 1 small red or green pepper (cut in strips) to saucepan, after tomatoes.
- Cross top of pizza with anchovy fillets and place black olives, halved, between the anchovies.
  Note: Pizza base may also be made from yeast bread recipes on page 106.

BÉCHAMEL SAUCE

1 slice onion
Bay leaf
2 cloves
Salt, pepper
Pinch mace or nutmeg   } Infusing ingredients
300 ml milk
25 g margarine
25 g flour
1-2 tablesp. cream (optional)

1. Place infusing ingredients and milk in a small saucepan. Heat gently but do not allow to boil. Stand for 15-20 minutes.
2. Strain milk into jug. Wash out saucepan.
3. Melt margarine, add flour, and cook for 1 minute on low heat.
4. Gradually add flavoured milk, stirring all the time to prevent lumping.
5. Bring to the boil, reduce heat and simmer gently for 3-5 minutes. Cool slightly.
6. Stir in cream and/or optional ingredients.

- *Sauce Mornay*
  Add 50 g grated hard cheese and a knob of butter to basic sauce.
- *Mushroom Sauce*
  Add 50 g sliced mushrooms that have been sautéed in 15 g butter or margarine, to basic sauce.

Use:
Used as sauce for filling savoury pancakes, vol-au-vents, etc.

► STUFFINGS

BASIC SAVOURY STUFFING

100 g fine white breadcrumbs
50 g butter or margarine
1 medium onion, finely chopped
1 tablesp. chopped parsley
¼ teasp. mixed herbs
Salt and pepper
1 tablesp. stock or milk, if dry

Melt fat, sauté onion for about 1 minute. Then stir in breadcrumbs, parsley, herbs and seasoning. Moisten, if necessary, with a little stock or milk.
Serve with: Most meats and fish.

VARIATIONS ON BASIC STUFFING

To each 100 g breadcrumbs add (omitting mixed herbs):
Celery and apple: 2 sticks chopped celery, 1 cooking apple, chopped.
Prune: 8 cooked prunes, chopped; 1 apple, chopped; 25 g chopped walnuts; grated rind and juice of ½ lemon.
Raisin and nut: 50 g raisins; 50 g chopped nuts.

► PASTRY

WHOLEMEAL PASTRY

100 g wholemeal flour
50 g plain flour
1 level teasp. baking powder*
Pinch salt
75 g fat (a mixture of butter and cooking fat gives the best flavour)
1 teasp. brown sugar
4-5 tablesp. cold water

1. Sieve plain flour, baking powder and salt into a bowl. Stir in wholemeal.
2. Cut up fat into small pieces, then mix into flour. Rub in with tips of fingers until it resembles fine breadcrumbs.
3. Dissolve sugar in 4 tablespoonfuls of water, then add to pastry, mixing with a knife. Add more water, if necessary.
4. Knead in bowl until smooth, then chill in refrigerator for 15-20 minutes before rolling out.
   * As wholemeal flour is inclined to be heavy, baking powder is added to give lightness.

BISCUIT CRUST OR FLAN PASTRY
(sometimes called rich shortcrust pastry)

125 g plain flour
Pinch salt
1 heaped teasp. icing sugar
75 g fat, e.g. margarine and lard
1 egg yolk
1 teasp. lemon juice
1 tablesp. (approx.) water

1. *Sieve flour and salt into a bowl. Rub in fat until it resembles fine breadcrumbs. Mix in sieved icing sugar.*
2. *Add water to egg yolk and, using a knife to mix, stir into flour, together with lemon juice. Add more water, if necessary.*
3. *Knead lightly in bowl, then chill in refrigerator for at least 15 minutes before using.*
   Note: The proportions in this recipe make sufficient pastry to line the average 18 cm flan ring. For a 20 cm flan, use 200 g flour to 125 g fat. For a 23 cm flan, use 250 g flour to 150 g fat. Extra water will be required. Other ingredients remain the same.

CHEESE PASTRY
Ideal for savoury flans, particularly those using cheese. This amount will line an 18-20 cm flan tin.
175 g plain flour
Pinch each salt, cayenne pepper, dry mustard
75 g fat, e.g. margarine
50 g grated hard cheese
1 egg yolk
Cold water

1. *Sieve flour, salt, mustard and pepper into bowl.*
2. *Cut up, then rub in fat with fingertips until mixture resembles fine breadcrumbs. Stir in cheese.*
3. *Add two tablespoonfuls of water to egg yolk and add to mixture, mixing with a knife. Add more water, if necessary, to obtain a stiff dough.*
4. *Chill in refrigerator for 15-20 minutes before use.*
   Note: Cheese pastry is more likely to burn than normal short crust. Cook at *not more* than 200°C (400°F)/Gas 6.

CHEESE STRAWS
1. *Roll out pastry 7 mm in thickness and cut into narrow 'sticks' 8 cm x 1 cm wide.*
2. *Place on a greased tin and bake at 190°C (375°F)/Gas 5 for 10-15 minutes until pale golden in colour.*

ROUGH PUFF PASTRY
200 plain flour
Pinch salt
150 g fat (½ butter or margarine,
    ½ lard or cooking fat if possible)
6-7 tablesp. (approx.) cold water
Squeeze of lemon juice

1. *Sieve flour and salt into a bowl.*
2. *Cut fat into cubes about 2 cm in size and mix into flour. Do not rub in.*
3. *Add lemon juice and water to make a fairly stiff dough.*
4. *Turn onto a floured board, and roll into a long strip — at least 30 cm long and 10 cm wide (1). Mark into 3 sections (2).*
5. *Fold bottom third up (3) and top third down over it (4), then turn pastry to the right and seal edges with rolling pin (5).*
6. *Start rolling by pressing 3 or 4 times over centre of pastry oblong, without using too much pressure or air will be forced out, then roll into a strip again and repeat folding 4 times.*
7. *Place in plastic bag and chill in refrigerator for 30 minutes before use.*

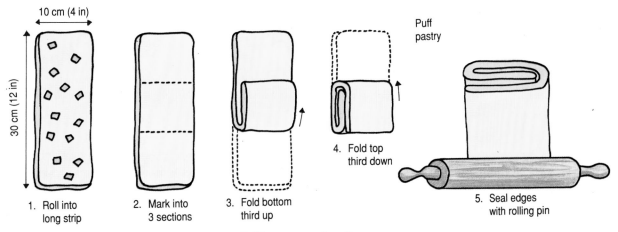

10 cm (4 in)
30 cm (12 in)

1. Roll into long strip
2. Mark into 3 sections
3. Fold bottom third up
4. Fold top third down
5. Seal edges with rolling pin

Puff pastry

Rolling out rough puff pastry

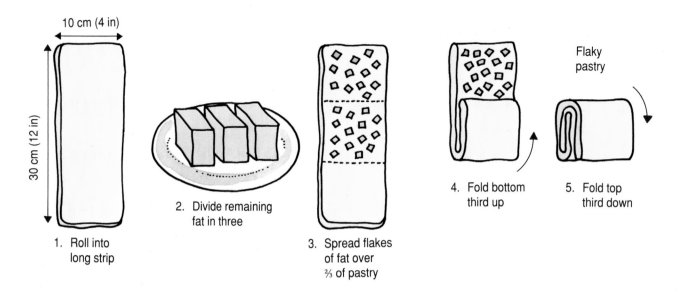

10 cm (4 in)

30 cm (12 in)

1. Roll into long strip

2. Divide remaining fat in three

3. Spread flakes of fat over ⅔ of pastry

4. Fold bottom third up

5. Fold top third down

Flaky pastry

Rolling flaky pastry

FLAKY PASTRY

This gives similar (slightly better) results but is slower to make.
200 g plain flour
Pinch salt
150 g fat (½ butter/margarine,
  ½ lard/cooking fat if possible)
6-7 tablesp. (approx.) cold water
Squeeze of lemon juice

1. *Sieve flour and salt into a bowl.*
2. *Soften fat by working with a knife on a plate. Divide into four and rub in one quarter as for short pastry.*
3. *Add lemon juice and water and mix to a soft dough.*
4. *Roll pastry into a long strip — at least 30 cm x 10 cm wide (a).*
5. *'Flake' ⅓ of remaining fat over top ⅔ fof pastry as evenly as possible — (c).*
6. *Fold bottom third up (d) and top third down (e), turn to right and seal edges with rolling pin.*
7. *Roll out carefully (see 4 above) and repeat twice more with remaining ⅔ fat.*
8. *Place in plastic bag and chill in refrigerator for 30 minutes before use.*
  Note: Both of the above pastries are rolled to between 3 and 7 mm in thickness and are baked in a hot oven, 220°C (425°F)/Gas 7.

CHOUX PASTRY

70 g plain flour
50 g butter/hard margarine
150 ml water (8 tablesp. approx.)
2 slightly beaten eggs

1. *Sieve flour onto a sheet of kitchen paper or foil.*
2. *Melt fat in water and bring to the boil. Tip flour in all at once and beat well with wooden spoon until paste forms a smooth lump in centre of pan. Do not overbeat,*
3. *Beat in eggs, about 1 tablespoonful at a time, beating well after each addition until mixture is thick and shiny. Omit some egg if mixture is getting too thin.*
4. *Pile into piping bag and allow to stand for 10 minutes before piping onto a dampened baking tin.*
5. *Bake at 200°C (400°F)/Gas 6.*

CHOCOLATE ÉCLAIRS

Choux pastry
150-300 ml cream
Melted chocolate

1. *Pipe éclairs using a 1 cm diameter nozzle into lengths on dampened baking sheet, using a knife to cut off pastry against edge of pipe.*
2. *Bake at 220°C (425°F)/Gas 7 for about 30 minutes until well risen, golden brown and crisp.*
3. *Place on wire tray, slit sides with sharp knife to allow steam to escape, and cool.*
4. *When absolutely cold, fill with whipped cream, and ice tops with melted chocolate, or chocolate or coffee glacé icing.*

Savoury Éclairs
It is also possible to fill éclairs with a savoury filling, e.g.
- Cream together 50 g butter with small packet of cream cheese. Add chopped parsley or chives and a squeeze of lemon juice.
- Make as above using chopped prawns or smoked salmon trimmings instead of herbs.

► PUDDINGS

LEMON MERINGUE PIE

Flan Pastry
150 g plain flour
1 tablesp. icing sugar
Pinch salt
75 g butter/margarine
1 egg yolk
2-3 tablesp. cold water
Filling
2 tablesp. cornflour (level)
150 ml water
Finely grated rind of 2 medium lemons
5 tablesp. lemon juice
2 egg yolks
75 g caster sugar
Meringue
2 egg whites
100 g caster sugar

1. Make pastry and chill in refrigerator. Roll out to fit a greased pie plate or flan ring 20 cm. Prod base with fork and chill for 15 minutes more, if possible.
2. Bake blind* in a fairly hot oven, 220°C (400°F)/Gas 6. Remove paper and beans and return to oven for 5 minutes.
3. Put cornflour and water into saucepan. Mix in lemon rind and juice and bring slowly to the boil, stirring all the time. Simmer gently until mixture thickens.
4. Remove from heat and stir in sugar. Cool a little, then stir in egg yolks. Pour mixture into cooked flan case.
5. Meringue: Whisk egg whites in a clean bowl until stiff. Fold in sugar gently, then pile or pipe meringue on to lemon mixture.
6. Bake in a cool oven, 140°C (275°F)/Gas 1, for about 30 minutes until meringue has crisped and points have begun to turn golden brown.
7. Serve hot or cold with cream.

* Baking blind: Roll out pastry to fit tin or plate. Prod base with a fork and chill for 15-20 minutes. Cut off surplus pastry. Line flan base with a circle of greaseproof paper and half-fill with dried beans to weigh it down. Bake at 200°C (400°F)/Gas 6 for 15 minutes. Remove beans and paper and return to oven for 5 minutes to dry out.

PINEAPPLE UPSIDE-DOWN CAKE

To Line Base of Tin

50 g butter/margarine	4 or 5 cherries
50 g brown sugar	4 or 5 walnuts
1 can pineapple rings, drained	

Madeira Mixture
100 g butter or margarine
100 g caster sugar
2 eggs
125 g flour
¼ teasp. baking powder
1 tablesp. pineapple juice

1. Grease the sides of an 18 cm round cake tin. Mix the butter and brown sugar together and spread over base of tin. Arrange rings of pineapple, cherries and walnuts in an attractive pattern over base of tin.
2. Make madeira mixture in usual way, moistening with a little pineapple juice. Spread carefully over pineapple, taking care not to lift fruit out of place.
3. Bake in moderate oven, 190°C (375°F)/Gas 5, for about 30 minutes, reduce heat to 180°C (350°F/Gas 4 and continue cooking for about 10 minutes until cooked through.
4. Place plate over tin and invert; cake should slip out easily. Serve with custard or a sauce made from tinned juice.

VARIATION

Use canned apricots or peaches as a substitute for pineapple.

PAVLOVA

4 egg whites
Pinch salt
225 g caster sugar
1 teasp. cornflour
¼ teasp. vanilla essence
1 dessertsp. vinegar
300 ml whipped cream
Selection of exotic fruits, e.g. kiwi, passion, ugli, banana

1. Grease a shallow ovenproof dish: set oven at 140°C (275°F)/Gas 1.
2. Whisk egg whites and salt until stiff. Add sugar, one tablespoon at a time, whisking until very stiff.
3. Beat in cornflour, vanilla, and vinegar.
4. Spoon into prepared dish, hollowing out the centre.
5. Bake for 70-75 minutes.
6. When cool, fill with whipped cream and prepared fresh fruit.

LEMON CHEESECAKE

Base
150 g digestive biscuits
75 g butter/margarine
50 g soft brown sugar

Topping
225 g cream cheese
2 tablesp. lemon juice
150 ml cream
2 eggs
Grated rind of one lemon
100 g caster sugar
1 tablesp. gelatine
3 tablesp. water

1. *Crush biscuits in blender or plastic bag, using rolling pin. Mix biscuits and sugar together in a bowl, melt fat and stir in.*
2. *Press into a loose-bottomed 20 cm flan tin. Chill.*
3. *Cut 2 or 3 slices from centre of lemon for decoration. Grate and squeeze lemon. Beat cheese and lemon juice in one bowl. Separate eggs. Place egg yolks, lemon rind and sugar in another bowl and whisk until light and creamy. Whisk in cream cheese.*
4. *Place gelatine and water in a small bowl to soak for 10 minutes. Then stir over simmering water until the gelatine has dissolved. Cool slightly and whisk into cheese mixture.*
5. *In a clean bowl, whisk egg whites until stiff. In another bowl, whip cream until stiff. Fold cream, then egg whites into lemon mixture.*
6. *Empty onto crumb base and smooth over. Place in refrigerator until set.*
7. *Decorate with lemon twists, angelica and piped whipped cream.*

BASIC COLD SOUFFLÉ

3 eggs, separated
75-100 g caster sugar
5 tablesp. milk
15 g sachet gelatine

2 tablesp. water + 2 tablesp. lemon juice
150 ml double cream

Variable Ingredient
Choose from one of the following:
1. 1 drained tin mandarin oranges, chopped, a little orange rind, 1 tablesp. orange liqueur.
2. 350 g fresh strawberries/raspberries, crushed with 1 tablesp. brandy.
3. 3 bananas, mashed, with 1 tablesp. rum.
4. 75-100 g plain chocolate, melted, 1 tablesp. rum.
Garnish
50 g flaked almonds/chopped nuts or sliced/whole fruit from which soufflé is made, e.g. strawberries/raspberries, oranges.

1. *Tie a double strip of greaseproof paper around a small soufflé dish (13 cm approx.), leaving 5-8 cm above the dish. Brush inside of paper with oil.*
2. *Place egg yolks, sugar and milk in a heat-proof bowl, standing over a saucepan of simmering water. Whisk with a rotary beater or a balloon whisk until thick and creamy. Remove from heat and whisk until cool.*
3. *Place water and lemon juice into a bowl, sprinkle gelatine over and leave to soak. Stand bowl over saucepan of simmering water and stir until gelatine has dissolved. Cool slightly, then stir into egg and milk mixture.*
4. *Whip cream until fairly stiff, then fold into mixture. Beat egg whites until stiff, then gently fold them into mixture with one variable ingredient until well blended.*
5. *Pour mixture into wet soufflé dish, then place in refrigerator until set — at least 3 hours.*
6. *To serve: Dip knife in hot water, then remove string and use a knife to carefully ease off greaseproof collar. Press flaked/chopped nuts into sides of soufflé and use appropriate fruit and piped whirls of whipped cream to decorate top.*

BREAD AND CAKES

WHITE YEAST BREAD

400 g strong plain flour
1 level teasp. salt
25 g fat (butter/margarine/lard)
15 g fresh yeast
300 ml tepid water
½ teasp. sugar

1. *Sieve flour and salt into a bowl and leave in a warm place.*
2. *Crumble yeast into a jug, add 150 ml warm water and sugar, and leave for a few minutes while rubbing in fat.*
3. *Meanwhile, rub in fat until it resembles fine breadcrumbs.*
4. *Make a hole in the centre of the flour, pour in yeast mixture, rinse out jug with remaining water and add*

enough to make a soft dough. Beat for a few minutes.
5. *Turn onto floured surface and knead for about 10 minutes.*
6. *Wash and dry bowl, grease, and place dough in bowl, covering with oiled polythene.*
7. *Leave to rise for 1 hour in a warm place until double its size. Grease and flour a ½ kg loaf tin.*
8. *Turn onto floured surface and knead again for a few minutes. The volume will decrease considerably.*
9. *Roll into rectangle the length of the tin, roll up with join underneath and place in tin.*
10. *Prove in warm place until double its size: 20-30 minutes.*
11. *Bake in a hot oven. 230°C (450°F)/Gas 8, for 35-40 minutes until base has a hollow sound when tapped. Cool on wire tray.*

BARM BRACK

450g strong plain flour
1 teasp. salt
¼ teasp. nutmeg
¼ teasp. cinnamon
50g butter/margarine
50g caster sugar
25g fresh yeast or 1 sachet of fast-action dried yeast
300 ml tepid milk
1 beaten egg
250g sultanas
50g mixed chopped peel
Syrup to glaze
2 tablesp. sugar ⎱
4 tablesp. water ⎰ boiled together

Traditional Irish Barmbrack
(W. and C. MacDonnell/Paula Daly)

1. *Sieve flour, salt and spices into a bowl. Leave in a warm place.*
2. *Crumble yeast into tepid milk. Stir in 1 teaspoonful of measured sugar and stand for 5-10 minutes in a warm place. (This is not necessary if using fast-action dried yeast.)*
3. *Rub fat into flour, mix in sugar. Make a hole in the centre and add beaten egg and yeast mixture. Beat well with a wooden spoon for 10 minutes until smooth and elastic.*
4. *Mix in fruit. Empty into greased, round 1 kg cake tin. Cover with oiled polythene and prove in warm place until it has doubled its size (1 hour).*
5. *Bake in a hot oven, 220°C (425°F)/Gas 7, for 10 minutes. Reduce to 220°C (400°F)/Gas 6 and continue cooking for 30-35 minutes more.*
6. *Brush with syrup glaze. Cool on a wire tray.*

QUICK WHOLEMEAL BREAD

450g wholemeal flour or
    225g white, 225g wholemeal flour
2 level teasp. salt
2 level teasp. dried yeast
350 ml water
2 level teasp. brown/white sugar

1. *Weigh and sprinkle flour and salt into a bowl. Warm slightly.*
2. *Take 4 tablespoonfuls of water from measured amount and place in a jug. Add sugar and sprinkle on dried yeast. Stir and leave for about 10 minutes until a froth has formed.*
3. *Make a hole in the centre of the flour, stir yeast into mixture. Rinse out jug with remaining liquid and add to dough, mixing well with a wooden spoon until the sides of the bowl remain clean.*
4. *Turn onto floured surface and knead for 5-10 minutes.*
5. *Place in greased loaf tin, smooth side up, and leave in a warm place, covered with oiled polythene until it has doubled in size: ¾–1 hour.*
6. *Bake bread at 220°C(425°F)/Gas 7 for about 40 minutes.*
7. *Cool on a wire tray.*

5 MICROBIOLOGY

Microbiology is the study of micro-organisms so small that they cannot be seen with the naked eye but only with the help of powerful microscopes. They include fungi, such as moulds and yeasts, bacteria and viruses. In Home Economics, the emphasis in microbiology lies in its relation to food processing, food spoilage, food poisoning and other diseases.

▶ CONDITIONS REQUIRED FOR GROWTH OF MICRO-ORGANISMS

All living things require certain environmental conditions in order to grow and to reproduce. When optimum (ideal) conditions are met, micro-organisms grow and multiply rapidly. When they are absent, multiplication cannot take place and the micro-organisms die.

REQUIREMENTS FOR GROWTH

1. Food	4. Correct oxygen level
2. Warmth	(see 4 below)
3. Moisture	5. Correct pH

1. FOOD

As moulds, yeasts and bacteria do not contain chlorophyll, they cannot manufacture their own foods as other plants do. They depend on ready-made sources of food to provide the chemical elements that they require, such as carbon, nitrogen, sulphur etc.

- *Parasites* are micro-organisms which feed on living matter, such as animals and humans. Many bacteria are parasites.
- *Saprophytes* feed and grow on dead and decaying matter — most fungi are saprophytes.

Feeding: Each micro-organism secretes enzymes directly onto the food, breaking it down into simple, soluble compounds which are absorbed through the cell wall.

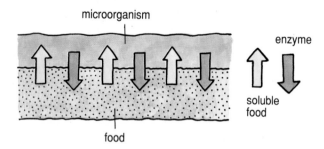

2. WARMTH

The optimum temperature for growth of micro-organisms is 30-45°C. This includes the human body temperature of 37°C.

Temperatures above 70°C will destroy most micro-organisms. Temperatures above 100°C will destroy bacteria,

although their heat-resistant spores need, on average, a temperature of 121°C for 15 minutes to destroy them. They would require 5 hours at boiling point (100°C) to have the same effect.

- Cold temperatures (-5°C to 15°C) retard growth and multiplication.
- Freezing inactivates micro-organisms but on thawing, they become active again.
- Psychrophiles (or psychotrophs) are micro-organisms which flourish at low temperatures, for example, -5°C to 20°C. Listeria are in this group.
- Mesophiles multiply at 30°C to 45°C — most micro-organisms fit into this category.
- Thermophiles prefer a higher-than-average temperature, for example, 55°C to 75°C.

3. MOISTURE

Micro-organisms need water, in liquid form, for metabolism. (They cannot utilise frozen water — ice.) Water is usually obtained from the food source, such as the soil. They grow best in moist foods rich in nutrients, such as milk, stock, meat and fruit. For this reason, dried foods are resistant to spoilage by micro-organisms.

4. AVAILABILITY OF OXYGEN

Micro-organisms may obtain their energy with or without oxygen.

- *Aerobic* organisms require oxygen for release of energy. Most micro-organisms are of this type.
- *Anaerobic* organisms obtain their energy in the absence of oxygen. An example is *Clostridium botulinum*, which causes a fatal form of food poisoning.
- Facultative organisms can adapt to either situation. *Example*: Staphylococci — bacteria which cause food poisoning and boils.

5. pH

Micro-organisms only reproduce within a specific pH range. Most micro-organisms prefer a neutral pH. Many moulds prefer a slightly acid pH — they often occur in fruit. Some bacteria prefer a slightly alkaline pH. Strong acids or alkalis destroy micro-organisms.

OTHER FACTORS WHICH AFFECT THE GROWTH OF MICRO-ORGANISMS

- *Time*: Micro-organisms need time to multiply.
- *Darkness*: Most micro-organisms flourish in darkness. Ultra-violet rays in sunlight destroy them.

DESTRUCTION/DEATH OF MICRO-ORGANISMS

Lack of any of the conditions described above will cause growth to slow down until the micro-organisms eventually die. Death occurs due to:

1. Lack of food.
2. High temperatures: Temperatures of 100°C will destroy micro-organisms.
3. Lack of moisture, although some bacteria produce spores when this occurs.
4. Strong acids/alkalis.
5. Ultraviolet rays, for example in sunlight.
6. Chemicals such as disinfectants, antibiotics and alcohol.

FUNGI

Fungi are simple plants which lack chlorophyll. They therefore cannot make their own food by photosynthesis. Instead, they absorb organic food externally (see 'Food' page 108). Fungi which feed on dead matter (saprophytes) include mushrooms which feed on soil, and moulds, which feed on many foods such as bread and cheese. Fungi which feed on living tissue (parasites) include those which cause disease in plants, animals and humans (ringworm, athlete's foot).

The three types of fungus related to food production/ spoilage are:

- Moulds — mucor, penicillium
- Yeasts — saccharomyces
- Large fungi — mushrooms, toadstools.

MOULDS

BASIC STRUCTURE

Each mould begins as a single cell or *spore*. When, under favourable conditions, this finds a suitable growth medium, it sends out a thread-like filament, or *hypha*, which grows down into the food, absorbing nutrients from it.

The hyphae of some moulds have cross-walls (*septae*) which separate the nuclei. Others (*non-septate*) have no walls and the nuclei are simply arranged along the length of the hypha.

When conditions are suitable, hyphae grow into a furry mass of intertwining filaments called a *mycelium*.

Reproduction may be asexual or sexual.

Mucor on bread (C. James Webb)

- *Asexual reproduction* occurs when the mycelium is well established. Vertical hyphae grow upward and form a sporing head at the top in which spores develop. This may take the form of a *sporangium* (a round structure) or *conidia* (finger-like chains of spores). When ripe, the dust-like spores are released and dispersed by air currents or water when, under suitable conditions, the cycle begins once again.

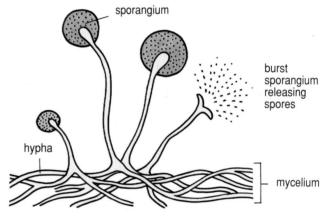

Mucor (rhizopus has a similar structure)

- *Sexual reproduction:* Two hyphae grow together. At the point of contact, the central wall breaks down and a thick wall develops, forming a *zygospore*. Spores develop within the zygospore. Its thick wall enables it to survive for long periods.

Spores will germinate into hyphae under suitable conditions.

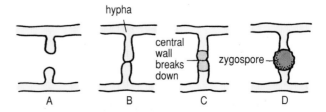

Sexual reproduction

COMMON FOOD SPOILAGE MOULDS

Phycomycetes

- *Mucor*: A group of saprophytic moulds which affect bread and other starchy foods. They reproduce sexually and asexually, producing white hyphae with greyish sporangia.
- *Rhizopus*: A saprophytic fungus similar to mucor. *Rhizopus nigrans* (black bread mould) forms on bread and causes soft rot on fruit and vegetables. Reproduction is usually asexual, producing a fluffy white mycelium and distinctive black 'pin-head' sporangia.

Note: The following moulds have three things in common:
- Their optimum temperature is lower than average — from 20°C to 25°C.
- Most have septae (dividing walls).
- They only reproduce asexually.
- The hyphae grow upward producing conidia, broom-like structures which have chains of spores radiating from the tip. When ripe, these break away.

Ascomycetes

- *Penicillium*: This is a group of saprophytic moulds. They form greenish-blue powdery colonies on many foods, including fruit, cheese and bread. Some species are used in the ripening of cheeses including Roquefort and Stilton to give them their characteristic colour and taste. Others are used in the production of the antibiotic, penicillin.

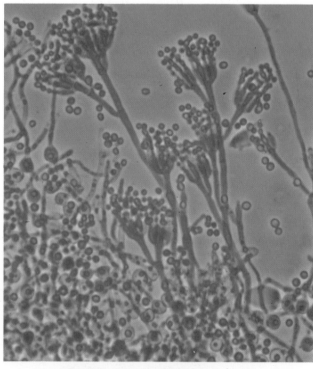

Penicillium showing hyphae and conidia
(C. James Webb)

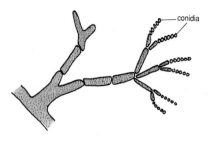

Penicillium

- *Aspergillis* is similar to penicillium. This is a saprophyte. It grows on grain and is a particular problem when large amounts of grain are stored. It also affects dried fruit and causes a black rot on fruit and vegetables. The mould may occur as a grey-green growth or as a black mould.

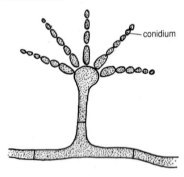

Aspergillis

LARGE FUNGI (BASIDIOMYCETES)

These produce large fruiting bodies visible to the naked eye. Some of these, such as mushrooms (*Agaricus campestris*) and truffles, are edible, while other fungi such as *Amanita* are extremely poisonous.

GROWTH OF MUSHROOMS

Like most fungi, a mushroom begins when a spore starts growing on a suitable medium, such as soil or a tree trunk. The hyphae spread over a wide area, forming a mycelium. When conditions are right, a tightly-packed, dense mass of hyphae grows upwards as a stalk, with a tightly-closed cap on top.

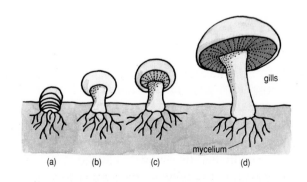

Development of a mushroom

As the mushroom ripens, the cap opens out and flattens and the gills become darker. From between the gills, spore-bearing bodies (*Basidia*) release millions of tiny spores to be dispersed by the air. These can be seen as a 'spore print' if a flat mushroom cap is left on white paper overnight.

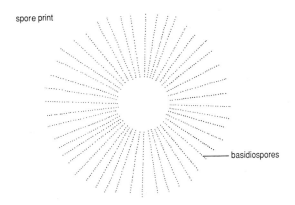

YEASTS (SACCHAROMYCETES)

STRUCTURE

Yeasts are single-celled fungi which are oval in shape and mainly saprophytic. The cell has a thin outer wall, is filled with cytoplasm and also contains a nucleus and food reserves. Wild yeasts are present in the air and are plentiful on fruit — for example, the bloom on a grape skin is caused by yeasts. They live mainly on acid and sweet foods such as jams and honey. *Saccharomyces cerevisiae* is the yeast which is cultivated for use in bread-making and brewing.

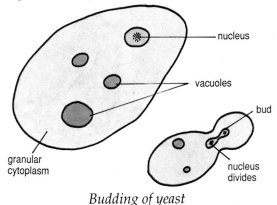

Budding of yeast

REPRODUCTION

Yeast cells reproduce themselves by *budding*. When yeasts are growing well in favourable conditions, a small bulge develops on one side of the cell, the nucleus moves towards it and divides. As the 'bud' grows, a wall forms, separating it from the parent cell, and it then breaks away. In rapidly-budding yeasts, new buds form before the previous bud has fully grown, leading to a chain of yeast cells.

CONDITIONS REQUIRED FOR GROWTH OF YEAST

As for normal fungi, yeasts require food, water, warmth and an acid pH. As yeasts can grow with or without oxygen, they are *facultative organisms*. Yeast is destroyed by temperatures in excess of 60°C. (Destruction begins at 44°C.)

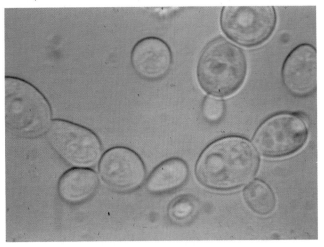

Yeast cells budding
(C. James Webb)

FERMENTATION

As yeasts feed, they break down sugar, producing carbon dioxide and alcohol. This is known as *fermentation* (page 77).

$$C_6H_{12}O_6 + \text{yeasts} \longrightarrow 2CO_2 + 2C_2H_5OH + \text{Energy}$$
(glucose)　　　　　　　　　(carbon　(alcohol)
　　　　　　　　　　　　　　dioxide)

1. Fermentation is utilised in *bread-making* to produce CO_2, which raises bread. (The alcohol is evaporated off.)
2. Fermentation is also important in *brewing* and *wine-making*. The alcohol is retained as a beverage and the CO_2 is driven off to produce still wine or beer. If some CO_2 is retained, the drink will be fizzy, as with champagne.

IMPORTANCE OF FUNGI

1. Various moulds are used in the manufacture of cheese.
2. Penicillin and other antibiotics are produced from moulds.
3. Many fungi are edible, including truffles and mushrooms.
4. Decomposition of dead plants and sewage is hastened by fungi in the air and soil which help recycle valuable nutrients.
5. Yeasts are important in bread, wine and vinegar making.
6. Yeast is a rich source of B vitamins and is used in the production of food supplements and tonics.

DISADVANTAGES

1. Fungi cause many harmful plant diseases. These include rusts and smuts on cereal crops, Dutch Elm disease, potato blight, mildew and dry rot.
2. Some such as *Amanita* are directly poisonous to humans.
3. They cause destruction by spoilage of many foods.
4. They cause human diseases such as athlete's foot and ring-worm.

Tests

1. To investigate fungal growth

Place a piece of damp bread on a dish under a bell jar. Seal join at the base with vaseline. Leave at room temperature for a few days. Examine the fungi with a hand lens, then under the microscope. The thread-like hyphae and coloured sporangia should be clearly seen.

2. To test the growth conditions of micro-organisms

Take four Petri dishes. In each, place a piece of damp bread. Cover and seal. Place: (a) in a freezer; (b) in a refrigerator; (c) in a warm place; and (d) pressure cook one at 15 lb (high) pressure for 15 minutes. Remove. Examine all after several days.

Results:

(a) _____
(b) _____
(c) _____
(d) _____

A similar experiment can be done by inoculating sterilised agar plates with a culture of harmless bacteria, using a sterilised wire loop. Leave in above conditions for 48 hours.

BACTERIA

Bacteria are tiny single-celled organisms. They occur in air, soil and water. There are also found on plants and in animals, particularly in the nose, mouth, throat, skin and bowel. They multiply readily, given suitable conditions, and cause a wide range of diseases. Some are parasites, feeding off living tissue, including the human bowel. Others are saprophytes and feed off dead matter such as food.

STRUCTURE OF BACTERIAL CELL

Bacteria have a very simple structure. They have a *rigid cell wall*. Inside this is the *cell membrane* which encloses the *cytoplasm* (cell liquid). In the cytoplasm are *ribosomes*, which manufacture protein, and *nuclear material*, which may be found in one or more places. Some bacteria possess *flagellae*, which grow out of the cell membrane and have a whip-like effect, moving the bacterium through liquid. Some bacteria are enclosed in a *capsule*, a jelly-like protective layer.

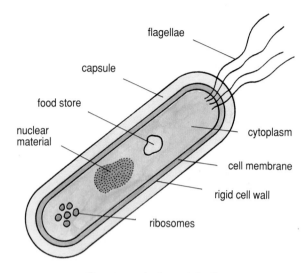

Structure of a bacterial cell

ENDOSPORES (BACTERIAL SPORES)

Particular bacteria (bacilli and clostridia) produce endospores or 'spores' when conditions are unfavourable to growth. These are not simply young cells, as is the case with fungal spores, but tough, dormant cells which are particularly difficult to destroy.

An endospore begins as a small area within a normal bacterium. It increases in size, grows a tough wall of protein around itself and, when sufficiently large, it is released from the parent cell as an endospore.

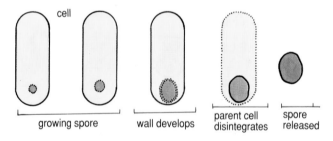

Formation of an endospore

Bacterial 'spores' only develop when conditions are unsuitable for growth, for example when it is dry or when no food is available. They can remain dormant for months and even years, but when favourable conditions occur, they germinate into typical bacterial cells.

Bacterial spores cause serious problems because they are highly resistant to heat, extreme cold and chemicals such as disinfectants which destroy normal vegetative bacteria. They must be subjected to a minimum steam temperature of 121°C for 15 minutes or to dry heat of about 150°C for 1 hour in order to destroy them.

CONDITIONS FOR GROWTH, (page 108).

GROWTH OF BACTERIA

Growth and reproduction in micro-organisms are essentially the same thing. In favourable conditions, bacteria reproduce rapidly by dividing in two, then into four and so on. This is known as *binary fission*. Large groups of bacteria are known as *colonies*, and may contain millions of cells. As colonies are visible to the naked eye, their colour and shape often help with identification.

Under optimum conditions, bacteria can reproduce every 20 minutes, so that a colony of several million could grow within a few hours.

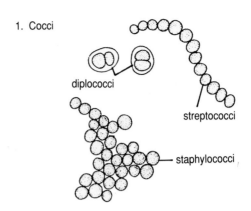

1. Cocci

diplococci

streptococci

staphylococci

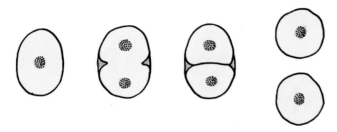

Cells reproducing by binary fission

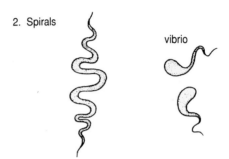

2. Spirals

vibrio

DEATH OF BACTERIA

Luckily for us, bacteria cannot multiply at optimum rate for long because:
1. Nutrient matter becomes depleted (bacteria run out of food).
2. Overcrowding occurs as cells compete for air, food and moisture.
3. During metabolism/growth, toxins and wastes are produced which retard and eventually stop growth. Eventually the whole culture dies.

TOXINS

These are poisonous waste products manufactured during rapid cell division of bacteria. They damage the cells of the infected host, causing inflammation, illness and sometimes death. They are a frequent cause of food poisoning.

CLASSIFICATION OF BACTERIA

1. *Spherical bacteria*
Coccus (plural: cocci)
These may occur:
- Singly — coccus
- In pairs — diplococci (one of these causes pneumonia).
- In chains — streptococci (these cause throat infections and scarlet fever).
- In clusters — staphylococci (these cause skin infections such as boils, and food poisoning).

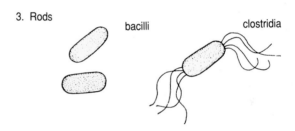

3. Rods

bacilli

clostridia

Bacteria are classified according to shape

2. *Rod-shaped bacteria*
There are many spore-forming, food poisoning bacteria in this group.
- Bacilli — the bacteria which cause tuberculosis (TB) are bacilli.
- Clostridia — *Clostridium welchii, Clostridium botulinum, Escherichia coli, Salmonellae* and the bacteria that cause dysentery belong to this group.
- Listeria
3. *Curved bacteria*
- Spiral (spirilla) — one of these causes syphilis.
- Comma-shaped (vibrio) — one of these cause cholera.

CLASSIFICATION BY STAINING

Because there is such a wide range of bacteria — over 230 genera or families — a more exact method of classification was considered necessary. This method, developed by Christian Gram, involves staining bacteria in order to identify them.

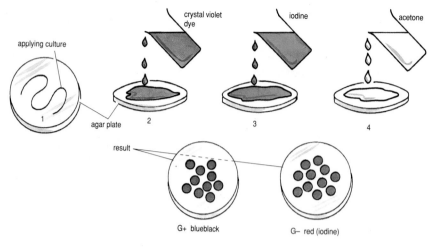

Gram staining

Gram Positive Bacteria (G+)	Gram Negative Bacteria (G–)
■ A thick single-layered cell wall (2% lipid)	■ Cell wall has two thin layers (20% lipid)
■ Produce spores	■ Do not produce spores
■ Immobile — few have flagellae	■ All are mobile and most have flagellae
■ Most are aerobic	■ Aerobic and non-aerobic
■ Low resistance to antibiotics and disinfectants	■ High resistance to antibiotics
■ Include streptococci, clostridia	■ Include Escherichia coli, salmonellae

GRAM STAINING

1. An agar plate is smeared with the culture and incubated.
2. Crystal violet dye is poured over the colony and then washed off with distilled water.
3. A solution of iodine is then poured over it.
4. An organic solvent such as acetone is applied to the stained bacteria. *Gram positive bacteria* are not decolorised. They retain a blue/black colour. *Gram negative bacteria* lose the violet colour, retaining the iodine.

IMPORTANCE OF BACTERIA

1. Used in the production of cheese, yoghurt, vinegar.

2. Produce vitamins B and K in the intestine; used as food supplements.
3. Break down waste matter into simple compounds so that it can be recycled.

DISADVANTAGES OF BACTERIA

1. Bacteria cause spoilage of food.
2. Bacteria cause a great number of diseases, such as food poisoning, e.g. salmonella poisoning and gastroenteritis; diphtheria, typhoid, cholera, scarlet fever, pneumonia, meningitis, dysentery, whooping cough.
   Note: Micro-organisms which cause disease are known as *pathogenic organisms* or *pathogens*. Those which do not cause disease are described as *non-pathogenic*.

► FOOD CONTAMINATION

The food we eat has a limited life. Perishable foods such as meat and dairy produce last no longer than a few days. Even preserved foods decompose eventually, particularly if they are badly sealed or stored.

Foods with a high water content are more likely to spoil as micro-organisms grow best when food is moist. Dried, frozen foods and foods with a high concentration of sugar or salt are less likely to suffer from spoilage.

TYPES OF SPOILAGE

- *Mould*: Food develops a furry growth on the surface.
- *Rot*: Is the disintegration of foods, such as fruit and vegetables.
- *Slime*: Is often caused by bacteria. It occurs on stale meat.
- *Colour change*: Certain growths show areas of colour, e.g. green from penicillium mould, apples go brown.

- *Fermentation*: Yeasts convert carbohydrate into alcohol and CO_2, e.g. fruit, jam.
- *Putrefaction*: Decomposition of proteins, produces foul odours, e.g. hydrogen sulphate (eggs), trimethylamine (fish).

CAUSES OF SPOILAGE AND CONTAMINATION

1. *Physical damage* such as bruising.
2. *Infection* by flies, vermin (rats, mice) and animals.
3. *Chemical contamination*: (a) insecticides in plant foods; (b) antibiotics in animal foods; (c) metal contamination.
4. *Enzymes* cause a chemical breakdown of food, including discoloration, oxidation and rancidity, as well as decomposition.

5. *Micro-organisms* cause many changes in food and often make it unsafe for human consumption.
   (a) *Moulds*, which are aerobic, grow on the surface of food. It may change colour and become sticky and soft.
   (b) *Yeasts*: These ferment food in aerobic and anaerobic conditions. Yeasts are attracted to foods whose concentration of sugar or acid is high.
   (c) *Bacteria* are naturally present on many foods.
   Vegetables are contaminated with soil bacteria and meat from those present in the intestines. Because the food requirements and temperature range of bacteria are similar to ours, they readily contaminate our food supplies and infect our bodies. Spores and toxins of bacteria cause serious problems.

FOOD POISONING

PATHWAYS OF INFECTION

Food poisoning occurs when food or water, which has been contaminated by poisons or pathogens, is ingested. The symptoms are: nausea, vomiting, abdominal cramps, diarrhoea and sometimes fever. Vulnerable people such as infants and elderly people are more badly affected. Death may result.

Food poisoning may be caused by : (1) natural food poisons; (2) chemicals; and (3) bacteria.

1. **Natural food poisons:** Some berries and fungi are naturally poisonous. Rhubarb leaves contain high levels of toxic oxalic acid. Green potatoes contain solanine, a toxin which is dangerous if large amounts are eaten.
2. **Chemical food poisoning:** This occurs when chemical compounds or metals accidentally enter food. Symptoms may occur very quickly.
- Metals such as copper, lead, zinc from equipment used in cooking or food production may dissolve into food liquid during storage. Traces of cyanide from silver polish may remain in cutlery. Cadmium from coloured casseroles may also cause contamination. Some metals such as lead have a cumulative effect and may poison over a number of years.
- Harmful additives may be used in food before their toxicity is known.
- Residues of chemicals including pesticides may contaminate plants.
- Drinking water may be contaminated with chemical effluent.
3. **Bacterial food poisoning:** This is by far the most frequent form of food poisoning. It may occur in two ways.

- *Infectious food poisoning* is caused by consumption of food which is contaminated with large numbers (perhaps millions) of pathogenic bacteria such as salmonella.
- *Toxic food poisoning* is caused by ingestion of a toxin which has been produced in food by bacteria — before consumption (symptoms occur quickly) or after consumption (symptoms take longer to show and disease lasts longer).

In both cases, the contaminated food may show no difference in appearance, taste or smell.

The bacteria which cause most outbreaks of food poisoning are:
- The salmonella group
- Staphylococci
- Clostridium welchii (perfringens)
- Listeria and Clostridium botulinum are included on the chart because, although outbreaks are rare, they are particularly dangerous.

FOODS MOST AT RISK

Moist high-protein foods such as meat, poultry, fish, eggs, stock, cream, custard, reheated dishes.

Precautions against listeria
1. The elderly and pregnant women should avoid cook/chill foods.
2. Read sell-by date of perishables.
3. Store cook/chill in fridge within 1 hour of purchase.
4. Read instructions and reheat thoroughly.
5. Use cook/chill chicken etc. within 24 hours.
6. Keep raw and cooked foods separate.
7. Wash packaged salads carefully.

Description	Sources and method of infection	Incubation time	Symptoms	Duration
Salmonella Rod-shaped, Gram negative bacteria. *Flagella* make them mobile. Facultative non-spore-forming. Optimum temperature 37°C.	Salmonella is the commonest cause of food poisoning, particularly *S. Typhimuriam*. *S. typhi* causes the serious disease, typhoid. Mainly found in intestines of animals and humans. Rodents, pets, birds and farm animals are common carriers. Intensive rearing and careless production methods help it to spread. It is excreted in the faeces of the infected person or animal in huge numbers. Many healthy people are carriers. The importance of scrupulous hygiene in lavatories cannot be over-emphasised. Flies are likely to transfer organisms from faeces to food. Meat and poultry are frequently infected. Sausages, eggs, shellfish which feed in polluted waters and water contaminated by sewage, are common causes of poisoning.	12-24 hours	Vomiting, Abdominal pain, Diarrhoea, Fever. Patients are highly infective.	1-8 days
*Clostridium welchii** now called *C. Perfringens* Rod-shaped, Gram positive; anaerobic; spore-forming.	Bacteria causing both infectious and toxic food poisoning. Carried in the intestine of birds, animals and humans. Organisms infect meat during slaughter and production. Present in sewage. As it grows in the soil, it may infect fruit and vegetables which must be thoroughly washed. The bacterium multiplies rapidly in food under anaerobic conditions, such as the centre of rolled joints of meat, stews, pies, particularly when cooked slowly. The toxin is produced in the intestine after consumption. Spores can survive long periods in air, soil, dust or water and will withstand boiling for 1-4 hours.	10-12 hours	Abdominal pain, Diarrhoea	12-24 hours
Staphylococci Particularly *S. aureus*. Round Gram positive (+) bacterium; found in clusters, like a bunch of grapes. Facultative, mainly aerobic, optimum temperature 30 to 40°C.	This bacterium lives on the nose, throat and skin of humans, particularly when there are skin infections, such as boils. If present on the udder of cows, it may infect milk. Humans are usually the cause of staphylococcal food poisoning. They pass the organism to food with unwashed hands. When growing in food, it produces a toxin which withstands prolonged boiling.	3-4 hours	Nausea, Cramps, Diarrhoea	24 hours
Clostridium botulinum Causes a form of food poisoning known as botulism: rod-shaped Gram positive bacillus. Anaerobic; spore-forming; produces deadly toxin in anaerobic conditions. Can be destroyed by a temperature of 121°C for 5 minutes.	A saprophyte which lives in soil and decaying matter. Cannot function below pH 4.5. Produces heat-resistant spores capable of withstanding hours of boiling. Produces a deadly toxin. (This can be destroyed in a few minutes by boiling.) The toxin can only be produced in anaerobic conditions, e.g. in cans; in the centre of fish. Most cases of botulism occur in non-acid home-canned/bottled produce. Cases occurring in commercially canned food, e.g. fish, are usually due to a flaw in the processing cycle, e.g. insufficient heat. Any can which appears to be blown, rusted or leaking should not be used.	12-36 hours (Death 1-8 days)	Headaches, Dizziness, Tiredness, Diarrhoea followed by constipation. The central nervous system is affected, causing slurred speech, blurred vision, paralysis of throat and finally, death.	Fatal in 60% of cases Recovery very slow,* often taking months * If antidote is administered.
*Listeria Monocytogenes** Rod shaped. Gram positive Facultative; Psychrophile (likes low temperatures). Optimum temperature 30°C, but it can survive at temperature as low as 4°C or as high as 43°C. Tolerates salt. * see previous page	Causes infective food poisoning, called Listeriosis. Lives in soil. Contaminates water, animals, vegetables. Likes an acid pH therefore is found in soft, unpasteurised cheeses. Likes foods with high water content, e.g. poultry, pâté, coleslaw. Major danger is cook/ chill products which are not stored at sufficiently low temperatures. Long incubation period in food — 2 weeks. N.B. Bring to high temperature when reheating. Microwave heating may be insufficient.	Long – up to 2 weeks	Slow to develop. Starts with fever. Passes into bloodstream. Rarely serious in healthy adults. Can cause serious diseases in susceptible victims, e.g. infants, elderly, pregnant women. Encephalitis, Meningitis, Miscarriage/stillbirth (can pass through placenta). Septicemia (blood poisoning) Fatality in such victims: 1 in 3	Several days.

OTHER FOOD-BORNE DISEASES

The following diseases are caused by organisms which use food or water as a vehicle of infection, rather than as a growth medium, as occurs with food poisoning organisms. These diseases take a long time to incubate — 1 to 2 weeks on average.

- *Typhoid* is caused by contaminated water or by food such as shellfish. It is also spread by humans through faeces.
- *Dysentery* is caused by shigellae in faeces and is spread by flies.
- *Cholera* is caused by vibrio cholerae, and is often the result of drinking infected water.
- *Scarlet fever* is caused by streptococci.
- *Brucellosis* } Passed from cows to humans in milk. Less common today due to disease control in cattle.
- *Tuberculosis* (TB) } Pasteurisation destroys such pathogenic organisms.

Most raw foods, e.g. plants and animals, carry bacteria.

PATHWAYS OF INFECTION

1. *On the farm*: Bad husbandry can result in plants being contaminated with insecticides. Animals may be contaminated with antibiotics. Disease may spread to food in milking parlours. Intensive rearing, poor transport conditions or unhygienic storage, for example of milk, can also cause contamination.

2. *Production plants*: When hygiene regulations are not complied with, disease can spread easily from one contaminated source to a wide network of foods. Poultry plants, abattoirs and food factories must observe strict rules of hygiene. Food must be kept chilled.

3. *Food shops, markets and catering establishments* can often be the cause of a food poisoning outbreak. Unhygienic practices include: displaying vegetables in sunlight outside greengrocers and placing meat in warm shop windows. Assistants with unkept hair and dirty fingernails are not acceptable. One should complain if any of these circumstances are noted.

4. *In the home*: The kitchen and lavatory can be dangerous sources of infection and must be kept scrupulously clean and disinfected. Persons working with food must maintain a very high standard of hygiene (see over).

PREVENTION OF FOOD CONTAMINATION

Food poisoning is a preventable disease. In Britain between 1981-87, reported cases doubled, from 10,000 to 20,000. The chief cause is carelessness and ignorance of food hygiene.

Hands should be washed before handling food
(S. and R. Greenhill)

Lavatories are a frequent source of infection
(S. and R. Greenhill)

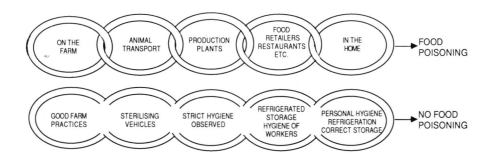

Breaking the food poisoning chain

PERSONAL HYGIENE

1. Every person working with food should follow *basic rules of hygiene*. Hands should be washed *after* using the lavatory, *after* handling raw food such as meat, and *before* handling food.
2. *Cover cuts* with waterproof dressings and change them frequently because cuts and sores attract and are always infected with bacteria.
3. *Avoid coughing and sneezing* over food. Avoid handling face and hair.
4. *Tie long hair* back and *cover clothes* with a clean apron.
5. Keep *nails* clean and short.
6. Those *suffering from food poisoning* should not work with food.

FOOD HYGIENE

1. *Keep all food covered* and *handle it as little as possible.*
2. *Cook food thoroughly,* especially poultry and minced meats such as sausages and hamburgers, to destroy bacteria.
3. Eat food soon after it is cooked. *Avoid keeping food warm* as this is the ideal temperature for bacterial growth.
4. *Leftovers* are common sources of infection. Cover, cool quickly and store in refrigerator. Reheat thoroughly. A temperature of 100°C (boiling point) for at least five minutes is necessary to destroy pathogens.
5. *Cooked and raw food must never be prepared on the same surface.* If raw meat is contaminated, cooking will destroy the bacteria. But if cooked meat is placed on the same surface, there is no further cooking and food poisoning may result.
6. *Never refreeze frozen products.*

KITCHEN HYGIENE

1. The kitchen must be well-designed to make it *easy to keep clean*. Surfaces should be easy to clean and be non-absorbent. Floors, walls and worktops should have as few joins as possible as these harbour germs.
2. *All utensils and equipment* should be washed thoroughly after use. Sinks, drains and floors should be *disinfected* regularly.
3. *Good ventilation* through windows and extractor fan is important to prevent humidity.
4. *Good washing-up facilities* are essential, using plenty of hot water. A dishwasher is ideal as it sterilises dishes.
5. *Cloths* are a frequent source of micro-organisms. They should be washed well after use, boiled or bleached regularly to sterilise them and dried in the fresh air.
6. *Refuse* should be disposed of efficiently and hygienically. Bins should be washed and disinfected regularly.
7. *Floors* must be swept, washed and disinfected regularly.
8. Keep *pets out of* the kitchen.

FOOD STORAGE

1. Plenty of dry, well-ventilated storage is essential. Damp, dirty storage areas will encourage the growth of micro-organisms, particularly moulds.
2. Clean and disinfect storage areas regularly.
3. Meat, fish etc. should be stored at 5°C or below — in a refrigerator. The practice of putting warm food in the fridge causes condensation on foods and raises the temperature — both are factors which promote microbial growth. (More on food storage, page 83.)

COMMERCIAL AND LOCAL AUTHORITY PREVENTION

1. Pasteurisation of milk, eggs and dairy produce.
2. Purification of water supplies.
3. Efficient sewage treatment.
4. Frequent inspection of food premises by health inspectors.
5. Food hygiene education, particularly for those in the food industry.

DISINFECTION AND STERILISATION

Disinfection is the process of destroying pathogenic organisms.

Sterilisation is the process of destroying all micro-organisms.

1. Heat, both dry and moist, can be used to destroy organisms. Washing hands, utensils, crockery and cloths in hot soapy water destroys many pathogens. Boiling destroys more. Even higher temperatures, i.e. 150°C, are required to destroy all organisms and their spores.
2. Ultraviolet rays can be used to sterilise air.
3. Chemicals also destroy pathogens. These include:
- soap and detergents
- chlorine for water supplies and swimming pools
- sulphur dioxide for fruit and fruit juices
- hydrogen peroxide for cuts and grazes
- phenols as general heavy duty disinfectants
- potassium permanganate for cleaning drains
- antibiotics such as penicillin.

See also page 205.

6 FOOD PRESERVATION

WHY FOOD IS PRESERVED

A knowledge of microbiology (Chapter 5, page 108) is assumed when studying the preservation of food.

Food is preserved:

1. To *save money*: Most home-preserved produce is cheaper.
2. To *use up food* such as garden produce when it is plentiful and so avoid waste.
3. To have *seasonal produce* available throughout the year.
4. To *introduce flavour* and variety to a menu, as with jams and chutneys.
5. *For convenience*: Preserved foods can be easily stored until required.
6. Preserved foods are *easier to handle*, distribute and transport on a large scale than are fresh foods.

CAUSES OF DECAY

Food is subject to a normal cycle of growth, maturity and decay. Food lasts longest in its living state, as growing fruit. Once picked or slaughtered, it rapidly begins to deteriorate. Decay is brought about by enzymes (organic catalysts present in cells that speed up chemical reactions).

Decomposition is also caused by micro-organisms such as moulds, yeasts and bacteria. These contaminate and destroy food, given suitable conditions such as warmth and moisture.

ENVIRONMENTAL FACTORS

Certain conditions speed up microbial growth. Others damage the food, thus hastening decay.

- *Warmth* – Milk goes sour, while meat and fish go 'off'.
- *Moisture* – Bread and fruit go mouldy in a moist kitchen.
- *Oxygen* – Causes fats to go rancid and cut fruit to brown.
- *Rough handling* – Causes fruit to bruise, brown and decay.

PRINCIPLES OF PRESERVATION

Preserving interrupts the process of decay in food by inhibiting or preventing decomposition.

1. It prevents the action of enzymes which speed up decay.
2. It prevents the growth of micro-organisms.
3. It prevents the re-entry of micro-organisms by thorough sealing.
4. The colour, flavour, texture and nutritive value should be kept as near as possible to that of fresh food.

In the past, food changed considerably when preserved.

Today, modern processes cause less change in colour, taste and appearance. Nutrients are either retained or are replaced, if lost in the processing.

Enzymes and micro-organisms work best in warm, moist conditions. They are destroyed by high temperatures, retarded by cool temperatures, and inactivated by low temperatures.

The following chart gives an approximate guide.

Causes of Decay	Optimum Temperature	Destroyed	Retarded	Inactive
Enzymes	20 to 40°C	70°C+	15 to –10°C	–18°C
Moulds	30 to 45°C	75°C+	15 to –10°C	–18°C
Yeasts	25 to 40°C	60°C+	15 to –5°C	–16°C
Bacteria	30 to 40°C	100°C	15 to –5°C	–18°C

Some bacteria produce endospores which are highly resistant to heat and chemicals and are therefore difficult to destroy. The temperature required to destroy them is higher than can be achieved by using normal kitchen equipment.

PH VALUE

Enzymes and micro-organisms will only work within a specific pH range — usually around neutral (pH 7). Some moulds favour a slightly acid environment. As all micro-organisms are inactivated by strong acids such as vinegar, these are sometimes used to preserve foods like pickles and chutneys.

PRESERVATIVES

High concentrations of substances such as sugar (65%), salt, vinegar (see above) and alcohol inhibit the growth of micro-organisms. Salt and sugar act as preservatives by dissolving in the water of the food cells, forming a concentrated solution. Water is drawn by osmosis from the cells of micro-organisms already present in an attempt to equalise the concentration. This dehydrates the cells and they die.

Food may be preserved by:

- Removing one of the requirements for growth of micro-organisms
  - Removing warmth ⟶ freezing
  - Removing moisture ⟶ drying
  - Removing air ⟶ canning, bottling
- Heat treatments to destroy micro-organisms/enzymes.
- Addition of chemicals which inhibit the action of micro-organisms and enzymes (sugar, salt, vinegar).
- Irradiation.

► METHODS OF PRESERVING

FREEZING

UNDERLYING PRINCIPLE

Enzymes and micro-organisms require warmth in order to function. They are inactivated by extreme cold. As ice crystals take the place of water in food, micro-organisms have no water available for metabolism. Quick freezing (–25°C to –33°C) converts the water present in food to tiny ice crystals. Slow freezing (between 0°C and –25°C) and fluctuating freezer temperatures cause large ice crystals to form which break the cell walls and upon thawing cause loss of moisture, texture and nutrients.

After freezing at –25°C, food is stored at –18°C. Commercial freezing takes place in a blast freezer at –30°C.

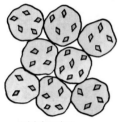 

quick freezing —
small ice crystals

slow freezing —
large crystals

Short-term cold storage (5°C) is used to keep perishable food in good condition for as long as possible without freezing. Refrigerator storage (between 1°C and 5°C) inhibits the growth of many spoilage organisms.

ADVANTAGES OF HOME FREEZING

1. Freezing is a simple, safe method of preserving.
2. A greater variety of foods can be frozen than preserved by any other method. Foods are available out of season.
3. Foods retain their colour, flavour, nutritive value and, in most foods, their texture better than any other method of preserving.
4. Much waste is avoided. Leftover food can be stored and used as required.
5. Bulk cooking and freezing save time and fuel and leave the cook more leisure time.
6. Frozen food is very useful in emergencies.

DISADVANTAGES OF FREEZING

1. The cost of buying the freezer
2. Maintaining the freezer
3. The cost of packaging

FOODS SUITABLE FOR FREEZING

Almost all foods may be frozen.

- Raw and cooked meats and fish
- Fresh fruit and vegetables
- Reheated dishes such as fish cakes and shepherd's pie

- Baked foods including bread and cakes
- Uncooked dough and pastry
- Sauces, soups, stews, pancakes, savoury dishes
- Puddings and cold sweets
- Breadcrumbs, stuffing, some sandwiches, packed lunches
- Prepared baby foods, advance cooking for parties, Christmas etc.

Note: Foods with a high fat content such as bacon go rancid. Use within three months.

FOODS UNSUITABLE FOR FREEZING

Do not freeze:

- Bananas: They blacken.
- Lettuce, cucumber and salad greens: They go limp.
- Whole tomatoes: Although tomato and other purées freeze well.
- Whole melon, pears. If freezing, do so in syrup.
- Milk, cream and plain yoghurt: They separate. Fruit yoghurt and whipped cream freeze satisfactorily.
- Whole eggs: It is possible to freeze the yolks and whites of eggs separately.
- Mayonnaise.
- Whole potatoes, although it is possible to freeze potato purée or partly-cooked chips.
- Foods containing gelatine.

PACKAGING

Freezing has a drying effect on food. For this reason, food must be well protected by strong packaging which will not tear or split. Packaging for deep freezing must be air-tight, waterproof and vapour-proof. Careless packaging results in loss of colour, flavour and texture.

Freezer burn: This is a toughening and discolouration of food where it has been exposed in the deep freeze. It usually occurs on protein foods such as meat and fish.

SUITABLE MATERIALS FOR FREEZER PACKAGING

- Polythene boxes: They are strong and reusable, but expensive.
- Polythene freezer bags: These are made of thick polythene. Thin bags are unsuitable for freezing.
- Heavy-duty freezer foil: This is useful for overwrapping.
- Foil containers: Some of these have lids and come in several shapes and sizes.
- Waxed cartons and tubs: Cream, yoghurt and margarine tubs and containers, especially those with lids, are useful and are free.
- Freezer tape: This is useful for sealing openings.
- Wire ties: These are necessary for tying polythene bags. (Take care not to use them in a microwave oven).

LABELLING

Keep a record of the contents of the freezer in a notebook, together with the weight and date of freezing. Tick off each item as it is removed. Individual packages must also be labelled, using a special freezer pen or crayon on freezer labels.

GENERAL RULES FOR FREEZING

PREPARATION

1. Only freeze best-quality foods. Fruit and vegetables should be in peak condition, while meat, poultry and fish must be absolutely fresh. Freeze as soon as possible after harvesting or purchase.
2. Freeze in usable quantities, preferably in small amounts, — the amount usable in one dish or meal.
3. Never freeze more than one-tenth of the capacity of the freezer in 24 hours. This will raise the temperature of the freezer, damage already frozen food and slow down the freezing process.
4. For the same reason, chill hot foods well before placing them in the freezer.
5. Turn the freezer to its coldest setting — fast-freeze — 2 to 3 hours before freezing fresh food. This reduces the freezer from storage temperature (–18°C) to freezing temperature (–25°C). Return switch to normal after 24 hours.

PACKAGING

1. Use moisture-proof, vapour-proof containers which will not tear or split.
2. Pack foods tightly and expel all air. A straw is useful for this purpose.
3. Seal well with wire ties or warm iron.
4. Allow 10–20mm head space over liquids to allow for expansion.
5. Overwrap sharp bones with foil.

FREEZING

1. Place food in fast-freeze compartment. Packages may touch the base or walls, but some circulation space between packages must be allowed.
2. Open-freeze soft foods which are likely to stick — sausages, fancy cakes, strawberries. Pack in appropriate containers when frozen.
3. Never refreeze frozen food such as meat which has thawed out. There is a danger that bacteria present will have time to multiply to dangerous levels due to the double thawing period. It is permissible to refreeze if the food has been cooked in the meantime, as with a casserole.

STORING

1. Store similar foods together and use in rotation.
2. Keep a record of contents of freezer.
3. Use up all food within the specified time. Store no food longer than 12 months. Foods stored past their correct date deteriorate in quality and food value.
4. Use up bought frozen food within 3 months.
5. Defrost the freezer* regularly — about twice a year at a time when stocks are low.
(* See Defrosting a freezer, Chapter 15)

THAWING

1. Food is normally left in the container while thawing.
2. Many dishes may be cooked without thawing. These include stews, meat pies, chops, steaks, fish fillets and fingers. Make sure they are thoroughly cooked.
3. Vegetables should be cooked from frozen to preserve colour and nutrients.
4. Joints of meat should be thawed before cooking.
5. Poultry must be fully thawed. Chickens take from 8–10 hours at room temperature before cooking. Turkeys may need up to 48 hours. Insufficiently thawed poultry can be highly dangerous.
6. Fruit should be thawed slowly in the refrigerator for approximately 6 hours and may be used slightly under-thawed.
7. Once thawed, food should be used up quickly to prevent bacterial deterioration.

SPECIAL POINTS TO NOTE WHEN FREEZING

MEAT

- Meat should be well hung prior to freezing.
- Have it jointed into suitably-sized pieces or prepare as for cooking.
- Separate steaks and chops with waxed paper. Salty meats such as bacon do not freeze well as salt prevents rapid freezing.
- Trim off excess fat to delay rancidity.
- Freeze at lowest possible temperature to reduce 'drip loss'.
- Freeze poultry unstuffed. Freeze giblets separately.
- Pack mince into suitable packs — about 450g (1 lb).

FISH

- Freeze within 12 hours of catching.
- Shellfish should be blast frozen.
- Prepare fish as for cooking — remove head, gut and bone.
- Divide large fish into fillets or cutlets.
- Separate fillets etc. with waxed paper, not foil.

STEWS AND CASSEROLES

1. Make up stew in the usual way, leaving sauce a little thin as it thickens on freezing.

2. Keep seasoning to a minimum as it intensifies on freezing. Avoid garlic — it goes musty.

3. Shorten cooking time by 20 minutes. Cooking will be completed during reheating time.

FRUIT

1. Prepare as for cooking, discarding bruised or over-ripe fruit.

2. Pack in polythene bags, sprinkling sugar between layers if wished.

3. Open-freeze soft fruits and pack when frozen.

4. Fruit gives best results when frozen in a syrup — 225g (8oz) sugar to 600ml (1 pint) water — or as a sweetened or unsweetened purée, allowing headspace.

VEGETABLES

1. Prepare as for cooking. Peel and cut into medium pieces. Leave small vegetables such as carrots whole.

2. Because the enzymes in vegetables cause deterioration — even at –18°C — it is essential to blanch vegetables before freezing in order to destroy enzymes. Blanch in boiling, salted water for required time (see chart).

3. Plunge blanched vegetables into ice-cold water to cool. Drain well.

4. Open-freeze, if wished, or pack in polythene bags or waxed cartons, removing all air.

BREAD AND CAKES

1. May be frozen as dough or as baked bread. The latter gives a better result.

2. Pastry freezes well, both cooked and uncooked.

3. Pack bread and plain buns in polythene bags. Decorated confectionary should be open-frozen, then packed in rigid containers such as plastic margarine boxes.

4. Batch baking saves fuel. Make two or more of each item and freeze one.

FREEZING COOKED DISHES

Prepare and cook in the normal way. Avoid overcooking. Be sparing with seasoning. Freeze, if possible, in oven-to-tableware as food can then be taken from the freezer to oven to table without disturbance. Place the dish to be reheated in a cold oven. This allows it to heat gradually as the oven is heating. Then continue cooking until heated through.

USING A MICROWAVE COOKER TO THAW

1. *Meat, steaks and chops*: Leave meat wrapped or place in covered container. Place in microwave, set to 'defrost' for 5 minutes. Stand for 10 minutes before using. Repeat if necessary, turning regularly.

2. *Joints (boneless)*: Place in microwave and set at 'defrost', for 10 minutes per 450g (1lb). Stand for 20 minutes. Return at 'medium' setting for 6 minutes per 450g (1lb), then stand for 20 minutes before using.

Note: Standing time is part of the process.

BLANCHING VEGETABLES FOR FREEZING

Vegetable	Time
Aubergines, sliced	4 min.
Brussels sprouts	3–4 min.
Carrots	3–5 min.
Cauliflower florets & broccoli	3 min.
Celery	3 min.
Corn on the cob(medium)	6 min.
Courgettes, sliced	1 min.
French and broad beans	3 min.
Mushrooms, sautéed in butter	1 min.
Onions, small	4 min.
Parsnips, turnips	2–3 min.
Peas	1 min.
Potatoes, chipped (frying oil)	2 min.

Note: Blanching destroys enzymes and many spoilage organisms.

Blanching method

1. Blanch vegetables in 4.5 litre (1 gallon) of water to each 450g (1 lb) vegetables.

2. Blanch in small amounts (about 450g).

3. Place them in a colander or wire basket and lower into boiling water, timing from the moment it returns to the boil.

4. Plunge colander into ice-cold water to cool for same time as blanching time. Drain well.

5. Pack into containers. Label and seal.

Maximum food storage times

Food	Months	Food	Months
Bacon	3	Pastry, cooked	6
Beef	8–12	Pastry, raw	3
Bread	1	Pâté	1
Cakes	3–6	Pies, savouries	3
Chicken	12	Pork	6
Eggs, separated	6	Poultry (except chicken)	6
Fish, oily	4	Reheats, e.g. fish cakes	2
Fish, pies, etc	2	Sauce	3
Fish, shell	2	Sausages	3
Fish, white	6	Soup	3
Fruit	1–12	Stews, etc	2
Lamb	6	Stock	3
Minced meat	3	Veal	6
Offal	3	Vegetables	9–12

OTHER METHODS OF PRESERVATION

HEAT TREATMENTS

UNDERLYING PRINCIPLE

High temperatures coagulate the cell protein of enzymes and micro-organisms, thus destroying them. This also occurs during cooking.

FORMS OF HEAT TREATMENT

1. *Pasteurisation* of milk, eggs (temperature 72°C, page 58).
2. *Sterilisation*, including canning and bottling, (temperatures over 100°C). The more acid in the food, the shorter the processing time.
3. *Preservation, using high concentrations of sugar or acid, to make jam or chutney.*

BOTTLING

UNDERLYING PRINCIPLE

Food in containers is brought to a sufficiently high temperature for long enough to destroy micro-organisms and enzymes. Air is eliminated in the process and a vacuum is created on cooling so that air cannot re-enter to contaminate produce. If a sufficiently high temperature is not reached, micro-organisms may survive and cause spoilage and food poisoning. Too high a temperature or processing for too long will result in soft, mushy food.

Bacterial spores present in vegetables and protein food require particularly high temperatures for long periods in order to destroy them. For this reason, it is extremely dangerous to attempt to bottle these at home as domestic equipment cannot reach the required temperatures (moist heat 121°C for at least 15 minutes or dry heat 150°C for one hour). Acid foods such as fruits or vegetables preserved in acid, such as pickles and chutney, can be preserved successfully, however.

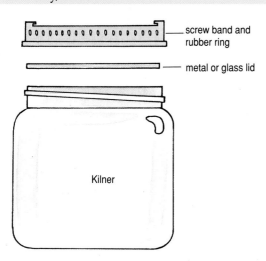

screw band and rubber ring

metal or glass lid

Kilner

Preserving jar

EQUIPMENT REQUIRED FOR BOTTLING

1. Large saucepan or pressure cooker.
2. A sugar thermometer.
3. Vacuum bottling jars. These are made of heat-resistant glass with wide tops for ease of filling. They have clip tops or metal or plastic screw bands holding glass or metal lids in place. Lids may have separate or attached rubber rings which help form a tight seal between jar and lid. Jars are available in several sizes.

Note: Ensure that rubber ring has not perished. Replace if necessary. Lids with attached rings should be used only once. Examine jars and lids for cracks, chips and flaws which might affect sealing.

RULES FOR BOTTLING

1. Fruit should be just ripe, sound, dry and absolutely fresh.
2. Jars, lids and rings should be clean and sound. Wash and rinse in hot water. Do not dry.
3. Prepare fruit as for normal cooking — for example, wash, peel, core, quarter. Pick over soft fruit and remove stalks.
4. Make a syrup by dissolving 225g sugar in 500ml water. Then boil for 5 minutes.
5. Pack fruit closely to top of jar, then fill up with syrup. (Add soft fruit/syrup alternately.)
6. Tap jar gently on a hard surface, turning to remove air bubbles (these may harbour micro-organisms). Wipe rim with kitchen paper.
7. Place rubber ring and lid on jar. Apply clip or screw band. Untwist the latter one-quarter turn to allow steam to escape.
8. Sterilise according to chart — in oven, waterbath or pressure cooker.
9. Wipe outside of jar. Allow to cool for 12 hours, tightening screw band occasionally.
10. Testing. When jam is quite cold, remove clip/screw-band and lift carefully by the lid to see if an air-tight vacuum has been created. If it comes away, check cause of failure (for example: chips, perished ring). Then either reprocess or use up quickly.
11. Label jar with name of fruit and date. Store in cool, dry, dark, well-ventilated place.

JAM-MAKING

UNDERLYING PRINCIPLE

1. Fruit is boiled to soften it and to destroy micro-organisms. Boiling point, 100°C, is sufficient to destroy the micro-organisms (the yeasts and moulds) and enzymes found in fruit.

Bottling methods

	Oven	Saucepan	Pressure cooker
	Preheat oven to 150°C (300°F) Gas 2. Stand bottles at least 50mm apart on a large tin containing 10mm water. Lids are laid loosely on top of jars after filling. Process 2kg fruit or under for shorter time shown below. The longest time is used for jars of fruit up to 6kg	Stand covered jars in a saucepan of water heated to 38°C (100°F). Jars should not be touching and a false bottom should be used in the saucepan. Cover jars with more warm water and heat slowly to simmering point: 85°C (185°F). Maintain according to time chart below.	Place trivet in cooker. Add 3cm warm water. Warm jars before filling. Put filled jars into cooker. Put on lid, heat until steady flow of steam appears. Put on weight and bring to 5lb pressure. Maintain as below. Reduce pressure for 10 minutes at room temperature.

Fruit	Boiling liquid	Hot liquid	Boiling liquid
Soft fruits, e.g.	35–60 mins	5 mins	1 min
blackberries	35–60 mins	5 mins	1 min
raspberries	35–60 mins	5 mins	1 min
strawberries	35–60 mins	5 mins	1 min
Apple slices	30–60 mins	2 mins	1 min
Gooseberries	40–60 mins	10 mins	1 min
Rhubarb	40–60 mins	10 mins	1 min
Stone fruits, e.g.	55–75 mins	20 mins	3–4 mins
peaches, plums	55–75 mins	20 mins	3–4 mins
Pears	65–85 mins	40 mins	5 mins
Tomatoes	70-100 mins	50 mins	15 mins

| Finishing: | Wipe outside of jar. Put on clips/screwbands. Test in 12–24 hours. | Using a jug empty out some water. Lift out bottles onto wooden surface. Tighten screwbands. Test in 12–24 hours. | Lift pressure cooker carefully. Open when pressure has reduced. Tighten screwbands. Test in 12–24 hours. |

2. Sugar is added which inhibits the growth of micro-organisms. Sixty-five per cent concentration of sugar is necessary to prevent growth of these organisms and also to prevent fermentation.
3. The setting of jam depends on a gum-like substance called *pectin*. This is present in most fruit and, with the right proportion of acid and sugar, it should produce a good set.

CHARACTERISTICS OF WELL-MADE JAM
Good jam will have a clear, bright colour and a fruity flavour. It should be well set, but not too stiff and will keep for one year.

PECTIN AND ACID
Jam will not set properly if pectin and acid are not present in the correct proportions.

Pectin is a polysaccharide which is present in the cell walls of fruit. It starts off in unripe fruit as insoluble pectose. On ripening, the pectose changes to the setting agent pectin and, as the fruit becomes over-ripe, the pectin changes to pectic acid which has no setting properties.

Acid helps to release the pectin from the cell walls. It also improves the flavour and helps to convert beet sugar into invert sugar which prevents crystallisation of jam. Fruits which are deficient in acid, such as strawberries and blackberries, should have lemon juice added when starting to make jam.

Presence of Pectin and Acid in Fruits

Good	Medium	Poor
Apples	Raspberries	Cherries
Blackcurrants	Plums	Pears
Green goose-	Apricots	Strawberries
berries	Early blackberries	Late blackberries

Note: Commercial pectin which is available in powder or liquid form may be used, if necessary, but follow the manufacturer's instructions. A mixture of under-ripe and ripe fruit will usually produce a good set, as will a mixture of a fruit rich in pectin — combining apples (high in pectin) with one low in pectin such as late blackberries.

1. Simmer fruit in water
2. Add 1 tsp. juice to 3 tsp. methylated spirits
3. Shake or stir and leave for 1 minute

solid clot good   a few clots medium   tiny clots poor

4. Pectin content

To test for pectin

TO TEST FOR PECTIN

Boil a little of the fruit to be tested in a small quantity of water until softened. Cool. Put 1 teaspoon of the fruit juice into a bowl. Add 3 teaspoons of methylated spirits. Stir and leave for 1 minute.

Results:

- A single firm clot: fruit is rich in pectin.
- A soft clot or 2 or 3 firm clots: fruit has average amount of pectin.
- Many small pieces of jelly: poor in pectin.

SUGAR

The amount of sugar used in making jam is vital to the success of the recipe. It is essential to have 65% sugar content, as too little will cause fermentation, giving off a smell of alcohol, and mould formation. Too much sugar causes crystallisation. Granulated sugar is commonly used. Some preserving sugar such as Sure-set has added pectin which assists the setting of jam. In this case, boiling time after adding sugar is reduced to 4 minutes.

ADDING SUGAR

1. Soften fruit completely before adding the sugar, which has a hardening effect on the fruit.
2. Stir jam thoroughly while the sugar is dissolving.
3. The sugar must be dissolved before the jam is brought to the boil. Otherwise crystallisation will occur.

RULES FOR MAKING JAMS AND JELLIES

1. FRUIT

Use sound, dry, under-ripe fruit. Do not use over-ripe fruit or the jam will not set. Prepare the fruit as for cooking: washing, peeling, removing stones and chopping, if necessary. Skins and cores are used in jellies: rind and pips in marmalade.

2. CONTAINERS

Use a large stainless steel preserving pan or saucepan. There should be sufficient room for the jam to boil vigorously. It should have a thick machine-ground base to prevent burning. Avoid chipped enamel pans, or brass or copper-lined pans which reduce the vitamin C content. Grease the base of the saucepan to reduce the possibility of sticking.

3. COOKING

The amount of water depends on the type of fruit. Soft fruits need no water. Simmer the prepared fruit gently to soften the skins and to extract pectin before adding sugar. Add warmed sugar, stirring until it is dissolved and then bring to the boil. Boil rapidly until setting point is reached. (Test for setting — see below.) Avoid stirring at this stage as it causes crystallisation.

Jams with large pieces of fruit such as strawberry jam or marmalade should be cooled for 10 minutes before potting to prevent fruit rising in the jars.

4. JARS

Jars should be without chips or flaws. They must be spotlessly clean, washed and sterilised in a low oven for 15 minutes to destroy micro-organisms and to prevent cracking when they are filled with hot jam.

5. POTTING

Skim jam. Stir and pour into heated pots, filling to within 1.5cm (½in) of the top. Wipe rims and cover at once with waxed discs and cellophane — dampening these slightly helps them to stretch tightly over the jars, achieving a perfect seal. Label and date.

6. STORING

Store in a cool, dry, dark place in order to preserve the colour, flavour and quality.

TO TEST FOR SETTING

- *Cold plate test:* Put 1 teaspoon of jam on a cold plate and leave aside. When setting point has been reached, the surface of the jam will wrinkle when pushed with a finger.
- *Temperature test:* Use a warmed sugar thermometer when boiling jam. It will register 104°C (220°F) when the correct sugar concentration, i.e. setting point, has been reached.
- *Flake test:* Take a spoonful of jam. If it falls from the edge of a clean wooden spoon in a broad flake instead of a continuous stream, the jam is set.

(a) Cold plate test

(a) (b)

(b) Temperature test

(c) Flake test

Tests for setting

STRAWBERRY JAM

(Yield: 2.25kg/5lb approximately)

1.6kg (3½lb) strawberries

3 tablesp. lemon juice

1.4kg (3lb) sugar

1. Hull and wipe over fruit. Remove over-ripe or bruised fruit. Cut large strawberries in two.
2. Place strawberries and lemon juice in greased saucepan and heat gently until strawberries have softened.
3. Add warmed sugar and stir over a low heat until sugar is dissolved. Bring to the boil and boil until setting point is reached. Skim.
4. Cool for 10-15 minutes, then stir and pour into warmed sterilised jars. Cover, label and date.

GOOSEBERRY JAM

(Yield 4.5kg/10lb approximately)

2.75kg (6lb) gooseberries (slightly under-ripe)

1 litre (2 pt) water

2.75kg (6lb) sugar

1. Top, tail and wash fruit. Place in preserving pan with water, bring to the boil and simmer gently for about ½ hour, until soft. Stir frequently to prevent sticking.
2. Add warmed sugar, stir until dissolved, then boil rapidly until setting point is reached. Skim.
3. Stand for 10-15 minutes, stir, pour into warmed jars, cover, label and date.

DRIED APRICOT JAM

(Yield 2.25kg/5lb approximately)

450g (1lb) dried apricots

1.75 litres (3 pt) water

Juice of 1 lemon

1.5kg (3lb) sugar

1. Wash fruit thoroughly to remove any grit, etc. Soak for 24 hours in measured water.
2. Put fruit and soaking water into saucepan with lemon juice and simmer gently for 30 minutes, until soft, stirring occasionally. Skim.
3. Add sugar, stir until dissolved. Bring to the boil and boil rapidly until setting point is reached, stirring regularly to prevent sticking. Skim.
4. Allow to stand for 10 minutes, stir, pour into warmed pots, cover, label and date.

APPLE JELLY

2.5kg (5½lb) unripe cooking or sour eating apples

(windfalls may be used)

Juice of 2 lemons

Water

450g (1lb) sugar to each 600ml (1 pt) juice

1. Wash apples, remove damaged or bruised parts, cut large apples in 4, halve small ones.
2. Put apples, including peel and core, into preserving pan, add enough cold water to cover and add lemon juice. Simmer until soft and pulpy and liquid is reduced by one-third.
3. Strain pulp through a clean cloth which has been tied at four corners of an upturned stool. A large bowl should be placed beneath to catch juices. Leave for several hours *or* overnight.
4. Measure juice and return to clean pan, adding 450g (1lb) sugar to each 600ml (1 pt) of juice. Stir until sugar has been dissolved.
5. Bring to the boil and boil rapidly until setting point is reached.
6. Skim, pour into warmed jars. Cover, label and date.

BLACKBERRY AND APPLE JELLY

Make as for apple jelly above, using half blackberries (hulled and washed) and half apples.

MARMALADE

900g (2lb) Seville oranges

Juice of 2 lemons

2.3 litres (4 pt) water

1.8kg (4lb) sugar

1. Wash oranges well, peel, remove some pith, if wished, and shred peel.
2. Chop flesh roughly; tie pips and some pith in muslin.
3. Put flesh, water, peel and pips into a bowl and steep

overnight, if possible, as this helps to speed up the softening of the peel.

4. Pour steeping ingredients into a preserving pan and simmer gently for 1½-2 hours, until peel is quite soft and liquid is reduced by half.
5. Remove bag of pips, squeezing well. Add warmed sugar and stir until dissolved.
6. Bring to the boil and boil rapidly until setting point is reached (about 15 minutes). Skim.
7. Stand for 10-15 minutes. Pour into warmed jars. Cover, label and date.

PRESSURE COOKER MARMALADE

Ingredients as for marmalade above, using half the quantity of water, i.e. 1.2 litre (2 pt)

1. Prepare fruit as for marmalade above. Put flesh, water, peel and pips (tied in muslin) into pressure cooker, without trivet.
2. Pressure-cook for 10 minutes at 10lb (medium) pressure.
3. Reduce pressure at room temperature.
4. (It may be necessary to change to a larger saucepan at this stage.) Remove pips, add warmed sugar and stir until dissolved.
5. Bring to the boil, and boil rapidly until setting point is reached. Skim.
6. Stand for 10 minutes. Stir, pot, label and date.

Note: Using a pressure cooker speeds up the fruit softening stage of jam-making.

- Remove trivet.
- Never have pressure cooker more than half full. If necessary, the amount of water may be further reduced and added later.
- Cook at 10 lb (medium) pressure.
- Reduce pressure at room temperature. Never attempt to force lid.

CHUTNEYS AND PICKLES

Pickles and chutneys are chemical methods of preservation in which substances are added which inhibit the growth of micro-organisms. These substances include sugar, salt and vinegar.

PRINCIPLE OF CHUTNEY AND PICKLE MAKING

- The chutney is boiled at 100°C. This destroys micro-organisms.
- The large amount of vinegar reduces pH so that micro-organisms cannot survive.
- The high concentration of sugar/salt causes water to pass from bacterial cell by osmosis, thus destroying bacteria.

1. CHUTNEYS

Chutney is a sweet pickle. It usually consists of a mixture of vegetables and fruit cooked in vinegar and flavoured with sugar and spices. Chutneys are served with cold or hot meats and cheeses, and are included in many recipes such as curries.

A chutney should have a thick, jam-like consistency, a mellow flavour and a good colour. Chutneys should not be eaten soon after making as they improve by being kept for at least 3 months to mellow.

APPLE CHUTNEY

(Yield: 2.75kg/6lb approximately)
1.5kg (3lb) cooking apples
1.5kg (3lb) onions
450g (1lb) sultanas or raisins
½ teasp. mixed spice
1-2 lemons
700g (1½ lb) brown sugar
600ml (1 pt) malt vinegar

1. Peel, core and chop apples. Peel and chop onions.
2. Put apples, onions, sultanas and spice into saucepan.
3. Grate lemon rind, strain juice and add each to chutney with sugar and vinegar.
4. Stir until sugar is dissolved, bring to the boil and simmer gently until mixture has a thick jam-like consistency.
5. Pour into warmed jars and cover with special synthetic skin covers — cellophane jam covers are unsuitable.
6. Store for a few months before using.

GREEN TOMATO CHUTNEY

(Yield: 1.5kg/3¼lb approximately)
450g (1lb) green tomatoes
225g (8oz) onions
225g (8oz) raisins
2 small pieces of dried root ginger
350g (12oz) brown sugar
1 banana
15g (½oz) salt
1 teasp. cayenne pepper
700ml (1¼ pt) vinegar

1. Wash and chop tomatoes. Peel and chop onions. Peel and chop banana.
2. Put above ingredients, ginger and raisins into pan. Cover and simmer until tomatoes are soft.
3. Stir in spices, sugar and vinegar and simmer gently until thick.
4. Pour into warmed jars. Cover, label and date.

2. PICKLES

A pickle is a preserve of fruit or vegetables in vinegar with sugar, salt and spices added. The ingredients are first salted for 1-2 days.

The vinegar used for pickling should have a minimum acetic acid content of 5%. Distilled (clear) or malt (brown) vinegar may be used. These are first 'spiced' to improve the flavour. Wine or cider vinegars may also be used, but these are more expensive.

SPICED VINEGAR

1 litre vinegar

About 4 teasp. picking spice *or*

1 teasp. cloves	1 teasp. peppercorns
1 teasp. whole allspice	¼ teasp. cinnamon
1 blade of mace	

Infuse all ingredients in a bottle for 1-2 months, shaking occasionally. Or, if required quickly, put all ingredients into a saucepan and bring slowly to the boil. Cover, turn off heat and allow to stand for at least one hour.

In either case, strain vinegar and use hot or cold.

MIXED PICKLE

Ingredients: a mixture of vegetables such as cauliflower, onions, cucumber, French beans.

1. Wash vegetables, peel onion and cut into fairly small pieces. Place vegetables in layers in a tall container, sprinkling salt between the layers (or soak in brine — 50g (2oz) to 50ml (1 pt) water). Leave for 24 hours.
2. Rinse vegetables thoroughly. Pack into sterilised jars. Cover with cold spiced vinegar and seal with melted wax or synthetic skin tops. Allow flavour to develop for 1-3 months before use.

DRYING (DEHYDRATION)

UNDERLYING PRINCIPLE

Both enzymes and micro-organisms need moisture to survive. If water is evaporated from the cells of food — as it is when drying — the salt and sugar concentration is increased and water passes from the cells of the micro-organisms by *osmosis* (in an attempt to equalise the concentration). This causes micro-organisms to become dehydrated and to die.

Even the small amount of moisture present in dried foods, however, may still support enzyme action. It is therefore necessary to *blanch* certain foods such as vegetables before drying them to destroy enzymes.

HOME-DRYING

Home-drying may be carried out in a very low oven, a hot press or even a warm kitchen. Herbs may be tied in bundles and hung upside down in a warm place such as the hot press for a few days.

► COMMERCIAL PRESERVATION

1. COMMERCIAL DEHYDRATION

In the past, and still today in countries with suitable climates, many foods like raisins were dried in the sun. As this is unhygienic, it has been superseded almost completely by air drying.

HOT AIR DRYING

Fruit and vegetables are prepared, blanched if necessary, and chopped. The food passes through a tunnel of hot air, on a perforated conveyor belt, until moisture content is reduced to 5-10%.

FREEZE DRYING (2-3% WATER)

Freeze drying was formerly called accelerated freeze drying. This is a combination of freezing and drying. The food is first frozen quickly (-30°C) to create small ice crystals in the food cells. It then passes into a vacuum chamber where the ice crystals are *sublimated* (they change from solid to vapour without passing through the liquid state), under moderate heat. This results in a honeycomb of empty cells producing a lightweight food. Freeze dried food is easy to pack, transport and store. It is quickly reconstituted and superior in flavour and nutritive value to normal dried food.

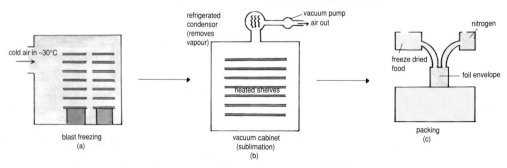

Freeze drying

ROLLER DRYING
Used to dehydrate milk, potato flakes and breakfast cereals (see page 58).

SPRAY DRYING
Used to dehydrate milk, eggs (see page 58).

EFFECTS OF DEHYDRATION ON FOOD VALUE
Dehydration results in some loss of vitamins A, B_1 and total loss of vitamin C. Less loss occurs when food is freeze dried.

■ CAKE MIXES
These consist of a mixture of ingredients such as flour, raising agent, fat, dried milk, caster sugar, and in some cases, dried pasteurised eggs. These are blended together with additives such as colourings, flavourings, emulsifiers, preservatives and anti-staling agents. It is essential that the moisture content is sufficiently low to prevent deterioration by micro-organisms and enzymes.

After weighing, ingredients are sieved, blended and aerated before being packed into vapour-proof envelopes or cartons. This prevents contamination or rehydration.

To use: Follow directions exactly, moistening as directed with egg, milk or water. Use as a basis for other dishes such as Eve's pudding and pizza.

1. Mixes are quick and easy to use. They are ideal for beginners.
2. They usually work out to be more expensive than fresh ingredients.
3. The taste, texture and volume are rarely up to expected standards.
4. These products also contain a great number of additives.

■ DEHYDRATED SOUPS, SAUCES AND CASSEROLE MIXES

MANUFACTURE
1. Meat, vegetables and other ingredients are tested and checked for quality.
2. Meat is steamed and minced. Vegetables are diced and blanched.
3. Fat and extractives from meat are concentrated and, with meat, are dried by hot air. Vegetables are dried separately.
4. Cereals, flour etc. are dehydrated to reduce moisture content.
5. Batches of soup/sauce are made by blending ingredients together in carefully controlled amounts.
6. Seasonings, flavourings and other additives are mixed in.
7. Samples are tested.
8. Mixture passes into filling machines which measure the exact amount into foil envelopes. These are then sealed.

FOOD VALUE
When reconstituted, the food value of dehydrated soups, sauces and casserole mixes is lower than that of a freshly-made soup or sauce. There is considerable loss of vitamin B_1 and, probably, a total loss of vitamin C. There is also some loss of vitamin A and other B vitamins. Calorific value is high. Milk, when added to sauces, increases food value.

EVALUATION
Dehydrated soups and sauces are quick to prepare and cook. They are easy to store and handy in emergencies. Like all dried foods, they contain several additives such as monosodium glutamate. Costs vary. Some packed soups such as asparagus soup would be cheaper than the home-made variety. Others like chicken broth are more expensive.

Home-made products are more nourishing, taste better and contain no mystery additives.

2. COMMERCIAL FREEZING
As this is carried out at below -30°C, the ice crystals formed are very small. Vegetables must first be blanched to inactivate enzymes.
- *Air blast freezing:* Food passes through a refrigerated tunnel on a conveyor belt while a blast of very cold (–30°C) air is blown over it. It is used for most commercial freezing.
- *Contact or plate freezing* is used to freeze flat pieces of meat and fish quickly. The food is packed, then placed between refrigerated shelves which touch it top and bottom. The food freezes in about 30 minutes.
- *Flow freezing* is similar to air blast freezing. Food has freezing air blown from underneath which keeps food 'on the move' and prevents it from sticking together. Used for peas, sweet corn etc.
- *Spray freezing:* Liquid brine or syrup is sprayed over food before packaging.
- *Immersion freezing:* Large, awkward shapes including chickens and fish are frozen by this method. Food is immersed in freezing brine.
- *Cyrogenic freezing:* Delicate foods such as prawns and strawberries are immersed in or sprayed with liquid nitrogen. Food is frozen within 30 seconds and results are very good, but it is an expensive method of freezing.

3. COMMERCIAL BOTTLING AND CANNING
The principle of bottling and canning (page 123) is a cheap and successful method of preserving food commer-

cially. Higher temperatures are used and strictly monitored to ensure safe preservation of food, including vegetable and protein foods. Food is prepared, blanched, cooked if necessary and filled into bottles or lacquered cans (for acid fruit). Syrup, sauce or brine is poured in. Air is removed. The cans are hermetically sealed. Cans are then sterilised for the required time, and cooled quickly.

Aseptic canning involves using ultra-high temperatures for a short time. This results in less loss of nutrients, colour and flavour.

Note: Leaking, dented, rusty or blown cans should never be used as there is a danger of serious contamination by food poisoning bacteria.

4. CHEMICAL PRESERVATION OF FOOD
Certain substances are used to preserve food because their presence inhibits the growth of bacteria.

UNDERLYING PRINCIPLE
The chemical dissolves in the water content of the food, forming a concentrated solution. Water from the bacterial cell passes into the food cells through the semi-permeable cell walls by the process of *osmosis* in an attempt to equalise the concentration. This dehydrates the bacteria present, eventually destroying them.

Some preservatives such as vinegar work by creating conditions unfavourable to microbial growth — a low pH, for example.

TRADITIONAL PRESERVATIVES
- *Salt* is used to preserve or 'cure' meat or vegetables — for example, bacon, corned beef, pickles etc.
- *Sugar*: Micro-organisms cannot survive a sugar concentration of 65% or higher. If too little sugar is used, moulds will grow and fermentation will take place. Too much sugar causes crystallisation.
- *Vinegar*: This contains acetic acid which lowers the pH of food to 2.7 — a level in which micro-organisms cannot survive. Pickles, chutney and ketchup contain high concentrations of vinegar.
- *Alcohol*: This contains ethanol, a substance which denatures the protein in food and destroys micro-organisms.

salt   sugar   vinegar   alcohol   smoking

Natural preservatives

- *Smoking*: Cured meat or fish is subjected to fumes from smoking wood which impregnate the outer layers with concentrated tars, phenols and aldehydes — all of which inhibit bacterial growth (see page 55).

PERMITTED PRESERVATIVES
1. sulphur dioxide
2. benzoic acid
3. sorbic acid
4. nisin
5. phenyls
6. potassium salts

Health regulations in this country permit the use of certain substances which 'inhibit, retard or arrest the deterioration of food caused by micro-organisms'.

The most commonly-used preservative is sulphur dioxide which is used in sausages, preserved fruit and vegetables. Other permitted preservatives are benzoic and sorbic acid, both of which lower the pH of food to a level unfavourable to micro-organisms. Gases such as nitrogen or CO_2 may be used when packing food in order to prevent oxidation and spoilage.

5. FOOD IRRADIATION
This is the process of using ionising radiation to preserve food, chiefly by destroying the micro-organisms. The food itself does not become radioactive. The food is sterilised in its container, thus eliminating the possibility of recontamination.

EFFECTS
1. It kills harmful micro-organisms.
2. It prolongs shelf life.
3. It kills insects and other pests in grains etc.
4. It delays ripening.
5. It prevents vegetables and cereals from sprouting.

ADVANTAGES
Irradiation, if properly carried out, can:
1. Prolong shelf life of many foods.
2. Reduce incidences of food-borne diseases.
3. Reduce the necessity for certain food additives and chemical treatments.
4. Make tropical foods more readily available.
5. Ease world food shortages by reducing spoilage and waste.
6. Provide sterile food for hospitals etc.

POSSIBLE DISADVANTAGES
1. It is impossible to know whether food has been irradiated or how much radiation has been used.
2. Certain micro-organisms may survive low level irradiation and may multiply unhindered in the almost sterile environment.

3. It is unsuitable for fatty foods — it damages some polyunsaturates.
4. There is some vitamin loss due to irradiation.
5. Even scientists are not certain about long-term effects.
6. Irradiation may be used to disguise bad manufacturing techniques or to sterilise food which has begun to go off.
7. There is a possibility of developing highly resistant micro-organisms.
8. There is a danger of using radioactive materials in processing plants.

Food safety committees in several countries, as well as an international committee of food experts (JECFI), have studied the whole area of food irradiation. They state that, subject to strict controls and up to a certain radiation level, irradiation is safe for preserving food.

Clear labelling of irradiated foods is considered very important. One of the labels currently used to identify irradiated food is shown here.

7 HUMAN PHYSIOLOGY

► INTRODUCTION

All living things are composed of small units called *cells*. The human body consists of millions of cells which vary considerably in shape. Some are long and tightly-packed together, as those in the muscles. Other cells are oval or round.

The outer layer of each cell is called the *cell membrane*. The cell is filled with a jelly-like liquid called *cytoplasm* in which are suspended various structures, including the nucleus. The *nucleus*, which is the life-centre of the cell, controls growth and cell division.

Other cell structures, called *organelles*, include:

- *endoplasmic reticulum*
- *ribosomes* } involved in protein synthesis
- *mitochondria* which are involved in energy production
- *vacuoles*: bubbles in the cytoplasm which may contain nutrients or waste.

Animals and plants grow and reproduce by cell division (*mitosis*).

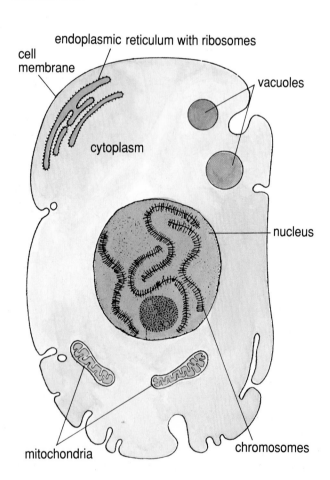

Basic structure of an animal cell

CELLS

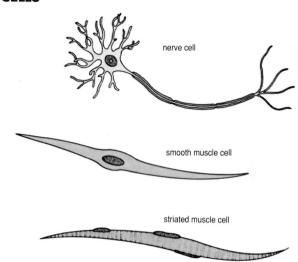

TISSUES

Groups of similar cells involved in a particular function are called *tissues*. There are four main types of tissue.

CONNECTIVE TISSUE

This forms the framework, connecting and supporting tissues of the body. Here are some examples of connective tissue.

- *Cartilage* covers ends of bones and forms part of the nose and ears.
- *Tendons and ligaments* connect muscle to bone. These contain collagen and elastin.
- *Elastic tissue* is found in arteries, stomach, bladder and lung tissue.
- *Adipose tissue* acts as a storage area for energy (fat) reserves. It forms an insulating layer under the skin and protects delicate organs.
- *Blood and bone* are also forms of connective tissue.

EPITHELIAL TISSUE

This consists of thin, flat sheets of cells. It is found on the skin, and the lining and outer membranes of many organs, reducing friction between surfaces and keeping them moist.

Many epithelial cells produce secretions. Examples include those in salivary glands and mucous membranes.

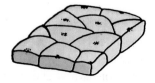

Epithelial tissue

NERVOUS TISSUE

The brain and spinal cord are mainly composed of nervous tissue. This consists of cells with long, branched extensions which carry impulses to other tissues.

MUSCULAR TISSUE

Muscle is necessary for all movements of the body, both voluntary and involuntary. There are three types of muscle.

1. *Voluntary muscle* is also called skeletal or striated muscle. This is the muscle in the limbs and trunk which forms the fleshy parts of the body. It is called voluntary muscle because it is under the control of the will — we decide whether to walk or move an arm. Voluntary muscle consists of tightly-packed bundles of parallel, multinucleated cells or fibres bound together with connective tissue. Each fibre is covered with visible stripes, consisting of thick and thin filaments. Movement occurs when muscles contract — when the filaments slide over each other, shortening the fibres.

2. *Involuntary muscle* is also called smooth muscle. This is found in the walls of hollow organs which need to contract, such as those of the alimentary canal, the bladder and the uterus. It is also found in blood vessels. Involuntary muscle consists of sheets of

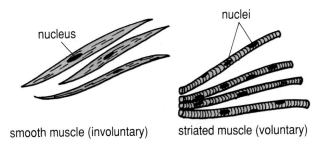

smooth muscle (involuntary)   striated muscle (voluntary)

cardiac muscle (branched)

spindle-shaped cells, each containing one nucleus. It has no striations and is very elastic. It is not under voluntary control and its contractions are long and slow.

3. *Cardiac muscle* is present only in the heart walls. It consists of short, irregularly-striated fibres, similar to voluntary muscle but with some branching between the fibres. It is largely under its own control, being neither a voluntary muscle nor a truly involuntary muscle.

► THE CIRCULATORY SYSTEM

This consists of
- the heart — which acts as a pump
- the blood vessels — which transport blood
- the blood — the medium of transport

THE HEART

The heart is a strong, muscular organ consisting of cardiac muscle (see above). It acts as a pump which forces blood all around the body, without stopping, for the lifetime of the individual.

POSITION

The heart is situated in the centre of the thorax towards the front. It lies between the two lungs, resting on the diaphragm. It is protected in front by the sternum and at the sides and back by the rib cage.

SHAPE

The heart is a pear-shaped hollow organ about the size of its owner's fist. Its widest part, called the base, is uppermost, while the apex, or narrow end, is pointing downwards and to the left.

STRUCTURE

- The heart consists of four chambers, with a central wall (*septum*) dividing the right side from the left side. There is no connection between the two sides. The right side of the heart contains only impure or deoxygenated blood, the left side having only oxygenated or pure blood.

- Each side is subdivided into an upper and lower chamber. The upper chambers, called *auricles or atria*, have thin walls and receive the blood coming into the heart. The lower chambers, called *ventricles*, have thick, muscular walls which pump blood out from the heart.

- A one-way valve, called the *tricuspid valve*, separates the right auricle from the right ventricle. A similar valve, called the *mitral or bicuspid valve*, separates the left auricle and left ventricle. Both consist of flaps (*tri* = three; *bi* = two) held in position by tiny tendons which prevent the blood from flowing backwards into the auricles.

- The outside of the heart is protected by a smooth membrane called the *pericardium* which helps prevent friction when it beats. The heart is lined with a similar membrane called the *endocardium*.

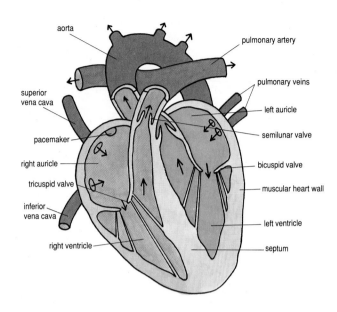

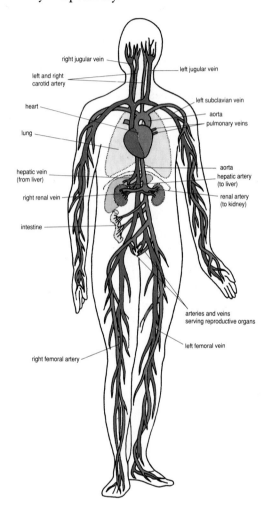

Circulatory system

THE CIRCULATORY SYSTEM

Every cell of the body requires a continual supply of oxygen and nutrients. The blood is the medium which distributes these to the cells. It also collects waste products, such as CO_2 and urea, for removal by the lungs and kidneys respectively.

THE BLOOD-VESSELS OF THE HEART

1. *The superior and inferior venae cavae* are large veins which return deoxygenated (impure) blood from the body tissues. The superior vena cava brings blood from the head, neck and arms, while the inferior vena cava brings blood back from the trunk, digestive organs and legs. Both superior and inferior venae cavae open into the right auricle.

2. *The pulmonary artery* is a large blood vessel which carries impure blood from the right ventricle to the lungs, where it is purified. A semi-lunar valve controls the entrance to this artery. After it leaves the heart, the pulmonary artery divides in two, with one branch going to each lung.

3. *Pulmonary veins* return oxygenated (pure) blood from the lungs to the left auricle of the heart, two pulmonary veins come from the right lung, and two from the left lung.

4. *The aorta* is a strong elastic artery which is the largest in the body. It pumps bright red oxygenated blood from the left auricle to the tissues of the body. Its opening is also guarded by a semi-lunar valve.

5. *The coronary arteries:* Just before the aorta leaves the left ventricle, two small arteries, the coronary arteries, branch out to form a network of blood vessels supplying the heart tissues with oxygenated blood. Two veins collect deoxygenated blood from the heart muscle and empty it into the right auricle.

Atherosclerosis: This occurs when the coronary arteries become coated with fatty deposits such as cholesterol, which make it difficult for the blood to pass through them. If a large blood vessel becomes blocked, a heart attack occurs, which may be fatal.

Heart circulation is a double system
A. Pulmonary Circulation: Heart ⟶ Lungs ⟶ Heart
B. Systemic Circulation: Heart ➤ Around body ➤ Heart

PULMONARY

1. The superior and inferior venae cavae empty deoxygenated blood from the whole body, with the exception of the lungs, into the right auricle.

2. The right auricle contracts, forcing blood through the tricuspid valve into the right ventricle.

3. The right ventricle contracts and forces the blood through the pulmonary artery to the lungs, where it is purified.

4. The pure, oxygenated blood returns from the lungs to the left auricle through four pulmonary veins.

SYSTEMIC

1. The left auricle contracts, forcing the blood downwards through the bicuspid valve into the left ventricle.
2. The left ventricle now contracts and the blood is pumped out of the heart through the aorta, which brings it all around the body.
3. Branching from the aorta, just after it leaves the heart, are three branches — one going to the head and one to each arm. The main branch of the aorta passes down behind the heart, bringing oxygenated blood to the tissues of the trunk.
4. A branch or artery passes into each organ, or area of tissue. It then breaks into smaller branches (arterioles) and becomes smaller and smaller. Eventually these tiny branches, called capillaries, form a network in every part of the body. Here oxygen and nutrients pass out into the cells, and the capillaries take up the waste products of cell metabolism (urea, CO_2).

The capillaries join up to form tiny veins which combine to form larger veins, eventually emptying into the inferior (or superior) vena cava. These flow into the right auricle and the circuit begins again.

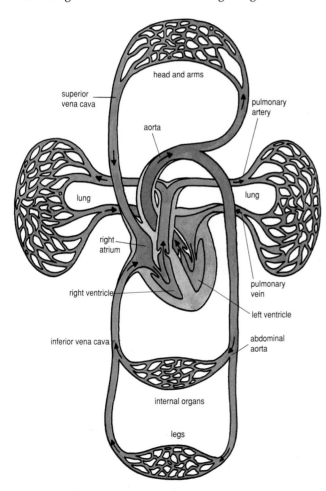

Diagrammatic representation of circulation

HEARTBEAT

The heartbeat is brought about by contraction (*systole*) and relaxation (*diastole*) of the heart muscle.

1. Blood flows into both auricles, causing pressure in them to rise.
2. Both auricles contract, forcing tri/bicuspid valves to open. Blood flows into the ventricles.
3. Both ventricles contract. This closes tri/bicuspid valves and opens semi-lunar valves.
4. The blood is forced upward through the pulmonary artery and aorta and out of the heart.
5. Relaxation (diastole) of auricles and ventricles follows each contraction.

FACTORS AFFECTING HEARTBEAT

Normal contractions of the heart are brought about by electrical impulses. These are created by special muscle cells in the right auricle called the *pacemaker*. This causes the muscle in the auricles to contract, which in turn stimulates another specialised group of cells (the *atrio-ventricular node*).

Heartbeat occurs about 72 times per minute — this can be checked by taking the 'pulse'. Abnormalities can be detected by an electrocardiogram (ECG).

Changes in the speed of heartbeat are affected by:

- The *medulla oblongata* in the brain — the accelerator nerves speed up heartbeat, while the vagus nerves slow it down.
- Age and body size affect heart-rate. An infant's heart, for example, beats faster than an adult's.
- Activity, exercise and excitement (which causes adrenalin to flow) increase the rate.
- Stimulant drugs can increase the rate, while depressants decrease it.

PULSE

This is the rhythmic increase in blood flow caused by the pumping action of the heart. The pulse may be measured by applying pressure to an artery near the surface of the skin, such as at the wrist, where a throb or pulse can be felt.

BLOOD PRESSURE

This is the force of pressure which the blood exerts against the arterial walls. It can be measured on a mercury scale. Normal blood pressure is shown as a fraction such as 120/80 — 120 is the strong pressure during systole; 80 is the weaker pressure during diastole which raises the mercury only 80mm on the pressure gauge.

FACTORS INFLUENCING BLOOD PRESSURE

1. Cardiac output — the volume of blood pumped by each heartbeat.
2. Resistance to the blood flow provided by the arteries.

High blood pressure or *hypertension* occurs when there is an increased resistance to blood flow. This may be temporary — being caused by excitement or stress — or more permanent, when the blood vessels become lined with deposits which narrow the bore of the vessels. High blood pressure can be helped by a low salt diet and a more easy-going lifestyle,

BLOOD VESSELS OF THE BODY

As the blood circulates around the body, it passes through three types of blood vessel. The structure of each blood vessel varies, according to its function:

Arteries: Capillaries: Veins

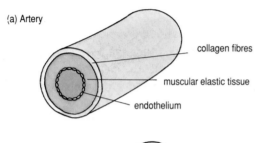

(a) Artery
- collagen fibres
- muscular elastic tissue
- endothelium

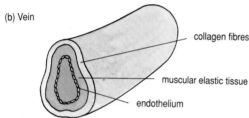

(b) Vein
- collagen fibres
- muscular elastic tissue
- endothelium

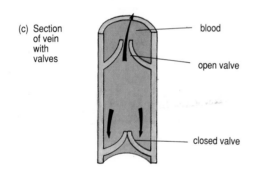

(c) Section of vein with valves
- blood
- open valve
- closed valve

(d) Capillary
- single layer of endothelial cells

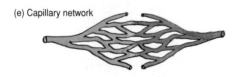

(e) Capillary network

Structure of blood vessels

ARTERIES

These are large blood vessels which carry blood *away* from the heart. They have thick walls, consisting of:
- an outer fibrous coat
- a thick layer of muscular elastic tissue
- an inner lining of endothelium

The elasticity of arterial walls, which is greatest nearest the heart, enables them to expand with each surge of blood pumping from the heart. Arteries divide into smaller branches (arterioles), which in turn form smaller and smaller branches, until they penetrate every portion of body tissue. Arteries carry oxygenated blood (exception — pulmonary arteries).

CAPILLARIES

These are tiny blood vessels which connect arteries with veins. Their walls are just one cell thick, consisting of endothelium. Water, oxygen and small molecules of digested nutrients can diffuse through the thin walls into the cells where cellular respiration takes place. The waste products pass back into the capillaries to be removed from the body. The blood in the capillaries, now dark in colour due to its CO_2 content, flows into tiny veins (venules).

VEINS

These are blood vessels which *return* blood to the heart from the tissues. They have the same three layers as arteries but thinner walls and a wider bore, the latter a factor which assists the return flow of blood to the heart. As the blood in veins has lost much of its force and is flowing against gravity, valves are present in the veins of the limbs to prevent a backward flow. Muscular contraction also assists the upward flow of blood by squeezing against the veins. Veins carry deoxygenated blood (exception — pulmonary veins).

THE BLOOD

Blood is a red liquid tissue, consisting of 55% fluid (plasma) and 45% solids — mainly cells. The average adult has five to six litres of blood. The blood is the principal medium of transport in the body. It carries oxygen and nutrients to the cells and collects waste products for excretion.

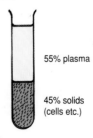

- 55% plasma
- 45% solids (cells etc.)

Composition of blood

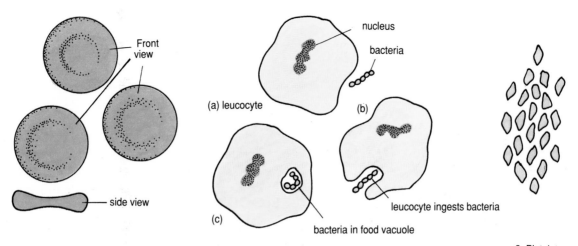

1. Red cells

(a) leucocyte

nucleus

bacteria

(b)

(c)

bacteria in food vacuole

leucocyte ingests bacteria

2. White cells

3. Platelets

PLASMA

This is a pale yellow fluid in which are dissolved many substances:

- Nutrients such as amino acids, lipids, glucose, mineral elements.
- Important proteins such as hormones, enzymes, antibodies and fibrinogen.
- Red cells, white cells and platelets.
- Sodium bicarbonate which keeps the blood alkaline.

Plasma itself consists of 90% water and 10% other substances, mainly protein.

RED BLOOD CELLS (ERYTHROCYTES)

These are minute concave discs which have no nuclei. They are formed in great numbers in the bone marrow. They contain the pigment *haemoglobin* which has the ability to pick up oxygen in the lungs to be carried to every cell. Red cells are soft and very flexible so that they can squeeze along the tiny capillaries. As they are easily damaged by this friction, they have a short life-span of 3-4 months. After that, they are broken down in the spleen and bone marrow into their components — the iron-rich haem and the protein, *globin* — and are then recycled.

The protein is used to make new cells and some of the iron passes to the liver where its pigments colour the bile. Most of the iron returns to the bone marrow to be made into more haemoglobin. Vitamins B_{12} and folic acid are necessary for the manufacture of haemoglobin.

HAEMOGLOBIN

This is a large and complex protein. Its importance in the blood is due to its ability to combine readily with oxygen. Haemoglobin absorbs oxygen in the lung capillaries to form *oxyhaemoglobin*, which makes the blood bright red in colour. In the tissues it releases this oxygen for combustion (cellular respiration). *Anaemia* occurs when the blood contains a reduced amount of haemoglobin.

WHITE BLOOD CELLS (LEUCOCYTES)

White cells or corpuscles are larger than red cells. Unlike red cells, white cells contain a nucleus. The blood has fewer white cells — there are over 500 red cells to each white one — although the number of white cells increases during infection. White cells have a very short life, lasting a maximum of 14 days. They are constantly moving about and changing shape. They can squeeze through capillary walls to fight invading micro-organisms. White blood cells are made in the bone marrow, spleen and lymph nodes.

There are several types of white cell which vary according to the shape of their nucleus. They include:

- *Lymphocytes:* These secrete proteins, called *antibodies*, which inactivate foreign molecules, called *antigens*.
- *Phagocytes:* These engulf and destroy invading bacteria.

The principal function of the white blood cells is to fight infection — pus on the site of a wound contains millions of dead white cells.

PLATELETS (THROMBOCYTES)

These are the smallest blood cells. They are, in fact, cell fragments produced from large cells in bone marrow. They are an important factor in blood clotting.

BLOOD CLOTTING

Blood does not clot in healthy blood vessels. Yet clotting is essential when blood vessels are cut or damaged, thus preventing death from loss of blood. As blood flows from a cut blood vessel, the damaged cells and platelets release an enzyme known as *thromboplastin* — made up of several factors which are not fully understood by science.

In the presence of *calcium*, thromboplastin converts *prothrombin* (a protein in the blood) to *thrombin*. Thrombin converts *fibrinogen* (a soluble protein in plasma) to insoluble stringy *fibrin*. This forms a network around the wound in which red cells and platelets are trapped. The *clot* formed in this way seals the opening and stops

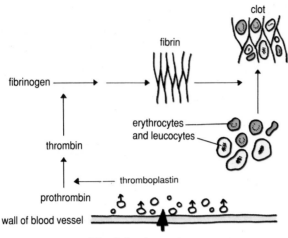

Blood clot formation

bleeding. This dries to form a *scab* which protects the wound while new cells form beneath.

- *Serum:* Plasma minus its fibrinogen.
- *Haemophilia:* A disease which usually affects males. It is caused by a deficiency of some of the plasma protein factors required for blood clotting.
- *Thrombosis:* when clots are formed within blood vessels.
- *Coronary thrombosis:* a blockage of a coronary artery due to blood clotting.

FUNCTIONS OF THE BLOOD

The blood is the principal medium of transport in the body.

1. *Oxygen transport:* Haemoglobin picks up oxygen in the lungs and carries it to the tissues for combustion.
2. *Carbon dioxide transport:* The blood collects carbon dioxide, following combustion (cell respiration), and carries it in the plasma to the lungs for excretion.
3. *Transport of food and chemicals:* Digested foods such as glucose and amino acids, pass into the capillaries of the small intestine and are carried by the portal vein to the liver and from there into the general circulation. Important proteins such as hormones and enzymes are also distributed by the blood.
4. *Transport of waste:* Toxic wastes from cell respiration, (for example, urea) are carried to the kidneys for excretion.
5. *Temperature control:* Heat generated by metabolism is distributed evenly by the blood. By constriction or dilation of blood vessels near the skin surface, the body may be kept warm or cooled (see page 152).
6. *Prevention of infection* by the action of white cells.
7. *Homeostasis* is the maintenance of correct balance of chemicals in the blood in order to provide the necessary environment for metabolism — for example, oxygen, pH, temperature.

SUMMARY OF BLOOD FUNCTIONS

1. Transport of oxygen
2. Transport of waste materials — carbon dioxide and urea
3. Temperature control
4. Transport of nutrients
5. Distribution of hormones and enzymes
6. Prevention of infection
7. Homeostasis — maintenance of ideal environment

BLOOD GROUPS

Not all people have similar blood. Factors may be present which could have fatal results if incompatible blood groups were mixed.

Antigens which may be present on the surface of the red blood cells of some people determine their blood group. Antigens are placed in two groups, A and B.

- Some people have antigen A in their red cells — they belong to blood group A.
- Some people have antigen B in their red cells — they belong to blood group B.
- A few people have both antigens — blood group AB.
- The largest number of people have neither antigen and belong to blood group O.

Blood also contains antibodies which would clump and destroy the red cells containing the matching antigen — that is, an antibody is never present in the same blood as its related antigen.

If a person with A antibodies in his/her plasma receives blood from blood group A, the red blood cells of the donor's blood would clump in the recipient's body with fatal results.

The chart shows which blood groups can donate to whom.

Blood Group	Antigens present	Antibodies	Can donate to	Can receive from
A	A	anti-B	A,AB	O,A
B	B	anti-A	B,AB	O,B
AB	A and B	neither	AB	O,A,B,AB
O	none	anti-A and anti-B	A,B,AB,O	O

As group O blood cannot be clumped, it can be given to people of any blood group. It is known as the *universal donor*. Those with blood group AB are known as *universal recipients*, as they can receive any blood.

THE RHESUS FACTOR

Apart from the blood groups just explained, there is a separate group of antigens found in 85% of humans. It is called the *Rhesus factor*, after the Rhesus monkey in whose cells the antigens were first discovered. Those whose blood contains these antigens are Rhesus positive (Rh+); those without them are Rhesus negative (Rh-).

This factor used to cause problems during pregnancy when an Rh+ father and Rh– mother produced an Rh+ baby. This caused the mother's blood to develop Rh+ antibodies which could endanger the life of subsequent babies. It is now possible to inject the mother with a serum to prevent agglutination (clumping) in her baby's blood.

THE LYMPH SYSTEM

FORMATION OF LYMPH

Lymph begins in the intercellular spaces between the tissues. All the cells of the body are bathed by *tissue fluid* or *extracellular fluid* (ECF). This is formed when some plasma filters through the capillary walls, leaving its large protein molecules behind in the capillaries, and slowly circulates between the cells. This fluid contains nutrients and oxygen. These diffuse into the cells, while the cells pass their waste (CO_2 and urea) into the fluid.

Most of the fluid and its waste products pass back into the blood capillaries, but some drains into minute porous vessels which begin between the cells. These carry what is now called the *lymph* to larger vessels, most of which eventually empty into the main *thoracic duct*. The main thoracic duct passes up through the trunk and empties the lymph into the bloodstream at the left subclavian vein. The right lymphatic duct drains lymph from the right side of the upper part of the body into the right subclavian vein.

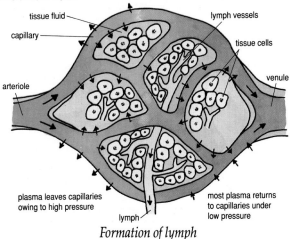

Formation of lymph

LYMPHATICS OR LYMPH VESSELS

Lymph vessels begin as blind-ended ducts between the cells and combine to form larger vessels (see above). Lymph vessels resemble veins, in that they depend on contraction of muscles to help the lymph along. Like veins, lymph vessels contain valves which prevent a backward flow. Lymph flows in one direction only — towards the neck.

LACTEALS

Lacteals are specialised lymph vessels present in the villi of the small intestine. They absorb digested fats which return to the general circulation with the lymph.

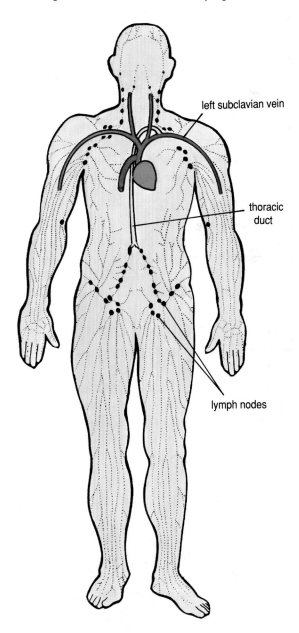

Position of lymph nodes in the body

LYMPH NODES GLANDS

Large lymph vessels have hundreds of lymph nodes or glands distributed at intervals throughout the body. They are numerous in the groin, abdomen, thorax, armpits and neck. Lymph nodes are composed of connective tissue. They contain special cells which engulf and destroy foreign bodies such as bacteria as they filter through the gland. A major infection may cause swelling (swollen glands) due to the activity of these cells. The tonsils, adenoids and spleen are composed of similar tissue.

Lymph nodes manufacture lymphocytes (white blood cells) which are involved in antibody production.

FUNCTIONS OF THE LYMPH

1. It is a medium of exchange between the blood and the cells.
2. It drains tissue spaces, returning plasma to the bloodstream, and thus helping to maintain homeostasis (correct internal environment).
3. It manufactures lymphocytes.
4. Lymph nodes reduce spread of infection by removing and destroying dangerous organisms.
5. Digested fats are absorbed and transported from the lacteals to the bloodstream.
6. Lymph is involved in the production of antibodies.

THE SPLEEN

The spleen is a small, spongy organ situated in the top left-hand corner of the abdomen, beside the stomach and under the diaphragm. It is composed of fibrous elastic tissue. The spleen is supplied with blood by the splenic artery; deoxygenated blood is removed by the splenic vein.

FUNCTIONS OF THE SPLEEN

1. It forms *red blood cells* in the foetus and, sometimes, in adults, if the spleen is diseased.
2. It *removes worn-out blood cells* by entangling them in its tissues, where they are broken down and recycled.
3. It *manufactures lymphocytes* which help to fight infection.
4. It *destroys bacteria* as they filter through in the bloodstream.

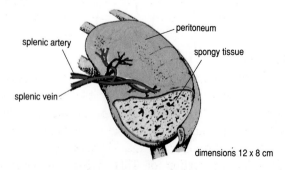

Structure of the spleen

THE ENDOCRINE SYSTEM

The main glands in the body can be classified as follows:

1. The *exocrine* or *ducted glands* which send their chemicals through ducts into the target organ nearby. Most of the glands of the digestive system are of this type.
2. The *endocrine* or *ductless glands* release their chemicals (hormones) directly into the blood flowing through the glands. These chemicals are carried by the blood through the body until they reach their target organs, where they cause changes to take place.

The endocrine system helps to control and to co-ordinate many body functions such as metabolism and reproduction. Its effects are often long-term — for example, growth, ageing. The chemical messengers are known as *hormones* (from a Greek word meaning 'to activate'). Normal, healthy glands regulate the amount of hormone they release to suit the requirements of the body — too much (*hypersecretion*) or too little (*hyposecretion*) can lead to disorders. Administration of the hormone will usually cure the latter problem.

The endocrine glands are:

1. Pituitary
2. Thyroid
3. Parathyroid
4. Adrenals
5. Islets of Langerhans
6. Gonads (testes, ovaries)

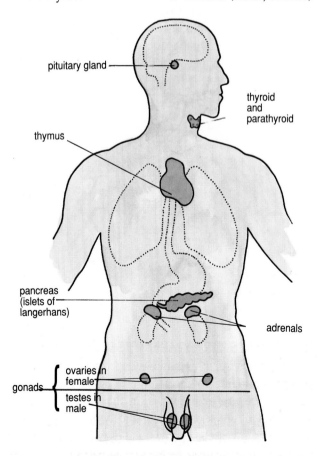

Position of endocrine glands

1. THE PITUITARY GLAND

This 'master' gland controls the activity of several other glands. It is a pea-sized structure at the base of the brain and is divided into two parts: the *anterior pituitary* and the *posterior pituitary*. The anterior pituitary secretes at least seven hormones.

(a) *Human growth hormone* (HGH) influences growth of cells. Too much causes giantism; too little causes dwarfism.

(b) *Thyroid-stimulating hormone* (TSH) stimulates the thyroid gland to secrete its hormone, thyroxine.

(c) *Adrenocorticotropic hormone* (ACTH) stimulates the adrenal cortex to release its hormones.

(d) *Luteinising hormone* (LH) stimulates production of sex hormones — progesterone in females and androgens in males.

(e) *Follicle-stimulating hormone* (FSH) acts on the gonads (sex organs). In females, it stimulates ripening of an ovum and oestrogen production. In males, it stimulates sperm production.

(f) *Lactogenic hormone* (LTH) stimulates milk production in females after birth.

(g) *Melanocyte-stimulating hormone* (MSH) affects the pigmentation of the skin.

Deficiency of all anterior pituitary hormones, due to disease of the gland, causes premature senility.

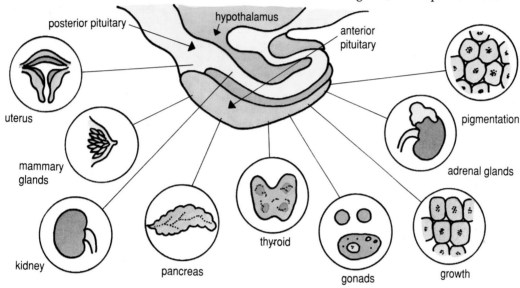

Target organs of the pituitary gland

The *posterior pituitary* secretes:

(a) *Oxytocin*, which stimulates contraction of the uterus in childbirth.

(b) *Antidiuretic hormone*, which controls water balance in urine and, therefore, in blood. Deficiency causes a form of diabetes — *diabetes insipidus*.

See chart over.

MORE ON INSULIN

Insulin controls carbohydrate metabolism and, therefore, the level of sugar in the blood. When blood sugar rises, insulin is released into the bloodstream. This hastens the conversion of glucose to glycogen, bringing the glucose level in blood back to normal.

DIABETES MELLITUS

Diabetes mellitus occurs due to lack of insulin. Because the extra glucose cannot be converted into glycogen and stored, large amounts stay in the blood and are excreted in urine (osmosis causes an increase in urine production). Protein and fat have to be converted to glucose when a

back-up supply of energy is required, depleting these reserves.

Excess insulin removes too much glucose from the blood, leaving the body with no energy source. Coma may result.

THYMUS GLAND

This is situated at the base of the neck. It is important in young children, as it helps fight infection by producing lymphocytes. When the thymus gland is damaged, growth is retarded and the child is susceptible to infection. From adolescence onwards, it shrinks and has no function.

FEEDBACK

Many hormones operate a self-regulating feedback system which prevents over-production of the hormone. For example, the thyroid-stimulating hormone (TSH) secreted by the pituitary gland stimulates the thyroid to produce its hormone, thyroxine. Thyroxine in the blood inhibits the production of TSH. When the level of thyroxine falls, the pituitary starts to produce TSH again.

Other Endocrine Glands

Gland	Position	Hormone	Effect	Hypersecretion (excess)	Hyposecretion (deficiency)
2. *Thyroid* — the largest endocrine gland	In the neck, in front of the trachea	Thyroxine	Controls rate of metabolism Controls growth in young	Raises metabolic rate. Thinness; sweating; Giantism Abnormal secretion causes enlargement of gland — causing goitre	Lowers metabolic rate: Obesity. Mental confusion. Dwarfism. Mental retardation in children (known as *cretinism*).
3. *Parathyroids* — 4 tiny glands	Embedded in back of thyroid in neck	Parathormone	Controls calcium level in blood	Excess causes a reduction of calcium. It is then taken from bones, making them brittle. Kidney stones.	Convulsions and muscular spasm known as *tetany* — can be fatal.
4. *Adrenal glands* (a) *Adrenal cortex*	They sit on top of each kidney. (outer layer)	1. Glucocorticoids including cortisone 2. Aldosterone 3. Sex hormones, e.g. androgens, oestrogen/pro-gesterone	1. Involved in metabolism of carbohydrate and laying down of glycogen in the liver. 2. Regulates salt/water balance in blood 3. Produce male/female characteristics in each person. (Both male and female hormones are present in both sexes.)	1. Cushing's disease (fat body & thin limbs) 2. Oedema (water retention) 3. Early sexual maturity. Causes male characteristics in women; the reverse in men.	Addison's disease: muscular weakness, apathy, weight loss; death, if not treated.
(b) *Adrenal medulla*	(Inside of gland)	Adrenaline Noradrenaline	Secreted in large quantities when body suffers fright or stress. Prepares body for 'fight or flight'; speeds up heartbeat and breathing; raises blood sugar, blood pressure, metabolism. Secreted soon after adrenaline. Increases blood pressure so that above reaction can be sustained.	Increased heartbeat and blood pressure	Rare
5. *Islets of Langerhans*	Make up 1-2% of pancreas, which is situated under the stomach	Insulin	Controls carbohydrate metabolism and level of blood sugar (see page 141).	Hyperinsulism. Low blood sugar; metabolism reduced; coma; death	High blood sugar Sugar in urine (Diabetes Mellitus) Thirst
6. *Gonads* (a) *Ovaries* (2) (female) (b) *Testes* (2) (male)	Inside the body in the base of the pelvis/abdomen Outside the body in the genital area	1. Oestrogen 2. Progesterone* Testosterone	Initiates changes at puberty, e.g. breast development, broadening of hips. Initiates and controls menstruation. Controls changes which occur during pregnancy and lactation. Controls sexual development and development of secondary male characteristics e.g. growth of hair on face and body; deepening of voice.		Interferes with menstrual cycle Miscarriage Possible sterility. Secondary characteristics may fail to develop.

THE RESPIRATORY SYSTEM

Oxygen is continuously required by the body in order to release energy for all body processes. The system whereby oxygen is taken into the body from the atmosphere and carbon dioxide is removed through the air passages and lungs is known as the *respiratory system* or *external respiration*. (Internal or cellular respiration which takes place in the cells is the complicated series of chemical changes involved in releasing energy from food.)

The respiratory system consists of:
1. *the respiratory tract* — the passages through which air passes when we breathe, including the lungs.
2. *the muscles* concerned with the mechanism of breathing.
3. *the centre in the brain* which controls breathing.

THE RESPIRATORY TRACT

This consists of the nose and mouth, the pharynx, the larynx, the trachea, bronchi and their branches within the lungs, the bronchioles.

- *The nose:* As air passes through the nose, it is warmed and filtered by the *cilia* — small hairs in the nose. Mucus secreted by the lining cells of the nose entraps dust and bacteria and moistens the air.

- *The mouth:* Breathing through the mouth is not as satisfactory as breathing through the nose, as the air is neither filtered nor 'conditioned'. This may cause in-flammation of air passages.

- *The pharynx:* This is a wide cavity at the back of the mouth. It divides into two passages: the *oesophagus* (gullet) and *trachea* (windpipe) in front. A muscular 'lid' — the *epiglottis* — closes over the trachea during swallowing to prevent food going down the 'wrong way'.

- *The larynx or voice box:* This is a wide area at the top of the trachea. The vocal cords stretch across it. As air passes through the vocal cords they vibrate, producing sound. Inflammation of the cords is known as *laryngitis*.

- *The trachea:* This is a hollow, muscular tube 10 cm long which is kept open by C-shaped rings of cartilage. Like the nose, the trachea secretes mucus and has hair-like projections which propel any excess mucus or foreign bodies upwards to the mouth. This substance, *sputum*, is usually infected with bacteria.

- *The bronchi:* The trachea divides into two branches — one bronchus entering each lung. The walls of the bronchi and the rings of cartilage become thinner as they pass farther into each lung. In each lung, they branch into *bronchioles*, smaller tubes which have no cartilage. They eventually end in bundles of *alveoli* (*air cells*) which have extremely thin walls.

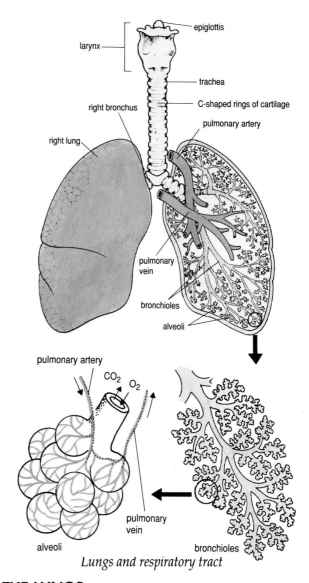

Lungs and respiratory tract

THE LUNGS

Position: The lungs almost fill the thoracic cavity, with the heart between them and the diaphragm beneath. They are enclosed by the rib cage and its intercostal muscles, with the backbone at the back.

Shape: The lungs are cone-shaped. The broad end or base sits on the diaphragm and the apex (pointed end) faces upwards.

Structure: Healthy lungs are a purplish-red in colour. They are covered by a double membrane called *pleura* which is lubricated to enable lungs to move freely.

The lungs are divided in folds or *lobes* — the right lung into three; the left one into two. The main blood vessels and the bronchi enter and leave at the *root* of the lung.

The lungs are composed of spongy, elastic tissue and contain *bronchi, bronchioles, air cells* (alveoli), *nerves, blood vessels* and *lymphatics* held together with *connective tissue*.

BLOOD CIRCULATION IN THE LUNGS

On leaving the heart, the pulmonary artery divides into two branches — one going to each lung. In the lung, they divide into smaller branches (arterioles). They gradually break up into capillaries which pass into every part of the lung tissue. The capillaries form a network around the air cells and exchange their carbon dioxide for oxygen (see below).

The capillaries, now containing bright red oxygenated blood, join up to form veins, and eventually form the four pulmonary veins which carry the oxygenated blood back to the heart from where it is pumped to the tissues.

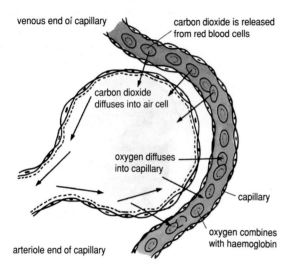

Exchange of gases in lungs

EXTERNAL RESPIRATION
(EXCHANGE OF GASES IN THE LUNGS)

The walls of the air cells and capillaries surrounding them each consist of a thin layer of *endothelial cells*. When air is breathed in, it passes through the air passages and fills the air cells. The air in the air cells has a high level of oxygen; the blood in the capillaries has a low concentration of oxygen. Because the walls of both air cells and capillaries are thin and *permeable*, the oxygen diffuses through the capillary walls to equalise the concentration. The haemoglobin in the red blood cells readily takes up the oxygen and brings it to the tissues.

The concentration of carbon dioxide in the lung capillaries is higher than that in the air cells. *Diffusion** of carbon dioxide takes place into the air cells and this 'stale' air is breathed out through the air passages.

INTERNAL RESPIRATION

This is also known as *cellular respiration*. It is part of the process whereby energy is released from the cell. When arterial capillaries bring blood to the tissues, the concentration of oxygen in them is high, while that in the cells is low, having been used up in energy production.

Oxygen diffuses* into the cells to equalise the concentration. The concentration of carbon dioxide in the cells is high and that in the blood capillaries is low. Carbon dioxide therefore diffuses from the cells into the capillaries. These return this deoxygenated blood to the heart via the superior and inferior venae cavae.

Diffusion: A gas moves from an area of high concentration or high pressure to one of lower concentration (low pressure) until the concentration is equal.

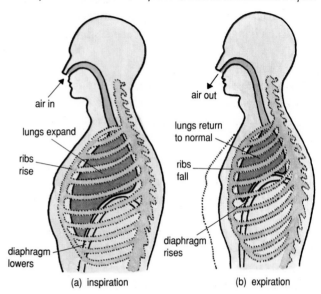

Mechanism of breathing

THE MUSCULAR MECHANISM OF BREATHING

The exchange of gases is brought about by muscular movements of the chest. These movements consist of:

1. *inspiration* or *breathing in*
2. *expiration* or *breathing out*

The thorax is an airtight cavity consisting of the rib cage and intercostal muscles with an arched muscle, the diaphragm, beneath. As we breathe in and out, the lungs, which are elastic, follow the movement of the rib cage.

1. *During inspiration:*
- The muscles of the diaphragm contract and flatten.
- The intercostal muscles contract, lifting the rib cage upwards and out.
- This increases the volume of the thoracic cavity, thus decreasing pressure in the lungs. As atmospheric pressure is greater, air rushes in to equalise it.
- The lungs, being elastic, fill up with air.

2. *During expiration:*
- The muscles of the diaphragm relax and it returns to its arched position.
- The intercostal muscles relax and the rib cage falls.
- This reduces the volume of the thoracic cavity, increasing the pressure.
- The air is forced out of the lungs.

RATE OF BREATHING

The amount of air taken into the lungs during normal breathing is called the *tidal volume*. It averages about 500 ml in an adult. The vital capacity of the lungs is the greater volume (up to 4 litres) taken in during deep breathing. The air remaining in the lungs at all times (1.2 litres) is known as *residual air*.

Adults breathe 15-20 times per minute. Children breathe faster. The rate of breathing is increased when necessary, as when exercise demands extra oxygen. Aerobic exercise can increase the vital capacity of the lungs. Respiratory diseases and smoking can reduce the efficiency of breathing and lead to oxygen shortage. This is particularly harmful during pregnancy.

NERVOUS CONTROL OF BREATHING

The *medulla oblongata* is the area of the brain controlling the breathing mechanism. Cells in this centre of the brain are sensitive to the concentration of carbon dioxide in the blood. When the level of carbon dioxide rises, as when a person runs, the medulla oblongata speeds up the rate of breathing. When carbon dioxide is low, as during sleep, the rate of breathing slows down.

The hormone, *adrenaline*, and sensitive nerves in the major arteries can also influence the rate of breathing by stimulating the medulla.

DISEASES OF THE RESPIRATORY ORGANS

These diseases include: tuberculosis (TB), pleurisy (infection of the pleurae), colds, sore throats, influenza, bronchitis (inflammation of the bronchi), pneumonia (caused by a virus or bacterium which causes an accumulation of mucus in the lungs); emphysema (alveoli walls break down, reducing the surface area through which gases may be exchanged); lung cancer (its main cause being cigarette smoking).

► THE DIGESTIVE SYSTEM

The food we eat cannot be used by the body cells until its molecules are broken down into smaller, soluble molecules. This is done by *digestion*:

1. *Physically**, for example, when food is chewed and churned about.

* See glossary.

2. *Chemically**, when chemicals called enzymes break the links between the large molecules with the addition of water. This process is called *hydrolysis* (from Greek, *hydro* = water; *lysis* = loosening).

A small area at the base of the brain, the *hypothalamus*, controls appetite. It initiates the feeling of hunger when glucose level is low.

- *Ingestion* involves taking food into the body — eating or drinking.
- The foods which must be digested before absorption can take place are *proteins, carbohydrates* and *lipids*.
- Substances made up of small molecules can be absorbed without digestion: water, mineral elements, glucose, alcohol and many drugs.
- Substances which cannot be digested (such as cellulose) and non-food substances (such as plastic) pass through the system and are eliminated.
- *Absorption* is the process whereby digested nutrients of small molecular structure pass through the walls of the intestine and, eventually, into the bloodstream.

THE ALIMENTARY CANAL

This is a continuous muscular tube through which the food passes from the time it is ingested through the mouth until the waste is eliminated from the anus (*egestion*).

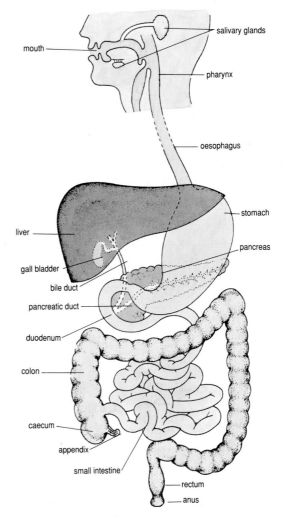

Alimentary canal

The alimentary canal is lined with mucous membrane which secretes digestive fluids containing enzymes which help to digest food. The muscles in the walls of the alimentary canal enable it to contract and relax in a wave-like movement called *peristalsis*, which pushes food along. The alimentary canal consists of:

- the mouth
- the oesophagus
- the stomach
- the small intestine
- the large intestine

Other glands associated with digestion by secreting important digestive enzymes etc. are:

- salivary glands
- pancreas
- liver

THE MOUTH

Digestion begins in the mouth. The teeth grind down food in order to increase its surface area for digestion. Saliva softens and moistens food, assisting in the sensation of taste (end of chapter 1).

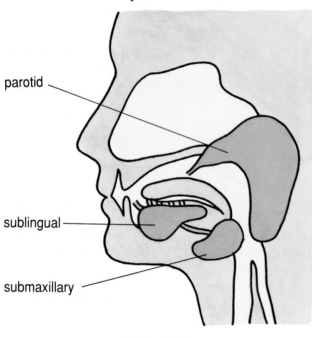

Saliva glands

SALIVARY GLANDS

Saliva is secreted by three pairs of glands:

1. the *parotid glands* at the back of the cheeks under each ear.
2. the *submaxillary glands* under the jaw.
3. the *sublingual glands* under the tongue.

These glands consist of secretory cells grouped around small ducts. Each duct leads to a main duct which leaves the gland and passes into the mouth.

Saliva is secreted continuously to keep the mouth moist, but the sight or smell of food increases its secretion. Saliva is an alkaline fluid, containing mucus and the enzyme *ptyalin (salivary amylase)*. It mixes with and moistens the food which is formed into a ball (*bolus*) by the tongue.

- Digestion in the mouth: Ptyalin converts cooked starch to dextrin (a short-chain starch) and maltose (a disaccharide).

THE OESOPHAGUS OR GULLET

- The tongue pushes food into the oesophagus in the act of swallowing. The oesophagus is a straight, muscular tube about 25 cm long, connecting the pharynx with the stomach. It contracts rhythmically in a wave-like movement called *peristalsis* which moves foods towards the stomach.
- *Digestion in the oesophagus:* Digestion of starch by ptyalin continues, but there is no enzyme secreted by the oesophagus.

THE STOMACH

- *Position:* The stomach is situated on the top left of the abdomen, immediately below the diaphragm. It lies to the left of the liver, in front of the pancreas, and touches the large intestine and the spleen.

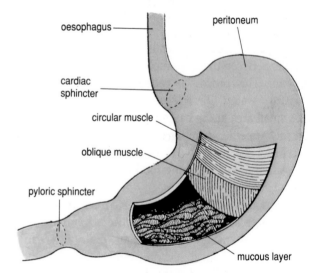

Structure of the stomach

- *Shape:* The stomach is a large, pouch-like, hollow organ. A tight ring of muscle, called the *cardiac sphincter*, is situated at the point where the oesophagus enters the stomach. This controls the amount of food entering and prevents food from passing back up the oesophagus. A similar muscle, the *pyloric sphincter*, controls food passing from the stomach into the duodenum. The stomach expands considerably after a large meal.
- *Structure:* The stomach is largely composed of muscle. Its walls have four layers:

1. A thin outer covering of *peritoneum*.
2. A *thick layer of smooth (involuntary) muscle*, arranged alternately lengthways, in a circle and horizontally. This gives elasticity and produces the strong contractions which churn the food about.
3. A *sub-mucous layer* (containing nerves and blood vessels).
4. A *mucous layer* which is deeply folded when the stomach is empty. Between the folds are numerous glands which secrete *gastric juice*. This consists of:

- water
- mucus, a sticky secretion which clings to the stomach walls, preventing the stomach from digesting itself!
- Hydrochloric acid (HC1) provides the necessary high acidity — pH 1-2 — for the action of gastric juices and enzymes. It neutralises ptyalin soon after it enters the stomach. It also destroys bacteria unless they are present in very large numbers.
- Gastric enzymes: *Pepsinogen* and *rennin* (see below).

DIGESTION IN THE STOMACH

Pepsinogen (stimulated by the hormone *gastrin*) is produced when food is eaten. When it is mixed with hydrochloric acid, it changes to *pepsin* — a *proteolytic* (protein-splitting) enzyme which breaks large protein molecules into shorter chains called *peptones*.

Rennin clots the milk protein *caseinogen*, changing it to casein. This combines with the calcium in milk to form *calcium caseinate* which is more easily digested by pepsin. This enzyme is most active in infants.

PHYSICAL ACTION IN THE STOMACH

The muscular walls contract and relax, churning the food about and mixing it with gastric juice until it reaches a creamy consistency known as *chyme*.

Food remains in the stomach from two to five hours, depending on the type eaten — proteins and fats remain longer than carbohydrates. It then passes into the *duodenum*.

FUNCTIONS OF THE STOMACH

1. Food is broken down physically to make it easier for digestive enzymes to work on the food.
2. The partial digestion of proteins by enzymes, pepsinogen and rennin, takes place in the stomach.
3. Stomach heat melts fats.
4. By acting as a food reservoir, the stomach reduces the amount of times food must be eaten.
5. It breaks down cellulose on plant foods, releasing carbohydrates for digestion.
6. Some absorption takes place in the stomach — of glucose, alcohol and drugs, for example.

THE PANCREAS

This is a long, pinkish-white gland which lies under the stomach. It stretches from the bend in the duodenum to the spleen.

- *Structure:* It is similar to salivary glands in structure, being made up of groups of secretory cells called alveoli which produce pancreatic juice. These open into tiny ducts which join up to form the main *pancreatic duct* which brings pancreatic juice to the duodenum.

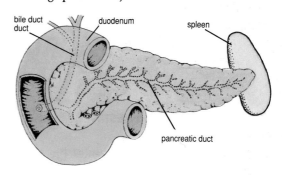

Pancreas and duodenum

The pancreas also contains groups of specialised cells — the *islets of Langerhans* — which produce insulin. These are part of the endocrine system (page 140).

- *Pancreatic juice:* This is a clear, colourless, alkaline fluid which flows into the duodenum. It neutralises hydrochloric acid, bringing the 'chyme' to pH 8. It has three enzymes:

1. *trypsin*
2. *amylase*
3. *lipase*

THE SMALL INTESTINE

This is a coiled tube 6-8 metres long which stretches from the stomach to the large intestine. It is held in place by a membrane — the *mesentery*. It consists of three sections:

1. the *duodenum*, which consists of the first 25 cm.
2. the *jejunum*, which is the main section.
3. the *ileum*, which is the last section.

- *Structure:* The walls of the intestine, like those of the stomach, have four layers.

1. an outer covering of peritoneum
2. a middle muscular coat
3. a sub-mucous layer
4. a mucous layer

The inner layer is deeply folded. The folds are covered with tiny hair-like projections called *villi*. These give the inner layer a velvet-like appearance and increase its surface area for absorption.

Each villus contains a *lacteal* or *lymph vessel*, and a network of tiny capillaries. Between the villi are glands which secrete intestinal juice (*succus entericus*).

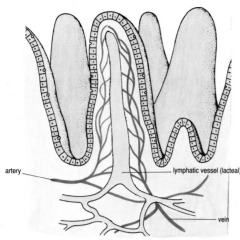

Structure of villi

DIGESTION IN THE SMALL INTESTINE

A. *Duodenum*

1. *Trypsin* acts on large protein molecules, breaking them into smaller chains such as *peptides*.
2. *Amylase* breaks down starchy carbohydrates to maltose.
3. *Lipase* splits fats, emulsified by bile*, into fatty acids and glycerol.

* *Bile:*

This is a greenish-yellow secretion of the liver (page 150) which contains no enzymes but which plays an important part in the digestion of fats by emulsifying them — breaking large fat globules into tiny droplets. This provides a greater surface area for the fat-splitting enzyme, lipase, to work on. Its alkaline pH provides the correct environment for the action of pancreatic enzymes.

B. *Jejunum*

4. *Peptidase* (or *erepsin*) breaks any remaining protein links, converting partly-digested proteins to amino acids.
5. Carbohydrate-splitting enzymes convert any disaccharides to monosaccharides:
   (a) *Maltase* converts *maltose* to *glucose*.
   (b) *Sucrase* converts *sucrose* to *glucose* and *fructose*.
   (c) *Lactase* converts *lactose* (milk sugar) to *glucose* and *galactose*.
6. Intestinal *lipase* breaks down any remaining fat to *fatty acids* and *glycerol*.

Digestion is now completed. Nutrients have been broken down into simple soluble products:

- amino acids
- monosaccharides
- fatty acids and glycerol

C. *Ileum*

Absorption

As the walls of the villi are extremely thin, digested molecules can readily pass through. The villi in the ileum are richly supplied with blood vessels and lacteals to carry away the products of digestion.

1. Monosaccharides and amino acids diffuse into the blood capillaries in the villi and are carried to the liver by the portal vein.
2. Emulsified glycerol and fatty acids pass into the lacteals in the villi where many are rearranged into lipids. They are carried by lymph vessels to the thoracic duct and, finally, into the blood at the left subclavian vein.

Absorption is largely a process of diffusion. Nutrients, which are in high concentrations as they pass along the intestine, diffuse into the blood/lacteals where nutrients are in lower concentrations.

Any substances that are not absorbed pass into the large intestine through the *ileocaecal valve*.

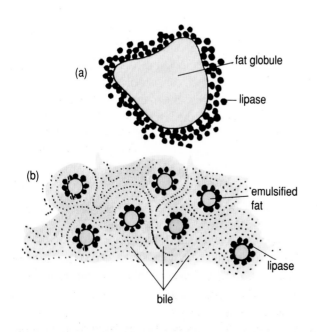

Emulsifying property of bile

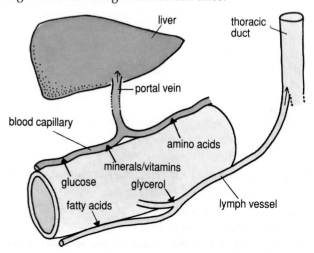

Absorption in the small intestine

THE LARGE INTESTINE

This tube has a wider diameter than the small intestine. It has a puckered outward appearance and is just under two metres long. It begins as the *caecum*, passes up the right side as the *ascending colon*, across under the diaphragm (*transverse colon*) and down the left side (*descending colon*). The last few centimetres, which consist of strong muscle, are known as the *rectum* (see diagram, page 145).

The structure of the large intestine is similar to that of other areas of the alimentary canal:

1. peritoneum
2. muscle layer
3. sub-mucous layer
4. mucous layer, which secretes mucus to lubricate the intestine

When food enters the large intestine, it contains large amounts of water. This must be reclaimed or the body would become dehydrated. Bacteria present in the intestine break down the waste matter. In doing so, they produce vitamins which are absorbed.

Some infections such as food poisoning lead to inflammation of the large intestine. When this occurs, efficient absorption of water is impossible and diarrhoea results.

The *faeces* are eliminated by strong contractions of the anal sphincter.

THE FUNCTION OF THE LARGE INTESTINE

1. Reabsorption of water, thus concentrating the faeces.
2. Absorption of any remaining nutrients such as mineral salts.
3. Elimination of waste known as faeces or stools, mainly cellulose and bacteria.
4. Manufacture of B vitamins and some vitamin K by intestinal flora (bacteria naturally present there).

Summary of Digestion

Digestive gland	Secretion	Enzymes and other substances	Substances acted upon (substrate)	Product
Salivary glands (mouth)	Saliva (alkaline)	Ptyalin or salivary amylase	Cooked starch	Dextrin Maltose
Gastric glands (stomach)	Gastric juice (acid)	Pepsin Rennin Hydrochloric acid (not an enzyme)	Protein Caseinogen (milk protein)	Peptones Casein
Liver	Bile (alkaline)	Bile salts (not an enzyme)	Lipids	Emulsified fat
Pancreas	Pancreatic juice (alkaline)	Trypsin Amylase Lipase	Protein Starch Lipids	Peptides Maltose Fatty acids, glycerol
Ileum	Succus entericus (alkaline)	Peptidase (erepsin) Lipase { Maltase Sucrase (invertase) Lactase	Peptides Lipids { Maltose Sucrose Lactose (milk sugar)	Amino acids Fatty acids, glycerol { Glucose Glucose, fructose Glucose, galactose

METABOLISM

The term *metabolism* is used to describe the sum total of chemical changes which occur in the body. It involves:

1. the digestion and absorption of food
2. storage of digested nutrients
3. making of body tissue from nutrients
4. their utilisation and the release of energy, creating the waste products CO_2 and urea.

Excretion (page 152) gets rids of these waste products.

- *Catabolism* is the breakdown of large molecules into smaller, simple molecules. This occurs during digestion or when food stored in the body is broken down. *Catabolism releases energy.*

- *Anabolism* is the process whereby large complex molecules such as proteins and glycogen are synthesised —

built up from simple substances. *Anabolism requires energy*.

Energy is required for all bodily activities. It is released from every cell during the process of *oxidation*. This can be shown simply as follows:

$$C_6H_{12}O_6 + 6O_2 \longrightarrow 6CO_2 + 6H_2O + \text{energy}$$

glucose oxygen carbon water
                  dioxide

To be more exact, energy is released in a series of complicated chemical steps controlled by enzymes. Energy release occurs in two stages. The first stage occurs when glucose combines with a compound of phosphorus, producing *pyruvic acid* — a three-carbon compound — with the release of energy. The second stage (the *citric acid* or *Krebs cycle*) produces a great deal of energy from pyruvic acid. This energy is stored as the compound *ATP* (*adenosine triphosphate*) — often called the 'energy bank' of the cell. Whenever energy is required, one of the phosphate groups in ATP breaks off, producing *ADP* (*adenosine diphosphate*) with the release of energy.

METABOLISM OF CARBOHYDRATES

All monosaccharides which reach the liver are converted to glucose.

- Some glucose is released immediately into the bloodstream and is oxidised to produce energy (see above).
- Some of the glucose is converted into *glycogen*, an insoluble starch-like chain of glucose molecules, which is stored in the liver and muscles until required.
- If more glucose is available than can be used by the body, it is converted into fat and stored as *adipose tissue* under the skin.

METABOLISM OF FAT

- Some fat is oxidised in the liver and muscles to provide energy. A little is used for structural purposes, as in the cell walls.
- The remaining fat is stored as an energy reserve in the form of adipose tissue beneath the skin and around delicate organs. This forms the largest energy store in the body which is only utilised when fewer kilocalories are consumed that are required by the body.

METABOLISM OF PROTEIN

Amino acids are carried by the portal vein to the liver cells.

- Some are *retained* by the liver itself. The remainder pass into the bloodstream and body tissues where they are built up again (*synthesised*) in order to form new cells, repair tissues and make protein chemicals such as hormones and enzymes.
- Excess amino acids are *deaminated* (the nitrogen is removed) in the liver. They are converted first to ammonia, then to urea, and excreted in the urine. The remaining part of the amino acid molecule is converted to glucose and used for energy production or stored as adipose tissue.

THE LIVER

The liver is a highly complex organ which carries out many important functions.

- *Position:* It is situated at the top right of the abdominal cavity, its upper surface fitting into the curve of the diaphragm. It lies beside the stomach and above the intestines.
- *Structure:* The liver is the largest gland in the body. It is dark in colour and triangular in shape. It has an outer covering of peritoneum. It is divided into two lobes, the right lobe being the larger of the two. On the underside, in the cleft between the lobes, is the entry and exit point of most of the liver vessels.

1. the hepatic artery
2. the portal vein
3. the hepatic vein
4. the hepatic ducts

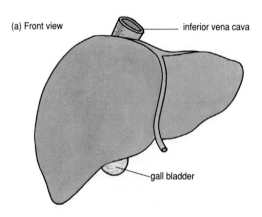

(a) Front view — inferior vena cava — gall bladder

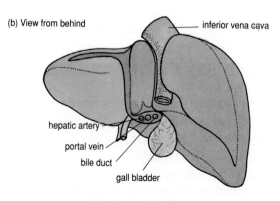

(b) View from behind — inferior vena cava — hepatic artery — portal vein — bile duct — gall bladder

Structure of the liver

HEPATIC CIRCULATION

The liver has a double blood supply.

1. A branch of the aorta, the *hepatic artery*, brings oxygen-rich blood to the liver, where it breaks into capillaries supplying the liver lobules.
2. The *portal vein* brings nutrient-rich blood from the intestine where they are acted upon or stored by the liver cells. Capillaries of the portal vein pass between the lobules. A small vein collects deoxygenated blood from each lobule. These unite to form:
3. The *hepatic vein*, which leaves the liver and empties into the inferior vena cava.

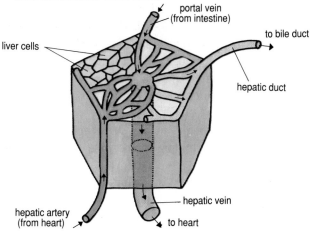

Hepatic lobule

- *Detailed structure (lobules)*: Liver cells are arranged in column-like groups called hepatic lobules. Each is fed by a branch of the hepatic artery and portal vein, and drained by a venule leading to the hepatic vein. Blood entering this vein has been depleted of its oxygen and nutrients.

  Small channels begin between the liver cells, collecting bile. These eventually collect to form the *hepatic ducts* — one from each lobe of the liver. The hepatic ducts combine to form the *bile duct* which brings bile to the duodenum. A branch of the bile duct leads to the *gall bladder*, a pear-shaped bag lying in the groove under the liver, where bile is stored and released as required.

  Bile is a greenish-yellow alkaline fluid, containing water, sodium bicarbonate, the pigment *bilirubin* made from the haemoglobin of dead blood cells, and mucus. Bile salts assist the pancreatic enzyme, lipase, by emulsifying fats.

FUNCTIONS OF THE LIVER

The liver has over fifty separate functions, many of which are concerned with screening and sorting digested food.

1. *Regulation of nutrients*

The liver regulates the amount of nutrients entering the blood stream to that required by the body.

2. *Formation of glycogen* (an energy reserve)

Water-soluble glucose is not easily stored in the body, as it would quickly be removed by the kidneys. To overcome this, the liver converts glucose to insoluble glycogen — a chain of glucose molecules. This is stored by liver cells and muscle tissue and is converted back to glucose when energy is required.

3. *Deamination*

Amino acids, which are not required for protein synthesis, are deaminated. This means that the amino group (NH_2), containing nitrogen, is removed from the amino acid molecule, converted to ammonia, and then to urea which is excreted by the kidneys. The remaining part of the molecule — COOH — is converted into glucose and used for energy production. If not required, this is converted to glycogen.

4. *Secretion of bile*

Bile assists the action of lipase by emulsifying fats.

5. *Storage*

The liver stores some fats, vitamins A, D and B group, and certain minerals such as iron, potassium and copper. These are released when required by the body.

6. *Protein synthesis*

Liver cells manufacture plasma proteins such as fibrinogen and prothrombin. It is also involved in the formation of antibodies.

7. *Destruction of red blood cells*

The liver completes the destruction of red cells and recycles their components. The haemoglobin pigment is used in bile; the iron is used to form new red cells.

8. *Detoxification*

The liver converts various toxins into harmless compounds and neutralises chemicals such as hormones which are no longer required by the body.

9. *Homeostasis*

The liver helps to keep the blood and body fluids at the correct concentration, composition and temperature so that they function property.

Summary of Liver Functions

1. Controls release of nutrients
2. Formation of glycogen
3. Deamination
4. Secretion of bile
5. Stores many nutrients, including vitamins A, D, B group, iron
6. Manufactures plasma proteins and antibodies
7. Helps to destroy and recycle red blood cells
8. Destroys toxins
9. Maintains homeostasis, i.e. ideal environment for body functioning

► EXCRETION

Excretion may be defined as the removal of waste products produced during metabolism. Many such wastes are toxic. The excretory organs include: the skin, the kidney, the lungs and the liver (which acts as an excretory organ by altering and storing some waste products). The large intestine is an organ of *elimination* rather than excretion.

THE SKIN

The skin is the largest organ of the body. It is composed of two layers — the *epidermis* on the outside and the *dermis* underneath. The thickness of the skin varies according to its position on the body — for example, the skin on the soles of the feet is the thickest.

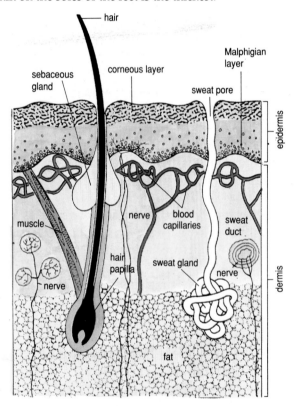

Structure of the skin (vertical section)

STRUCTURE

1. The epidermis

The surface of the epidermis is known as the *corneous layer*. It consists of flat, dead cells which form a protective, waterproof layer on the skin. These cells are constantly being worn away and replaced by an upward growth from beneath. Under the corneous layer are layers of living cells. At the bottom of the epidermis is a layer of actively-growing cells called the *malpighian layer*. This contains the pigment melanin which determines the colour of the skin.

2. The dermis

The dermis is a thick layer consisting of connective tissue in which are distributed sweat glands, hair follicles, capillaries, nerves and lymphatics. The top of the dermis is raised into projections called *papillae*. These contain many of the nerve endings of the skin. At the base of the dermis is a layer of fat cells, the thickness of which varies with the individual. This layer of fat cells is called *adipose tissue* or *subcutaneous fat*. It acts as an energy store and helps to insulate the body.

- A *sweat gland* consists of a coiled tube lined with secretory cells which takes fluid from the network of capillaries surrounding it and releases it through the sweat ducts which open onto the skin surface as *pores*. The fluid known as *sweat* consists of water, salt and urea. The capillaries bring oxygen and nutrients to the skin and remove CO_2.
- *Hair follicles* are really ingrowths of epidermal cells. Active cells, multiplying at the base of the follicle, form the hair.
- *Sebaceous glands* produce sebum, a greasy substance which lubricates each hair and helps to make the skin supple and waterproof. A tiny muscle attached to each hair follicle contracts when we are cold or frightened, creating 'goose pimples' and making the hair 'stand on end'. This provides insulation.
- *Nerves* are plentiful on areas such as the fingertips. Different types of *nerve receptors* enable us to feel sensations such as temperature, pressure and pain.

Summary of Skin Functions
1. To protect the inner tissues
2. To excrete waste (sweat)
3. As a temperature regulator
4. As a sensory organ
5. It manufactures vitamin D (page 18)
6. It acts as an insulator (fat cells)

FUNCTIONS OF THE SKIN

1. *Protection:* The malpighian layer screens the body from the harmful ultraviolet rays of the sun. The corneous layer keeps skin waterproof and prevents infection by micro-organisms and loss of moisture.
2. *Excretion:* Water and traces of waste such as salt and urea pass onto the surface of the skin through the sweat ducts and pores.
3. *Temperature regulation:* The skin regulates body temperature in two ways:
   (a) By *evaporation of sweat*. Heat is taken from the surface of the body in order to evaporate the sweat. This cools the body.

(b) *Vasodilation and vasoconstriction* — the expansion and contraction of skin capillaries. When we get too warm, the capillaries near the surface of the skin dilate and allow blood to lose heat by convection and radiation (this is what happens when we blush!). The reverse happens when we are cold. The capillaries contract, reduce the volume of blood to the skin (we get pale),

thereby lessening heat loss. Sweat production is also reduced to retain heat.
4. *Sensory organ:* The skin responds quickly to sensations such as heat, cold and pain. The nerve ends in the skin transmit this information to the brain which may act on it, as when we remove our fingers from a hot object.

THE URINARY SYSTEM

THE KIDNEYS

■ *Position:* The kidneys are situated on the back wall of the abdomen, just below the diaphragm, one on each side of the lumbar vertebrae. Each is embedded in fat which protects it. An adrenal gland rests on top of each kidney.

■ *Structure:* The kidneys are two dark red, bean-shaped organs about 12 cm long. The inner border, or *hilum*, faces the backbone. Here the renal artery enters, and the renal vein leaves, bringing blood in and out of the kidney.

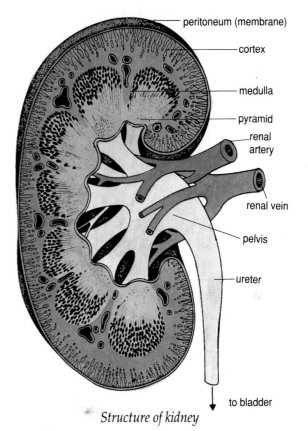

Structure of kidney

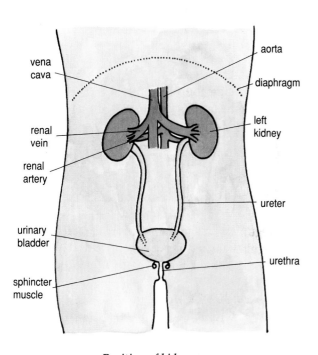

Position of kidneys

The kidney consist of:
■ an outer fibrous membrane of *peritoneum*
■ the *cortex*, a dark-coloured, fleshy layer
■ the *medulla*, a lighter-coloured area which contains the 'pyramids'. These pass into the *pelvis* of the kidney, a funnel-shaped collecting tube which narrows to form the *ureter* which leaves at the hilum and passes downwards to the *bladder*.

■ *Detailed structure (nephrons):* Each kidney contains over a million tiny units called *nephrons*. These act as filters, separating urine from blood. Each begins as a cup-shaped funnel called *Bowman's capsule* which is filled tightly with a capillary network called a *glomerulus*. These capillaries originate in a branch of the renal artery (the *afferent arteriole*).

From Bowman's capsule, a twisted tube (the *proximal tubule*) passes down into the medulla, makes a narrow U turn (the *loop of Henle*), returns to the cortex and coils a few more times. This is called the *distal tubule* (as it is more distant from the capsule). It then straightens out, passes back into the medulla to form a collecting duct, joining up with similar tubules on the way. Eventually they all pass into the pelvis of the kidney.

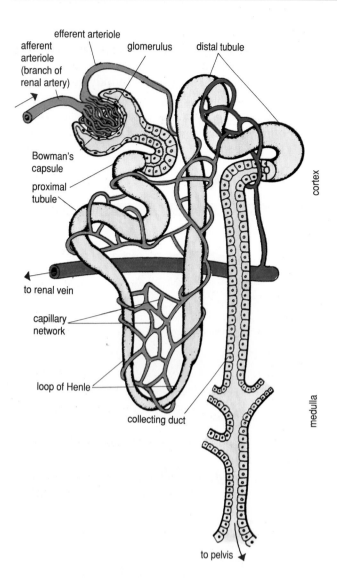

Structure of a nephron

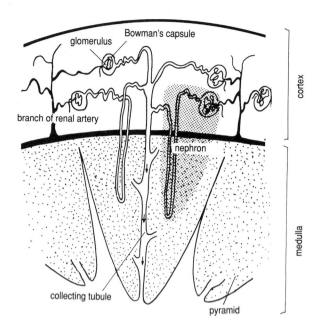

Detailed structure of kidney

The venous capillaries, now deoxygenated, have picked up CO_2 in the normal way. They unite to form veins which empty into the renal vein. One leaves each kidney and joins the inferior vena cava which returns the filtered blood to the heart.

The urine passes into the pelvis of the kidney, and down the ureter to the *bladder*. This is a hollow, elastic organ which stores urine until a certain degree of pressure stimulates its sphincter muscle to relax, releasing the urine through the urethra.

SUMMARY OF THE FUNCTIONS OF THE KIDNEYS

1. The removal of waste products such as urea from blood.
2. They regulate the amount of water in the body (osmoregulation, see next page).
3. They regulate the amount of glucose, salt and other substances in blood.
4. They are a major homeostatic organ, adjusting the concentration of body fluids and regulating the pH of blood.

COMPOSITION OF URINE

Water 96%
Urea* 2%
Salt 1%
Other substances (1%): uric acid, calcium, potassium, ammonia.

■ *Urea* is an organic compound containing nitrogen which has been produced during the breakdown of protein.

RENAL CIRCULATION

The renal artery, carrying blood which contains many impurities, enters the kidney at the hilum under great pressure. It passes into the cortex, breaking into capillaries and eventually forms the glomerulus. The walls of both the glomerulus and the capsule surrounding it are extremely thin, and water, salts, urea etc. are passed into the tubule under great pressure. A tiny (efferent) arteriole leaves the glomerulus and immediately breaks into a network of even smaller capillaries which completely surround the proximal tubule and loop. Here, 80% of the *filtrate* is reabsorbed by the capillaries — mostly useful nutrients such as glucose, amino acids, vitamins etc. Harmful substances are not reabsorbed. Tiny projections called microvilli which line the tubule assist this selective absorption. More reabsorption takes place from the distal tubule until the *urine* — which the filtrate is now called — reaches the correct dilution.

- *Osmoregulation:* This is the delicate balancing of the water level of the body. It is controlled by the pituitary hormone, *antidiuretic hormone (ADH)*. When large amounts of water have been lost by the body as through diarrhoea or excessive sweating, ADH stimulates the tubules to return more water to the blood, thereby increasing the concentration of urine. The opposite occurs when the blood become too dilute — for example, by drinking a lot of liquids. ADH production is suppressed; the tubules return less water and the quantity of urine is increased. Inability to produce ADH causes *diabetes insipidus*.

THE NERVOUS SYSTEM

The human body consists of millions of cells which make up many organs and systems. None of these work in isolation — they are all interdependent. The system which controls and co-ordinates all these activities is the nervous system.

The nervous system is, in fact, made up of three systems:

1. The *central nervous system* (brain and spinal cord)
2. The *peripheral nervous system* (spinal and cranial nerves)
3. The *autonomic nervous system* (controlling involuntary movements)

NERVE CELLS (NEURONS)

In order to understand clearly how the nervous system works, it is necessary to study the basic unit of the system — the *neuron* or *nerve cell*.

A neuron consists of:

1. a *cell body* containing a nucleus;
2. an *axon*, which is a long fibre extending from the cell body. This may be covered by a fatty sheath (the *myelin sheath*) which insulates and protects it.

The cell bodies are in, or near, the brain and spinal cord. The fibres extend all over the body, often for considerable distances. A *ganglion* is a group of cell bodies just outside the spinal cord.

There are two main types of neuron which differ in structure and function:

1. *Sensory* or *afferent neurons*
2. *Motor* or *efferent neurons*

1. SENSORY NEURONS

These convey impulses from the body, e.g. skin to the central nervous system (CNS). They consist of:

(a) a *sensory receptor* at the end of the neuron which picks up stimuli (sensations)
(b) a *dendron*, which carries the stimulus to —
(c) the cell body
(d) an *axon*, which transmits the stimulus through branched nerve endings (*synaptic bulbs*) to the CNS

2. MOTOR NEURONS

These carry impulses from the CNS to each part of the body. The consist of:

(a) an *irregular cell body* surrounded by *dendrites* which carry impulses into the cell body
(b) the *axon*, which is a long nerve fibre protected by the myelin sheath which brings impulses to —
(c) the *end plate* — a branching of nerve fibres attached to the muscles

ASSOCIATION NEURONS

These link motor and sensory neurons. They are only found in the brain and spinal cord.

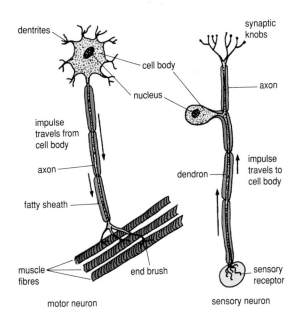

Nerve cells

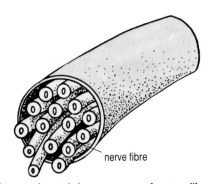

A nerve (containing sensory and motor fibres)

NERVES

A nerve consists of a bundle of nerve fibres bound in connective tissue. It contains both motor and sensory fibres.

- *Nerve impulses:* These are electro-chemical reactions which travel along nerve fibres at high speed, in one direction only (much like a lighted fuse). The nerve fibre is stimulated at one end. This causes an impulse in the next section and so on, along the fibre. Oxygen is required for the transmission of nerve impulses.

- *Synapse:* This is the chemical connecting link between neurons or nerve fibres. It occurs only in the CNS. Neurons do not connect directly with one another. There is a tiny space between the end of one and the beginning of another. This space is called a synapse. It is bridged by a hormone, acetyl choline (ACh), which is secreted by the end of the axon and reaches the end terminals of the dendrites, chemically transmitting the impulse across the gap. After each transmission, an enzyme destroys ACh so that it is ready for the next.

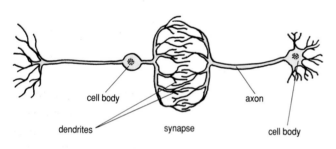

Synapse

CENTRAL NERVOUS SYSTEM (CNS)

This consists of the brain and the spinal cord. The brain is like a central computer which receives information, interprets it and stores it or transmits instructions. For example, it receives a stimulus, such as a sound or light, and decides to react in a certain way — for example, blink in response to the light.

The peripheral system (that is, nerves) gathers the information, feeds it into the central nervous system and then transmits its instructions to the body muscles, cells etc.

THE BRAIN

The brain is protected by the skull and surrounded by a protective triple membrane — the *meninges*. The inner membranes are bathed with *cerebrospinal fluid*. The brain's three main divisions are:

- the *cerebrum* which is the largest part (*forebrain*)
- the *cerebellum* at the base of the skull (*midbrain*)
- the *medulla* oblongata which connects the brain with the spinal cord (*hindbrain*)

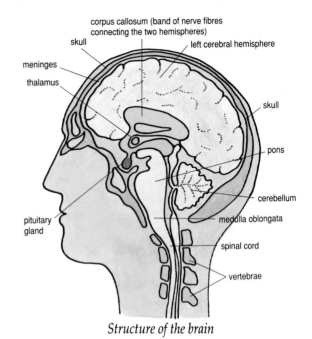

Structure of the brain

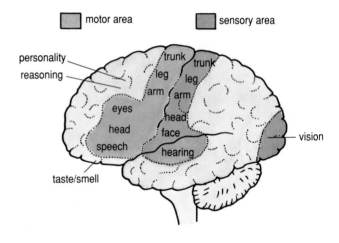

Sense centres of the brain

1. THE CEREBRUM

This is composed by two deeply-folded hemispheres — the right and the left. Its exterior, the *cerebral cortex*, is made up of grey matter, consisting of billions of tightly-packed nerve cells or bodies. The white matter beneath consists of billions of nerve fibres — extensions of the cell bodies in the cortex

Different areas or 'centres' in the brain control certain functions (see diagram). The frontal lobe of the cerebral cortex is very well developed in humans. It is concerned with behaviour, personality and intellect. It is also the area which stores information and memory.

The motor centres at the top control the voluntary movements of the body. Those on the *right side* of the brain control movements on the *left side* of the body and vice versa. This is because the nerve fibres leaving these areas cross to the opposite side at the *pons*. The major areas of the brain are connected by nerve fibres.

The *hypothalamus* is a small area in the centre of the brain. It controls hunger, thirst, body temperature and water content, as well as stimulating the release of certain hormones from the pituitary gland beneath it. The *thalamus* is concerned with sensations of pain and pleasure.

The *reticular formation* nearby acts as a 'censor', allowing only the most important messages through to the brain. It also 'shuts down' most of the impulses during sleep.

2. THE CEREBELLUM

This is situated at the base of the back of the brain. It is involved with muscular control and balance and helps to co-ordinate muscular movements.

The *pons* (bridge) connects the cerebrum and cerebellum with the medulla oblongata and spinal cord.

3. MEDULLA OBLONGATA

This is the centre of *involuntary* reactions. It controls breathing, heartbeat and blood pressure. It also plays a part in digestion.

THE AUTONOMIC NERVOUS SYSTEM

This is the system which controls *involuntary actions* such as those of the digestive system, heart and lungs which are not consciously controlled. It consists of two separate parts which have opposing influences — one stimulating contraction, the other inhibiting contraction. They are:

1. The *sympathetic nervous system* which helps the body to respond to an emergency, providing muscles with more oxygen and glucose by speeding up breathing and heartbeat and converting body stores of glycogen into glucose.
2. The *parasympathetic nervous system* shuts down these responses, restoring the body to normal. It also controls the degree of contractions which occur.

PERIPHERAL NERVOUS SYSTEM

This consists of the (1) *spinal nerves* and (2) *cranial nerves* which carry impulses to and from the central nervous system.

They transmit impulses from *receptors* to the central nervous system and transmit *impulses* from it to the muscles.

1. *Spinal nerves:* Between the vertebrae, at intervals, the spinal cord sends out thirty-one pairs of nerves leading to the main muscles of the body.

2. Twelve pairs of *cranial nerves* lead from beneath the brain. They control important sensations in the head and neck, including the optic and auditory nerves and the vagus nerve, leading to and from the heart, lungs and digestive organs.

THE SPINAL CORD

This is a long cylinder of nerve tissue, stretching from the medulla oblongata to the lumbar vertebrae. The bony vertebrae of the spine protect it from damage. The spinal cord thickens as it passes up through the body as nerve fibres join it from different parts. On the outside, the spinal cord consists of *white matter* made up of nerve fibres which convey impulses to and from the brain. The *grey matter*, which forms an H-shape in the centre, consists of *nerve cell bodies*. The grey and white matter in the spinal cord are the reverse of that in the brain.

The brain and spinal cord are bathed with *cerebrospinal fluid* which supplies them with nutrients and protects them from damage.

FUNCTIONS OF THE SPINAL CORD

1. It carries impulses to and from the brain.
2. It acts as a centre for reflex action.

REFLEX

A reflex action is a rapid, involuntary response by an organ to a stimulus. It is not necessary for the message to reach the brain before the action takes place. The 'knee-jerk' reaction shows how it works. *Receptors* in the leg muscle send impulses along a *sensory fibre*. The impulses pass through a *connector neurone* in the grey matter of the spinal cord instead of passing to the brain and cross over to a motor fibre which tells the muscle to contract.

Conditioned reflexes are actions which were originally conscious actions, such as learning to walk or to drive a car but which, with practice, are done without thinking.

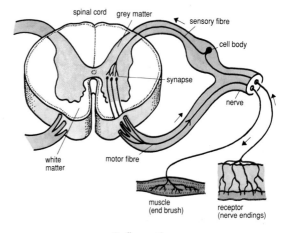

Reflex action

► THE REPRODUCTIVE SYSTEM

Reproduction is the means whereby a species is perpetuated. In humans, the reproductive function is closely involved with emotional needs and drives such as love and security.

The *gonads* are the reproductive organs in which gametes (reproductive cells) are formed. In the male, the gonads are the *testes* which produce *spermatozoa (sperm)*. In the female the gonads are the *ovaries* which produce *ova*.

THE MALE REPRODUCTIVE ORGANS

The reproductive organs of the male lie outside the body because the cooler temperature is more suitable for the production of sperm. These organs consist of the following.

- The *testes* are two oval organs which lie in a loose covering of skin called the *scrotum*.
  Each testis contains a mass of *seminiferous tubules*, the walls of which contain cells which manufacture sperm.
- The male hormone *testosterone* is also produced in the testis.
- The mature sperm pass into a duct which leads to a coiled tube outside each testis, called the *epididymis*.
- From this a larger tube, the *vas deferens* or sperm duct, passes out of the scrotum up into the body.
- Near the bladder it divides in two. One branch leads to the coiled *seminal vesicle*, while the other opens into the urethra at the base of the bladder.

- Near this point two glands, the *prostate* and *Cowper's gland*, together with the vesicle, produce a fluid in which the sperm are suspended.
- The urethra passes downwards into the *penis*, which is composed of connective tissue with a sponge-like structure. The spaces in the connective tissue fill with blood during sexual intercourse, causing the penis to become erect.

The *pituitary hormones* LH and FSH (see page 141) stimulate sperm production at puberty, as well as secondary male characteristics such as hair growth and a deepening of the voice.

THE FEMALE REPRODUCTIVE ORGANS

- The two *ovaries* lie within the pelvis, on either side of the womb and underneath the kidneys. They are small oval organs, each about the size of a bean. Each one contains thousands of immature ova or eggs embedded in fibrous tissue.
- From each ovary leads a *Fallopian tube* which passes into the *uterus* or womb, a pear-shaped muscular organ. This has an opening at the base guarded by a strong circle of muscle called the *cervix*.
- From this, a narrow, muscular tube, the vagina, passes outwards and opens into the groin.
- The bladder lies in front of the uterus and releases its urine through the urethra which opens in front of the vagina.

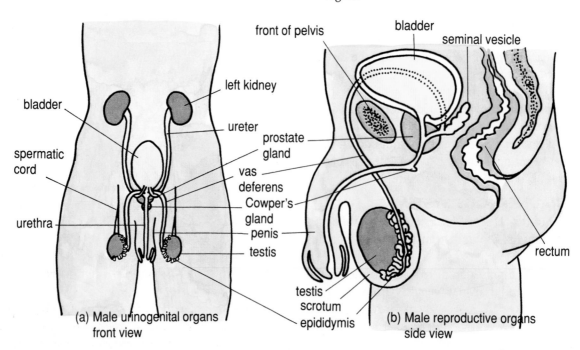

Male reproductive organs

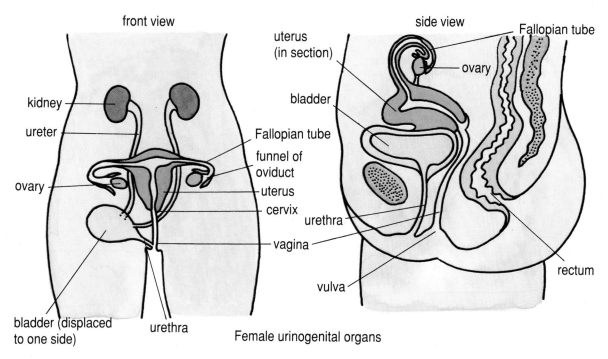

front view

kidney

ureter

ovary

bladder (displaced to one side)

urethra

uterus (in section)

bladder

Fallopian tube

funnel of oviduct

uterus

cervix

vagina

vulva

side view

Fallopian tube

ovary

urethra

rectum

Female urinogenital organs

Female reproductive organs

OVULATION

A female child is born with thousands of potential ova which lie dormant until puberty. The *hormone, FSH,* stimulates the ovaries to begin maturing one ovum each month. One by one, each ovum grows larger and a sheath rich in nutrients (the *Graafian* or *ovarian follicle*) develops around it. This enlarges and eventually pushes the ovum through the wall of the ovary into the funnel-shaped opening of the Fallopian tube. This is the moment of *ovulation*. It occurs in the second week after a period and it is the time during which fertilisation is most likely to occur.

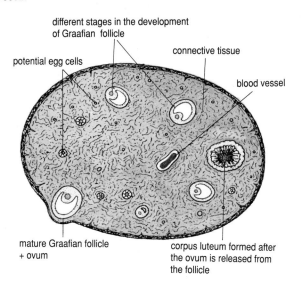

different stages in the development of Graafian follicle

potential egg cells

connective tissue

blood vessel

mature Graafian follicle + ovum

corpus luteum formed after the ovum is released from the follicle

Structure of an ovary

As the ovum travels along the Fallopian tube towards the uterus, the follicle which remains in the ovary continues to grow, eventually forming the *corpus luteum*. This secretes the hormone *progesterone*, which begins to prepare the body for pregnancy by thickening the uterine lining.

If fertilisation does not occur, the corpus luteum shrivels up and the progesterone level falls rapidly.

If the ovum is fertilised, the corpus luteum enlarges and secretes even more progesterone. This increases the blood supply to the uterus, further thickening the uterine wall and halting the development of follicles in the ovaries, preventing further ovulation. Pregnancy is the result.

THE MENSTRUAL CYCLE

1. As the follicle ripens, it secretes *oestrogen*, a hormone which causes thickening of the *endometrium* (lining of the womb) and an increased blood flow to the uterus.
2. After ovulation, the corpus luteum secretes progesterone which causes further thickening and blood flow in the uterus.
3. When fertilisation does *not* occur, production of progesterone stops. The uterine lining disintegrates and, as a result of contractions of the uterus, the uterine lining is expelled from the uterus through the vagina.

Menstruation, or a period as it is usually called, occurs about fourteen days after ovulation. The cramps often experienced are caused by uterine contractions. Some

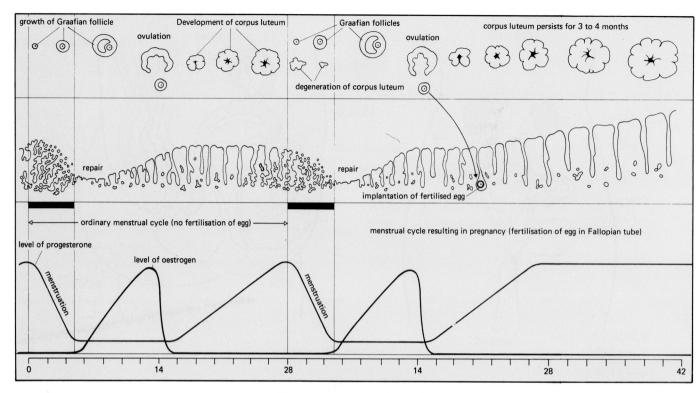

The menstrual or ovarian cycle

people also experience pre-menstrual tension (PMT), which is thought to be related to the withdrawal of progesterone.

Menstruation begins at puberty and continues each month (except during pregnancy) until the *menopause*, when it ceases.

FERTILISATION

Fertilisation occurs when a male sperm unites with a female ovum. This is also called *conception*. During sexual intercourse, semen is ejaculated into the female vagina. The semen contains millions of spermatozoa or sperm. Each sperm consists of a head containing a nucleus, and a tail which enables it to swim upwards through the cervix into the uterus and Fallopian tubes. In most cases, the sperm die before they reach the tubes. But if an ovum is present, the sperm surrounding the ovum attempt to penetrate it. When the nucleus of one sperm unites with the nucleus of the ovum, conception has occurred.

PREGNANCY

1. The fertilised ovum, called a *zygote*, divides in two. Each cell divides again and thus the growth of the embryo begins.
2. The cells multiply rapidly as the *embryo* moves along the Fallopian tube until it reaches the uterus in about a week.
3. Here the embryo sinks into the thick lining of the uterus (*endometrium*) and sends small projections into

it to hold itself in place and assist absorption of nutrients from its walls.
4. This area develops into the *placenta*.
5. The *placenta* provides the embryo with nutrients and oxygen from its mother's blood. It also receives carbon dioxide and urea from the blood of the embryo. The supplies of blood do not mix, but the placenta acts as a filter through which some substances can pass and many harmful products are held back. (Some drugs, and viruses such as rubella can pass through, however. For this reason, pregnant women are advised not to smoke, drink alcohol or take any drug, even aspirin, during pregnancy.)

The placenta stimulates increased production of oestrogen and progesterone and eventually makes its own progesterone. These hormones control many changes, for example:
- thickening of the uterus
- accumulation of fat and fluid
- enlargement of the breasts

Progesterone also inhibits uterine contractions preventing *miscarriage*.
6. The uterus grows large to accommodate the growing embryo.
7. The cells begin to group together in tissues. In eight weeks the embryo, now called a *foetus*, has a head, trunk and limbs. It is surrounded by a sac containing *amniotic fluid* which protects it from injury.

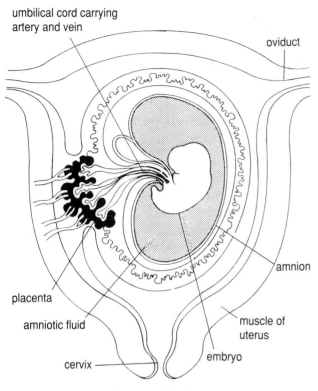

Embryo within the uterus

umbilical cord carrying
artery and vein

oviduct

placenta

amniotic fluid

cervix

embryo

muscle of
uterus

amnion

8. By about six months, all the organs of the foetus are fully developed but it remains in the uterus until it is strong enough to survive independently. The whole period of pregnancy, the *gestation period*, is about forty weeks.

9. *Birth:* When the baby is ready to be born, it usually lies with its head down, facing the cervix (the neck of the womb). Progesterone secretion (which inhibited uterine contraction) diminishes. Stimulated by the hormone *oxytocin*, labour begins. The uterus contracts rhythmically with increasing strength and frequency.

After a time, the cervix dilates, the *sac membrane* ruptures and the amniotic fluid flows out. In the final stages of labour, vigorous contractions expel the baby which must now begin to breathe on its own.

The *umbilical cord*, which attaches the placenta to the abdomen of the baby, is severed. As a result of further contractions, the placenta or afterbirth is expelled with the remains of the umbilical cord.

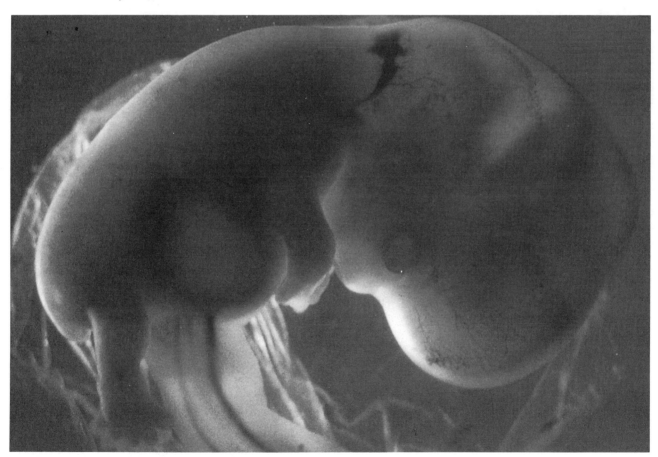

► GLOSSARY

The following glossary explains some of the terms used in the preceding chapters. It is also useful for revision work. Further details on scientific terms may be found in Madden, *Food and Nutrition* (pages 195–203), or in an Intermediate science textbook.

Acetic acid: Also called ethanoic acid, present in vinegar.

Acetyl choline (ACh): A hormone secreted by neuron endings at the synapse to transmit impulses.

Acid: An acid is any molecule which donates protons. Acids have a sour taste, are corrosive, turn litmus red and have a pH of 1 to 6.

Additives: Substances such as colourings deliberately added to foods.

Aerobic: A term used to describe micro-organisms which require oxygen to survive.

Agar: A type of jelly obtained from seaweed. Used for the culture of micro-organisms.

Agglutination: Clumping together of red blood cells. Caused when incompatible blood groups are mixed.

Alkali: A water-soluble molecule which accepts protons and neutralises acids. Alkalis have a pH of 8–14 and turn litmus blue. Sodium bicarbonate (bread soda) is a weak alkali; caustic soda a strong one (pH 14).

Amino acids: Sub-units of protein, containing an amino (NH_2) and carboxyl (COOH) group.

Anaemia: Deficiency of haemoglobin in red blood cells.

Anaerobic: Used to describe micro-organisms which live without oxygen.

Antibody: A protein in blood plasma which attacks and destroys invading organisms.

Antigen: Proteins on red blood cells which stimulate antibody production.

Antioxidant: A substance which reacts with oxygen, preventing it from combining with food molecules and thus causing oxidation or rancidity. Example: ascorbic acid.

Atom: The smallest part of an element which can take part in a chemical reaction.

Base: A molecule that accepts protons. Most bases are water-soluble and are called alkalis.

Binary fission: Splitting of a nucleus, and then a cell, in two, to produce two new cells. One form of cell reproduction.

Blanch: To place in boiling water with the object of whitening, removing a strong taste or destroying enzymes before further processing such as freezing or drying.

Bond: The joining of atoms together to form a molecule. There are various types of bonds. They are broken by adding a water molecule (hydrolysis).

Bowman's capsule: A cup-shaped structure in the cortex of the kidney in which capillaries are coiled.

Budding: The method whereby yeast reproduces itself.

Calciferol: Vitamin D.

Calorie: A unit of energy. A kilocalorie is the amount of heat required to raise the temperature of 1 litre of water by 1°C.

Carbohydrate: A nutrient made up of carbon, hydrogen and oxygen. Example: sugar, starch.

Carboxyl group: This is an acidic molecule (COOH). It is present in the amino acid structure.

Catalyst: A chemical which speeds up a reaction. Enzymes are catalysts.

Cellulose or dietary fibre: An indigestible carbohydrate (polysaccharide) found in plant foods.

Central nervous system (CNS): The areas of the nervous system which include the brain and spinal cord.

Change, chemical: A change which involves the breaking up and rearranging of molecules. It produces a new substance with different properties from the original substance. It is often impossible to reverse. Examples are: combustion of coal, protein digestion, rusting.

Change, physical: A change which may produce a difference of state or appearance but which does not produce a new substance. Examples: ice changing to water, water changing to vapour, puréeing of food.

Cholesterol: A hard, waxy fat synthesised in the body and found in food. It helps to form deposits on artery walls, leading to atherosclerosis.

Coccus: A spherical bacterium.

Collagen: A form of connective tissue.

Colony: A large group of bacteria. May be cultivated on agar.

Combustion: Combining of oxygen with a fuel. It gives off energy and waste products such as CO_2.

Compound: Two or more different elements chemically joined together. Salt, for example — NaCl = 1 atom of sodium and 1 atom of chlorine.

Compounds, inorganic: Usually compounds which do not contain carbon. They include mineral elements and water.

Compounds, organic: These contain carbon. Most foods are organic compounds.

Corpuscle: Blood cell — red or white.

Cryogenic freezing: Instant freezing using liquid nitrogen.

Deamination: Removal of NH_2 (amino group) from the amino acid molecule.

Dehydration: Removing moisture, as from food. A method of preserving.

Diabetes: A disease in which the pancreas produces insufficient insulin for the metabolism of glucose.

Diffusion: The movement of a substance from an area of high concentration to one of low concentration, in order to equalise the density.

Digestion: The physical and chemical breakdown of foods into simple, soluble molecules.

Disaccharide: Two monosaccharides bonded together. Example: sucrose.

Elastin: One form of connective tissue.

Element: A substance made up of atoms which cannot be broken down into a simpler susbtance. Examples: carbon, calcium.

Emulsion: A mixture of two immiscible liquids — those which would not normally mix together. Example: French dressing — oil and vinegar.

Emulsifier: A substance containing a hydrophilic (water-loving) and hydrophobic (water-hating) group. They hold a liquid and lipid together. Example: lecithin in egg yolk is an emulsifier.

Endocrine glands: Ductless glands which produce hormones.

Endospore: A dormant cell of a bacterium which is resistant to heat, cold and chemicals.

Enzymes: Organic catalysts which speed up chemical reactions.

Evaporation: When molecules in a liquid escape from its surface and change into gas. Boiling increases evaporation.

Exocrine glands: Glands which send secretions through ducts into the bloodstream.

Fibre: see Cellulose.

Fibrin/fibrinogen: A clotting protein present in blood.

Galantine: A cold dish of minced meat, herbs and flavourings, often used to stuff meat or fowl. It is boiled or roasted, pressed and glazed.

Gametes: Male and female cells involved in reproduction.

Ganglion: A group of neuron cell bodies near the spinal cord.

Gelatine: A mixture of proteins and amino acids, its main component being gelatin. In water, it absorbs up to 10 times its own weight. Obtained from bones and connective tissue.

Glycogen: Sometimes called animal starch. A substance made of units of glucose, stored in muscle and liver. It is converted back to glucose when required for energy.

Haemoglobin: A pigment in red blood cells which carries oxygen. It is a conjugated protein containing iron.

Homogenisation: The process of forcing milk through small apertures in order to break up and more evenly distribute its fat globules.

Hormone: A chemical released into the blood by endocrine glands. It activates other body cells in target organs.

Humectant: An additive used to prevent moisture loss from convenience foods.

Hydrogenation: The saturation of carbon atoms in an unsaturated fat by adding hydrogen. This results in a hard fat.

Hydrolysis: This occurs when a compound reacts with water. The compound is broken down into simpler substances.

Invert sugar: A mixture of glucose and fructose produced when sucrose is hydrolysed (see Hydrolysis).

Joule: A unit of energy.

Leucocytes: White blood cells.

Liaison: A thickening agent such as flour. Used in soups, sauces.

Lipids: Fats and oils.

Lymphocyte: A white blood cell which produces antibodies to fight infection.

Matter: Any substance which occupies space and has mass. It can exist as a solid, liquid or gas.

Mesophilic organisms: Those that grow at medium-range temperatures.

Metabolism: The various chemical reactions in living things, involved in the breaking down of food and building up of new tissues.

Microwaves: Very high frequency electromagnetic waves.

Molecule: The smallest group of atoms capable of a separate existence.

Monosaccharide: A single sugar unit. Carbohydrates are composed of monosaccharide units.

Mucous membrane: A mucus-secreting membrane which lines body cavities or passages that are open to external environment.

Mucus: A slimy protective secretion of mucous membranes. Example: nasal secretion. (Note difference in spelling, mucous/mucus.)

Mycelium : A mass of intertwining hyphae (in moulds).

Myomeres: Groups of short muscle fibres present in fish flesh.

Nephron: The working unit of the kidney. Millions of nephrons filter urine from the blood.

Neuron: A nerve fibre. Several neurons make up a nerve.

Osmosis: The diffusion or movement of water molecules through a semi-permeable membrane from a weak solution to a stronger one until their concentrations are equal.

Oxidation: The reaction between oxygen and another element. Internal respiration is the process whereby oxygen combines with the carbon of food in the tissues, to produce energy, with the release of CO_2 and waste.

Pectin: An insoluble polysaccharide present in the cell walls of fruit and capable of setting jam.

Pernicious anaemia: Deficiency of vitamin B_{12} which is necessary for red blood cell formation.

Phagocyte: A cell which can ingest and destroy invading micro-organisms.

pH scale: This is a measurement of acidity and alkalinity on a scale from 0 to 14. A pH of 7 is neutral.

	HC1		caustic soda
1 ◄	2 ─────	7 ──────►	14
strong acid	water		strong alkali

Plasma: The liquid component of blood.

Platelets: Tiny cell particles which help blood to clot.

Polysaccharide: A chain of monosaccharides. Examples: starch, cellulose.

Proteolytic enzymes: Enzymes which break down proteins into shorter chains or amino acids.

Prothrombin: A clotting agent in blood which changes to thrombin.

Psychrophilic micro-organisms: Those which thrive at low temperatures. Example: listeria.

Rancidity: A form of decomposition of fat.

Reduction: The removal of oxygen from a substance. It is the opposite to oxidation and occurs simultaneously with it. Antioxidants work by reduction. Reducing sugars can remove oxygen from a substance (see Fehling's test, page 13).

Respiration, external: Taking in of oxygen and removal of CO_2 through the lungs.

Respiration, internal: See Oxidation.

Retinol: Vitamin A.

Rhesus factor: The presence (Rh+) or absence (Rh-) of certain antigens in blood.

Riboflavin: Vitamin B_2.

Roughage: Fibre or cellulose which stimulates the intestine.

Solution: A homogeneous mixture of two or more substances. The most common solutions involve a solid dissolving in a liquid.

Solute: The substance which dissolves.

Solvent: The liquid in which a substance dissolves. A saturated solution contains as much solute as the solvent can hold.

Spirillum: Spiral bacterium.

Spore: A normal reproductive cell produced by micro-organisms, such as moulds. Note: not to be confused with endospore or bacterial spore which is a heat-resistant, dormant cell which is difficult to destroy.

Stabiliser: A substance which keeps oil and water dispersed after emulsification.

Sublimation: A change of state from a solid to a vapour without passing through the intermediate liquid state. This occurs in freeze drying.

Synapse: A chemical link across nerve endings which are not connected.

Thermophilic micro-organisms: Those which can survive at higher than normal temperatures.

Thiamine: Vitamin B_1; quite unstable to heat.

Tocopherol: Vitamin E.

Toxin: A poison produced during metabolism.

UHT: Ultra-heat treatment; a method of preserving milk for several months. Milk is heated to 135°C for 1 second.

Vacuum: An airtight space from which air is excluded.

Yeast: A unicellular fungus.

HOME

EARNING

Most of us are paid regularly, either weekly or monthly. *Gross income* is the amount of money we earn before any deductions are made. *Gross annual income* is the amount we earn in one year, such as wages/salary, commission or interest on savings.

Nett income is the amount of money left after compulsory deductions have been made — in other words, the amount we have to spend.

In order to work out a budget, it is necessary to calculate our monthly and weekly income.

DEDUCTIONS
- Income tax
- Social insurance
- Government levies, e.g. Health, Youth Employment
- Superannuation: payment towards pension
- Health insurance such as VHI
- Payment into savings schemes

INCOME TAX (PAYE)
This is the principal method by which the government raises money to run the country. It is deducted by the PAYE (Pay As You Earn) system. This means that each employer deducts tax from employees' wages and pays it directly to the government.

People who are self-employed must arrange to pay their tax to the government. Failure to pay tax may result in prosecution and fines.

Each taxpayer has a code number and fills in a tax return form at the end of every financial year. Various tax-free allowances are made before tax is deducted.
- A personal allowance
- PAYE allowance
- Allowances on interest on mortgage repayments, life assurance premiums, Voluntary Health Insurance (VHI). (These allowances may vary from time to time.)
- Allowances for certain dependent relatives

When these allowances are subtracted from the total income, the remainder is taxed on a sliding scale.

Those on low incomes pay little or no tax because they do not earn more than their total allowances.

Employees also pay:
- PRSI at 5.75% up to £17,300 per annum
- Health Act contributions of 1.25% of gross income up to £16,700 per annum
- Employment contribution of 1% of gross income.

TAX-FREE ALLOWANCES
Find out the current allowances and fill in accordingly.

Income Tax Allowances	1990 Single/Married	19-- Single/Married	19-- Single/Married
Personal allowance	2,050/4,100		
PAYE allowance	800/1,600*		
PRSI allowance	286/572*		
Interest on mortgage, house repairs, 90% (maximum allowed)	80% up to 2,000/4,000 interest paid		
Children	Nil, unless incapacitated		
Dependent relative	110		
VHI	Full premium		
Life assurance	25% of premium		
Superannuation	Full premium		

* Only double if both spouses are employed. No income tax payable if income is under £3,250/6,500
+ £300 each child

Rates of Taxable Income (after deduction of allowances)			
Rate	19– – Single/Married	19– – Single/Married	19– – Single/Married
30% 48% 53%	First £6,500/13,000 Next 3,100/6,200 Balance		

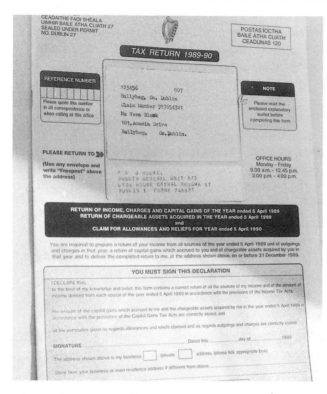

PAY-RELATED SOCIAL INSURANCE (PRSI)

Most employees over 16 years of age must pay social insurance, regardless of income. Contributions are calculated as a percentage of the employee's earnings, the cost being shared between the employer and employee. PRSI contributions are usually deducted at source by the employer and paid to the government, along with the employee's income tax.

Certain persons such as low-paid workers, deserted wives and unmarried mothers are exempt from paying employees' contributions.

Benefits available include:

- Unemployment benefit
- Disability benefit
- Maternity benefit
- Deserted wives' benefit
- Widow's pension (contributory)
- Old-age pension (contributory)
- Death grant
- Redundancy (a lump sum payable to insured workers when they are made redundant)

To qualify for benefit: A claimant must have contributed PRSI for a minimum of 39 weeks *in the year prior* to the period in which benefit is being claimed. Contributions are credited to those who are unemployed or receiving other benefits.

Remember: Both contributions and benefits are pay-related. This means that those on low incomes both pay and receive benefits lower than those on high incomes.

CURRENT DETAILS IN ANNUAL BOOKLET
Summary of Social Insurance and Social Assistance Services

SPENDING

Most people find that their spending, unlike their income, is irregular. Some bills come once or twice a year; others every month or two. Each day we spend money on items such as food and bus fares. At certain times of the year, a family has extra expenses, such as at Christmas time or back-to-school time. Unexpected spending such as house repairs and doctors' bills crop up now and then.

Weekly	Monthly	Quarterly or bi-monthly	½ yearly/ Annually	Occasionally
Food, Fares	Mortgage/ HP	ESB, gas, Phone	Insurance, Licences	Furniture Repairs

Note: Many people fail to see the difference between a *need* — something we *must* have to live or work (for example, food, shelter, warmth) — and a '*want*' such as a holiday. A car would be a 'need' for a commercial traveller but a 'want' for many other people. The higher our income, the more we can satisfy our wants as well as our needs. But remember — essentials/needs must be catered for first.

Each family has different priorities, depending on:
1. Income
2. The stage of the family — newlyweds, those with growing children, pensioners
3. The number in the family

A single girl living at home, for example, will have less essential spending than a young family which has to pay rent or mortgage repayments and buy furniture and children's clothes.

Because spending is so irregular, we need to put aside much of our income on pay-day so that it is there when we need it for essentials.

Lots of people complain about not being able to make ends meet, yet few sit down and plan how to spend their money.

BUDGETING

Budgeting is the process of managing one's income so that essential spending is first provided for before discretionary (less essential) spending. Budgeting is a question of balance — balancing money coming in (income) against money being spent (expenditure).

A budget is a plan for spending. A good budget plan helps reduce anxiety over money, whatever our income, and gives us more control over our lives. If money is safely put aside for essentials, we can feel safe in the knowledge that what is left over can be spent on luxuries such as entertainment, without having to worry over future bills.

A family budget should be a joint effort. Both husband and wife should be equally involved in planning how family income should be spent.

ADVANTAGES OF BUDGETING

1. It keeps expenditure under control, allows for major bills and seasonal spending.
2. Without a plan, there is a danger of over-spending on luxuries and not having enough money for necessities.

3. A budget cuts down on impulse buying and irresponsible spending.
4. Written budgets show where overspending occurs and where economies can be made.
5. It gives children a good example in the handling of money.
6. Failure to plan spending, particularly when credit is used, can lead to serious financial problems.
7. Budgeting reduces stress and anxiety and results in a greater sense of security and independence.

DRAWING UP A HOUSEHOLD BUDGET

1. Collect bills, receipts etc. List major essential spending in the previous year (e.g. mortgage, insurance etc.) and add them up. (Add a little for increases/inflation or change in circumstances — for example, a new baby.)
2. Work out what you spend weekly on items such as food or travel. Multiply by 52. Add to previous total and divide by 12. This tells you the amount you should set aside per month to cover essentials. Keep this money in a deposit account so that it is available for monthly withdrawals.
3. List your income for the coming year, excluding possible income such as overtime.
4. List expenditure (see chart).
   - Essential
   - Less essential, but still important
   - Set aside a sum for savings/emergencies, if the budget allows.
   - The remainder can be spent on non essentials such as holidays or entertainment. Don't forget to set aside a sum for high spending times such as Christmas or back-to-school time.
5. Pencil in the estimated amount of bills in the month they are expected. As you pay them, fill in the true amount in pen. This gives you a clear picture of where you stand — what bills to expect, when to expect them, and what bills are paid.

Check this budget each month against what you spend. It may be necessary to alter the budget if circumstances change (if a new baby arrives) or at retirement. You will soon see if you are spending too much in one area and leaving things short in another.

Income	Jan	Feb	Mar	Apr	May	Jun	Jul	Aug	Sept	Oct	Nov	Dec
Husband's earnings } Wife's earnings } after deductions												
Social welfare benefits e.g. FIS, Child Benefit, Unemployment Benefit, Pension/Interest on Savings												
Total Income												
Expenditure												
A. Essential												
Rent/Mortgage												
Food												
Electricity												
Other fuels (coal, gas, oil)												
Household (cleaning, repairs)												
House and contents insurance												
Basic clothes												
Essential travel												
B. Less essential/occasional												
Telephone												
Car expenses/petrol/fares												
Furniture/appliances												
Health insurance												
Education expenses (e.g. books)												
Medical (e.g. doctor, dentist, chemist)												
C. Savings												
Short- and long-term savings												
Life assurance												
D. Personal Spending												
Pocket money, hobbies												
TV (HP/licence etc.)												
Entertainment to include: Dining out/alcohol/cigarettes holidays/trips												
Christmas spending/presents												
Total Expenditure												
Debit/Credit												

ALLOCATING THE INCOME: recommended expenditure

Housing 25%	— Rent or mortgage repayments; house insurance; house and garden; maintenance and repairs.
Food 25%	— Feed the family a well-balanced diet, thus reducing doctors' bills. Economise by careful shopping. Use cheaper cuts of meat. Avoid convenience foods.
Household 20%	— Fuel for cooking, lighting, heating. Furniture and equipment; household linen; cleaning materials; telephone. Keep fuel bills down by insulating well.
Clothing 7%	— Clothes, shoes and dry cleaning. This will be a priority where growing children are concerned. Shop during sales or make your own clothes to economise.
Car/Fares 7%	— This will be reduced considerably if you live near work or use a bicycle. Commuting is expensive.
Education/Health 5%	— School books/sports etc. Doctors', dentists', chemists' bills; VHI. Those availing of free education and those on medical cards will have less expenditure here.
Personal, Entertainment } *6-7%*	— Cosmetics, hairdresser, gifts, hobbies, stationery, books, sports and pets. Cinema, theatre, discos, babysitting. Remember that certain hobbies such as gardening, woodwork and dressmaking *save* money — many cost little, e.g. walking, cycling, football, joining a library.
Savings 5%	— Set aside a regular sum towards emergencies. Life assurance might be included here.

This list is an approximate guide only. Different families have different priorities. Take a look at how money was spent on average in Ireland in the 1980s. Note the amount spent on alcohol and tobacco! Is this necessary?

Expenditure	1980	%	1987	
Housing	7.2		8.8	
Fuel/light	6.1		6.3	
Household durables, e.g. furniture	5.5	} 20.7	3.9	} 21
Household non-durables	1.9		2.0	
Food	27.7		25.0	
Alcoholic drink/Tobacco	8.2		8.0	
Clothing/footwear	8.9		6.7	
Transport	14.9		13.6	
Services and other expenditure	16.8		22.0	
Miscellaneous goods	3.8		3.5	

BUDGETING ON A LOW INCOME

Many families have a constant struggle to make ends meet. Those on a low income may qualify for Family Income Supplement (FIS) to top up their income, particularly if they have children. Those receiving Social Welfare/Assistance or benefit have to exist on extremely low incomes. These people have to spend nearly all of their money on essentials and cannot usually afford to save.

Sample budget for a family on a low income	
Food	35%
Rent	20%
Fuel (heat, light, cooking)	20%
Clothes, particularly for children	10%
Fares	10%
Miscellaneous	10%

BUDGETING AND YOUNG PEOPLE

Young children can learn to budget and save some of their pocket money. Older children benefit from a clothes allowance — a quarterly sum from which all clothes must be bought. This teaches them the value of money and gives them some responsibility.

Sample Budget for a Young Person	
Keep*	35%
Fares	10%
Lunches/snacks	10%
Clothes	15%
Entertainment	15%
Savings/Insurance	10%
Miscellaneous, including hobbies	5-10%

* Contribution to parents towards expenses incurred
e.g. heating, lighting, laundry.

WEEKLY ACCOUNTS

It is a good idea to keep a simple account of each week's spending. In this way, it is easy to see where the money is going and how much is left to spend. Each evening, jot down your daily spending. You will soon see if you are living beyond your means and, if so, where to cut back.

Example of Daily spending		
Date	Goods or Services	Cash
14 Feb.	Bus fares	2.00
	Butcher	4.00
	Supermarket	10.50
	Snack lunch	3.50
	Newspapers	1.20
	Flowers	3.00

Bills may be paid:
- By cash
- By cheque
- By credit payment — for example, credit card, HP (see below).
- Credit transfer (giro). Bills can be paid into the bank which will transfer the money to the bank account of the company.

► CREDIT

Credit comes in many forms — mortgages, overdrafts, budget accounts, credit cards, hire purchase. All forms of credit add up to the same thing — Buy now and pay later.

When you borrow money (or delay paying for an item), you will have to pay dearly for the privilege. Credit companies and banks charge high *interest* on the money they lend. This puts up the cost of an item, so it is usually more sensible to save first. *Repayments* to the credit company are made in fixed instalments.

The Annual Percentage Rate (APR) of interest must be displayed on any credit agreement or advertisement.

Many household items are bought on credit

ARE YOU A GOOD RISK?

Credit is based on trust. Before any organisation will lend you money, it must find out if you are trustworthy — whether you are a good risk. It is necessary to fill out a detailed form stating job, income and existing credit arrangements. It is usually necessary to obtain a reference or a *guarantor* — someone who will pay up if you *default*, particularly if you are under eighteen.

FORMS OF CREDIT

1. HIRE PURCHASE (HP)

This works on the principle that the buyer hires goods and pays for them in regular instalments over a certain period of time. During this time, the buyer has the use of the goods but does not own them until the final instalment has been paid.

The buyer pays the cash price of the goods, plus a high rate of interest. A deposit may be required. A person under eighteen needs a guarantor.

A hire purchase agreement should state clearly in writing:
1. The cash price of the goods
2. The amount of each instalment
3. The full hire purchase price, including interest
4. The date on which instalments fall due

5. A clear description of the goods
6. Details of your rights should you wish to return the goods or if the goods prove faulty
7. The APR: Annual Percentage Rate (interest)

Note: *Read any agreement carefully* — especially the small print. *Do not sign* the agreement until you fully understand it. Once signed, the agreement is legally binding. A stamped copy of the agreement must, by law, be sent to the buyer within fourteen days of signing the agreement.

Remember: The hire purchase company is entitled to repossess the goods if the hirer defaults (stops paying). A court order is required to repossess if more than one-third of the hire purchase price has been paid.

2. CREDIT SALES DEFERRED PAYMENT
This method is similar to hire purchase except that:
1. A deposit is always paid.
2. The goods become the property of the buyer once the first instalment has been paid. The retailer cannot repossess the goods in the case of default, but must sue for the money in court.

3. BUDGET ACCOUNT
This is a form of revolving credit frequently offered by department stores. It works like this.
- An agreement is made to pay a fixed sum to the shop every month.
- After the first payment, goods up to ten times the monthly payment may be bought in the store.
- As the months go by, the amount outstanding reduces and more goods may be purchased as long as the credit limit is not exceeded and regular repayments are made.

Disadvantages
- Interest on these accounts is quite high.
- You are restricted to shopping in one shop or a chain of shops.

4. CREDIT CARDS (VISA, ACCESS)
These cards allow the holder to buy goods or pay for services up to a pre-arranged monthly limit. A monthly

account is issued on which purchases are itemised. If the whole bill is paid promptly, for example within 28 days, some companies charge no interest. Otherwise a percentage of the balance must be paid off and interest is charged on the remainder until it is cleared. Credit cards are very convenient, which makes it very easy to overspend and get into debt. They are not recommended for compulsive spenders! A yearly government levy is also charged.

5. CHARGE CARDS
These are similar to credit cards, except that the account must be paid in full at the end of each month, otherwise very high interest rates apply. An annual charge is made. Examples: Diners Club, American Express.

6. OVERDRAFT FROM BANK
One of the simplest and cheapest forms of credit is to get permission to overdraw your bank account by a fixed amount.

CREDIT AND THE LAW
The consumer is protected by:
1. Hire Purchase Acts, 1946 and 1960.
2. The Sale of Goods and Supply of Services Act 1980, which tightened up some hire purchase loopholes to further protect the consumer.

ADVANTAGES OF CREDIT
1. The buyer has the use of the goods long before they could be bought for cash.
2. Without credit, large items such as cars and houses could be bought by very few people.
3. With inflation and rapidly increasing prices, it is often almost impossible to save for a large item before it goes up in price.
4. It avoids the risk of carrying large sums of money.
5. It encourages a flow of cash and goods, thereby increasing employment.
6. There is a low (or no) initial outlay.

DISADVANTAGES OF CREDIT
1. Interest rates are high and no longer eligible for tax relief.
2. There is a real danger of taking on too many credit commitments and not being able to keep up the repayments.
3. Credit is too tempting for the weak-willed and spendthrift.
4. Unscrupulous door-to-door salesmen may use unfair persuasion on housewives, pensioners etc. at home on their own, by persuading them to buy items they do not need on credit.
5. Although the item may be used from time of purchase, it is not owned until the final instalment is paid.

LEASING

It is now possible to lease goods which in the past were bought on credit — for example, cars, TV sets, cookers. While expensive, there are a number of advantages. The item is replaced by a new one after a number of years. It may be serviced/repaired free-of-charge during the leasing period.

► SAVING

It is a good idea to start saving the moment you earn your first pay packet. This means that it quickly becomes a habit and that money will be there when you need it. Living 'one day at a time' is not wise when it comes to money!

A family should have two savings accounts:
- One for short-term goals — a car, holiday, or Christmas.
- One for long-term saving which can be drawn on in the case of a genuine emergency. Long-term saving can also be used as a pension or to save towards major expenses such as further education or buying a house.

INVESTING YOUR MONEY

The main considerations are:
1. *Rate of Interest:* This varies depending on where you put your money and the type of scheme or account you use. Rates of interest are based on the bank rate. Shop around for the best rates.
2. *Tax:* Most interest earned from saving is taxable. In most cases it is paid directly to the government, using the Deposit Interest Retention Tax (DIRT) system. Some schemes such as savings bonds are tax free.
3. *Ease of withdrawal:* With many accounts, withdrawals may be made on the spot (on demand) up to a certain limit. Notice is required before withdrawing large sums, or in certain schemes which give a better rate of interest.
4. *Safety:* Any scheme which is state-guaranteed is absolutely safe, as the state will pay out in the event of the bank etc. becoming insolvent. Any company with *trustee status* is also safe, as the government guarantees its funds.

Large banks and building societies are safer forms of investment than investing in the stock market or new unproven investments.

1. GOVERNMENT-SPONSORED SAVINGS SCHEMES

AN POST

An Post schemes are those that operate through post offices. They are state-guaranteed and provide a wide choice in methods of saving. They also have more branches than any other savings bank.

1. Post Office Savings Bank
This is a deposit account. Money can be deposited or withdrawn easily in any post office and each transaction is entered into a deposit book. Notice in writing must be given when withdrawing large sums. Loans are now available by arrangement with a merchant bank.
Disadvantage: Interest is taxed.

2. Savings Stamps
This is a similar scheme designed for children to encourage them to save. Children buy stamps and paste them into a post office savings book. When this is filled, the children are encouraged to use it to open a savings bank account, as in 1 above.

3. Index-linked* National Instalment Savings
Under this scheme, a person agrees to save a certain amount every month for a year.** This is left on an account for two further years when an index-linked bonus is paid. A further bonus is given if savings are left for five years. Interest is tax free.

* Index-linked means that payment is in ratio to the consumer price index, which is linked to the economic situation such as rate of inflation etc. It ensures that total interest will never be less, in real terms, than the amount saved.

4. Savings Certificates
These are bought in units of £10. The money must be left for five years and a high rate of interest is paid.** This is reduced if the money is withdrawn before the five years are up. Interest is tax free.

5. Index-linked Savings Bonds
These are bought in multiples of £50. They provide a good rate of interest** with a bonus if the bonds are not

cashed in for three years. All interest is tax free. One week's notice is required for withdrawal.

** Check leaflets available in post offices for latest interest rates/conditions.

INDUSTRIAL CREDIT COMPANY/AGRICULTURAL CREDIT CORPORATION

These are state-sponsored development banks. Their purpose is to raise money for investment in Irish business (ICC) and Irish agriculture (ACC). Deposit accounts may be opened, but withdrawal may be difficult as there are few outlets.

PRIZE BONDS

Prize bonds costing £5 each are available at banks and post offices. No interest is paid, but each bond is placed in a weekly draw for large amounts of money. Bonds may be cashed in easily.

TRUSTEE SAVINGS BANKS (TSB)

These provide:
1. Deposit account (easy withdrawal).
2. Investment account (long-term savings at a higher interest rate than deposit account).
3. Current account (cheque book accounts)

All monies are state-guaranteed and the rate of interest is usually a little higher than that of commercial banks. TSB provide loans and many other banking facilities not provided by An Post. They also have longer opening hours than other banks.

Rate of Interest on Ordinary Deposit Accounts (find current rates)**			
	1990	19– –	19– –
PO Savings Bank	7.75%		
ACC/ICC	7%		
TSB	6%		
Associated Banks	5.75%		
Building Society	9.2%		
Credit Union			

Interest on any of the above (except credit unions) is subject to Deposit Interest Retention Tax (DIRT). This is paid by the bank directly to the government. Investors may be liable to pay further tax. Savings Bonds, Savings Certificates and National Instalment Savings are completely tax free.

2. OTHER METHODS OF SAVING

COMMERCIAL BANKS

These are large financial institutions including the Bank of Ireland and Allied Irish Banks (referred to as the *Associated Banks*). They provide loans and many other facilities.

Inside a bank

There are two basic types of account:
- *Current account:* You have the use of a cheque book, but money earns no interest — in fact you pay the bank fees or charges. A bank card or cheque card is provided to facilitate the cashing of cheques and the use of the ATM (Automatic teller machines). Bills can be paid by *direct debit* (money will be taken from your account and paid into another account). A *statement* (list of transactions) is posted out regularly so that one can keep a check on the account. *Loans* and *overdraft facilities* (permission to withdraw more than the amount in your account) are provided.
- *Deposit account:* Money can be deposited or withdrawn at any time within banking hours or by use of cash dispensing machine — 24 hours a day.

    Bank deposit accounts are mainly used to save money. Interest is paid automatically into the account. A statement is issued at intervals or a deposit book may be provided.

Automated teller machines (ATM) such as PASS and Banklink enable cash to be withdrawn from a current or deposit account, once it is in credit, at any time of the day or night. They also provide other facilities such as bank statements, bill paying etc.

BUILDING SOCIETIES

Up until recently, building societies only provided saving facilities and loans for house purchase. Today they provide many of the services available from banks such as foreign exchange.

It is a good idea to save with a building society as house loans may only be given to investors.

■ Shares account: Money can be deposited or withdrawn at any time on production of deposit book and identification. Notice is required for large withdrawals.

Other types of account provide a higher rate of interest, but 1-3 month's notice may be required for withdrawal.

CREDIT UNIONS

These are local co-operative organisations. They are run largely on a voluntary basis, which keeps overheads low. Members usually come from a specific area or workplace. Although the interest rate is low, so also is the lending rate of interest if you wish to borrow money — much lower than comparable institutions. Opening hours vary — many are open evenings to facilitate members.

IRELAND

Credit unions specialise in small savings and will only provide fairly small loans. Savings must be kept in the account for the length of any loan. All money in a credit union is insured against loss and money is therefore safe.

LOTTERIES

Lotteries are not a form of saving. They provide a very low possibility of winning a substantial sum. Money put in a lottery is lost. Lotteries encourage gambling and often result in deprivation when those who can least afford it gamble social insurance payments in the hope of the elusive 'big win'.

▶ INSURANCE

The purpose of insurance is to share risks among insured people so that the loss will not be too great for the few who are unlucky. Those insured pay into a central fund (the insurance company) from which any losses are paid out. Money is not paid back if you do not have a claim.

Insurance may also be used as a form of long-term saving as with a pension scheme, towards further education or simply as an investment to earn interest.

Some insurance such as PRSI and car insurance are compulsory. Most insurance schemes are voluntary.

INSURANCE TERMS

■ The *premium* is the sum of money paid annually or by instalments to the insurance company.

■ The *policy* is the scheme in which the insured person is involved.

■ The *policy document* specifies the conditions of the scheme and the amount of cover provided.

■ The *claim* is the request for compensation — as the result of an accident, for example — and the amount paid out.

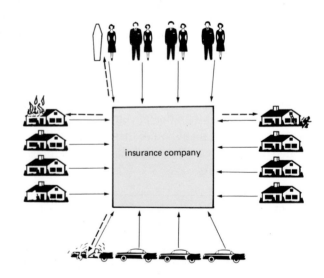

insurance company

■ *Assurance* covers something which is *certain* to happen — death.

■ *Insurance* covers something which *may* happen such as a fire.

■ *A broker* is an agent who advises on aspects of insurance/assurance and receives commission.

1. LIFE ASSURANCE

This is a form of assurance taken out on the life of a person. When that person dies, the beneficiary — usually the spouse — receives a lump sum of money in ratio to the yearly premiums paid. There are three types of life assurance.

(a) Standard Whole Life Assurance

This involves two parts — a 'risk premium' (that is against death) and a 'savings element' which will be invested by the company and paid back to the policyholder at the end of the policy term, say at 60 years, with any profits accumulated. It guarantees either payment of a lump sum if death occurs during the life of the policy, or a pay-back at the end of the policy term with profits from the investment.

(b) Term Assurance

The individual is insured for a fixed term, say 20 years. A lump sum is paid if the policyholder dies within this term. If death occurs after that, nothing is paid out. As it has no savings element, it is the cheapest form of life assurance. It is ideal for a young wage earner with dependants who cannot afford large life assurance premiums.

Convertible term is the name given to a term policy on which the insured person has the option to change to a whole life or endowment policy.

A mortgage protection policy is a form of 'reducing term' assurance (that is the pay out is lower, the later death occurs). It is used to cover the life of a mortgage holder for the amount outstanding so that the mortgage is paid off if the mortgage holder dies.

(c) Endowment Assurance

As this has a higher savings element, it is the most expensive form of life assurance. It provides a minimum guaranteed payout at the end of a fixed period, say 15 years. This is reduced considerably if it is 'cashed in' early. A lump sum is also paid out on death. Endowment assurance is often used as a form of pension or savings for further education of children as it has tax advantages.

Tax allowances are given to those paying life assurance in order to encourage people to provide for their families and thus save the state the expense of providing for dependants should the breadwinner die.

Annuity: This is a method whereby a person can invest a lump sum with an insurance company, for example to prepare for retirement. A pre-arranged sum is paid out to the investor (like a salary or pension) until death.

2. HOUSEHOLD INSURANCE

A wide range of cover is provided by various insurance companies. Insurance should be provided for:

(a) The house: In the event of damage by storm, flood, fire etc.

(b) The contents: The insuring of normal items such as furniture, carpets, curtains and household equipment so that they are covered for damage, fire or burglary.

(c) Valuables: Jewellery, furs and expensive equipment such as a camera, stereo or video should be covered by a separate all-risks policy which also insures them while outside the house.

Note: Make sure to raise the cover regularly when renewing insurance premiums in order to maintain the real value of replacing the property. Most premiums are now index-linked.

3. CAR INSURANCE

Every person who drives a car must by law be insured in order that any damage caused by an accident can be paid for. There are two types of policy:

(a) Third party. This is the least amount of insurance one may have and is the cheapest form. It covers the driver for any injuries or damage to the property of other people, who are the third parties, but it does not cover the driver or his/her car. An extra premium will insure the car for fire and theft.

(b) Comprehensive: This covers injury and damage to all parties and property. It is more expensive.

4. MEDICAL INSURANCE

There are two principal types of private medical insurance.

(a) Permanent health insurance (PHI) which covers an individual who may be permanently or temporarily incapacitated and therefore unable to work. It pays out a regular income to the incapacitated in ratio to premiums paid.

(b) Voluntary Health Insurance (VHI).
Voluntary Health Insurance covers:

- treatment such as surgeons' costs, for those whose income is above the limit for hospital services (category III of the health services)
- private or semi-private hospital or nursing home maintenance
- basic maintenance
- out-patient benefits.

In the latter case, expenses such as doctors' and specialists' fees, X-rays, physiotherapy and so on are added up. If the total in any one year comes to over a specified limit (see below), the balance, up to a set limit, is paid by the Voluntary Health Insurance board.

Current limit —1990 £105 per person; £170 per family

19__ £____ per person; £____ per family

5. OTHER TYPES OF INSURANCE
(a) Social insurance (PRSI) (page 169)
(b) Travel insurance

ADVANTAGES OF INSURANCE
1. Families are more secure when they know that the main wage earner is insured so that they will be provided for should the breadwinner die.
2. Insurance protects against the shocks of life — fire, theft and accident — and attempts to compensate for them.
3. Insurance can be used as a form of saving or as a pension for old age.
4. Tax relief can be claimed on life, health and medical insurance.

One of the most basic lessons each of us needs to learn is how to shop wisely. Lots of helpful advice is given in consumer magazines, on TV and in newspapers but it needs to be put into practice. 'Caveat emptor', an old Latin phrase, still applies — it means 'Let the buyer beware'.

Manufacturers spend lots of time and effort finding out our weaknesses such as our favourite colours and things we like and dislike. They use this knowledge to help them to design packets, advertisements and even shops which encourage us to spend more and more of our hard-earned money. It is up to us to be just as smart as they are by becoming conscious consumers, being aware of prices, looking for good quality and knowing our legal rights.

SHOPPING — A SERIES OF CHOICES

Shopping is basically a matter of making decisions. The scarcer the money, the more important these choices are. Close attention must be paid to what we are buying and how much it costs. But in the rush to save money, do not forget quality. It is essential that each item we buy is suitable for its purpose and reasonably long lasting. (A bargain is not a bargain if it does not fulfil its purpose.)

Examine each item carefully, checking labels for information — price, weight, size, guarantee, washing instructions etc. Anything we buy should be:

- Of good quality
- Good value for money
- Suitable for its purpose
- Well designed and made
- Suitable for our needs
- Capable of withstanding normal wear and tear — with obvious exceptions such as food.

SHOPS

Individual shops are often close to home. They give a personal service and will often oblige with small amounts of a product, e.g. one or two rashers. Small shops are usually more expensive than large shops but may stay open late or at weekends. Some of them will deliver goods and offer credit facilities.

Supermarkets and other large shops offer a wider variety of goods. They are cheaper because supermarkets buy in bulk. They have a good turnover of perishable goods which are more likely to be fresh. The self-service system cuts down on staff which facilitates the lowering of prices. Be careful, however. Such shops are designed to make you spend as much money as possible, with essentials at the back of the shop and sweets and other non-essentials under your nose at the checkout!

Computerised checkouts. Do they benefit retailer or consumer?

There are a number of things to look for before choosing a supermarket.

- Both the assistants and shop should be clean and hygienic.
- A list of basic food prices should be displayed.
- Perishables such as meat, fish and dairy produce should be displayed in chilled cabinets.
- Raw meat and cooked meat or fish should be kept separate.
- Wide aisles, sufficient checkouts and a car park are important.

Be conscious of how much you are buying because there is a strong possibility of overspending in a supermarket. Many supermarkets do not normally offer credit or delivery facilities, although most large chains accept credit cards.

SHOPPING TIPS:

- Make a list and keep to it.
- Shop once a week to cut down on impulse buying.
- Get to know the price of basics and shop around for good value.

- Check weights and date stamping.
- Avoid shopping when tired or hungry. Otherwise you will be more likely to buy more.
- When buying perishables, 'a little and often' is the best policy.
- Shop locally to avoid travel costs.
- Only bulk buy if you are sure it is good value and if you know you will use up the product.
- Clothes/household linen etc. should be checked carefully for size. The care label should indicate the type of fabric and how to clean it.
- Keep receipts, instruction leaflets and guarantees in a safe place.

SHOPPING TERMS AND PRACTICES

- *Special offers:* An offer is only 'special' if it is an item you need. Some supermarkets reduce a number of basics each week. A wise shopper will stock up on such non-perishable bargains if they are good value. Compulsive buyers might be better off avoiding special offers.
- *Loss leaders:* These are special offers which are sold at cost in order to encourage people to shop in a particular supermarket. It is now illegal to advertise or sell goods below cost.
- *Trading stamps:* These are stamps given when a certain amount of money is spent in a shop or garage. When a certain number of stamps have been saved, they may be exchanged for 'gifts'. The main beneficiary in the trading stamp system is the trader — a price reduction would be more beneficial to the consumer.
- *Own-brand goods:* Certain products are sold cheaply in supermarkets in practical packets under the supermarket name or under names such as 'Yellow Pack' or 'Thrift'. These may be good value, but it is safer to try just one item to make sure it suits before bulk buying.
- *Bulk buying:* This may be cheap, but not always. Only non-perishables should be bought this way. There is a danger that the family will grow tired of the product, such as a particular variety of soup, or that they will be extravagant if there is a large amount in reserve. Extra money and transport are required when buying in bulk.
- *Prices:* The cost of many items that we buy is often influenced by factors over which we have little control. Such factors include world market conditions, inflation, fuel costs, weather, scarcity and wage increases. There are also the hidden costs of packaging and advertising.
- *Computerised checkouts:* Many supermarkets now use *bar codes* to key the prices of all items into a computer. Checkout operators simply run the bar code over a scanner which rings up an itemised receipt on the cash register. This is a useful form of stock control for the retailer, but it can cause problems for shoppers as prices are only displayed on shelves — not on each item. If the stock is not placed exactly behind prices on the shelves, it is impossible to know the price.

► CONSUMER INFORMATION

A consumer is a person who obtains goods and services in return for payment of money. Due to the increasing complexity of goods and services, as well as to combat advertising pressures, it has become necessary to increase the output of consumer information.

As a result of constant pressure from consumer groups, the amount of information available to the consumer from manufacturers of products has increased enormously. Large companies, banks etc. provide a wide range of information about their services.

One of the best examples of consumer information is food labelling and grading.

FOOD LABELLING

The EC has many stipulations regarding the sale of food, both fresh and processed. For example, eggs, fruit and vegetables must be *graded* according to size, quality and origin. The contents of tins and packages must be accurately described. The ingredients must be listed in decreasing order by weight (the principal ingredient heads the list). *Additives*, which are strictly controlled, must be listed. The *net weight* — the weight without the tin or packaging — must be given, as well as the name and address of the manufacturer or producer and clear cooking/heating instructions. Perishables should be 'date-stamped'.

A well-labelled product

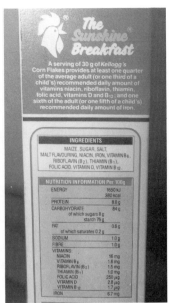

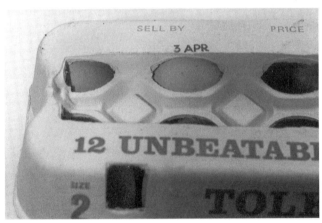

Food labelling/date stamping

- *Date stamping:* This is the system of stamping perishable goods with the date by which the product should be sold. It allows for 1-2 days' storage at home before the product is consumed. Foods commonly date-stamped are often vacuum packed foods. They include rashers, cooked ham, sausages, cheese, yoghurt, milk, cream, eggs, meat pies and cakes.

   New legislation is being prepared which will recommend 'use by' rather than 'sell by' dates. This will allow less margin for error.
- *Unit pricing:* This shows the price per unit — for example per gram or millilitre — making it easier to compare packets of different size to find out which is best value.

   For example: 100 g coffee at £1.30 = 1.3p per gram
                    200 g coffee at £2.50 = 1.25p per gram
   In this case, the larger jar is cheaper.

   It is an expensive and time-consuming facility for the retailer to provide, but it is useful for the consumer.

CARE LABELLING

As there is now such a wide variety of fibres and fabrics, mixtures, blends and finishes, it has become necessary to standardise washing processes into groups.

- The International Care Labelling scheme shows symbols for the washing, drying, ironing and dry-cleaning processes. A cross through a symbol shows that the process must not be used (see also page 259).

   Care labels should be stitched securely into garment seams, so that they will last the life of the garment. Cardboard swing tickets, which are removed after purchase, are not such a good idea.

grade		3	2	1	0
treatment	symbol	no special caution	caution prescribed	special care	treatment prohibited
washing	wash-tub	95°	60°	30° or 40° according to articles	✕
chlorine bleaching	triangle	Cℓ			✕
ironing	iron	⚬⚬⚬	⚬⚬	⚬	✕
dry-cleaning	dry-cleaning cylinder	Ⓐ	Ⓟ	Ⓕ	✕
	colour	green	green orange	orange	red
		—	◯	|||	✕
drying		dry flat	line dry	tumble dry	drip dry

Care labels

STAR MARKING

This is an indication of temperature used by the manufacturers of refrigerators, freezers and frozen foods (see chart, page 255).

SEALS OF APPROVAL/QUALITY MARKS

Some of these are obtained independently by manufacturers to show that their products are good quality and/or safe. Examples: Guaranteed Irish, Wool Mark, Real Leather, the British Standards Institution's 'Kite' mark and its Irish equivalent, the Irish Standards Mark.

Design Centre

caighdeán eireannach

kite mark

woolmark

GUARANTEED IRISH (LTD)

This programme provides marketing support of Irish manufacturers by promoting the use of the Guaranteed Irish symbol in retail outlets. It is funded by manufacturers. Products using the symbol must be manufactured in Ireland and have a high standard of quality. If guaranteed terms are not observed, the symbol may be withdrawn.

APPROVED QUALITY SYSTEM

This is a mark awarded to any Irish company whose *products* or *services* conform to stringent standards set down by the Irish Quality Control Association. When companies apply for the mark, the association's inspectors visit the premises to check processes such as training, quality control, manufacture, hygiene and customer service. Annual inspections are carried out to ensure maintenance of quality. The mark is withdrawn if standards are not maintained. The aim is to improve quality and service in Irish industry.

INSTRUCTIONS

Large and/or complicated equipment should be accompanied by a set of clear instructions on how to use it. Most well-known manufacturers provide instruction booklets with equipment such as washing machines, dishwashers, sewing machines etc. Check that foreign products have instructions printed in English. Instructions on packets of food, cleaning agents etc. are also important.

Note: It is a good idea to keep all instructions, guarantees etc. in a file or large envelope in a safe place in the kitchen so that they are easy to find when needed.

Consumer information is also provided by consumer associations, magazines and other media.

► CONSUMER PROTECTION

THE LAW

The rights of the consumer are protected by a wide range of laws. But even the law cannot protect the consumer from his/her own ignorance and mistakes — only consumer education and information can.

When you buy an item, you are entering into a legal contract between yourself and the shopkeeper. If the goods prove to be faulty, it is the shopkeeper who is responsible and who is bound to refund you your money. (See Sale of Goods Act, 1893, below.) It should not be necessary for you to deal with the manufacturer. You, the buyer, need not accept an exchange or credit note. If the goods are faulty, a cash refund should be given by the shopkeeper.

If, on the other hand, you change your mind about size or colour, the shopkeeper is not obliged to exchange the goods (although this is often allowed as a gesture of goodwill). If you ill-treat the goods, for example if a sweater is washed incorrectly, you have no redress.

SOME IMPORTANT CONSUMER LAWS

1. Sale of Goods Act, 1893
This Act stipulates that goods are of merchantable quality. They must be fit for the purpose for which they are sold and live up to the description given — for example, real leather.

2. Sale of Food and Drugs Acts, 1875 and 1936
These Acts make it an offence to put any ingredient into food which is dangerous to health.

3. Food Hygiene Regulations, 1950 and 1971
These regulations control hygiene in shops and food premises. Inspectors from the Department of Health frequently bring legal proceedings under this Act.

4. Health Acts
Many health acts, for example the Foods Standards Act 1974, control various aspects of food manufacture and distribution, including the use of additives. They cover the preparation and sale of food in hotels, restaurants, hospitals, shops and factories.

5. Weights and Measures Acts, 1878 and 1961
These Acts deal with the accuracy of all weighing and measuring machines — for example, scales, petrol pumps, spirit measures used by publicans.
6. Hire Purchase Acts, 1946 and 1960 and
7. Sale of Goods and Supply of Services Act, 1980
These two Acts deal with laws relating to hire purchase.
8. Consumer Information Act, 1978
This Act relates to trade descriptions, which makes it an offence to make a false description — for example, handmade or waterproof, where it is not; false price claims, for example reduced from £10 when it is not. The Act also makes it illegal to publish misleading advertisements.
9. Sale of Goods and Supply of Services Act, 1980
This Act relates to warranties, guarantees, (see below), quality of goods and exclusion clauses which might restrict the rights of the buyer.

Guides to the Consumer Information Act and Sale of Goods and Supply of Services Act are available from the Office of Consumer Affairs.

GUARANTEES

A guarantee is a contract, usually between the manufacturer and the consumer, in which the manufacturer accepts responsibility for any (or certain) faults which occur in a product within a reasonable time. Most manufacturers of good-quality articles offer a guarantee. Some guarantees are for one year, others three, five or even ten years. The consumer may be required to fill in and post a guarantee form to the manufacturer or else retain the receipt as proof of purchase.

Remember, however, that the contract of sale is between the buyer and the shopkeeper. It is the shopkeeper who is legally obliged to sell goods of 'merchantable quality' (Sale of Goods Act, 1893). The retailer is responsible for the goods she/he sells.

The Sale of Goods and Supply of Services Act, 1980, makes it quite clear what a guarantee should involve. It should:
■ Be clearly legible.
■ Refer to specific goods.
■ State the name and address of the person to whom claims should be made — usually the manufacturer.
■ State the duration of the guarantee from date of purchase.
■ State clearly the procedure for claiming.
■ State clearly what the manufacturer undertakes to do.
■ State what extra charges such as postage may be incurred by the buyer.
■ It may not attempt to limit a consumer's legal rights.
Note: No guarantee will cover goods which have been mistreated.

CONSUMER PROTECTION

GOVERNMENT AGENCIES
As well as the protection given by law for the consumer (see Acts above), the government has initiated several schemes to protect the consumer.
1. *The Consumer Information Act* established the post of *Director of Consumer Affairs* with responsibility for informing the public about consumer rights, encouraging reliable codes of advertising, and instituting court proceedings against advertisers who persist in misleading the public.
2. *The Ombudsman* is appointed by the government to represent the individual who has failed to get satisfaction when dealing with complaints relating to government departments. The Ombudsman acts on behalf of the individual citizen by investigating officials within local authorities, health boards, An Post and Telecom Eireann etc.
3. *EOLAS:* The Irish Science and Technology Agency (formerly IIRS) is concerned with research, development, monitoring and control of areas such as technology, environment and energy. It controls patents and inventions and operates by advising and product-testing for industries — for example, construction, chemical, electronic and telecommunications. *NSAI (National Standards Authority of Ireland)* participates in establishing Irish Standards (using the Irish Standards Mark) and represents Irish industry in ensuring Irish products reach EC and international standards.

THE IRISH SCIENCE AND TECHNOLOGY AGENCY.

4. Safety controls are set down by the Consumer Protection Section of the Department of Industry and Commerce regarding consumer goods which might be dangerous, and can include the banning of dangerous objects. For example, children's night attire must comply with a fire safety regulation and toys must be safe and non-toxic. Anoraks and other outer clothing for children may not have draw cords which have caused strangulation in the past. Electrical goods must conform to strict safety regulations.
5. *The National Social Service Board (NSSB)* gives information on many government services. *Social Service Centres* have been established throughout the country which give advice on legal, social, health and consumer problems.

CONSUMER PROTECTION

VOLUNTARY ORGANISATIONS

1. *Community Information Centres*

Like social service centres (see NSSB above), these provide legal, social and consumer information. They are staffed largely on a voluntary basis.

2. *Consumers' Organisation*

A number of voluntary organisations have helped to improve the situation for the Irish consumer. Residents' associations, the Irish Housewives' Association and the Consumers' Association are just three examples of such.

The Consumers' Association of Ireland helps the consumer in the following ways.

- It provides information. It publishes informative consumer booklets such as *Consumer Choice* and distributes other consumer publications.

- It acts as a lobby at government level, endeavouring to improve consumer legislation and to introduce a more efficient system of justice to deal with small claims arising from consumer purchases.

- It represents Irish consumers when dealing with government departments, state bodies and private industry. Nominees of the association are appointed to boards and councils.

- It provides publicity on consumer issues in the media, as well as providing speakers on consumer matters to schools, clubs etc.

3. *The media*

As interest in consumer affairs has grown, there has been a corresponding increase in the coverage given by the media to consumer topics.

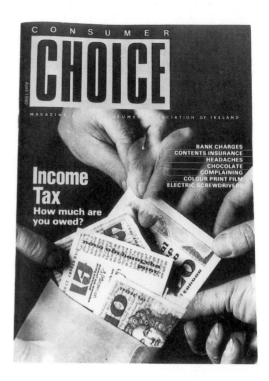

Newspapers publish market reports, indicating the cost of fish, fruit and vegetables. Most papers have a consumer column which gives advice and/or publishes complaints. Magazines, radio and even TV programmes now devote more time to consumer affairs. (A BBC consumer programme, 'That's Life', has an exceptionally high rating.)

This increase in media coverage generates more interest in consumer matters, fulfilling two of the main functions of the media: to inform and to educate.

10 HOUSING

CHOOSING A PLACE TO LIVE

A home provides warmth, shelter and security. The place in which we choose to live is influenced by many factors.

1. Whether we want to rent or buy.
2. The amount of money we can afford to spend/borrow and the amount that we have saved as a deposit.
3. The area and type of neighbourhood in which we wish to live (location).
4. Convenience to work, schools, shops and other amenities (location).
5. The type of house/apartment we prefer.
6. The condition of the house/apartment.
7. Availability.

ACCOMMODATION

One has only to look in the property columns of any newspaper to see the wide variety of accommodation available. We can choose from many types of accommodation.

- *A bedsitter* is a combined bedroom and livingroom, usually with a small kitchen area. A private bathroom may be included but it is more common to share bathroom facilities. Bedsitters are useful for single people as they are cheap and easy to keep. They are usually furnished.

- *A flat* is a set of rooms which form a residence. A self-contained flat will have its own front door and include a bathroom and kitchen. Sharing facilities such as these can be unsatisfactory and can lead to problems regarding times of use, cleaning etc. An apartment is simply an American term for a flat. It usually describes a purpose-built luxury flat rather than the more usual type of flat in an old converted house.

- *A maisonette* (French for 'small house') is a self-contained part of a house and is usually on two levels.

- *Mobile homes* are useful for young couples who need accommodation quickly, particularly if they have a site available (this often applies in rural areas) but not enough money to buy or build a house. Modern mobile homes are large and well fitted. They may be connected to services such as ESB, water and sewerage.

- Houses may be rented or bought.

FURNISHED OR UNFURNISHED PROPERTIES

- Houses, flats and maisonettes which are available for sale are usually unfurnished. They are less frequently sold furnished.

- Rented accommodation is more usually furnished. In this case, settling in costs less as there is no outlay on furniture.

RENTING A PROPERTY — HOUSE OR APARTMENT

1. Study newspaper advertisements and phone around to find the normal price being charged for the type of accommodation that you require.
2. Prices vary according to: (a) the location; (b) the size of property; (c) its condition; (d) nearness to public transport etc.
3. Arrange to view a few properties. Check the following before making a final choice:
   - How much is the rent? Is it paid weekly or monthly, by cash or cheque? How often may it be increased?
   - Is it self-contained or do you have to share facilities?
   - Are there extra charges, for example for heating, maintenance etc.?
   - Is it clean, comfortable and well maintained?
   - Check electricity, heating, phone and how they are paid for. A meter gives you control of your own consumption.
4. Check the conditions of the lease.
   - Duration of tenancy: How often is the lease renewed; may you sublet, for example, in the summer?
   - What notice is required on either side before vacating the property?
   - Who is responsible for maintenance and insurance?
5. If everything is acceptable, get your solicitor to check the lease, if any. Then you may sign it.
6. Arrange a date for moving in and for paying rent. It is usual to pay one month's rent in advance, plus a deposit to cover any damage to the flat or its contents.
7. Insure your own belongings as soon as you move them in.

DISADVANTAGES OF RENTING FLATS

- Can be noisy — many shared facilities such as stairs, heating.
- Often no garden or garage.
- Lifts frequently out of order.
- Lack of play space, storage space.
- May be cramped. Problems with disposing refuse may arise.
- May have service charges.
- Lack of community spirit — often vandalism and graffiti.

SHARING

Single people may prefer to share accommodation with a friend. This is cheaper as the rent is divided by two or three, and much the same amount of light and heat will be used by one person as by two or more. It is also less lonely, particularly if you have just moved into a strange city. It is important in this case that the costs and workload are decided upon in advance and shared. Otherwise resentments and arguments may spoil the arrangement.

LEGAL ASPECTS OF RENTING

The terms on which one rents a premises must be agreeable to both parties. This may be a verbal agreement, but a written agreement is safer for both parties, although it will involve payment of a fee and stamp duty. Every point in the lease must be clear and unambiguous.

SOME RIGHTS THAT A LANDLORD MIGHT EXPECT IN A LEASE

A landlord:
1. Is entitled to a fair rent, paid on an agreed date.
2. Is entitled to charge a deposit, which may be forfeited by the tenant if property is damaged (normal wear and tear excluded). A receipt for the deposit must be given.
3. Is entitled to notice, if a tenant wishes to leave, of one week if rent is paid weekly, or one month's notice if rent is paid monthly.
4. Is not liable for repairs unless local by-laws stipulate this or it is stated in the agreement. She/he will probably be liable for external repairs.
5. May not disconnect services such as electricity and water.

SOME RIGHTS THAT A TENANT MIGHT EXPECT IN A LEASE

A tenant:
1. Is entitled to privacy, if the landlord has not reserved the right to enter the premises in the agreement.

2. Is entitled to have guests to stay, but is not entitled to sublet unless this is mentioned in the agreement.
3. Is entitled to due notice (see 3 above).
4. Is entitled to have the deposit returned if there is no damage done.
5. Cannot be evicted without a court order.
6. May not redecorate or carry out work on property without permission.
7. Cannot use the property for commercial purposes, as for a business.
8. Unless the agreement stipulates when and how often rent may be increased, the landlord may increase rent at will.

Note: Take care that you understand all the clauses in the agreement. Discuss with the landlord any point with which you do not agree and have any changes written into the agreement.

Never sign any document without examining it carefully, preferably with the help of a solicitor. As the landlord is not legally obliged to provide a rent book, it is up to you to keep a record of all payments and/or receipts.

RENTING FROM THE LOCAL AUTHORITY

Local authorities provide houses and flats for those in need of housing who would find buying or renting privately beyond their means. There is an income limit — for example, under £12,000 per annum.

Allocation of houses is decided by a *system of priorities* (points) which vary between councils. Preference is given to those who live in accommodation which is unhealthy, overcrowded and/or dangerous. Extra priority is given to large families and those in medical need of housing. In urban areas, there is often a waiting list, particularly for houses in more desirable areas. Dwellings provided range from small flats — often allocated to the elderly or single parents — to four bedroomed houses.

Rent is subsidised by the local authorities. *Fixed rent* (which is being phased out) remains static and does not take into account the income of the tenant. *Differential rent* is fairer. The housing department assesses the rent according to the tenant's circumstances. If there is a change, such as a rise or fall in income, the rent is altered accordingly.

Local authority tenants may not sublet their dwellings. They may apply for a *transfer* to another house or area for reasons such as employment. Tenants may buy their houses from their local authority. The price is based on the original cost of the house. Grants and loans are available.

BUYING A HOUSE

ADVANTAGES OF BUYING A HOUSE

1. It provides security.
2. It is a good investment and will usually increase in value.
3. When you rent a house, the money is only paying for accommodation. When buying by mortgage, it is buying you an asset — something that you can sell which is of value.
4. Tax relief is allowed on the interest you pay on a mortgage.

DISADVANTAGES OF BUYING A HOUSE

1. It is very expensive, with many extra costs involved such as legal fees and bridging loan.
2. A large sum must be saved for a deposit.
3. It may be difficult to get a loan, particularly if one is on a low income. Many low-income families live in rented accommodation. They may be entitled to a cheap local authority loan.
4. Much time and effort is spent looking at houses, arranging finance and legal work. Renting is simpler.

Annual Outgoings	
Buying	*Renting*
Mortgage repayments	Rent
Mortgage protection policy	Maintenance charge (in some cases)
Insurance of house	Insurance of personal contents
Insurance of contents	
Repairs, redecoration and maintenance costs	Repairs and redecoration (depending on lease)
Fuel — heating, lighting etc.	Fuel
Furniture	Some furniture
	Saving (towards a house)

CHOOSING A HOUSE

MONEY

The main consideration which influences many other factors is the amount of money you have saved, and how much you can afford to borrow.

LOCATION/NEIGHBOURHOOD

- Rural or urban: One area may be overcrowded and noisy, while the other may lack amenities.
- Large or small estate?
- Newly-built or mature area?
- Is it near your family, work, shops, schools, public transport, amenities such as parks and playgrounds?

Avoid busy roads, densely built-up areas, derelict areas, rubbish dumps and large industries which may be noisy or pollute the air. Check local authority plans of the area for changes in zoning, proposed re-development, road widening etc. These may reduce the value of your house should you wish to sell it. A pleasant aspect is an asset but you will probably pay more for it. Main rooms should face south.

TYPE OF HOUSE

Do you prefer:

- A bungalow, detached, semi-detached, or terraced house?
- A large house or a small one? With a garage?
- Old or modern? Modern houses need less maintenance.
- New or previously occupied?
- Is the garden suitable, attractive and well maintained? Is it too large to maintain if you have little time or interest in gardening?

LAYOUT OF HOUSE

- Does the interior of the house suit your lifestyle and the size of the family?
- Are there sufficient bedrooms and a spare room in which to play or study?
- A well-planned kitchen is extremely important. If not, you will have to spend a large sum of money renovating it.
- A modern bathroom and downstairs lavatory would be considered essential today.
- Do not be put off by the taste of the previous owner — redecoration is relatively cheap, particularly if you do it yourself.
- In older houses, plumbing, electrical and structural repairs are a bigger problem and expensive to rectify.

STRUCTURAL FEATURES

- Get a surveyor/architect to check these, if possible.
- Roof, chimney, gutters, drainpipes: Are they sound, without leaks or missing slates? Viewing a house on a wet day shows up more faults.
- Foundations: Are they sound, with a damp proof course?

Check structural features!

- Walls: Look for cracks, dampness, crumbling plaster or pointing.
- Floors and woodwork: Look for dry rot and woodworm.
- Doors and windows should be sound and well fitting.
- Plumbing should have sound pipework, drainage, large storage tank, lagging on pipes and cistern.
- Heating: What type of system and fuel?
- Is there insulation, especially in the attic?
- Is there an immersion heater or backboiler?
- Electricity: Is it safe, with plenty of modern, flat 3-pin sockets?

COSTS INVOLVED IN BUYING A HOUSE

A house is probably the most expensive purchase that you will ever make. Because of this, it is essential to save as much as you can before buying one. In this way, you will have enough cash to pay for the main hidden expenses involved. These include:

1. *Deposit* of at least 10% of the cost of the house.
2. *Stamp duty* (4–6%): A government tax.
3. Your *solicitor's fees*: Charged in ratio to the cost of the house (average 2% of house price).
4. *Legal fees* for mortgage, stamp duties and searches.
5. *Lender's survey fees:** You pay these when you apply for a loan, but have access to the report.
6. *Your survey*: It is advisable to employ an architect/surveyor of your own, particularly if the house is old.

The total cost of the deposit and these fees comes to several thousand pounds, but the largest sum involved is the balance of cash for the house. Most people borrow this.

*Some building societies may charge an application fee.

RAISING THE MONEY TO BUY A HOUSE

TAKING OUT A MORTGAGE

When you borrow money with a house as security, it is known as a *mortgage loan*. The lender (mortgagor) holds the title deeds, which are papers proving ownership, until the loan is repaid in full.

Money for house purchase may be borrowed from:
1. Building societies
2. Banks
3. Local authorities/Housing finance agency
4. Insurance companies (for endowment loans)
5. Agricultural Credit Company (ACC, Chapter 8) which gives mortgages to farmers using the land deeds as security.

RESTRICTIONS ON LOANS

The following restrictions are made on most loans.
1. *Amount lent*: The borrower may only borrow two and a half times his/her annual salary, excluding overtime. A spouse's salary will be considered by some lenders. The purpose of this restriction is to ensure that monthly repayments will not be too great a burden on the family, particularly if one partner leaves work to rear the children. The lender may have to repossess the house if repayments are not kept up.
2. *Period of repayment*: This is usually twenty to thirty years. Banks average twenty years, building societies twenty-five and local authorities will allow thirty years to repay the loan. A borrower over fifty may have more difficulty in obtaining a loan and may be forced to repay the loan in a shorter time, possibly fifteen years.
3. *A good record and deposit*: The borrower is expected to have a steady job and to have a good financial record with no bad debts. He/she is expected to have saved the deposit for the house.
4. *The property* must be of a certain quality and standard so that it is a *good investment*. The lending company may refuse to lend money for an old house, particularly if it is in a bad state of repair or on a short lease. It is easier to get a loan for a new house, particularly if you are a first-time buyer.

BORROWING

1. Borrowing from a building society
   - Building societies may restrict their loans, lending only to people who have been saving with them.
   - Borrowing is restricted to up to 80% of the house price.
   - Rates of interest fluctuate with the economy. They are not fixed.
   - Income tax relief is allowed on a certain percentage of the interest paid annually. This figure may also fluctuate.
   - Loans are usually repaid in monthly instalments over 20-25 years.
   - Conditions/rates vary slightly between one building society and another.
   - Endowment loans are available (see below*).
2. Borrowing from a bank
   - Very similar to building societies.
   - Repayments are usually monthly, over 20-25 years.
   - Mortgage interest varies according to the current bank rate. Interest is allowable for tax relief.
   - Banks also supply 'bridging loans' which bridge the time gap between buying a new house and selling an old one. Bridging loans also tide the buyer over while waiting for a building society loan. Rates of interest on bridging loans are high.
   - Endowment loans* are also available from banks.

   Endowment Loans
   - This type of loan is tied up with an endowment policy provided by an assurance company. When this matures (in 20 or 25 years), or if you die before that, your loan is paid off.
   - Tax relief is better with this type of loan as interest on the life policy and loan are allowable.
   - There is no need for a mortgage protection policy as the borrower's life is assured.
   - The rates of interest are higher for older borrowers.
3. *Local authority loans*
   Finance for local authority loans is made available through the state-run Housing Finance Agency*. Those who wish to obtain a local authority loan must first apply to a bank or building society who make special (no deposit) conditions for those earning under £10,000 per annum. Local authorities only accept loan applications if letters of refusal from both bank and building society are submitted.

LOCAL AUTHORITY HOUSE LOANS

There are three basic types of local authority loans.
1. Annuity loan — similar to bank/building society loans.
2. Income related — repayments calculated on a percentage (20-22%) of income.
3. Convertible — one starts with B, changing to A within 5 years.

The general conditions for all three Local Authority house loans are (with some variations):
- Borrower must earn under £10,000 per annum (farmers valued under £44).
- Up to 90-95% of house price may be borrowed.
- Maximum limit of mortgage is in the region of £22,500.
- Period of loan — up to 30 years.
- Interest charged/repayments:
1. Annuity loans: 9.5% (varies with inflation).
2. Income related repayments: 20-22% of income, revised each year — it rises or falls as income rises or falls. As repayments are usually lower than other types of loan, this takes longer to pay off. Applicants must be under 55. (Those between 40 and 55 qualify for a smaller loan because of age.)
- All loans include a mortgage protection policy.
- Tax relief is given on interest paid.
- Those eligible:
  (a) Single and married people
  (b) First-time buyers only

Exceptions
- When existing accommodation is unfit to live in or overcrowded.
- When employment necessitates a move to another area.
- Exceptional circumstances, such as marital breakdown, or loss of house due to fire or flood.

SPECIAL CATEGORY APPLICANTS

These get preferential treatment — for example, no qualifying income limit, higher loans.
1. Those who rent, own or are buying a local authority house (or living in a Defense Force house) and are prepared to hand it back.
2. Those on council housing list for more than one year, living with a child or two other persons and in need of rehousing.
3. Members of a registered housing co-op may be eligible.
4. One-parent families.
   - *Housing Finance Agency plc**
   This is a state-run limited company which works closely with the Departments of the Environment and Finance. It no longer provides loans directly to the public. Instead, it provides finance to local authorities so that they can provide loans for low-cost accommodation such as council housing. Their finance is also used for housing grants — for example, for conversion of a house for a disabled person. They raise funds through borrowing, issuing bonds and dealing in stocks and shares.

- *Five-year mortgage subsidy*
This is a subsidy paid in yearly instalments over a five-year period. It is only available to those buying a new house who have never owned a house before — that is those qualifying for a new house grant (see below).

PROCEDURE FOR BUYING A HOUSE — STEP-BY-STEP

1. Make a preliminary visit to several lending agencies to see if you are eligible for a mortgage. Find out their interest rates, conditions and the amount they are prepared to lend you.
2. Look through the property pages of newspapers. Enquire from estate agents. Go to visit a few houses within your price range, including show houses in housing estates.
3. Narrow your choice down to one or two and have a full survey carried out on your final choice.
4. Check local planning authorities for any developments such as road widening in the vicinity which may affect your house.
5. Apply formally for a loan and hire a solicitor.
6. You may be required to put down a small deposit to 'hold' the property — the solicitor should be consulted.
7. Your solicitor will now be studying the contract before getting you to sign. Contract will include details of the deposit, full price, date of completion of contract (that is, exchange of title deeds) and a detailed description of what is involved in the sale — fixtures, fittings etc.
8. You now sign the contract to buy (subject to loan approval) and pay the deposit (usually 10% of the purchase price).
9. Your solicitor now checks the title, registration etc. During this time you should get confirmation of loan approval from the lending agency.*
10. *Completion of sale.** When the seller's and buyer's solicitors are satisfied that everything is in order, the seller signs the house over. The buyer's solicitor hands over the cheque for the balance of the house purchase price. The title deeds pass to the lending agency (who will retain them until the mortgage is paid off) and the buyer signs the final documents and receives the keys.

* During this period delays are common. For this reason it may be necessary to take out a bridging loan to provide house purchase finance while waiting for the mortgage loan cheque.

BUYING FROM A BUILDER

Most people buy their first house in a new housing estate from a builder. Check the following.

1. Price of house, amount of deposit and when the balance must be paid. The builder may require you to pay in instalments as the house progresses.
2. Avoid a *price variation clause*. This allows the builder to increase the price of the house after you pay the deposit because of increased costs.
3. Obtain a *floor area certificate* if you want to qualify for grants, mortgage subsidy and stamp duty exemption.
4. Make sure that you get a *six-year guarantee* against structural faults.
5. The builder's contract should provide for a maintenance period during which they will be responsible for repairing faults.
6. Have any changes or extras written into the contract. Check the amount allowed towards 'choices' such as wallpaper or bathroom fittings. Having your own choice will be more expensive. Your solicitor should check most of the points above as well as checking that the builder:
   - Has planning permission.
   - Completes the estate, with its roads, landscaping and footpaths. If he fails to do so, you may be refused a loan.
   - Completion date: Is it specified on the contract? If there is a delay, you may have to pay dearly with a bridging loan.

HOUSE PURCHASE TERMS

- *Auctioneer or estate agent*: A person who auctions, sells or arranges rental of property such as houses, lands, flats etc. For this service the client/seller is charged a fee based on the price of the house. Advertising costs are extra.
- *Auction*: At an auction, a house is sold to the highest bidder. The deeds must be checked beforehand by a solicitor. When the auction is over, the buyer must pay one-quarter of the house price at once and the remainder within one month.
- *Certificate of reasonable cost*: This is granted by the Department of the Environment to those builders who have complied with certain minimum standards and who have put the house on the market at an acceptable price. Failure to obtain a certificate may result in loss of grants and many other benefits.
- *Contract*: This is the written agreement between buyer and seller which states the terms on which the house is bought. The terms 'subject to contract' and 'subject to loan' should be written into any agreement or deposit so that, if the loan is rejected or if there is a genuine problem over the sale, you will get your deposit back.
- *Conveyancing*: Transferring the legal ownership of property from one person/company to another.
- *Floor area certificate*: This is a certificate supplied by the builder of a new house to the buyer for the purpose of

grants and stamp duty exemption. It states that the floor area does not exceed 125 square metres.

- *Freehold*: This means that the house and the land on which the house is built belongs to the owner forever and no ground rent has to be paid. All houses built since 1978 are freehold.
- *Grants*:
  1. New house grant (currently £2,000): This is available to persons who: (a) are buying a new house; (b) have never bought a property before; and (c) who intend living in the house/flat themselves. The property must conform to certain standards set by the Department of the Environment, be under 125 square metres and have a six-year builder's guarantee. Payment of the grant is made by authorities within one year.
  2. House improvement grants: These include sums of money paid by the Department of the Environment for provision of bathrooms/water/sewerage supplies to houses without these facilities. A special grant is available for adapting a house for a disabled person. Other grants may be available from time to time — for example, repair of rural dwellings.
- *Housing co-operatives*: This is a system whereby a group of people pool their resources and share all the costs — architect, builder, solicitor, land, materials — of building a group of houses. This cuts expense to a minimum and is a cheap method of having a house built. Local authorities offer help and advice.
- *Leasehold*: This means that title to the land is held by a person or company other than the new owner. If this is the case, you will have to pay *ground rent*. It is now possible to pay a sum of money — roughly nine times the ground rent — to the landlord in order to obtain the freehold of a property.
- *National house building guarantee scheme*: This is a voluntary scheme operated and financed by builders which guarantees new houses in the scheme up to £15,000 against major structural defects for six years. All building societies, the Housing Finance Agency and most local authorities require that the houses they mortgage have guarantee certificates under this scheme. Department of the Environment inspectors carry out technical inspections of sites and houses on at least three occasions under the scheme. If a defect is found, it must be reported at once, in writing, and the builder is required to put it right. If the builder goes out of business, the operators of the scheme will see that repairs are carried out.
- *Planning permission*: When building a house or when making any alteration which changes the appearance of the house or increases its size by more than 18 square metres, it is necessary to obtain planning permission from the local authority.
  1. Outline planning permission: This gives a general agreement to the structure being built. Plans must be submitted showing location and drainage and an outline of the building.
  2. Full planning permission: This requires detailed inspection of the house plans by the local authority. An advertisement must be placed in a local newspaper stating that you are applying for planning permission so that anyone who so wishes can object to your plans.

     Detailed plans of the structure including floor plans, elevations and drainage must be submitted, together with a copy of the newspaper in which you advertised for planning permission listing your name, address and details of interest in the land. The local authority must accept or reject your plans within two months. If rejected, one may appeal to An Bord Pleanala.
- *Property*: A building or piece of land, or both together.
- *Registration of houses*: Most new houses built in this country are registered in the Land Registry Office. Each change of ownership is recorded. When a house is being sold, the buyer's solicitor can check in the register that each change of ownership was legal and correct. Older, unregistered houses are more complicated to deal with.
- *Solicitor*: A person who specialises in legal procedures such as house purchase. He or she prepares the contracts and checks local authority services, future plans and the title (ownership) at the Land Registry Office. It is advisable that buyer and seller engage different solicitors. Otherwise there may be a conflict of interest if the same solicitor acts for both parties.
- *Stamp duty*: This is a form of tax on house purchase. It is payable on all previously occupied houses and on new houses larger than 125 square metres. It is calculated as a percentage (4%) of the value of the house. New houses less than 125 square metres in size — this includes the average three- or four-bedroomed house — are exempt from stamp duty.
- *Surveyor*: A house may be professionally surveyed by a surveyor, an architect or an engineer. A survey is more important if the house you intend buying is an old one. A survey should describe, in writing: the condition of foundations, walls, roof, plumbing and wiring; whether each fault can be put right and, if so, the approximate cost of the work. The building society's surveyor's report is now made available to the potential buyer.
- *Title deeds*: Legal documents proving ownership.

► BUILDING A HOUSE

1. SELECTING A SITE

- The best site is on slightly sloping, well drained land. Hollow sites hold dampness.
- It should be reasonably near, but not too near, main roads.
- If you build near water, there may be subsidence or flooding.
- Do not build near large trees as the roots may damage the foundations.
- Reclaimed land is unsuitable for building as it will subside.
- Gravel, sandstone and chalk are the most suitable soils for building.
- Houses should be sheltered from the prevailing wind.
- Water and sewerage should be reasonably near or preferably laid on.

ASPECT

- There should be free access of sunlight and air.
- The ideal aspect for a house is facing southeast or northwest, as it ensures that most of the rooms have sunlight for much of the day.
- Southwest walls should be protected by trees or other houses as this gets the full force of the prevailing wind.
- Pleasant view is desirable, with curved rather than straight roadways and adequate open spaces.
- Facilities such as shops, schools, parks and public transport should be nearby.
- The building must conform to local by-laws and should not interfere with any other building.

2. DESIGN AND HOUSE PLANS

The house should be planned to be aesthetically pleasing, with a well-thought-out arrangement of rooms and passages. It should ensure maximum efficiency and comfort. The materials used should be durable, of good quality and suitable for their purpose.

BASIC REQUIREMENTS

- There should be some open space around the house, with a pleasant outlook front and back — for example, on gardens.
- There should be sufficient interior space to facilitate comfortable living, with space to build on, if necessary, and sufficient storage space.
- Each room should have sufficient daylight and ventilation (windows).
- There should be an efficient, pure water supply and a good drainage system.
- Good water heating and house heating systems are important.

- There should be a well-designed, easy-to-clean bathroom and lavatory.
- There should be a modern kitchen with provision for storage, food preparation, cooking, washing and cleaning.
- A safe, efficient electrical and lighting system is essential.
- There should be effective roof, wall, window and floor insulation.

A good architect will submit drawings and specifications (the detailed lists of materials and procedures to be observed by the builder), having first discussed such things as the type of building, number of rooms required etc. with the client. He will apply for planning permission, get estimates from a selection of builders and, if required, for an extra fee will supervise building work in progress.

A selection of house plans is available in specialist bookshops. These are sufficiently detailed to be copied by builders. This saves a considerable amount of money. (Planning permission, see page 191.)

CONSTRUCTION FEATURES

FOUNDATIONS

The stability of a house depends on its foundations. There are three types of foundation.

1. *Strip foundations* (see below) are those most frequently used.
2. *Raft foundations* are broad foundations extending under the whole structure. They are used on unstable or badly-drained soil.
3. *Pile foundations* are used under very tall buildings.

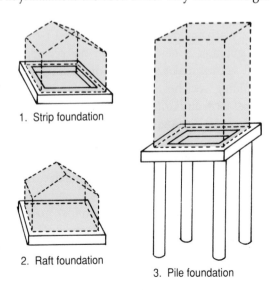

1. Strip foundation

2. Raft foundation

3. Pile foundation

Three types of foundation

Strip foundations

These foundations are laid in trenches at least 50 cm deep which are partly filled with concrete. This forms a solid base on which to lay the walls.

Floor foundations

Hard core, consisting of rough stones and broken bricks, is laid over the floor area. Concrete is poured over this and a damp proof membrane (see below) is laid on top. It is finished with another layer of concrete to form the sub-floor.

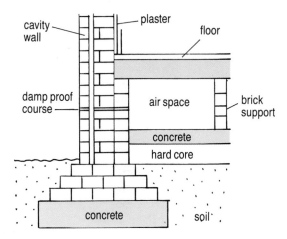

Foundations of house

DAMP-PROOF COURSE (DPC)

Brick walls and concrete floors readily soak up moisture from the ground beneath unless a waterproof barrier is used. Under local authority building regulation, all walls, both internal and external, and ground floors of habitable buildings are required to have a damp-proof course (DPC) to prevent rising damp. Flexible, bituminous felt or heavy-duty plastic strips are laid at about 150 mm from the ground between two levels of wall bricks. Floors are damp-proofed with heavy-duty polythene sheeting. Floors and any woodwork must be above the level of the DPC. Many old houses suffer from damp because they have no damp-proof course.

FLOORS

These may be solid or suspended.

1. *Solid floors*: The ground floor of most modern houses consists of a sub-floor of concrete, finished with a thin screed of fine concrete. Stone slabs provided a solid floor in very old houses. Neither are resilient nor comfortable.

2. *Suspended floors*: Parallel joists of wood are fixed at intervals between one wall and another. Tongued and grooved floor boards are fixed at right angles to the joists with nails. All wood used in house construction must be well-seasoned and treated to prevent warping and rotting such as dry rot. Cheap houses may use

chipboard instead of tongued and grooved floor boards, but there may be stipulations against this in a mortgage agreement as chipboard can be badly damaged by water. It is also quite inflammable.

WALLS

Most house walls are built from concrete blocks, bricks or preformed concrete. Air bricks should be placed at intervals beneath the DPC to allow underfloor ventilation in houses with raised wooden floors.

Bricks are fixed together with mortar and, when neatened on the outside, the plaster between the brickwork is referred to as *pointing*.

Cavity walls: These are used on exterior walls of modern houses. A cavity wall is really two walls with a space (80 to 100 mm) between them. The air between the walls acts as an insulator, keeping the house warm, reducing noise and preventing dampness from seeping in from outside. Cavity walls are often further insulated by filling the space between them with polystyrene sheeting.

A load-bearing wall supports the roof and/or upper floors. *Partition walls* are of light construction — for example, plaster board fixed onto a wooden frame. They separate some of the rooms of the house.

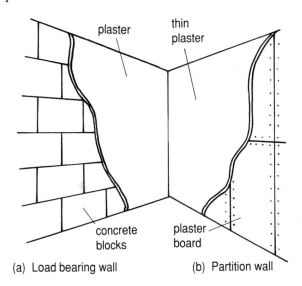

(a) Load bearing wall   (b) Partition wall

Types of wall

Wall Finishes	
External	*Internal*
Plaster	Plaster board, spread
Pebbledash	with fine plaster, then
Wood cladding	painted or papered
Brickwork	Wood cladding
Decorative stone	Brickwork
	Decorative stone

DOORS AND WINDOWS

These may be made from wood or metal. They should fit well and be securely anchored to the walls. Wood should be of good quality and well seasoned. It should be primed and painted with a weatherproof finish. Wood needs regular painting or it will warp and rot.

Aluminium double-glazed windows and doors are light weight, do not rust or warp and require no painting.

They are available in silver, white and bronze anodised finishes. Other metals such as iron and steel need to be primed with a metal primer and painted regularly to prevent corrosion. If they are poorly maintained, they may warp or buckle. Because of this they are rarely installed today.

Note: Safety glass should be used in glass doors to reduce injury.

► INSULATION

An uninsulated house can lose 75% of all heat produced. Insulation:

1. Reduces heat loss and therefore keeps the house warmer.
2. Reduces fuel costs and therefore saves money.
3. Acts as a noise barrier.

The simplest time to insulate a house is at the time of construction.

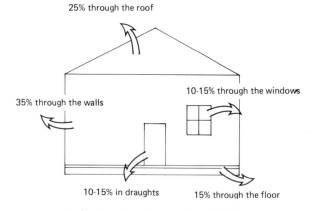

Average heat loss in an uninsulated house

PRINCIPLE OF INSULATION

Bad conductors of heat are used to prevent the passage of heat into the atmosphere outside. Air is trapped between layers, reducing heat loss. Bad conductors of heat include air, polystyrene, wool and fibreglass.

1. Roof insulation

This is the most worthwhile form of insulation. As heat rises, 25% of it is lost through an uninsulated roof. By insulating the roof this loss is reduced in direct ratio to the thickness of the insulation (100 mm of insulation is ideal). Remember to insulate over, but not under, the storage tank to prevent it freezing. Leave spaces at the eaves (outer edges of the attic) for ventilation. Insulate all pipework with split-foam sleeving, as the attic is colder once insulated.

- Fibreglass blanket strips are laid across or between the joists. Eighteen to 20 rolls are required for an average house.
- Loosefill pellets of polystyrene or Vermiculite are poured between the joists.

- Foam is sprayed underneath the roof which sets as a solid foam. This is expensive, but ideal for attic conversions.

2. Draught proofing

This is a cheap and quickly effective form of insulation.

- *Draught excluders* are fitted around windows and doors. Cheap temporary excluders such as strips of self-adhesive foam may be used. More permanent excluders are metal and plastic strips which are tacked into place. Some have rubber or brush-like extensions for the base of doors.
- *Curtains*: Heavy, lined and interlined curtains reduce heat loss at night when they are drawn across windows and doors. Insulated linings for curtains are also available.
- *Floors*: Thick, fitted carpets with a good underlay reduce heat loss through floors. Corrugated foil sheets can be tacked between joists under the floor, if it is possible to get underneath.
- *Cracks* in floorboards, skirting, around windows and doors should be filled with an appropriate wood or plaster filler before redecorating. Fill large cracks in the floor cheaply with papier mache or a mixture of sawdust and wallpaper adhesive.
- *Chimneys* allow a considerable amount of heat to be lost into the atmosphere. Block up unused fireplaces. Cover occasionally-used fireplaces with a solid fire-screen.

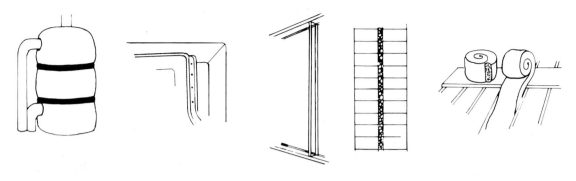

lagging jacket on cylinder   draught-proofing on door   double-glazed window   insulated cavity wall   attic insulation, using glass fibre blanket

Forms of insulation

3. *Walls*

Most houses built today have cavity walls. The 5 to 10 cm air space between the walls provides some insulation. Modern houses have polystyrene sheeting attached to one of the walls to further improve insulation.

The air space may also be filled with plastic foam which is pumped through holes drilled in the outer wall. It is an expensive operation and needs to be carried out by professionals.

In older houses with solid walls, the inside of the wall may be lined with sheets of polystyrene or dry lining, then wallpapered afterwards. Internal or external wood cladding may also be used. Both improve insulation.

4. *Double-glazing* (current cost averages £4,000-£5,000)

This is by far the most expensive form of insulation. A relatively small percentage of heat loss occurs through windows (about 15%). Double-glazing reduces this by half. It is therefore only worthwhile double-glazing windows which need to be replaced in any case because they are in a bad state of repair.

The principle of double-glazing is to use the still, dry air sealed between the layers of glass to reduce outward convection of heat. It also reduces condensation and entry of noise.

5. *Hot water cylinders and pipes*

Cylinders should be insulated with a cylinder jacket to prevent heat loss. Water pipes should be lagged with some form of insulating material such as split-foam tubes.

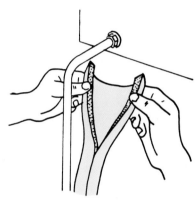

Lag water pipes with split foam sleeving

VENTILATION

Air is a mixture of gases.

	Fresh air	*Stale air*
Oxygen	20.96%	16.96%
Nitrogen	79.00%	79.00%
Carbon Dioxide	0.04%	4.04%
Temperature	variable	saturated
Impurities	variable	smoke, micro-organisms, un-pleasant odours

- *Oxygen* is a colourless, tasteless, odourless gas. It burns easily.
- *Nitrogen* is also a colourless, tasteless, odourless gas. It is an inert gas — that is, it does not support reactions such as combustion and oxidation.
- *Carbon dioxide* is a colourless gas with a sweetish taste and smell. Air containing more than 0.04% would be considered impure. CO_2 is released into the air by:
  1. breathing of animals and humans
  2. burning of fuel
  3. fermentation, as with rotting vegetation
  4. respiration of plants

AIR POLLUTION

Really pure air is difficult to find. Air is usually contaminated with impurities (see below), particularly over large towns and cities. Impurities are harmful to humans and animals as well as to vegetation and buildings.

Air is purified by:
- rain, which washes down impurities
- wind, which diffuses impurities
- sunlight, which destroys many organisms
- green plants, which take in CO_2 and release oxygen by day (photosynthesis)

HOUSEHOLD VENTILATION

Good ventilation of homes and work places is essential for healthy living. A good system of ventilation removes stale air and replaces it with fresh air without causing a draught or lowering room temperatures too much. An occupied room should have a complete air change at least once an hour.

Air Pollution

	Pollutant	Origin	Results	Methods of Prevention
1.	Carbon dioxide	All forms of combustion including breathing.	Increased susceptibility to respiratory infection. Poisonous in large amounts.	Improved ventilation. Use of solar/wind energy instead of fossil fuels.
2.	Carbon monoxide	Car exhausts. Incomplete industrial or domestic combustion.	Combines with haemoglobin in blood, reducing oxygen level. Large amounts cause unconsciousness and death.	Restricting use of cars in built-up areas. Modify engines. Decentralisation.
3.	Sulphur dioxide	Industrial combustion (oil refineries etc.)	Lung damage, respiratory infections. Damage to plant life, animals and buildings.	Remove sulphur from fuels. Decentralisation of industry.
4.	Pathogens, e.g. bacteria and viruses	Unhygienic habits: coughing and sneezing carelessly; droplet infection	Respiratory infections, TB. Many infectious diseases.	Improved ventilation. Improved hygiene. Vaccination. More fresh air and exercise.
5.	Tar, smoke, nicotine	Cigarette smoking.	Heart disease, lung cancer, respiratory diseases, e.g. bronchitis.	Avoid smoking. Improve ventilation. Ban smoking in public places.
6.	Minute particles/ irritants, e.g. dust, soot, ash	Domestic and industrial combustion. Mining etc.	Respiratory infections. Allergies, e.g. hay fever.	Improved ventilation. Smokeless fuels. Use of solar/wind energy.
7.	Hydrocarbons and lead	Car exhausts.	Lung, eye irritation. Affects nervous system, plant life.	Modify car engines. Restrict use of cars in built-up areas.

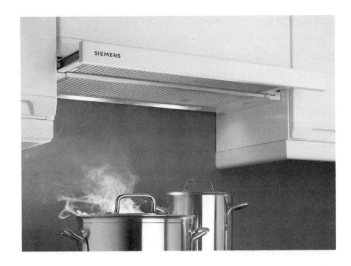

PRINCIPLES OF VENTILATION
- Warm air expands, gets lighter and rises, creating convection currents — therefore outlets should be high up in a room. Fresh air enters through lower openings.
- Moisture-laden air condenses on cold surfaces if not removed.

PURPOSE OF VENTILATION
- To remove stale, impure air, which is damaging to health.
- To remove unpleasant odours.
- To introduce fresh air in such a way that it brings about convection currents.
- To ensure that the air is neither too dry nor too humid.
- To prevent or reduce condensation.

BADLY VENTILATED ROOMS CAUSE:
- Drowsiness, headache and even fainting
- Lack of concentration
- Condensation — leading to rusting etc.
- Increased risk of colds and other infections, as germs flourish in badly-ventilated rooms
- Long-term exposure to bad ventilation can cause serious respiratory diseases such as bronchitis and lung cancer due to smoking

HUMIDITY
Humidity is the amount of water vapour in the air. Warm air can hold a higher level of moisture than cold air. Humidity is increased within a home by *breathing, cooking, laundering* and by the *combustion* of many heating appliances. Kitchens and bathrooms have a high level of humidity. They therefore require extra ventilation using such items as *extractor fans* (page 262).

High humidity levels cause condensation and aggravate bronchial conditions. *Low humidity levels* cause drying of air, irritate the air passages and aggravate sinus and similar complaints.

Many home heating systems, including electrical and central heating, cause drying of the air. *Humidifiers* are used to counteract this. Humidifiers may consist of simple water containers that are clipped onto radiators. These return moisture to the air. Electric humidifiers use a fan to blow moisture into the air.

CONDENSATION
This is the process whereby the high level of water vapour in the air converts to water droplets when it comes into contact with a cold surface or cold air. Kitchens and bathrooms are frequently affected by condensation (kitchens need an air change ten to twenty times each hour).

CONDENSATION CAN CAUSE:
- Bronchial complaints
- Growth of moulds and fungi
- Rusting of metals and damage to equipment
- Damage to wall coverings and paintwork, necessitating frequent redecoration

TO PREVENT CONDENSATION
- Improve system of ventilation — for example, by using an extractor fan.
- Improve insulation: Double-glazed windows are less cold on the inside, so are less affected by condensation.
- Improve heating system — for example, so that walls are less cold.
- Avoid cold, glossy surfaces which increase condensation.
- Use hygroscopic (water absorbing) materials for furnishings.

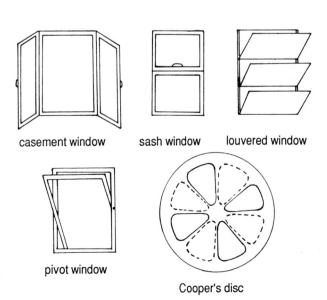

casement window   sash window   louvered window

pivot window

Cooper's disc

METHODS OF VENTILATION

- *Natural methods*: These take advantage of natural air movements, such as warm air rising, to extract air. Examples are doors, windows, fireplaces, airbricks etc.
- *Artificial methods*: Extractor fans, cooker hoods, air conditioning.

WINDOWS

- Casement windows open like a door. Some have a small top opening to allow stale air to leave.
- Sash windows: The top can be lowered to allow stale air to escape; fresh air enters between the panes. Opening the lower window causes draughts.
- Louvre windows: 3-4 panes of glass are fixed on a hinged frame. When open, louvred panes direct incoming air upwards.
- Skylight such as Velux windows inserted in roof. They ventilate and introduce light without causing draughts.

FIREPLACE

Warm air escapes up the chimney. This works most efficiently when the fire is lighting. Fresh air enters through doors etc. to replace it. Wind blowing over the chimney improves ventilation by drawing air upwards.

AIR-BRICKS

These may be found near the top of rooms that have no fireplace. They are also used below floor level to ventilate the underfloor area in order to prevent dry rot.

COOPER'S DISC

A double circle of glass or metal is fixed over a hole in a window or wall. Both circles have holes cut in them. When ventilation is required, the circles are twisted by a knob or pull-cord so that the holes are positioned on top of each other, allowing air to enter.

AIR CONDITIONING

This generally combines heating and ventilation. It consists of an air conditioning and heating unit that draws in air, filters it and either warms or cools it according to the time of year. It humidifies the air to about 50%, then releases it back into the house. The air is blown around the building through ducts which are driven by a powerful electric fan. The unit should be serviced annually and the filter needs regular cleaning — about every two months.

11 WATER AND SANITATION

► WATER SUPPLY AND HEATING

A supply of pure, uncontaminated water is a basic requirement in every home.

Rain is our main source of water. When it falls, it seeps through the soil until it reaches a *non-porous layer* such as rock. There it accumulates and may form a *spring* or, when drilled, *a well*. While pure, rain water picks up impurities as it falls.

Shallow wells which are drilled to a first layer of non-porous rock are not good water sources as they are easily contaminated with fertilisers, animal dung, run-offs from silage pits etc.

Deep wells which penetrate to a second impervious layer are less likely to be contaminated, although all water should be tested to make sure that it is safe to drink. All wells are lined with an impervious material such as steel to prevent further contamination. A *pump* is usually fitted which brings water in pipes to houses. Pipes must be at least 50 cm below ground level to avoid risk of frost. A *filter* which removes suspended impurities and a *water softener* may be fitted.

LOCAL AUTHORITIES

Local authorities are responsible for the water supply and drainage in towns and cities. They enforce building regulations and by-laws to ensure that there is no risk of contamination of the fresh water supply. Polluted water is extremely dangerous. Effluent discharge into waterways is illegal.

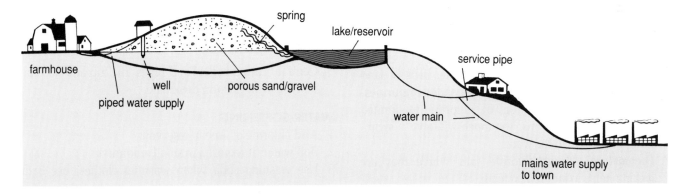

Water Pollution			
Cause	*Origin*	*Effect*	*How to prevent or reduce effect*
1. *Suspended solids*, e.g. dust, sand, grit, pollen	Soil, air, domestic and industrial waste	Clogs up pipes. May be toxic or irritant	Filtering and 'settling' during storage
2. *Bacteria and organic waste*	Human and animal waste e.g. sewage and slurry, soil, vermin	Dysentery, typhoid, cholera, food-poisoning e.g. gastro-enteritis	Correct sewage disposal and treatment. Water purification. Immunisation
3. *Dissolved minerals*, e.g. (a) calcium and magnesium (b) lead	(a) Soil (b) Old pipes, cisterns	(a) Hard water (b) Accumulation in body is fatal	(a) Boiling or adding chemicals, e.g. lime, borax (b) Replace lead plumbing. Modern plumbing is non-toxic
4. *Toxic chemicals*, e.g. in pesticides and weed killers	Farming and gardening procedures	Many are directly poisonous, often fatal	Avoid use, e.g. practise organic farming. Use with extreme caution; difficult to remove from water

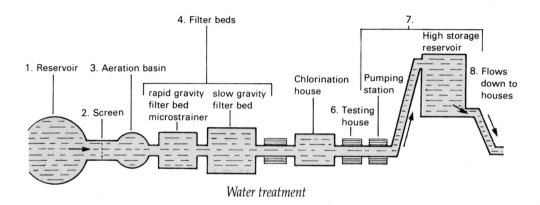

Water treatment

RESERVOIRS

The local authorities store water for cities and towns in large reservoirs or lakes. These must be on high ground so that there is sufficient pressure to supply the whole area with water. Water in reservoirs is kept pure by the action of fresh air and sunlight and also by oxygen-producing plants called algae which are present in the water.

WATER TREATMENT

The water leaving the reservoir may be treated in one or more of the following ways.

1. *Filtration*: Water is passed through filter beds of sand and gravel which remove many suspended impurities.
2. *Chlorination*: The addition of chlorine in limited amounts destroys germs. Too much will give a 'swimming pool' taste to the water.
3. *Fluoridation*: Adding fluoride salts where they are lacking helps to strengthen teeth.
4. *Softening*: Adding chloride of lime softens hard water.
5. Water may also be purified in small amounts by *boiling* or *distillation*.

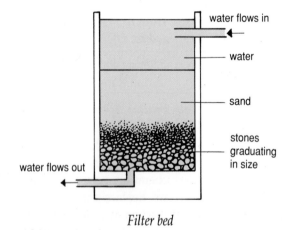

Filter bed

HARD WATER

As it passes through soil and rock, water absorbs many of the minerals present such as lime. These may cause what is known as *hardness* of water. Absorption of minerals is helped by the CO_2 which is absorbed by rain-water as it falls.

Hard water contains:
- Calcium or magnesium bicarbonates
- Calcium or magnesium sulphates

Hard water is water which does not easily make a lather.

EFFECTS OF HARDNESS IN WATER

1. Difficult and wasteful to make a lather with soap.
2. Hard on skin; leaves hair dull.
3. Scum clings to skin, clothes, baths etc.
4. Kettles 'fur' up and take longer to heat which wastes fuel.
5. Central heating boilers and pipes 'fur' up and become blocked with calcium carbonate.

WATER SOFTENING

1. Add chloride of lime in reservoir.
2. Boil water (if required in small amounts).
3. Use washing soda when washing clothes; use bath salts in baths.
4. Use a commercial water softener* such as Permutit.

* These contain a plastic material called a demineralising resin which replaces the calcium or magnesium ions in the water with harmless sodium ions. These softeners are attached to the household water system. They should be topped up with salt now and then to replace the sodium.

HOUSEHOLD WATER SUPPLY

Water is carried to towns in large pipes called *mains*. A *service pipe* leads from the mains into each house. A *stop cock* (a type of valve) outside the house enables water to be turned off during repairs. The service pipe usually enters the house under the kitchen sink where there is another valve. It feeds fresh water through the cold tap in the kitchen. The main branch passes up to the attic where the water is stored in a storage cistern or tank. This must be at a high level in order to provide sufficient water pressure to feed the system.

THE STORAGE CISTERN

This is made of galvanised iron or strong plastic and holds about 230 litres of water. This tank supplies water to cold water taps, the lavatory and the water heating (immersion) system. The water from this tank is not

Average individual usage					
Washing/Bathing	Lavatory	Laundry	Household Cleaning	Cooking	Drinking
40.5 litres	40.5 L	23 L	23 L	6 L	3 L

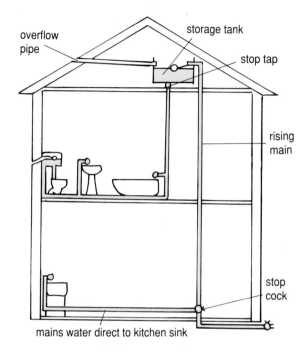

Cold water supply

drinking water as it may be contaminated with dirt and dead insects from the attic.

The tank should be covered and insulated. A *ball valve* controls the entry of water into the tank by opening when the tank empties and closing when it is full. An *overflow pipe* brings water outside the house in cases of overfilling due to failure of the ball valve.

WATER PIPES
Pipes are made from copper or plastic*. Copper is stronger but expensive. Water pipes in the attic should be lagged to prevent damage by frost; hot water pipes should be lagged to prevent heat loss. Taps may be made from chrome-plated metal or stainless steel. Some taps have a decorative acrylic top.

* Cold water pipes only

Daily water requirement: about 140 litres per person per day.

HOT WATER
A good supply of hot water is one of the most important labour-saving assets in the home. Hot water may be supplied by:
1. Individual water heaters
2. Direct systems
3. Indirect systems

WORKING PRINCIPLE OF WATER HEATING
Most systems are based on the principle of *convection* — water expands when heated, rises from the heat source, then falls as it cools. It may be necessary to supplement convection by using a *pump*. As overheating may cause over-expansion and boiling, it is necessary for safety that large water heating systems have an *expansion pipe* which empties into a tank in the attic.

INDIVIDUAL WATER HEATERS
Small amounts of water can be boiled in a kettle, but large heaters are required to meet the needs of a family.

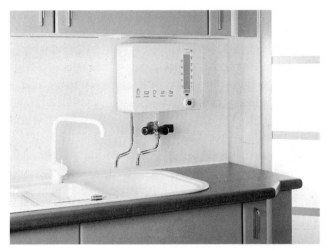

Single point heater

1. INSTANTANEOUS HEATERS
These are sometimes called geysers and may be heated by gas or electricity. They are installed over or under a sink or bath. While the average model, called a *single point heater*, is only large enough to supply one or two litres per minute, multi-point heaters can supply sufficient hot water for baths and all household requirements (4 litres per minute).

When the tap is turned on, water passes from the cold water supply through a narrow coil of pipes (gas) or over a heated plate or element (electricity). The water may be heated to warm, hot or boiling temperatures, depending on the thermostat setting. A *pilot light* ignites the gas when water is turned on.

Note: *It is essential that gas heaters of any type have a proper outlet to expel the carbon monoxide (toxic gas) produced. They require a balanced flue (page 211) to extract the gas; otherwise there is a very real danger of asphyxiation.*

Advantages of instantaneous water heaters
- Piping hot water is always on tap.
- As only the amount of water needed is heated, there is no waste.
- They are ideal for flats etc. where it would be wasteful to have a system which heated large amounts of water all day when occupants are out.

Disadvantages of instantaneous water heaters
- Gas heaters produce unpleasant, toxic fumes which must be removed.
- If the flue becomes blocked, these heaters are very dangerous.
- They are expensive if constantly in use.
- Large appliances can look unsightly on the wall.

Note: Electric/gas instant shower units work on the same principle.

2. ELECTRIC IMMERSION HEATER

An immersion heater consists of *a long electric element in a metal sheath* fitted inside the hot water cylinder. This is usually situated in the hot press. A *dual immersion* is more economical. It consists of two separate elements — a short one which heats the upper half of the cylinder, and a long one which is turned on when large amounts of water are required. A 3 kW heater heats water quickly and economically.

An immersion heater is thermostatically controlled. When heating the cylinder from cold, it stays on until water is heated to the set temperature, then switches off. It only turns on now and then to maintain that temperature. If the cylinder is well lagged, maintenance of temperature will use little electricity.

Advantages of an electric immersion heater
- Quick, efficient and clean.
- Hot water always available if kept on constantly.
- Thermostatically controlled.
- Useful in summer when alternative forms of water heating (such as back boiler/central heating) are not in use.

Disadvantages of an electric immersion heater
- Quite expensive to run, but less so if well lagged.
- Installation costs — must be fitted by an electrician.
- Possibility of power cuts.
- Slow to heat up from cold.

DIRECT SYSTEM OF WATER HEATING
(INCLUDING BACK BOILERS)

1. Water is heated at a single source of heat such as a gas or electric boiler. In this case, we will take a look at a back boiler behind a fire or in a solid fuel cooker. Back boilers are strong, heat-resistant water tanks, often made from copper.
2. The hot water rises and is stored in an insulated storage cylinder, usually in the hot press.
3. Cooled water flows from the base of the cylinder down to the boiler where it is heated and begins the cycle once again.
4. An expansion pipe from the top of the cylinder allows steam and over-heated water to escape into the storage tank in the attic.
5. As hot water is drawn, it leaves the top of the cylinder and flows through pipes to the sink or bath.
6. Cold water from the tank in the attic flows into the base of the cylinder to take its place.

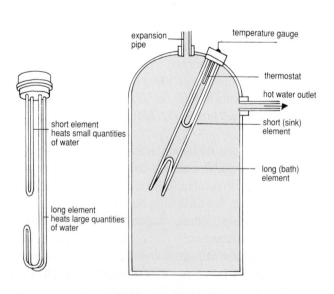

Dual immersion heater

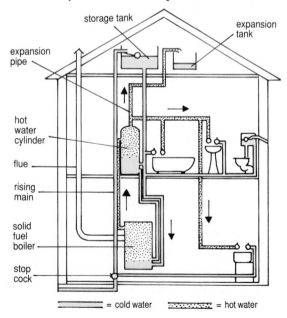

Direct hot water system

Advantages of back boiler

- Economical, as the fire/cooker is usually being used to heat the room in any case.
- This means that your hot water supply is more or less free while the fire it lit.

Disadvantages of back boiler

- Time-consuming and dirty, involving setting, cleaning and stoking fires (not the case with electric/gas boilers).
- Unsuitable in summer, needing supplementary heating such as an immersion heater.
- The constant flow of fresh water through the system may cause scaling of pipes in hard water areas.

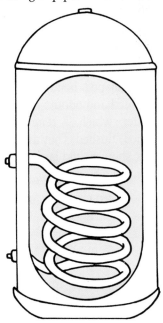

The heat exchanger inside a cylinder

INDIRECT SYSTEM OF WATER HEATING

This is usually part of a central heating system. It may also be used in hard water areas to prevent scaling of pipes.

1. Water for the central heating system is heated in a boiler — see (a) in illustration.
2. A pipe brings the hot water upwards to the storage cylinder (b) using natural convection or a pump (c).
3. Instead of flowing directly into the cylinder as in the direct system, the water flows through a coil of pipes (d) (*heat exchanger*) within the cylinder. Heat from these pipes *indirectly* heats the cylinder of water.
4. The central heating pipe leaves the cylinder and returns to the boiler to be heated once again (e).
5. A separate pipe brings water from the top of the cylinder to all hot water taps in the house (f).
6. As hot water is used up, water from the storage tank in the attic flows down into the cylinder to replace it (g).

An expansion pipe (h) and separate small *storage tank* (i) are required for an indirect system in case the water in the enclosed system, which may be dirty, overheats.

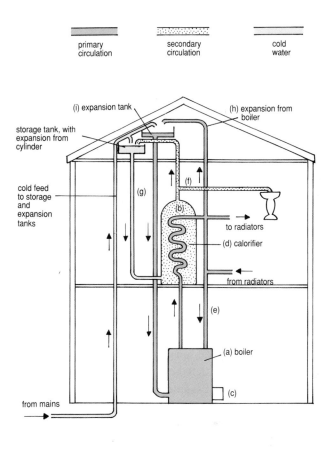

Indirect hot water/heating system

Note: At no time does the water in the central heating system — sometimes called the primary system — mix with the household supply of hot water (the secondary system). They are entirely separate. The central heating system is completely enclosed with the same water circulating continuously. The system is never drained except for repairs.

SAVING FUEL ON WATER HEATING

1. Storage cylinder and pipes should be well lagged.
2. Plumbing should be arranged so that there is the shortest possible distance between cylinder and taps.
3. Showers use less water than baths.
4. Avoid washing single items with hot water. Wait until you have a full wash before running hot tap and then use the stopper or plug.
5. Reduce temperature on the immersion heater thermostat.

► WASTE DISPOSAL

Domestic waste consists of:
1. Organic waste:
   - food, plants, peelings etc.
   - sewage
2. Inorganic waste: cans, plastic, delph, glass, metal, fibre.

RECYCLING

Due to an increasing awareness of the importance of conservation, there is a greater emphasis on recycling waste materials. Any items which can be recycled should be separated from general waste, saving money on bin collections and contributing to a cleaner environment.
- Any vegetable waste should be placed on a compost heap.
- Certain food waste may be used by animals.
- Paper should be given to waste paper collections.
- Bottles/cans can be deposited in a bottle/can bank.

DISPOSAL OF WASTE

A weekly local authority refuse collection collects household waste in cities and towns and deposits it on tipheads. These are usually situated in lowlying (infill) areas suitable for reclamation. Layers of waste are covered with soil and eventually grassed over. Small towns provide a dumping area used by local people to dispose of their refuse.

In rural areas, each householder must make arrangements for disposal of waste. A pit is usually used which is eventually covered with soil. Refuse pits/dumps should be as far as possible from houses to avoid infestation by flies and vermin.
- Waste disposal units (page 251) may be used to grind down kitchen waste.
- Kitchen bins should be covered, emptied daily, and then washed and disinfected.
- Dustbins are made of heavy-duty zinc, galvanised iron or plastic. They should be kept covered and not too near the house as they attract flies. Wrap moist waste in newspaper before disposal. Use plastic bags as bin liners, but tie them securely to avoid littering the neighbourhood. Dustbins should be raised up off the ground — for example, on two bricks — to avoid attracting vermin and to allow air to circulate.

DRAINAGE

Drains are a system of pipes which remove effluent from baths, sinks and lavatories. They also dispose of rain water.

A good drainage system should:
1. Not pass under a house.
2. Be laid in straight lines, where possible, to avoid blockages.
3. Rest on concrete.
4. Have inspection covers at intervals, especially on corners.
5. Be constructed of large diameter (150 mm) glazed stoneware, cast iron or heavy-duty plastic piping.
6. Slope away from the house, to assist flow.
7. Be well ventilated.
8. Be laid deeply enough to be unaffected by frost.
9. Have gullies or traps containing water between drains and house to prevent odours etc. from permeating the house.
10. Fresh water and sewerage pipes must never be laid close together in case of leaks.

TRAPS

These are U- or S-shaped bends in drainage systems which prevent bacteria and odours re-entering the house. They contain water, which is renewed each time the appliance is emptied/flushed. They are found under:
- All sinks, baths, showers and lavatories.
- In gullies, outside the house.

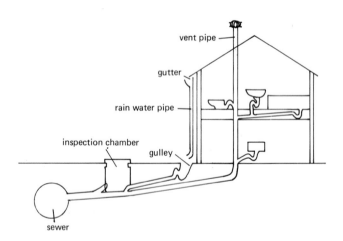

HOUSEHOLD DRAINAGE SYSTEM

1. Waste pipes from sinks, bath and shower empty into an external gully and then into the main drain.
2. Lavatories and bidets empty into separate pipes which are ventilated on top. From there they empty into the main drain underground.
3. A system of underground drains and sewers brings effluent to the sewage treatment plant.
4. At the plant, sewage is:
   (a) Filtered and broken up.
   (b) Allowed to settle in huge aerated tanks. The solids settle to the bottom. Anaerobic bacteria break down solids and the liquid is subjected to bacterial action

which renders it harmless. It is then discharged into rivers or the sea. The solids may be discharged far out at sea or dried and used as fertiliser.

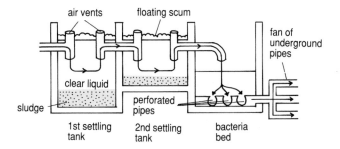

A septic tank

5. Rural areas: Waste is disposed into septic tanks where it lies over a period of time while bacteria decompose sewage into relatively harmless compounds. The liquid waste is released gradually through a fan of pipes laid deeply underground. The tanks must be well-ventilated and drained occasionally. Covers must be secure to avoid accidents. Biodegradable detergents should be used in such systems.

LOCAL AUTHORITIES

Responsibility for provision of pure water and removal of sewage lies with each local authority. Building regulations relating to drainage are very strict in order to ensure the health and hygiene of the community at large.

When house plans are submitted to local authorities, drainage and plumbing systems are carefully checked. Planning permission is required for any major alteration to a drainage system.

It is illegal to discharge untreated sewage into rivers or the sea. Factory effluent such as chemicals can harm animal and vegetable life. Detergents etc. should be *biodegradable* — easily broken down by bacteria. Otherwise they cause foaming at sewage works and damage plant and marine life.

Unsatisfactory drainage could cause:
1. Serious diseases such as cholera, dysentery, typhoid, gastro-enteritis and other food poisoning diseases.
2. Unpleasant odours.
3. Infestation by flies and vermin.
4. Contamination of pure water supply if not laid in separate trenches.

CLEANING AGENTS USED ON DRAINS

1. *Disinfectants*: These destroy pathogenic bacteria. They can be divided into two groups: natural and chemical disinfectants.

Natural disinfectants are:
- Heat — fire, steam, boiling water.
- Ultraviolet radiation — sunlight.
- Fresh air — many micro-organisms dislike oxygen.

Chemical disinfectants are:
- Soap and detergents.
- Hydrogen peroxide.
- Chlorine.
- Carbolic acid.
- Phenols (found in heavy-duty disinfectants made from coal tar such as Jeyes Fluid).
- Commercial products such as Dettol and Lifeguard.

2. *Bleaches*: These destroy micro-organisms by chemical oxidation of cells. They also remove colour and odours. Many bleaches contain *sodium hypochlorite* and have a strong smell. Other bleaches are chlorine, sodium perborate and hydrogen peroxide. Most bleaches are poisonous and should be used carefully. Restrict use with septic tanks. Commercial products include Parozone and Domestos.

3. *Lavatory cleaners*: Most are crystalline powders which clean and disinfect without scouring. Bleaches may also be used in lavatories, but must never be used with crystalline lavatory cleaners as, together, they form dangerous chlorine gas. Commercial products include Harpic and Sanilav.

4. *Drain cleaners*: Most contain sodium hydroxide which melts away any grease in the drainpipe. Some also contain abrasives which wear away dirt/grease by friction. They may be used on a regular basis to keep drains clear and are also used specifically to free blocked drains. They also have a disinfectant effect on the drain. One commercial product is Clearway.

5. *Washing soda*: This is a strong alkaline crystal of sodium carbonate. It is useful for keeping drain pipes grease-free.

Note: The above cleaning agents, like many others, are poisonous. Keep them locked away and out of the reach of children. Protect clothes and hands when using.

12 HEAT AND ELECTRICITY

THE PRINCIPLES INVOLVED IN HEATING

1. HEAT TRANSFER

Heat is transferred (moves from one area to another) in three ways:
- Conduction
- Convection
- Radiation

CONDUCTION

By this method, heat passes from one molecule of solid or liquid matter to the next. For example, when the point of a poker is placed in the fire, heat travels along the poker until the whole poker has eventually been warmed.

As it is a slow method of heat transfer, this principle is rarely used in heating appliances. But it is important in relation to electricity and insulation.
- Good conductors of heat: metals and water
- Bad conductors of heat: air, wood, fabrics, rubber

Bad conductors of heat such as fibreglass and polystyrene are slow to transfer heat and sound. They are used to insulate and soundproof buildings, cookers, refrigerators and other appliances. Contact grills, sandwich toasters etc. cook by conduction.

CONVECTION

This is the process whereby heat travels by the movement of molecules. When cold liquid or gas (for example, air) is heated, the molecules move apart, make it less dense and therefore lighter, so it rises. Cold liquid or gas then flows in beneath to replace it. This sets up convection currents.

Most central heating systems and many individual heaters such as convector heaters utilise this principle. Fans or pumps may be used to speed up the natural convection of hot air or liquid. Ovens are mostly heated by convection. The top of the oven is therefore the hottest part. Many cooking methods such as boiling, baking and steaming are based on convection.

RADIATION

By this method, heat passes in straight rays or waves from the heat source to an object without warming the air through which it passes. Convection currents of air rise from the heated object — for example, a wall or settee. They then pass across the room, falling as they cool until the whole space is heated. Open fires, radiant gas and electric heaters and radiators all utilise this principle. Grilling and toasting are cooking methods which use radiant heat.

2. THERMAL EXPANSION

(A) SOLIDS EXPAND ON HEATING AND CONTRACT ON COOLING

Application of principle
- *Thermostats* are devices which keep the temperature of heating and cooking appliances steady. The working of some thermostats depends on a *bimetal strip*. This consists of a strip of brass which expands readily on heating, and a strip of Invar — a metal which expands very little on heating. When heat is applied the brass expands, causing the strip to bend. This breaks the electrical circuit, switching off the appliance. Most appliances have a light which indicates when the current is off or on.

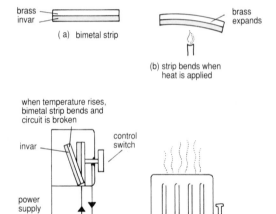

Thermostats

- *Fire alarms* work on the same principle, except that, in this case, the bending of the strip *makes* electrical contact and sets off the alarm.

(B) LIQUIDS AND GASES EXPAND WHEN HEATED

This increases their volume and decreases their density so that they become lighter and therefore rise.
Application of principle
- Hot water cisterns: when hot water floats above cold water.
- Heating and ventilation: hot air rises and cold air enters underneath — as in convector heaters.
- Baking: CO_2, trapped in dough, expands and pushes the dough upwards.

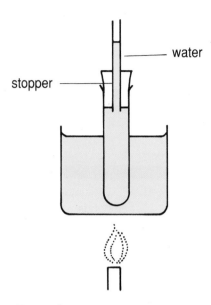

Test to show expansion of liquids

Test Showing Expansion of Liquids
Place a test tube filled with water in a water bath, as shown. Gradually heat the water bath. The level of water will be seen to rise up the narrow tube.

(C) WATER EXPANDS ON FREEZING
Application of Principle
- Burst water pipes in winter.
- Expansion of liquid foods on freezing, requiring 'head space' to be left.

3. EVAPORATION
Matter exists in three states: solid, liquid and gas. Water is solid below 0°C; liquid between 0°C; and 100°C and gas (vapour) over this temperature.

A change in physical state is usually caused by adding or removing heat from a substance.

EVAPORATION IS THE PROCESS WHEREBY A LIQUID CHANGES TO A GAS.
While it can take place at any temperature, evaporation is increased by high temperatures and also by air currents such as wind, dry air and a large surface area. Think of clothes hanging out to dry. On a still, damp, cold day, they will almost be impossible to dry. On a dry, cold day they will dry more quickly. But on a hot, windy day they will dry very quickly.
Application of principle
- Clothes drying — see above.
- Staling of bread and cakes.
- Commercial dehydration of foods: They are chopped, to increase surface area, then passed through a heated drying tunnel, thus evaporating moisture from food. Spray drying utilises the same principle.

BOILING CAUSES A RAPID CHANGE FROM LIQUID TO GAS.
This can be seen when a saucepan of water boils. Steam rises from the liquid and the level of liquid reduces. Each liquid has its own specific boiling point (water = 100°C). This can be changed: (a) by adding substances such as salt or sugar to the water, which raise the boiling point, e.g. in jam making to 104°C; (b) by raising or lowering pressure.

WHEN AIR PRESSURE IS LOWERED, THE BOILING POINT OF WATER IS LOWERED.
Application of principle
- On top of a mountain, where air pressure is lower than at sea level, water boils at a lower temperature (therefore, tea cannot be made properly).
- Low air pressure can be achieved by sucking out air, using a vacuum pump. This is utilised when evaporating milk and freeze drying foods such as potato powder.

INCREASING AIR PRESSURE RAISES THE BOILING POINT OF WATER.
Application of principle
- Pressure cookers seal in the air. As the heat is increased, the pressure builds up, causing the water to boil at a higher temperature (122°C), thus cooking the food faster.
- Sterilisers and autoclaves in hospitals and factories work on the same principle. The high temperature (120°-150°C) kills all micro-organisms.

EVAPORATION CAUSES HEAT TO BE ABSORBED FROM THE SURROUNDING AREA.
Application of principle
- In sweating, heat is taken from the body to evaporate the sweat, thus cooling it.
- Refrigeration utilises the above principle. A liquid refrigerant such as Freon 12 is made to evaporate. This draws heat from the refrigerator/freezer cabinet, making it cold (page 255).

4. CONDENSATION
THIS IS THE CONVERSION OF GAS OR VAPOUR TO A LIQUID.
Application of principle
- Breathe on a cold mirror. The vapour in your breath will condense — change back to liquid on the cold surface.
- Condensation is found on cold mornings when warm, moist air condenses on windows.
- It occurs particularly in kitchens and bathrooms when large amounts of steam condense on cold surfaces, often causing streams of moisture to run down the walls or windows.

HUMIDITY IS THE PRESENCE OF WATER VAPOUR IN AIR.
Kitchens, bathrooms and crowded, enclosed areas have a high level of humidity. Why?

Very high humidity leads to condensation on walls etc. and rusting of metals.

SUBLIMATION occurs when substances change from a solid to a gas without going through the intermediate liquid state. For example, ice changes directly to vapour without first changing to liquid. This occurs to clothes on a line on a frosty day.

The principle is utilised in accelerated freeze drying, (see Chapter 6, Preserving).

► MEASURING HEAT AND ENERGY

Fuel is a source of potential energy. Energy is released when oxygen combines with the carbon in fuel in the process of combustion or burning.

Heat and energy may be measured in different ways:
(a) In calories and kilocalories.
(b) In joules and kilojoules (approximately 4.2 times greater than (a))
(c) British Thermal Units (BTU) which are used to measure heat from fuels, such as coal, oil and gas. This unit of measurement has now been replaced by the joule.

Temperature — relative hotness and coldness — is measured with a thermometer using:
- *The Celsius (or Centigrade) scale*, which is now the international scale ($0°C$ = freezing point of water; $100°C$ = boiling point).
- *The Fahrenheit scale*: $32°F$ = freezing point of water; $212°F$ = boiling point.

Conversion from Fahrenheit to Celsius
Subtract 32 and multiply by 5/9.
Conversion from Celsius to Fahrenheit
Multiply by 9/5 and add 32.

► HEATING A HOME

The basic sources of heat for homes in this country are solid fuel, oil, gas and electricity.

It is difficult to work out which is the most economical. Prices are constantly fluctuating. Fuels such as solid fuel, which seem cheapest, are less efficient. Others become scarce at times or are subject to strikes. It is safer not to be too dependent on any one type of fuel — an all-electric house is not much use during an electricity strike!

Conservation of fossil fuels is important for future generations. Remember to use all fuels economically and to insulate your house and its equipment thoroughly to reduce heat loss.

SOLID FUEL
This term includes coal, turf, wood and smokeless fuels such as anthracite. All fuels contain carbon. Those with the most carbon produce the greatest amount of energy — wood 50%; turf 60%; coal 88% and anthracite 94%. What remains is smoke, soot, ash and waste gas.

SMOKELESS FUELS
These include anthracite, a natural fuel, and brand names such as Coalite and Phurnacite, manufactured from Welsh dry steam coal.

Smokeless fuels:	But they are:
■ are more efficient than coal. ■ burn more slowly, giving off more heat. ■ produce less ash and smoke. ■ therefore cause less pollution than coal. ■ must be used in smoke-control areas.	■ more expensive. ■ most must be used in closed stoves and fires. ■ most are slow to ignite.

Advantages of solid fuel heating
1. Relatively cheap to run.
2. An open fire is a focal point in a room and pleasant to sit by.
3. Water heating can be combined with room heating by using boiler grates.
4. Open grates assist ventilation.
5. They do not dry the air.

Disadvantages of solid fuel heating

1. Solid fuel systems are less efficient than most other forms of heating.
2. Much heat is lost up the chimney.
3. Fuel is bulky to store and deliver.
4. Difficult to control heat level and slow to build up heat.
5. It is time consuming — fuelling, cleaning and setting fires.
6. Can be too hot in summer so that alternative methods must be used for operations such as water heating.
7. It is dirty — stoking, emptying ashes. Rooms need redecorating more often.
8. Most solid fuels pollute the atmosphere.

OPEN FIRES

Open fires provide a cheerful form of radiant heat. Modern grates are well designed, with draught controls, restricted chimney throats and sealed grates. These improvements over old-fashioned grates reduce heat loss up the chimney and radiate more heat into a room.

BOILER GRATES OR BACK BOILERS

These have a metal water-tank built into the back of the fireplace or solid fuel cooker. This is fed with cold water from the storage tank in the attic. The water is heated and rises by gravity to be stored in the hot water cylinder (in the hot press). This provides a constant supply of hot water when the fire is lighting and, in the case of large, high-output boiler grates, will also feed several radiators to provide partial or full central heating.

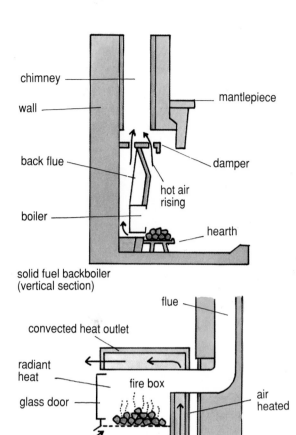

solid fuel backboiler
(vertical section)

solid fuel room heater
(vertical section)

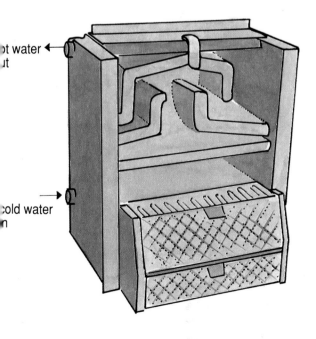

A back boiler

ENCLOSED FIRES — STOVES OR ROOM HEATERS

These are sealed metal boxes which may be fitted into an existing fireplace. They may also be freestanding with their own flues. Some are designed for use with smokeless fuels only. Others burn different fuels — for example, wood-burning stoves. Stoves are more efficient and economical than open fires as they burn fuel more slowly. They heat by radiation and convection and less heat is lost up the chimney, but ventilation is reduced. Some incorporate a back boiler and many can be left to burn overnight. While most are closed when operating, some models have doors that can be opened so that the fire can be seen. This, however, is less efficient, causing the fire to burn more rapidly.

SOLID FUEL CENTRAL HEATING BOILERS

Most solid fuel central heating boilers burn smokeless fuels as they are more efficient and cause less soot, ash etc. They are fuelled only once a day and produce very little ash. Automatic or hopper-fed boilers feed ovoids (manufactured smokeless fuel) from above through a hopper, reducing frequency of hand-fuelling to every 48 hours or so.

A solid fuel room heater

Danger! It is essential that solid fuel heating systems are correctly installed. The system should be suitably ventilated and fitted with a properly located *safety release valve* to prevent explosion in cases of overheating.

OIL

Petroleum (crude oil) is the source of all fuel oils. The oils are refined for various purposes. The oils most frequently used for domestic heating are *paraffin* and *fuel oil*. Paraffin is cheap and is used in individual heaters, stoves and lamps. Fuel oil is used in vaporising burners, such as those in central heating systems and oil fired cookers.

Advantages of oil heating
1. Oil is an efficient fuel. It lights readily and there is little waste.
2. Oil-fired central heating is fully automatic, requiring the minimum of attention.
3. Oil is relatively easy to deliver and to store.
4. Portable oil heaters can be moved from room to room, when unlit.
5. Causes little pollution.

Disadvantages of individual oil heaters
1. Fire is a great risk with portable oil heaters. They should conform to safety standards, be sturdy and difficult to overturn — and should cut out if they do overturn. *Do not* use in areas of traffic, near draughts or where children are unsupervised.
2. Unpleasant fumes are given off, particularly when not kept clean. Clean regularly.
3. Oxygen in the air is used up. They require a good system of ventilation.
4. Bulky to store — large tank required for central heating.

OIL-FIRED CENTRAL HEATING BOILERS
There are two types of oil used for central heating boilers, depending on the type of burner in the boiler.
1. *Vaporising oil*: The fuel is vaporised and the vapour is burnt within the boiler.
2. *Pressure jet oil*: Oil is forced from a jet at high pressure, forming a spray which is burned. This is a noisier method than burning vaporising oil.

Both oils are used in fully-automatic systems. Boilers should be serviced once or twice a year, depending on usage. Each house has an individual oil storage tank, holding about 1,300 litres. Communal tanks, with individual meters, are used in blocks of flats and some housing estates.

GAS

Natural gas is piped to some of our largest cities and towns. It is found under the sea bed and is piped ashore. Gas mains carry gas underground and a service pipe leads into each house. Within the house, a valve or tap controls its entry and a meter records consumption in cubic metres. Gas is a very clean, concentrated and efficient form of fuel.

Bottled gas is usually liquid butane gas. It is sold in pressurised cylinders and is useful in areas where piped gas is not available, as in rural areas, caravans and boats.

Small single or double gas burners are useful as a standby form of heating/cooking. Cookers, refrigerators and heaters such as Super Sers may be connected to bottled gas cylinders. Butane gas may also be used for central heating. It is stored in tanks outside the home.

Advantages of bottled gas
1. Gas is paid for in advance.
2. It is efficient and clean.
3. Useful when no piped gas is available.

Disadvantages of bottled gas
1. Cylinders are heavy to lift.
2. They are large and unsightly.
3. Good ventilation is required.

USING BOTTLED GAS
1. When buying bottled gas, get clear directions for connecting and using the cylinder.
2. *Ensure adequate ventilation*. It is unwise to use them in bedrooms or enclosed spaces.
3. Keep appliances and connections clean.
4. Store cylinders away from heat and direct sunlight.
5. On suspicion of any gas leak, do not use a match or lighted cigarette as it might cause an explosion. Contact the supplier or gas board.

Advantages of using natural gas
1. An efficient form of fuel. It is clean and easy to control.
2. Modern appliances light automatically and heat up quickly.
3. It is versatile. It may be used for cooking, water heating, individual heaters and central heating.
4. Natural gas needs no storage as it is piped direct.
5. Does not pollute the atmosphere.

Disadvantages of using natural gas
1. Fairly expensive, although special reductions are made for new customers. Cost reduces as consumption increases.
2. It dries the air and releases toxic fumes. An efficient flue or other form of ventilation is required. Some heat is lost this way.
3. Flueless heaters like Super Sers may only be used in large, well-ventilated areas.
4. Gas tends to have an unpleasant odour.
5. Appliances must be installed, serviced and repaired by a qualified fitter.
6. Slight danger of leaks and explosion.

Note: Gas appliances need oxygen to burn. This is drawn in at the base. It is essential to have rooms containing gas heaters *well-ventilated*, as the burning gas produces carbon dioxide and water vapour, which must be removed. Most gas heaters are built into an existing fireplace and the chimney is used as a flue to remove fumes. If not, large heaters and other appliances require a *balanced flue* which must *be fitted through an outside wall*. This is a form of *sealed double pipe fitted to the back of an appliance which removes toxic fumes and at the same time warms incoming fresh air.*

A closed gas fire

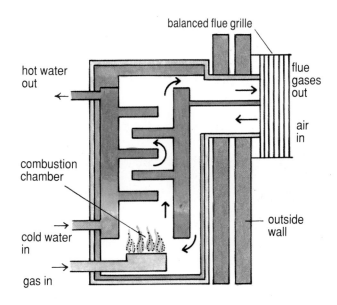

A gas-fired boiler with balanced flue

GAS HEATERS
- *Radiant heaters* are usually installed in a fireplace. They have gas jets which heat a fireclay grille. This radiates heat. Free standing models like Super Sers have a gas cylinder within the body of the heater.
- *Radiant/Convector heaters*: These are of similar construction. But as well as radiating heat, air is drawn in at the base, heated, and recirculated through a grille at the top.
- *Convector heaters*: These are usually wall mounted with a balanced flue to provide ventilation. Gas jets heat the air within the heater. The air rises, passing out through a grille at the top of the heater.

Gas central heating boilers: These may be floor standing, wall hung or form the back boiler to a fire. A pilot light ignites the gas burners when switched on. These heat water which circulates through pipes. A balanced flue is incorporated in all boilers.

ELECTRICITY
Electricity provides the widest variety of home heating appliances. It can be used to provide space heating or to power individual room heaters anywhere there is a 13 amp socket.

Advantages of electric heating
1. It is the most efficient form of heating. There is no waste, ash or fumes.
2. It is available on demand with no labour involved.
3. It is a very clean form of heating and simple to use.
4. No storage or delivery arrangements are necessary.
5. There is a wide range of heaters available, with modern features such as fans, time switches etc.

Disadvantages of electric heating

1. Electricity is usually the most expensive form of heating, although this is offset by its efficiency.
2. It dries the air.
3. Power cuts can disrupt supply. It is therefore advisable to have an alternative form of power for heating/cooking.
4. Heaters do not heat the water supply. A separate immersion heater is necessary.

An electric convector heater

ELECTRIC HEATING APPLIANCES

Electricity can flow freely through many cables and appliances. When the flow is resisted, heat is produced in the appliance or heater.

Most electric heaters are connected to a 13-amp fused plug. They have a selection of heat settings and a thermostat to maintain a steady temperature. Electric heating

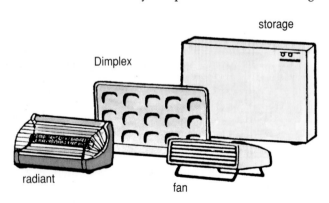

Electric heaters

appliances include: radiant (one and two bar) heaters or electric fires, lightweight infra-red heaters*, convector heaters, fan heaters, heated towel-rails, oil-filled radiators such as Dimplex, and storage heaters.

* Those used in kitchens/bathrooms should have a safety pull cord switch.

ROOM HEATERS/INDIVIDUAL HEATERS

These may be fixed or portable.

- *Fixed heaters* are attached to the wall, and are therefore safer when children are around.
- *Portable heaters* include a wide range of electric fires. They are convenient, can be moved from room to room and are quick to heat up. They are not as safe as fixed heaters, as they may be overturned and it is possible to trip over trailing flexes.

An electric fan heater

- *Radiant heaters*: Most heaters which glow red with heat are radiant heaters. Most have a reflective backing behind the heat source to throw out as much heat as possible. Two-bar electric fires, infra-red heaters, gas radiant heaters, bottled gas room heaters such as Super Ser and paraffin heaters are all radiant heaters.
- *Convector heaters*: These may be heated by electricity, gas or oil (less usual). Air is heated by the heat source (gas jets, electricity wires). The air expands, rises and passes out through a metal grille at the top of the heater. Cold air is drawn in through the bottom of the heater to replace it, thus setting up convection currents which heat space quickly and efficiently.
- Storage heaters (page 214).

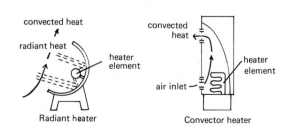

SAFETY PRECAUTIONS WHEN USING HEATERS

1. Buy a reliable make which conforms to accepted safety standards.
2. Open fires and radiant fires should be protected by a secure fireguard.
3. Ensure that the room is well ventilated. Gas heaters should be connected to a flue or used only in a ventilated area.
4. Never leave clothes to dry over any heaters. This causes overheating and may lead to fire.
5. Never move oil heaters once lit.
6. Keep heaters clean and well serviced.
7. Special precautions are necessary when children are about. Never leave unsupervised small children in a room with unguarded radiant fires.

CENTRAL HEATING

Central heating heats several rooms from one central heat source which may be heated by oil, solid fuel, gas or electricity.

Full central heating is usually fully automatic and heats the whole house to a comfortable temperature — about 15-22°C. *Partial central heating* may heat part of the house — for example, a back boiler which only heats downstairs radiators. *Background heating* heats the whole house a little but needs to be supplemented by individual heaters in cold weather.

SMALL BORE CENTRAL HEATING — A WET SYSTEM

This system involves heating water in a boiler, then pumping it through narrow diameter (*small bore*) pipes around the house to feed one or more radiators in each room. As the water becomes relatively cool, it returns to the boiler to be heated up again. Water is supplied from the storage tank in the attic. But as this is an enclosed system (the same water circulates continuously through the system), water rarely flows from the tank except after draining the system. This system usually includes an *indirect water heating* system in the hot water cylinder (page 203). An *overflow pipe*, leading to a separate water

storage tank, is required in the attic in case of expansion due to overheating.

A small bore system should have:

1. *A minimum guaranteed temperature in each room*: living areas — 20°C approximately; bedrooms, bathrooms and kitchens — a couple of degrees lower.
2. *A powerful boiler and circulating pump* (powered by electricity).
3. *Thermostats* — one on the boiler, one in the living area which turns off the boiler when indoor temperature is sufficiently warm. Individual radiators may have a thermostatic control valve.
4. Automatic *on/off switch* on a twenty-four hour clock.
5. An independent *hot water heating switch* for summer time.
6. *Radiators* made from pressed steel in single or double panelled form or low, skirting-style radiators. They work more efficiently when situated under a window.

Radiators may interfere with the layout of a room as furniture, curtains etc. cannot be placed directly in front of them.

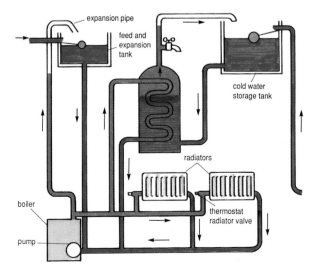

Small bore central heating system

time switch

room thermostat

Central heating boilers

(a) Wall mounted

(b) Floor standing

ELECTRIC STORAGE AND/OR UNDERFLOOR HEATING — A DRY SYSTEM

Storage heaters consist of heating elements embedded in blocks of fireclay or concrete. They are well insulated with fibreglass and enclosed in a slimline steel outer casing. The elements heat up the fireclay for nine hours at night on cheap off-peak electricity. The heat is gradually released during the day, with an afternoon boost of heat. Newer models use a fan to provide heat quickly when required.

Storage heaters and underfloor heating are designed to take advantage of off-peak electricity. They are wired directly into the system — they cannot be unplugged — and they have their own meter on which electricity is charged at a cheaper rate.

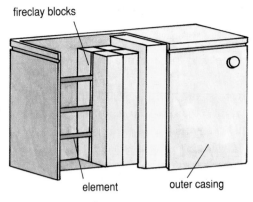

Storage heater

Advantages of storage heaters
1. Cheaper than normal electric heating, as economy rate is utilised.
2. Quiet and efficient in use. No maintenance necessary.
3. Installation less disruptive than other forms of central heating.
4. Further heaters can be added with little disruption as funds permit.

Disadvantages of storage heating
1. Heating is not easy to control and cannot be turned off quickly on a warm day. The heaters are slow to heat up and cool down.
2. Running costs are quite high.
3. Heating may need to be supplemented on cold days.

UNDERFLOOR HEATING

This works on the same principle as the storage heater. In this case, elements are embedded in concrete or other heat-storing material in the floor of a house. The concrete slowly releases heat during the day, with an afternoon boost to provide heat in the evening. This form of heating is also wired into an off-peak, cheaper rate meter.

Disadvantages of underfloor heating
1. Only really suitable for concrete floors — bungalows and commercial premises such as office blocks.
2. Must be installed during the building of a house.
3. If the system needs repair, it may be necessary to take up the floor. Accidents such as flooding could present serious problems.
4. Some find the underfloor warmth to be uncomfortable.
5. A separate water heating system is required.

AIR CONDITIONING/WARM AIR CENTRAL HEATING

Air is heated or cooled in an air-conditioning unit which may be run on gas, oil or electricity. Incoming air is filtered and 'conditioned' or humidified. It is blown around the building by a powerful electric fan and travels through ducts which are concealed in the floor and ceiling spaces.

It passes into each room through grilles placed at floor level.

This method of heating has been largely discontinued in Irish homes as it does not heat water. It also aggravates asthma and other allergies and is not suitable for installing in ready-built homes.

It is more suitable for industrial and commercial buildings, particularly in countries where extremes of temperature necessitate a cooling system in summer, and where pipes might burst if an alternative system were used.

COMPARING COSTS OF CENTRAL HEATING SYSTEMS

When installing central heating, consider:
1. *Installation costs*: Storage heaters would be one of the cheapest as there is little structural upheaval.
2. *Running costs*: Solid fuel and oil are cheaper than electricity.
3. *Efficiency*: How much heat are you getting for your money? A guaranteed temperature should be provided in each room, 18-20°C.
4. *Insulation costs*: These will repay their costs quickly by increasing heat efficiency, thus saving fuel.
5. *Convenience*: A fully-automatic system may cost more, but saves much time and labour.
6. Safety.

ECONOMISING ON CENTRAL HEATING

1. Insulate house well.
2. Switch off radiators/grilles in rooms not in use.
3. Do not set thermostats too high. Reduce them as weather gets warmer. Install radiator valves.
4. Keep doors closed to avoid heat loss.
5. Have system serviced regularly — at least once a year.

Paying for heat (1990)		
	1990	Today
Coal (per 50 kg)	£6–7.00	£
Anthracite (per 50 kg)	£9.00	
Briquettes (per bale)	£1.45p	
Central heating oil (per litre)	.28p	
Bottled gas (per cylinder)	£10.90p	
Natural gas (per therm)	.60p	
Electricity (unit) (normal tariff)	.07p	
Economy rate (unit)	.03p	

ELECTRICITY

Electricity is the flow of electrons (particles of atoms) from one atom to another. It is not a fuel, but a form of energy generated by turbines in power stations. It is difficult to store electricity. Although this can be done in batteries, it is usually generated as it is required.

ELECTRICAL TERMS

1. *Current*
   This describes the flow of electricity. It is measured in amps.
2. *Ampere (amp)*
   This is a measure of the rate at which an electric current flows. Amperage is determined by the amount of electricity used by an appliance. For example, electricity will flow to a vacuum cleaner at 1 amp; to an electric cooker, when fully turned on, at 30 amp. It is necessary to know the amperage when buying a fuse. A fuse must have the same, or slightly higher, amperage as the appliance.
   To find amperage: divide wattage by voltage, for example, 2,000 W ÷ 220 V = 9 amp.

3. *Volt*
   This is a measurement of electrical pressure or the force driving the current. It can be compared with water pressure. Electricity flows quickly when pressure is high and it provides greater power. It is less powerful when pressure is low. Standard voltage in Ireland is 220 V.

4. *Watt*
   This is a measure of the rate at which an appliance uses electricity. An appliance of high wattage uses a lot of electricity. A cooker uses up to 13,000 W (a microwave oven 600-900 watts). A kilowatt (kW) equals 1,000 watts and is used to measure appliances of a high wattage.
   To calculate wattage:
   Multiply volts by amps: 6 amps x 220 V = 1,320 watts.

5. *Kilowatt-hour (KWH) or unit of electricity*
   This is the unit of electrical consumption. If an appliance uses 1,000 watts for one hour, one unit of electricity is used.

6. *Earth* (green/yellow covering)
This is a metal connection between an appliance and the ground. Should a fault occur, such as a short circuit which makes an appliance live (capable of fire or shock), the current is conveyed harmlessly to earth. If an unearthed appliance is faulty, the current passes instead through the user causing shock or even death.

7. *Conductor*
A material which offers little resistance to the flow of electricity is considered to be a *good conductor* — for example, metal and water. A material which resists electrical flow is called a *bad conductor* or an *insulator*. Rubber, plastic, ceramics, fibreglass and dry air are bad conductors.

8. *Thermostat*
This is a device for controlling temperature in order to maintain a certain level of heat (page 206).

9. *Resistance*
Some conductors offer greater resistance to electrical flow than others, making it harder for the electricity to get through. Tungsten wire, in electric light bulbs, has such a high resistance; it glows white-hot. Hair driers, toasters and hot plates use nickel-chromium wire in their elements to create resistance and therefore heat.

ELECTRICITY SUPPLY

The main supply cable enters a house and passes into a sealed fuse box which may only be opened by ESB employees. From there it passes to the meter which records the consumption of electricity. It then passes into the main fuse box or consumer unit. There may be a second meter which records the consumption of off-peak electricity.

READING THE METER

Modern meters have a revolving digital counter which records consumption automatically. The Electricity Supply Board (ESB) read the meter and bill the consumer at two-monthly intervals. The previous reading is subtracted from the present reading to obtain the consumption of units during this period. For example:

Present reading	210,300
Previous reading	208,200
Consumption	2,100

This is multiplied by the cost per unit (see chart).
Meters in new houses are in sealed compartments, accessible from the outside to facilitate meter reading and avoiding estimated bills when householders are not at home.

THE FUSE BOX

This is the central distribution point for household electricity. The main supply is divided here into several 'circuits', each with its own fuse or switch. There is generally one fuse for each circuit — lighting circuits will have low (5 A) amp fuses. Large appliances, such as immersion heaters and washing machines will need a 16 amp fuse. A cooker needs a 35-60 amp fuse.

Circuits may include:
- Upstairs lighting
- Upstairs power points
- Immersion heater
- Downstairs lighting
- Downstairs power points
- Cooker

The fuse box also carries a main fuse or switch which should be removed or switched off when repairs are being carried out.

Fuses: A fuse is a deliberate weak link in an electric circuit. It is usually a Bakelite or porcelain container through which a wire, which is thinner than the rest of the circuit, passes. If too much current flows into a circuit, the wires could become dangerously hot. To prevent this, the fuse wire melts, cutting off electricity to the faulty area.

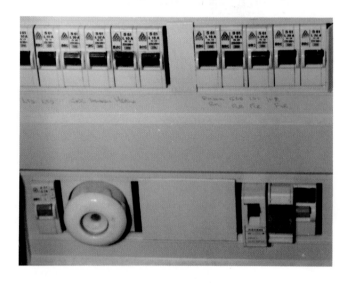

Modern installations use consumer units which contain miniature circuit breakers or trip switches instead of fuses. These switch off automatically when a fault occurs and are simply switched on again when the fault is corrected. These also incorporate an earth leakage circuit breaker (ELCB).

CAUSES OF BLOWN FUSES

- *Short circuit*: When positive and negative wires touch due, perhaps, to loosening of wires in a plug or appliance.

- *Overheating* of appliances — for example, due to faulty thermostat.
- *Overloading* the circuit by using more appliances at one time than the fuse can cope with.

TO REPLACE A FUSE

Gently unscrew the main fuse. Look for the blown fuse. The coloured disc at the end of the spent fuse may be loose, indicating which one needs replacing. Unscrew the faulty fuse and replace it with a new fuse of the correct amperage. Before switching on the main fuse, check cause of problem — for example, plugs, appliances or over-loading — and correct it. Never try to repair fuses.

DISC COLOUR	CIRCUIT
6 Amp	lights
10 Amp	lights
16 Amp	socket outlets (radial circuit)
20 Amp	water heater
35 Amp	socket outlets (ring circuit)
35 Amp	4-plate cooker

TYPES OF CIRCUIT

There are two types of circuit used in homes.

1. *The radial system* was used in old houses. Each socket and appliance had its own direct wire to the fuse box. It was a complicated system, involving a large number of fuses and large amounts of wiring.
2. *Ring circuits*: All modern homes use this circuit. A continuous length of wiring passes from the fuse box around the house and back again. To this circuit a large number of sockets may be connected, as long as the total does not exceed the strength of the fuse. Extra outlets are easily added.

Lighting has separate *5 amp circuits* — for example, for upstairs lighting, another for downstairs. Cookers, immersion heaters and any other major appliances need individual (radial) circuits, each with its own powerful fuse.

WIRING

Electric wiring is generally made of copper as it is an excellent conductor. Most cables and flexes contain three wires, each of which is insulated with a different coloured plastic.

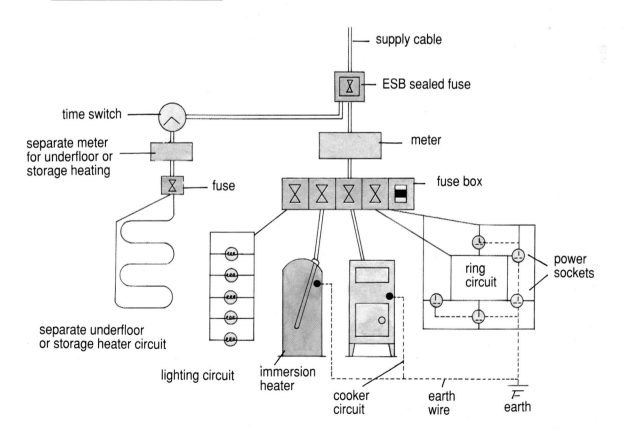

A typical household electrical system

- *Live wire*, coloured brown, carries electric current from the generator.
- *Neutral wire*, coloured blue carries current back to the generator.
- *Earth wire*, coloured green/yellow, carries faulty current to earth.

    (Old installations: live — red; neutral — black; earth — green).

Flexes for lighting and certain non-metal appliances such as shavers and hair dryers do not require an earth wire as these are *doubly insulated*.

SOCKETS, PLUGS AND SWITCHES

Modern electrical installations use flat three-pin, fused (13 amp) *plugs*. These are inserted into shuttered *sockets* which are safe because children cannot push objects into them. *Switches* break and connect the electric circuit by metal contacts which touch when the switch is on and separate when it is off.

WIRING A PLUG

1. Unscrew large central screw. Remove cover.
2. Loosen cord-grip screws and remove cartridge fuse.
3. Loosen screws of three terminals.
4. Strip back sufficient outer flex covering so that it finishes just inside the cord grip.
5. Measure the length of each wire to its appropriate terminal.
6. Trim frayed or thin wires and pare insulation from wires.

7. Fix wires in position: Live (brown) wire to L (fused, right-hand side) pin. Neutral (blue) wire to N pin on left-hand side. Earth (green/yellow) wire to E pin at top of plug. Tighten screws.
8. Replace cartridge fuse — 3 amp for lights; 13 amp for appliances. A fuse of too high amperage could cause a fire.
9. Tighten cord grip, replace cover and test.

ELECTRICAL SAFETY

1. *Never* mix water and electricity. Dry hands before touching electrical appliances.
2. *Never* overload sockets — for example, by using two double adaptors.
3. *Never* have electric sockets or switches in a bathroom. A pull cord may be used for bathroom heaters and shavers.
4. *Never* bring portable electrical appliances into a bathroom.
5. Keep electrical equipment in *good condition*. Replace frayed flexes and wires, cracked sockets and plugs. *Service equipment* when necessary.
6. *Avoid* trailing flexes. Do not run wiring under carpet, as it may fray and cause a fire.
7. *Switch off* appliances before cleaning and kettles before filling.
8. *Pull out plugs at night*, particularly TV plugs.
9. Use a *qualified electrician* for all wiring and installations. Avoid 'amateur' repairs of flexes etc.
10. *Use correct fuses*, earthed equipment and three-pin sockets only.
11. *Rewire houses* after 25-30 years, as wiring has a limited life.
12. Only use electrical appliances which carry an *electrical safety approval mark*.

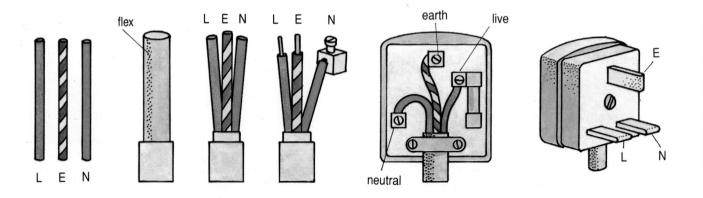

Wiring a plug

► INTERIOR DECORATION

When planning the decoration of a room, consideration must be given to three factors which will influence the end result: colour, pattern and texture.

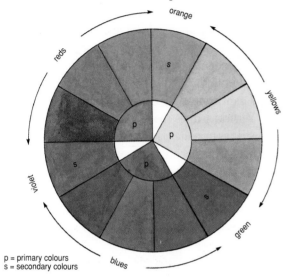

p = primary colours
s = secondary colours

The colour wheel

1. COLOUR

Daylight is made up of all the colours of the rainbow. The *colour spectrum* consists of all these colours spread out, each one blending into the next, although it was common at one time to describe the spectrum as having seven distinct colours: red, orange, yellow, green, blue, indigo and violet.

The most basic or *primary colours* are red, yellow, green and blue, which are strong and bright. Sometimes red, yellow and blue are called the primary colours because paints of these colours can be mixed to create many other colours.

Secondary colours are those between the primary colours — purple between red and blue, orange between red and yellow.

Shades are obtained when a colour is darkened by adding black and *tints* are obtained when white is added to lighten a colour.

The way in which we perceive colour can be influenced by many factors: the amount of light in the room, the particular hue, textures and so on. Use of certain colours will appear to alter the proportions of a room. Some colours such as red advance, crying out for attention. Others such as white or cream recede, making the room seem larger and the ceiling higher.

Colour can be cleverly used to highlight good features such as cornices. Colour can also disguise bad features — if ugly radiators or doors are painted the same shade as the wall behind them, they will be far less noticeable than if they were picked out in a contrasting colour. Avoid mixing too many colours — one or two colours should be dominant.

Colours may show up differently under artificial lighting. Examine furnishings etc. under both natural and artificial light before making a decision.

To make a room feel larger, decorate in light colours. The lighter the colour the more light is reflected and the larger the room feels.

To make a large room feel smaller or cosier, use warm colours to bring the walls inwards and the ceiling downwards.

Dark colours and warm colours advance. A single wall painted in a dark colour will be drawn into the room

Cool colours recede. A wall painted in a light cool colour appears further away than it really is.

To lower a ceiling, use a colour which is slightly darker than the walls but not so dark that it feels oppressive.

To raise a ceiling, use a colour which is lighter than the walls. Increase the effect by painting the walls right up to the level of the ceiling.

SOME COLOUR FACTS

- *Hue*: A colour — blue, green red.
- *Tone/value*: A measure of the lightness or darkness of a colour. There may be several tones between the palest and the darkest shade/tone of any colour.
- *White and pale colours* reflect light and make a room seem larger by receding into the background.
- *Dark colours* absorb light. They make an area look smaller by making the walls or ceilings seem nearer.
- *Warm colours* such as yellow, orange and red stimulate. They are best in cold north-facing rooms.
- *Cool colours* like blues and greens are restful colours. They can be used in sunny south-facing rooms without making them seem cold.
- *Neutral* — black, grey and white. Grey and white are good background colours. Black and white may be used to provide accent.
- *Pastels* are very pale, soft shades of blue, green, pink, lilac and yellow. They are delicate and considered to be 'feminine' colours. They are often used in nurseries.
- *Analogous colour scheme*: This is based on two adjacent colours in the spectrum, e.g. greenish blue and blue.
- *Monochromatic scheme*: This is based on various tones of one colour, e.g. beige carpet, cream walls, tan/cream patterned furniture, beige/cream curtains. It is very effective and is a wise choice for those who have little confidence in their sense of colour.

- *Harmony*: When colours go well together, when they do not clash, they are said 'to harmonise'.
- *Contrast*: When one colour shows up well against another, e.g. red on white. Colours opposite each other on the colour wheel contrast well.

2. PATTERN

A pattern is a decorative design which may form part of a surface — woven cloth, brickwork — or be printed on it. Patterned wall coverings, fabrics and floor coverings are all available and vary considerably in size and design.

- Take care when using patterns. Too much pattern looks fussy and untidy.
- Pattern can appear to change the proportions of a room. Vertical stripes make a room seem higher; horizontal stripes or patterns have a widening effect.
- Large bold patterns are only suitable for large rooms. Small patterns look well in small rooms.
- Co-ordinating patterned wall-coverings, curtains, tiles etc. are now available in a wide range.

This room illustrates the use of
(a) pattern — curtains, chaircovers, carpet;
(b) texture — carpet, lampshade, accessories

3. TEXTURE

This term describes the thickness, roughness or feel of an object. Most rooms combine smooth and rough textures in equal amounts. Textures give an interesting third dimension to a room.

A blue monochromatic scheme

Smooth finishes: Glass, mirror, metal, gloss paint, ceramics, e.g. tiles

Rough (textured) finishes: Carpets, tweeds and other upholstery fabrics (e.g. velvet, linen, hessian), brick, stonework, embossed and flocked wall-coverings, carved furniture, rough ceramics, wall hangings

- Smooth surfaces reflect sound and light. They can produce glare and noise and be cold and uninviting.
- Textured surfaces absorb sound and light. They are quiet and comfortable to live with, but may darken a room.
- Textured surfaces may be difficult to clean. Smooth surfaces are used extensively in kitchens and bathrooms because they are easily cleaned.
- Textured surfaces will make a room seem smaller; smooth surfaces reflect more light, making it seem larger.

Accessories such as photographs, paintings, ornaments and plants provide interest, pattern and texture. They give a room a homely, 'lived-in' atmosphere.

PLANNING A COLOUR SCHEME

1. Consider the house as a whole. Different areas should relate to one another, each room blending with the next.
2. This can be achieved by using the same background colour throughout, such as white or cream walls, or a beige carpet. It also makes the house look bigger.
3. Keep carpets and furniture in fairly neutral shades. The colour scheme can be altered later without great expense.
4. Each room should have a dominant colour, with contrasting colours used for accent.
5. Check colours in both natural and artificial light. Bring swatches/samples home.
6. Consider the size and the 'mood' of the room. Small rooms are usually best decorated in pale colours/small patterns. Large rooms can take bold colour and large patterns.

▶ WALL FINISHES

Surfaces may be covered with paint, wallpaper or tiles.

1. PAINT

Paint protects surfaces and improves their appearance. Wood and metal should be painted regularly to prevent damage by rotting and rust.

COMPOSITION OF PAINT

Paint is a thick viscous substance. It may be oil or water based. It contains:

Pigment	+	Binder	+	Solvent
or		or		or
Powder		Medium		Thinner

Pigment may be natural or synthetic. It gives paint its colour and ability to cover. Lead should not be used in paint as it is toxic.

Binder: Linseed oil or resin. Modern paints may also contain substances such as vinyl or polyurethane to strengthen the paint.

Solvent: This helps to spread the paint. After application it evaporates. (a) White spirit or turpentine is the solvent used in oil based paints and (b) water in emulsion paints.

Driers are often included in paints today to speed up drying.

MANUFACTURE OF PAINT

Pigment and powder are mixed by grinding together. Then other ingredients are blended in. Paint is sold in 250 ml, 500 ml, 1 litre, 2½ litre and 5 litre tins. It is also available in many colours, textures and finishes, including gloss, eggshell and matt finish.

WATER-BASED PAINTS

- *Emulsions:* Modern emulsions contain plastic binders such as acrylic and vinyl which give them a washable, hard-wearing finish. They are easy to apply, quick to dry, and paint brushes are easily washed out with water.

  Emulsions are used mainly for interior walls and ceilings. They are available in matt, eggshell and semi-gloss (silk) finishes.
- *Non-drip (thixotropic) emulsions:* These are thick jelly-like paints which are easy to apply and are particularly handy for beginners. Because of their thickness, one coat is often sufficient to obliterate previous paintwork. They should not be stirred and, therefore, colours cannot be mixed.

  Solid emulsion is an even thicker paint, particularly useful for ceilings. It is usually sold in paint trays, is spillproof and is applied with a roller.
- *Distemper* is a cheap paint generally used for ceilings. As it is non-washable, it flakes easily and must be removed before repainting. It is rarely used today.
- *Exterior emulsions:* Many contain powdered cement or stone, plastics and silicones (to give a waterproof finish). Some have a textured finish. These paints may last for about ten years without repainting. They are expensive.

OIL-BASED PAINTS

These paints contain pigments, a binder such as linseed oil, and solvent. They are more difficult to apply than other paints, slower to dry and have a strong smell. They are more hardwearing, water-resistant and easier to clean than are emulsions. Clean brushes with solvent.

- *Gloss paint* is suitable for wood work, metal (e.g. window frames), and small areas of wall. It is highly water resistant and is therefore useful in kitchens and bathrooms. It is hardwearing but more expensive than emulsion. A matching undercoat is usually required. High gloss (wet look) paints are also available.

- *Non-gloss finishes*: Manufacturers now produce a wide range of non-gloss, oil-based finishes, including eggshell, lustre, satin, silk and matt. Apart from their finish, they are similar in composition and use to gloss finishes.

- *Strengthened paints* such as polyurethane contain strong plastics as binders which provide a particularly durable finish. As they dry quickly, they are more difficult to apply than are other paints. They are ideal for areas subjected to hard wear including skirtings, doors and furniture.

MODERN PAINTS AND FINISHES

- *Thixotropic or non-drip paints* are available in gloss and emulsion forms.

- *Flame retardant*: Paint is highly inflammable and this paint has been developed for high-fire risk areas, such as kitchens, boats and caravans, as it inhibits flames. It is the only paint which can be used over polystyrene ceiling tiles. Brand name: Timonex.

- *Textured paints* contain plastic fibres to give a textured or stippled finish and are usually water-based.

- *Bituminous paint*: Contains a tar-like substance which is water-resistant and protective. Used inside gutters, on flat roofs, etc.

- *Anti-mould/fungus* paint contains chemicals which resist mould growth.

- *Anti-condensation* paint absorbs moisture.

- *Creosote* and *anti-woodworm* treatments.

PAINT SYSTEM

It is usual to apply paint in three stages.

1. *Primer* is used on untreated surfaces. This gives extra protection and helps further coats of paint to adhere well. It seals wood and helps prevent rusting of metals.

2. *Undercoat*: This helps to obliterate previous colours and provides a key for gloss paint. Two coats of water-based paints are usually applied, the first acting as an undercoat. Oil-based paints generally have matching, non-gloss undercoats. One or two may be needed.

3. *Top coat*: This provides the finish and must be carefully applied (see below).

Amount of paint required: This varies according to porosity of the surface being painted and the number of coats required. Coverage is usually written on the tin.

Average coverage per litre:

Gloss }	
Emulsions }	15 sq. m (163 sq. ft)
Non-drip	11 sq. m (119 sq. ft)

1. Prepare surfaces
2. Apply primer
3. Undercoat
4. Sand down to create key
5. Top coat

Stages in painting with gloss paint

PAINTING EQUIPMENT

Apart from paint, many of the following items will be required when painting.

Brushes: Good quality bristle are best — 2.5 cm, 5 cm, 7.5 cm, 13 cm.

Roller and roller tray, sandpaper, paintstripper, white spirit, ladder, scraper, filler, masking tape (for windows), cloths, protective ground sheet.

PAINTING A ROOM

PREPARATION

1. Prepare room. Remove curtains, blinds and as much furniture as possible. Take up carpets or cover with plastic or dust sheets. Remaining furniture, which should be placed in the middle of the room, must also be covered.

2. Wear suitable protective clothing.

3. Prepare surfaces.
   - Remove any loose material around cracks and holes and fill with appropriate filler. When dry, sand down with sandpaper.

- Wash dirty surfaces with warm soapy water. Rinse and dry.
- Sand down gloss paint to provide a key. Badly flaking paint should be removed with a chemical stripper such as Nitromors. Vacuum to remove dust etc.

4. Apply suitable primer to untreated wood or metal.

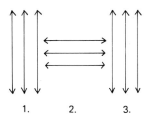

a. 1. Apply paint in an up and down movement.
   2. Spread paint with a to and fro movement.
   3. Lay off with a light, up and down movement.

c. Painting a door

b. Paint wall in 1m. sections, from top to bottom, right to left.

Tips for painting

PAINTING

1. Paint in this order: ceiling, walls, woodwork.
2. Follow instructions on tin on whether to stir, dilute etc.
3. Apply primer, if necessary, then one or two undercoats. Finish with top coat and allow to dry.
4. Apply paint as follows. Dip brush or roller into paint, removing excess. Start painting in up-and-down strokes, then across in strokes. Then, finally, lay off paint with light up and down strokes to wipe out brushmarks.

   Do not paint with erratic diagonal strokes. Blend joins well.

5. Roller paint ceiling and walls in 50 cm squares, starting at the top right-hand corner and working down in panels (see diagram).
   Finish edges with small paintbrush.
6. Doors: Paint frame the day before, if possible. Flush (plain) doors: paint as above. Panelled doors: paint edges first, then mouldings, then four panels, then the area around the panels (see diagram).
7. Windows: Use masking tape to protect glass, if wished. Paint frame the day before. Leave window open when painting and drying. Work from top to bottom, starting with the sections nearest the glass.

2. WALL-COVERINGS

Wall-coverings introduce colour, pattern and, in some cases, texture to a room. They come in standard rolls, 10.14 m (11 yd) x 0.52 m (20-21 in.) wide and are available in a wide variety of designs. They vary in thickness. For example, cheap paper is thin and is difficult to apply as it tears easily. Vinyl is stronger, as well as being washable.

MANUFACTURE

- Strengthened paper is cut, coated with pigments and dried.
- Design is printed onto paper by printing machines.
- Expensive papers may be block or silkscreen printed.
- Paper to be embossed is passed between moulding rollers.
- Resin may be applied to surface to give a wipeable finish.

PAPER WALL-COVERINGS

- *Lining paper*: Thin white paper used under wallpaper to improve the surface finish or as base for painting. It may be hung horizontally or vertically. The seams of lining and wallpaper should not lie one on top of the other.
- *General purpose papers* come in various thicknesses, colours and designs, with the design printed on the surface. If designs must be matched, extra paper is required.
- *Washable papers* have a surface coating of resin or silicone, giving some water resistance. They can be gently wiped with a damp cloth but will not withstand regular washing.
- *Embossed papers*: These are heavy papers with the design pressed into them. They provide texture and disguise minor wall blemishes. They may require matching and heavy-duty paste. Avoid flattening design by over-rubbing.
- *Wood chip paper* is an inexpensive paper made from two thin layers of paper with chips of wood pressed

between them. It gives an attractive, textured finish, disguises uneven walls and is usually painted over.

- *Anaglypta* is a very thick, embossed paper and useful for covering uneven walls. It can be painted over, giving a panelled effect on walls and ceilings. Heavy-duty paste is required.
- *Flock* is a design produced by gluing nylon fibres onto a heavy vinyl or paper background. Suitable for period decor.

VINYL WALL-COVERINGS

- *Vinyl papers* consist of a layer of PVC on a paper backing. They are durable, waterproof, easy to handle and clean. They remain strong when wet and can be gently scrubbed when heavily soiled. They are especially suitable for kitchens, bathrooms and heavy-wear areas.
- *Ready-pasted vinyls* have a coating of dried paste on the paper. When soaked in the trough provided, the lengths of paper can be hung after draining without pasting.
- *Novamura* is a thin layer of polyethylene foam. The wall is pasted and the wallcovering applied to it.
- *Metallic-finished vinyls*: This is a foil-type finish which can highlight an interesting feature such as an alcove. It is not suitable for large areas.

Other wall coverings
- Fabric including hessian, grass cloth
- Ceramic and vinyl tiles; mosaic tiles
- Mirrors
- Wood panelling
- Cork tiles, brick, stone

PAPERING A ROOM

EQUIPMENT AND MATERIALS REQUIRED
Pasting table (or clean floor)
2 stepladders
Bucket for paste
Steel ruler and T-square
Stripping knife
Sharp scissors and handyman's knife
Wallpaper brush
Plumbline and pencil
Wallpaper (Ensure all rolls have same 'batch' number.)
Suitable paste*

* Paste: standard; heavy-duty for heavier papers; antifungicidal paste, essential for impervious vinyl papers.

WORK IN THIS ORDER
1. Paint ceiling (emulsion).
2. Paint woodwork (using under and top coats).
3. When paint is dry, apply wall-covering.

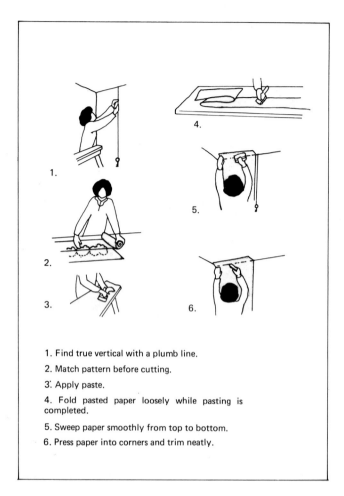

1. Find true vertical with a plumb line.
2. Match pattern before cutting.
3. Apply paste.
4. Fold pasted paper loosely while pasting is completed.
5. Sweep paper smoothly from top to bottom.
6. Press paper into corners and trim neatly.

PREPARATION
1. Wear old clothes and prepare room as for painting.
2. Prepare wall. Soak old paper well with warm water or a solution of wallpaper stripper. Scrape off carefully, using a stripping knife. Vinyl paper may be peeled off, leaving backing paper behind as a lining. Electric steam strippers are useful for large areas and for removing several layers of paper. They may be hired.
3. Wash down walls and allow to dry.
4. Fill any cracks or holes with filler. Allow to dry.
5. Sand down walls to remove bumps and any pieces of paper.
6. Size porous or newly plastered walls. Size is a watered-down solution of paste: 50% prepared paste; 50% water. It seals walls and allows paper to move more easily during hanging.
7. Remove light switches and any other removable fitting before papering the immediate area. Be sure to disconnect the fuse first.

HANGING WALLPAPER
1. Make up paste according to instructions.
2. Start at the centre of a chimney breast or to the right side of a window (if right handed), working away from the light source.

3. Measure wall. Measure a length of paper, allowing 50 mm top and bottom for trimming. Using a set square, mark and cut paper. Match a second length of paper before pasting and hanging.

4. Place paper face down on table. Paste liberally, using pasting brush from centre to edges. Fold pasted ends together.

5. Using a plumb line, mark a vertical line with pencil on the wall.

6. Standing on a ladder, place top of paper to top of wall. Place edge of paper carefully along vertical pencil line and press in gently from centre outwards — from top down. Brush out air bubbles and avoid creases. Unfold paper and repeat with lower half.

7. Press paper close to skirting, making a crease. Lift slightly and cut with scissors. Trim top of paper evenly with knife or scissors.

8. Match, measure and cut next strip. The edges should form a butt join and not an overlap.

9. Use plumb line again at each corner, as they are rarely 'true'.

10. Paper neatly around doors, windows etc.

CALCULATING AMOUNT OF PAPER REQUIRED

1. Measure height of walls from skirting to ceiling.

2. Divide height into 10.04 m, the standard length of a roll (4 lengths can usually be cut from one roll unless room is high or pattern is large).

3. Multiply 0.52 m (width of paper) by number of lengths obtained from one roll. This gives the amount of space which one roll covers.

4. Measure the perimeter of the room. Divide this by the answer to 3 above. This gives the number of rolls needed. Allow extra paper if matching is necessary. Allow less if there are large areas of door, window and fireplace.

Cost of wallcoverings/paint			
	1990	19--	19--
Vinyl wallcovering (per roll)	£4–6		
Wallpaper	£2–5		
Wood chip/lining paper	£2–3		
Gloss paint (per litre tin)*	£5.50–6.50		
Emulsion (per litre tin)*	£4.50–5.50		
*larger sizes are cheaper per litre			

► FLOOR FINISHES

CONSTRUCTION OF FLOORS

Floors may be solid or suspended (Chapter 10).

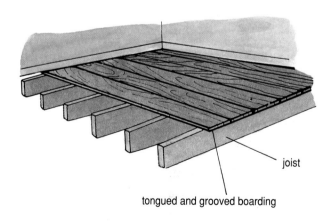

joist

tongued and grooved boarding

A suspended floor

FLOOR COVERINGS

These may be *hard* or *soft*.

Hard finishes include wood floors, quarry tiles, ceramic tiles and stone. Soft finishes include carpets, rugs etc. Vinyl is neither a really hard nor a soft finish.

FUNCTIONAL REQUIREMENTS OF FLOORS

- Tough and durable
- Resilient (flexible)
- Warm
- Attractive
- Comfortable
- Hygienic
- Easy to clean and maintain
- Stain, heat and water resistant
- Non-slip when wet or dry
- Quiet

The type of room will influence the choice of floor covering. For example:

- A kitchen or bathroom requires an easy-to-clean, stain-resistant, non-slip finish.
- A living room should have a comfortable, quiet, attractive finish, preferably easy to maintain and clean.
- A hall demands a hard-wearing surface which does not show footprints, for example a heavy domestic carpet.

WOOD FLOORS

Wood provides a rich, durably-attractive finish which is easily maintained if sealed with several coats of polyurethane. It is hard, noisy, damaged by heel marks and not suitable for wet areas. Existing floorboards may be sanded and sealed if they are in good condition. Gaps should be filled with the appropriate filler.

Note: Sub floor must be absolutely flat — a cement base is best.

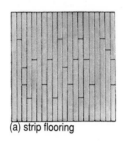
(a) strip flooring

(b) wood block

(c) wood mosaic

Wooden floors

- *Strip flooring*: Softwood or hardwood strips already sanded, sealed and attached to a firm backing. Easy to fix.
- *Wood block floors (parquet)*, made from hardwood, are laid in herringbone or basket-weave design over concrete subfloor, then sanded and sealed.
- *Wood mosaic*: Thin strips of hardwood arranged in decorative panels on a fabric backing, making them easy to fix.

CARE AND MAINTENANCE OF WOOD FLOORS
- Avoid soaking with water. Mop up spills at once.
- Sweep daily to remove harmful grit.
- Clean regularly with a damp cloth. Polish unsealed floors with wax polish.
- Worn finishes will have to be sanded and re-sealed.

CARPETS

CONSTRUCTION

The pile of a carpet is the surface one walks on. It consists of loops or tufts of yarn fixed or woven into a tough jute, nylon or foam backing. Pile can be short (velvet), long, twisted, sculptured or embossed (pile of differing heights). The pile can be cut or uncut.

The backing is the simple woven base into which the main carpet is woven or inserted. It was traditionally made from jute or sisal (used to make twine). Today it is usually made from polypropylene. A second backing is often added to give extra comfort, springiness and durability. This is usually made of synthetic foam or latex adhesive.

- *Woven carpets*: These are made by weaving a wool/nylon thread in and out through a jute backing. The pile, which can be long or short, should be closely woven and secured firmly into the backing.

  Wilton carpets have the threads woven into the backing, providing a thicker carpet but limiting the number of colours used.

  Axminster carpets catch each tuft separately into the backing. This is more economical so that these carpets are cheaper but they do not wear quite as well as Wilton carpets. Unlimited colours may be used with Axminster weaves and most patterned carpets are made in this way.

  Note: Axminster and Wilton are methods of weaving and not brand names or indications of quality.

- *Tufted carpets* are made by inserting tufts of yarn into a woven backing. The tufts are held in place by adhesive and a backing of latex foam may then be applied. As these carpets are quicker to make, they are cheaper than woven carpets, yet quite comfortable and hardwearing. Colour may be introduced by the use of different coloured yarns or by printing (not as satisfactory). Sculptured or embossed effects are created by using cut and uncut pile or pile of differing depths.

Axminster weave

knife
plain Wilton weave

foam-backed cord carpet

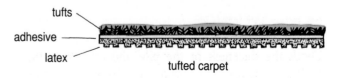
tufts
adhesive
latex
tufted carpet

Carpet construction

YARNS USED FOR CARPETS

- *Wool*: This is the traditional and still the most popular yarn used for carpets. It is warm, resilient, durable, dyes well, is springy, doesn't flatten easily and is resistant to liquids. It is expensive, but is often blended with other yarns to provide a cheaper but equally hardwearing carpet. As wool is susceptible to moths, ensure carpet is moth-proofed.
- *Synthetics*: These include the acrylics (such as Acrilon, Courtelle), nylon and polypropylene. All are reasonably hardwearing, easy to clean, flame resistant and cheaper than wool. But they tend to soil more easily (due to static build-up) and are permanently damaged by burns, as from cigarettes. Many have an unpleasant sheen and cheaper varieties tend to pill — that is gather into balls of fluff. Polypropylene is very water-resistant and is used for kitchen carpets (as these are unhygienic they are not recommended). It is also used for carpet backing into which carpet threads are woven.
- *Cotton, rayon* used for cheap carpets/rugs, as in bathrooms.
- *Blends*: A combination of two or more fibres which provide the best qualities of each. For example, 80% wool and 20% nylon combine the warmth and resilience of wool with the durability of nylon. Blends also reduce the cost.

CHOICE OF CARPETS

Carpets are usually classified as:
- Light domestic use (bedrooms)
- Medium domestic use (dining rooms)
- General domestic use (living room)
- Heavy domestic use (living room, hall, stairs)
- Luxury domestic/heavy contact (living room, hall, stairs, hotels, etc.)
- Washable kitchen and bathroom carpets are also available.

1. Consider the amount of traffic to which the carpet will be subjected. A hall will require a heavy-duty carpet, while a bedroom probably will not.
2. Consider the colour scheme. The carpet is often the most expensive item in a room. A basic or neutral colour will last through several changes of decor.
3. Unpatterned, plain carpets show up every speck; patterned carpets are easy to maintain. Pale colours are impractical where there are children.
4. Do you require: (a) a large *carpet square*? (b) a *fitted carpet*, extending from wall to wall? (c) *carpet tiles*, which are very practical as they can be changed around?
5. Check the thickness of the pile, the quality of the backing. Tug the tufts, bend them back. The carpet label or brand name is often an indication of quality.

6. Get a *written estimate* to include carpet, underlay and fitting. Carpets can be tacked in position, held in place with *carpet grippers* or loose laid.

UNDERLAYS

All carpets benefit from the use of an underlay, although it is not essential when foam-backed carpets are used.

TYPES OF UNDERLAY

- *Felt* is available in various thicknesses. It is cheap but tends to flatten.
- *Foam*: Polyurethane and latex are thicker and softer than felt. It is durable although expensive and cannot be used with underfloor heating.
- *Layered*: A layer of rubber/latex and felt is more durable than foam. It is softer and more comfortable than felt, as well as being more expensive.

ADVANTAGES OF AN UNDERLAY

1. It makes a carpet feel more comfortable underfoot.
2. Provides insulation.
3. Reduces noise.
4. Improves wear of carpet by reducing friction.

CARE OF CARPETS

1. Vacuum regularly to remove harmful dirt and grit which damage fibres.
2. Avoid dragging heavy furniture over carpets. Use castors, if possible.
3. Wipe up spills at once.
4. Shampoo occasionally, according to composition.
5. Hand sweep new carpets to avoid removing too much fluff. Delay vacuuming for one month to allow it to settle.
6. Protect from fading on sunny days by drawing curtains.
7. Turn non-fitted carpets and move stair carpets to prevent uneven wear. Move around furniture where possible.

PLASTIC FLOORING

Plastic flooring is ideal for use in kitchens and bathrooms and is also attractive enough to use in dining rooms and halls. The sub-floor must be absolutely flat. A layer of hardboard may be necessary.

COMPOSITION

1. *Binder* such as PVC (polyvinylchloride
2. *Filler* such as asbestos
3. *Pigments*

TYPES OF VINYL

- *Plain vinyl or PVC* consists of 35%-70% vinyl. It is available in sheet or tile form. The design may be: *printed*, that is, on the surface only under a transparent film of PVC (this may wear away) or *inlaid*, forming part of the material.

- *Vinyl asbestos* (PVA): Asbestos or other fillers are mixed with vinyl (25%). It is usually sold in tile form, is hard-wearing, water and stain resistant. It is not as flexible as plain vinyl. It is therefore less comfortable than other vinyls.
- *Cushioned vinyl* is backed with a layer of foam. It is more comfortable, quiet and warm than plain vinyl. It is easy to put down as it does not have to be glued in position and is easy to clean. It is unsuitable for use over underfloor heating. Available in sheet form only.

ADVANTAGES OF VINYL

1. Hardwearing, easy to clean.
2. Flexible, resilient; resists indentation, e.g. heel marks.
3. Resistant to acids, alkalis, water and grease.
4. Reasonably soft, comfortable, warm and quiet.
5. Available in sheet (2 m wide) or tile form (30 cm square).
6. Available in a wide range of colours, designs — some with a veined or marbled effect, others are embossed to look like ceramic tiles.
7. Easy for the amateur to lay, using special adhesive.
8. Cheap, hygienic and not too slippery.

CARE OF VINYL

1. A wash and rinse, using a non-soap detergent like Flash is usually sufficient to keep it in good condition.
2. Many manufacturers supply a special cleaner and polish.
3. Avoid using abrasives as they will damage the surface.
4. Avoid wax polishes as they soften the vinyl, making it prone to scratching. Water-based emulsion polishes are more suitable.
5. Self-shine polishes such as Seel cause a build-up of residue after a time. This sticky layer must be removed every six months or so, using a solvent recommended by the manufacturer.

OTHER FLOOR COVERINGS

- *Linoleum* is made from linseed oil, resins, cork etc.
- *Cork* is a natural material obtained from trees and may be sealed or unsealed. It is useful for bathrooms but is not particularly hardwearing.
- *Stone, quarry, cement and ceramic tiles* are hardwearing and easy to clean. No resilience and very hard on the feet, if standing on them for long periods. Very expensive. Must be used on solid cement base.

CHOICE OF FLOOR COVERINGS:

ROOM BY ROOM

1. *Kitchen:* Floor covering must be water- and stain-resistant. It should be easy to clean, yet resilient and

Ceramic tiles — ideal for kitchen

non-slip. Vinyl tiles or sheeting lives up to the above requirements, but it may be damaged by dry heat — for example, hot pans. Ceramic tiles are resistant to water and stains and are easily cleaned, but they are slippery, very hard and cold. Objects dropped on them break very readily. A carpet is totally unsuitable.

2. *Bathroom:* As for kitchen. Cork has a warm appearance and is water resistant. It is reasonably hardwearing when sealed. Bathroom carpet is comfortable and absorbent but not very hygienic, especially around the lavatory.
3. *Bedroom:* Light domestic-quality carpet which is foam backed; linoleum or vinyl with rugs.
4. *Living room, hall, stairs and landing:* Top-quality, hardwearing, woven carpet. Twist pile and patterned carpets show less wear. Carpet tiles are practical but not as attractive as other carpeting. Vinyl or wood block may also be used and looks well, if polished.

Cost of floor coverings (sq. metre)			
	1990	19--	19--
Wood mosaic	£15–25		
Vinyl tiles	£5–10		
Ceramic tiles	£10–25		
Carpets			
a. Heavy domestic 80% wool/20% nylon	£20–30		
b. Tufted, foam back, medium nylon	£5–10		
c. Carpet tiles	£10–20		

Floor polishes and cleaners

Type	Composition	Used on	Directions for use
Solid wax polish	Mixture of *waxes*, e.g. Carnuba wax, dissolved in solvents such as white spirit. *Silicones* are often added for high gloss and water-resistance. *Perfumes* may be used.	■ Wood floors ■ Cork ■ Linoleum	■ Never use on vinyl ■ As these do not clean, the floor must be cleaned before use. ■ Apply sparingly. ■ Rub in thoroughly.
Liquid wax, e.g. Beautiflor	As above, but contains more solvent and less silicone.	■ Wood floors ■ Linoleum	■ These clean as well as polish. ■ Apply sparingly. ■ Less slippery, due to reduced silicone.
Emulsion polishes, e.g. Seel, Kleer	Blend of waxes and resins emulsified in water. When this evaporates, a hard, shiny finish results.	■ Vinyl floors ■ Rubber, cork ■ Linoleum ■ Sealed wood	■ Floor must be thoroughly cleaned first – these do not *clean* the floor. ■ Spread evenly with soft cloth or mop. ■ Leave to dry for about 20 minutes. ■ High-gloss finish: no need to buff. ■ As this polish becomes sticky after a time, build-up must be removed every six months or so, using a proprietary remover or steel wool.
Combined cleaner/polish	Emulsion-type polish with cleaning agents added.	■ Slightly soiled floors, as above	■ Use as above: build-up not as severe.
Non-shine floor cleaners	Strong, low-foaming detergents, often with some of the following added: bleach, disinfectant, ammonia, perfume.	■ Vinyl floors ■ Ceramic tiles ■ Rubber ■ Quarry tiles	■ Used to clean floors. ■ Dissolve according to directions, usually in warm water. Wash floor using mop or floor cloth. ■ Rinse thoroughly. ■ Do not apply polish until absolutely dry.
Carpet shampoos: (a) wet, e.g. 1001	Detergent containing alkalis, e.g. ammonia	Carpets	■ Follow directions: usually dissolve in required amount of warm water. ■ Apply sparingly with sponge or carpet shampooer. ■ Do not allow carpet to become too wet. ■ Dry thoroughly before replacing furniture or walking on carpet.
(b) dry, e.g. Dry Foam, Shake 'n' Vac	Absorbent powder, e.g. fuller's earth, and grease solvent.	Carpets	■ Shake on surface of carpet, brushing in lightly. ■ Leave for required time, then vacuum off.

► LIGHTING

Good lighting is essential in a home to:
- Provide light for activities
- Prevent eyestrain and accidents
- Make the home more attractive

PROPERTIES OF LIGHT

When light rays fall on a surface, they can be:
1. *Reflected* — bounced off a pale or shiny surface.
2. *Refracted* — bent as they pass through thick or ridged glass.
3. *Diffused* — scattered by passing through translucent substances such as lamp shades, or falling on non-reflecting surfaces.
4. *Absorbed*: No light is reflected as by dark surfaces.
5. *Dispersed*: Broken down into its component colours as by a crystal or prism.

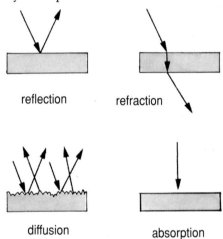

reflection   refraction

diffusion   absorption

Properties of light

NATURAL LIGHTING

Natural lighting is the most suitable light for work and recreation as it does not cause eyestrain. It is introduced into the home by use of:
- Windows: Large windows admit plenty of light but cause heat loss unless double-glazed. Small windows restrict the amount of light entering. This can be improved by painting the room in white or pastel shades which reflect light.
- Doors, glass bricks.
- Perspex and other transparent plastics.

COLOUR

- White and pale colours reflect light.
- Dark colours including black absorb light. They should therefore not be used in north-facing rooms or rooms with small windows.
- Mirrors increase the amount of light by reflecting it around the room.

ASPECT

North-facing rooms look dark. Large windows will increase the amount of light in the room.

South-facing rooms get lots of light. Such rooms are pleasant to live in as they get sun for most of the day.

ARTIFICIAL LIGHTING

This should be one of the first considerations when room planning, as wiring and fittings must be installed before redecorating. Lighting can be functional — for working, reading etc. — or decorative, when used in improving decor.

Electric light is the most efficient, versatile and safe form of lighting.

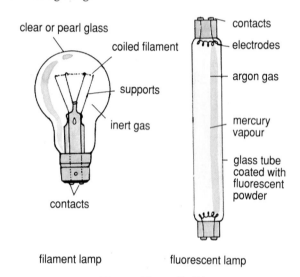

filament lamp   fluorescent lamp

Types of lamp (bulb)

ELECTRIC LIGHTING

There are two types of electric lamp or bulb: filament lamps and fluorescent lamps.

A filament lamp consists of a glass bulb filled with an inert gas such as argon. A thin filament of tungsten wire passes into the centre of the bulb, forming a single or double coil — the double coil gives out more light. The tungsten becomes white hot when the light is switched on, owing to its resistance to the flow of electricity. These lamps last about 1,000 hours. Their strength is measured in watts: 25 W; 40 W; 60 W; 75 W; 100 W; 150 W; 200 W.

Bulbs can be made from clear glass, pearlised glass (to prevent glare), coloured glass or part-silvered bulbs, used for spotlights.

Fluorescent lamps consist of a narrow glass tube coated on the inside with a fluorescent chemical, i.e. one which glows. A small electrode at each end of the tube heats up when current flows, causing mercury (also present in the tube) to vaporise. This produces ultraviolet light which makes the fluorescent lining glow with light. Fluorescent tubes are available in lengths from 30 cm to 2.5 m. Wattage and price increase with length.

Advantages of fluorescent lamps

1. They give three to four times as much light as a filament lamp of the same wattage.
2. They last about three times as long, but turning them off and on frequently will shorten their life.
3. They give a bright shadowless light very like daylight. They are ideal for kitchens and workrooms.
4. They are cool in operation and are therefore suitable for pelmet lights.

Disadvantages of fluorescent lamps

1. They are more expensive than filament lamps.
2. They may cause glare, although shades will eliminate this.
3. They hum on starting and, sometimes, when in operation.

LIGHTING CAN BE:

1. *General*, throwing light in all directions as when a translucent fitting is used.
2. *Direct*, as with a spotlight, with all light thrown in one direction. Direct lighting is required for close and desk work.
3. *Indirect*, where light is thrown onto a pale wall or ceiling, reflecting it back into a room.
4. *Diffused light*: Translucent shades or fluorescent lamps disperse light evenly around the area.

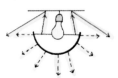

semi-indirect fitting

reflector fitting

indirect light fitting

diffused fitting

direct fitting

Effects of fittings on light

GOOD LIGHTING:

1. Should provide sufficient light for the job in hand. Extra light is required for close work.
2. Should not cause glare. Pearlised bulbs are preferable.
3. Should be consistent without flickering and causing shadows.

4. Hazardous places such as steps etc. should be well lit.
5. Colour affects light. Dark colours absorb light, while light colours reflect it.

A well-lit hall and stairs, essential for safety

LIGHTING SAFETY

- Lighting circuits should have a low (5 amp) fuse.
- Switches should be placed near to doors so that lights may be turned on upon entering a room.
- Use bulbs of the correct size and wattage for the fitting. Never exceed recommended wattage.
- Avoid placing shades too near bulbs as this could cause a fire. Use heat-resistant shades.

LIGHTING A ROOM

Lighting can add atmosphere and interest to almost any room, as well as providing the necessary light for work and living.

Good lighting adds atmosphere to a room

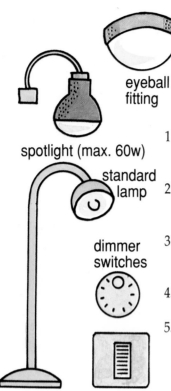

spotlight (max. 60w)

standard lamp

dimmer switches

eyeball fitting

recessed

downlighter

track lights

display lighting

uplighters

MODERN LIGHT FITTINGS AND FEATURES

1. *Dimmer switches* enable the light output to be reduced or increased. The normal switch is replaced by an electronic device.
2. *Track lighting*: A metal channel carries a continuous live, neutral and earth wire. Spotlights mounted on special adaptors can be moved to any part of the track.
3. *Flexible desk lamps* have pivoted joints or pliable stems which enable the lamp to be turned in almost any direction.
4. *Recessed ceiling lighting*: Spotlights are set into a recess in a deep ceiling. They do not provide much light.
5. *Display or decorative lighting*: Light fittings can high-light paintings, plants etc. For example, *up-lighters* on the floor throw light upwards. *Down-lighters* direct light down, as on shelves, ornaments etc.

Modern light fittings

*A bright kitchen, well lit
by day and night*

When planning the lighting of a room, consider:

1. *The purpose of the room*: A background light is required in most rooms with local lighting at work areas — for example, kitchen sink, for reading etc.
2. *Safety*: Buy good-quality, reliable fittings. Lamp bases should be steady. Shades should not be too near bulbs.
3. *Installation*: Lamps may be plugged into 3-pin sockets, but plugs should be fitted with a 5 amp fuse (not the 13 amp fuses supplied with the plug). Wiring circuits should have a low amperage.

4. *Functions*: Lighting should have a sufficiently high wattage to give the correct light for each activity. Older people may need stronger lights. Light for reading, sewing, studying etc. should fall on the work without causing glare.
5. *Appearance*: Shades and bases should suit the decor of the room in style and colour.
6. *Cleaning*: Light fittings should be easy to clean. Dust regularly to avoid reducing the light output.

LIGHTING ROOM BY ROOM:

SUGGESTIONS

Living room:	Central, diffused fitting with two portable lamps, one for reading.
Dining room:	Background lighting; 'rise and fall' lamp over table.
Kitchen:	Fluorescent tubes, one or two, depending on shape and size of kitchen. Strip lighting under wall cupboards to light up work area.
Hall, stairs, landing:	One light in the hall with an attractive fitting. One light shining on the steps of the stairs, with a two-way switch. If necessary, one light on landing.

Bedrooms: Central, diffused fitting. Strip light at dressing table. Bedside light for each occupant.

Children's rooms: Emphasis on safety. Central, diffused fitting. A dimmer switch is useful to provide a night light for small children.

A desk lamp for studying is advisable for older children.

Bathroom: Central, diffused or fluorescent fitting. Light over mirror with pull cord. All other switches should be positioned outside bathroom.

► FURNITURE

Good furniture should be attractive, well-designed and functional. Materials used in furniture-making include wood, plastic, metal, glass and textiles.

WOOD

Wood is classified as:

1. *Hardwood*, which comes from slow-growing trees such as ash, beech, elm, mahogany, oak and teak. It is tough and strong with finer, more attractive graining than softwood. For this reason it is expensive.

2. *Softwood*, which comes from fast-growing, coniferous trees, is used extensively in house construction and carpentry as it is cheap. Examples are fir, pine, spruce (collectively known as deal).

Wood is an expensive material and there is much waste (e.g. offcuts) in its production. It also has the disadvantage that it can warp and swell.

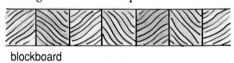
blockboard

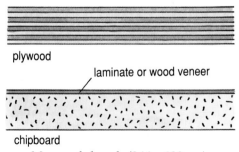
plywood

laminate or wood veneer

chipboard

Man-made boards (244 x 122 cm)

3. *Man-made boards*: These are available in sheets 244 cm x 122 cm (8 ft by 4 ft). They are cheap, less likely to warp and more economical because of their large size. But they are also less durable, are badly damaged by water, and therefore are unsuitable for external use. Most of them require a veneer* to disguise their unattractive appearance.

■ *Hardboard*: Thin, dark sheets made from compressed wood pulp (3 mm thick). They may be enamelled, laminated or perforated to make pegboard.

• *Plywood*: Thin sheets of cheap wood glued together with the grain of each layer running in alternate directions for strength. They are often laminated or veneered* with a thin layer of hardwood.

• *Chipboard* is made from chips of wood glued together under heat and pressure. It is graded according to thickness, quality and strength. Laminated chipboard is used extensively for kitchen units and work tops. Wood veneered chipboard is available for furniture-making and shelving.

* A veneer: This is a thin layer of material, e.g. hardwood, fixed to the surface of cheaper woods or man-made boards with adhesive. It is easily damaged by rough handling and water.

WOOD FINISHES

Wood furniture is usually treated to:

1. Preserve it, protecting it from rot and insects
2. Improve the colour
3. Bring out the grain
4. Make it easier to maintain
5. Make it moisture and stain resistant

■ *Stain*: Transparent wood colouring, which may be oil or water based. Stains are available in light and dark wood shades, as well as in some colours. They are usually matt finished and do not protect the wood unless they are incorporated in a French polish or varnish.

■ *Varnish*: This is a transparent finish, consisting of a mixture of resins (e.g. polyurethane), solvent (e.g. methylated spirits) and usually a stain.

Polyurethane varnishes or seals are strong and ideal for floors and furniture which get lots of wear. Stains and varnishes are applied like paint. Maintenance consists of rubbing with a damp cloth and/or a little silicone cleaner.

■ *French polish*: Made from a mixture of resin (e.g. shellac) and solvent (e.g. methylated spirits) usually with stain or colour added. It produces a high gloss and is ideal for fine-grained hardwoods such as mahogany. French polishing is a specialised job. It is applied in several layers, using a cloth.

French polish is easily damaged by heat and moisture, particularly alcohol and perfumes. Wipe up spills at once; use mats under hot dishes and drinks. Maintain by rubbing with a soft cloth, polishing lightly occasionally.

OTHER WOOD FINISHES

- Cellulose is a matt finish used on modern cabinets such as TV sets.
- Paint, lacquer (a high gloss varnish) and enamel.
- Wood preservatives, including creosote, anti-wood-worm treatments.
- Wax polish, which is made from beeswax and a solvent.
- Furniture cream: Liquid wax containing a blend of wax, water and an emulsifier. Many contain silicones which make them resistant to dirt and water.
- Furniture oil such as linseed or teak oil is used on teak to nourish and protect the wood, but it is not heat-resistant.

PLASTICS

A wide variety of plastics is used in the home today, not only for making furniture, but also for kitchens, bathrooms and other household utensils and containers.

Formation of plastic

MANUFACTURE

Plastics are chemical compounds consisting of long chains of carbon atoms. The raw materials for plastic manufacture are oil, air, salt and water. When these are mixed and subjected to varying degrees of temperature, pressure and humidity in the presence of a catalyst, a chemical reaction called polymerisation takes place. This causes the smaller molecules to join together to form a plastic. For example, hundreds of ethylene molecules form polyethelyne (or polythene for short); styrene molecules form polystyrene.

CLASSIFICATION

1. *Thermoplastic resins* such as polythene, polyvinyl chloride (PVC) and nylon are fairly soft and pliable.
   - They will soften on heating and harden again on cooling.
   - When pared, they produce long, thin slivers.
   - They are damaged by solvents such as petrol and benzine, but not by acids and alkalis.
   - Examples of use: kitchen buckets, basins, plastic toys, packing (polystyrene), filling for upholstery, vinyl wall paper.
2. *Thermosetting resins* including Bakelite, Melamine and laminated plastic are hard plastics. Because the molecules of these plastics form bonds where they meet, they are damaged when heat is applied.
   - Once shaped, thermosetting resins cannot be softened. They will harden, blister and crack when heat is applied.
   - When pared, these plastics produce small, powdery chips.
   - They are damaged by strong alkalis and acids but not by other household substances such as solvents.
   - They are more breakable than thermoplastic resins.
   - Examples of use: hard, brittle plastics — chairs and much furniture. Plastic tableware, laminated plastic* (for example, work tops), bathroom fittings, light fittings, electrical goods (hair driers, mixers), plugs and sockets.

   * Laminated plastics (e.g. Formica) are made by compressing several sheets of paper, including a decorative surface paper. Thermosetting resin is used to bond them together. They are used as a veneer on chipboard etc.

ADVANTAGE OF PLASTIC

1. Lightweight but strong
2. Quiet
3. Versatile. Can be used in many ways. A wide range of colours and textures is available
4. Cheap
5. Comfortable to handle
6. Does not rust or scratch readily
7. Resilient and pliable
8. Hygienic

DISADVANTAGES OF PLASTIC

1. Damaged by dry heat — for example, saucepans, cigarettes.
2. Damaged by harsh abrasives and sharp knives. Avoid chopping food on them.
3. May be damaged by certain solvents, acids, dyes etc.

STYLES OF FURNITURE

Styles and fashions in furniture change gradually over the years. They can be loosely grouped as follows: antique, traditional and modern.

1. *Antique furniture* refers to furniture over 150 years old. Georgian, Regency and other pre-Victorian furniture would be considered antique. This furniture is beautifully made by hand, using materials of the best quality and workmanship, but it is very expensive. Good modern reproduction furniture is cheaper (but still expensive) and is often machine made.
2. *Traditional furniture* includes much of the furniture of the past hundred years. Victorian and Edwardian furniture is heavy, ornate and often too large for a modern house. Welsh dressers, Windsor chairs and other cottage-style furniture is enjoying a revival today.
3. *Modern furniture*: This tends to be simple in design, less ornate than antiques, with low lines. It often uses glass, chrome, brass and plastic as well as wood. It is usually machine made and functional. It suits the modern home and is easy to clean.

   Well-designed furniture should be attractive and functional, i.e. suitable for its purpose. It should be durable, easy to maintain and clean, but not too 'way out' as this will soon become dated.

POINTS TO CONSIDER WHEN BUYING FURNITURE

1. *Cost*: Price is generally an indication of quality. Cheap furniture is usually a bad investment.
2. *Construction*: Joints should be well-made and fit well. Drawers should slide in and out easily. Doors should fit well. Finishes such as varnish should be smooth and evenly applied. The inside/underside of furniture should be neat and well finished off. Handles and fittings should be of good quality.
3. *Design*: Furniture should look attractive, be well proportioned and suitable for its purpose. A chair or bed should be comfortable, a table strong and steady.
4. *Quality* is usually in ratio to the cost. Good quality furniture is made from well-seasoned wood and durable fabrics. Quality marks: Design Centre, Quality Irish.
5. *Durability*: All furniture should be reasonably durable, more so if it is to be used by children.
6. *Maintenance*: Furniture should be stain-resistant and easy to clean. Pale shades are impractical. Fabrics should be washable.
7. *Comfort*: This is particularly important in the case of chairs, beds etc. Test by sitting/lying in/on them before purchase.
8. *Style*: Furniture should suit the decor of the room in style, period and colour etc.
9. *Check delivery, guarantees* and any extras. Find out how to care for any furniture you buy.

UPHOLSTERED FURNITURE

This usually consists of a wooden framework, sometimes sprung, which is padded with hair, foam or synthetic wadding, then covered with an attractive, hardwearing fabric. Sofas and armchairs are upholstered. It is difficult to judge the composition of such furniture as it is covered by fabric. For this reason:

- Look for a reliable make, with informative labels giving details on composition and materials used.
- The frame should be strong and well built from hardwood.
- The chair should be well padded with hair or foam.*

  * Note: Many foams produce toxic fumes when burned. Flame-resistant foams are now compulsory on new furniture (see page 369).

- Webbing should be taut and well secured.
- Outer fabric should be closely woven, durable, easily cleaned and flame resistant (page 369). Some fabrics are impregnated with *silicones* to prevent absorption of moisture when spills occur. Removable covers, particularly cushion covers, are a good idea.
- Examples of furnishing fabrics: real or artificial leather (PVC), Dralon, velvet or corduroy, wool (tweed and moquette), heavy cottons (Chintz), linens and linen union (a linen/cotton mixture), synthetics and mixtures of those above.

Upholstered armchairs provide comfort

FURNITURE FOR STORAGE

Furniture for storage should be functional and sufficiently large to store the amount and type of equipment required. Wall storage takes up less space than floor storage. Keep items which are in constant use near at hand.

Each room should have enough storage for the items used in that room. For example, dining rooms need storage for china and cutlery, while halls need storage for coats etc.

- *Modular unit systems* are readymade arrangements of wall furniture which build up to form one complete unit.
- They may take the form of simple ladder-style shelving units or more substantial arrangements of cupboard and desks to house TV, drinks, ornaments etc.
- Both cheap and expensive varieties are available. Modules can be added to over a period of time.
- Many can be dismantled when moving house.
- Unit systems are compact and space saving and are suitable for kitchens, bedrooms, living and dining rooms. (See Kitchen Storage, page 249.)

Storage provided by modular bedroom units

CABINET FURNITURE

- Cupboards, wardrobes and chests of drawers should be solid and stand firmly on the floor.
- Doors and drawers should fit well, yet open easily.
- Drawers and cupboards should be the right size for their purpose. Wardrobes etc. should be divided into areas for hanging, shoe storage etc. Ceiling-high units provide storage for seasonal items such as luggage etc. which are used occasionally.
- A modular system of wardrobe, dressing table etc. is a streamlined and space-saving arrangement for bedrooms (see page 245). Some are permanently built-in; others can be dismantled when moving house.

CHAIRS AND TABLES

- These should be strong and steady, with sturdy legs.
- *Chairs* should be comfortable and support the back.
- Easy-chairs should support the shoulders and should not be too low or too deep.
- Arms should be at a comfortable height.
- There should be a comfortable space (18 cm) for legs between a chair seat and table.
- Upholstery should be practical, durable and easily cleaned.
- *Tables* should be a comfortable height (usually 76 cm from floor).
- Table tops should be heat and moisture resistant and easy to clean. Laminated plastic is ideal for kitchen tables. Wooden tables will require a protective finish such as a polyurethane seal. Otherwise table mats must be used.
- Drop leaf or extending tables are useful when numbers vary.
- Round tables take up more space than square or rectangular tables.

BEDS

A bed should be comfortable, yet provide sufficient support for the back. The only reliable way to test it is to lie on it! It should be at least 15 cm longer than the height of the user. Beds consist of:

1. *A base* which may be spring edged (expensive but comfortable) or *box edged*, with a wooden frame boxing in the springs. This one is less comfortable than the spring-edged base, but it wears better. Solid wood or *rubber webbing* provides a base for bunk beds and some cheaper beds. Iron beds (rare today) have *stretch wire* bases.

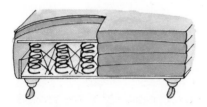
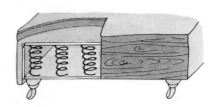
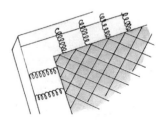

Bed bases

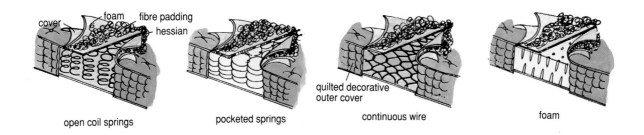

cover · foam · fibre padding · hessian

open coil springs   pocketed springs   quilted decorative outer cover · continuous wire   foam

Types of mattress

2. *Mattress*: This consists of an arrangement of springs which are padded above and below with horsehair, foam or synthetic wadding, then covered with ticking and an attractive, well-secured covering. *Individual springs*, *continuous springing* and *pocketed springs* are available — the latter being the most hardwearing and comfortable, but also the most expensive.

Foam mattresses consist of a rectangle of latex or polyether foam, which is available in various densities and thicknesses. These are useful for those suffering from asthma as they do not encourage dust.

Convertible beds, which fold to look like a settee, are useful where accommodation is limited, as are bunk beds, raised beds and folding beds. *Headboards* may be made from a wide variety of materials. They help to protect the wall behind the bed. Examples of headboards are wood, quilted, cane, brass and wrought iron.

Bed sizes: Standard single bed: 100 x 200 cm
               Standard double bed: 150 x 200 cm

 SOFT FURNISHINGS

Soft furnishings include curtains, bedspreads, chair covers and cushions. Soft furnishing fabrics should be:

Curtains	Upholstery
■ Reasonably durable	■ Tough and durable
■ Hang and drape well	■ Resistant to abrasion
■ Preshrunk	■ Preshrunk
■ Easy to clean, preferably washable	■ Spongeable or washable
■ Dirt resistant	■ Stain resistant
■ Resistant to fading	■ Resistant to fading
■ Colour fast	■ Closely woven to prevent sagging
■ Flame resistant	■ Flame resistant — padding material should be non-toxic when burnt

Co-ordinated soft furnishings

Curtains can be made to alter and to improve badly proportioned windows. Long curtains are attractive and insulate well, but they require more material and are therefore more expensive than short curtains.

1. *Net curtains* give privacy, especially if the room is overlooked. They can be made from cotton, polyester or Dralon — often made into thicker weaves. They should be easy to wash and should drip dry.

CURTAINS

Curtains are used for several reasons: (a) to decorate; (b) to provide privacy; (c) to insulate; and (d) to shut out light.

Tall, narrow windows can be made to look wider by extending the track beyond the window at each side.

Make a small window appear larger by extending curtains at each side and hanging mock café curtains below.

Festoon blinds remain gathered when down. Austrian blinds lose gathers when lowered.

Short curtains in a dormer window should clear the window by day.

Curtain track placed outside the bay window saves fabric, but floor space is lost when drawn at night.

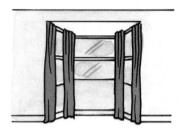

Curtains arranged within the bay.

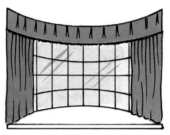

Short curtains and pinch-pleated pelmet on a bow window.

Curtains can be used to alter the appearance of windows

2. *Main curtains*: The choice will depend on the type of window, style of room, amount of wear and tear, and the amount of money available. Curtains should blend with the overall decor of the room. They can be the same colour as the walls, making the room look larger, or they can contrast with the walls. Large prints and designs look best in large rooms. Use small prints for small windows and small rooms. Extra fabric is required for matching.

   - *Shrinkage*: Many furnishing fabrics shrink — often up to 10%. Allow extra fabric when calculating to allow for this. Allow a deep, temporary hem until first washing in case of shrinkage. It is a good idea to wash fabric before making it up.
   - *Fading*: Most fabrics fade eventually. Lining helps to prevent fading. Pastels fade less than strong or dark colours.
   - *Washability*: Check this upon purchase. Velvets and heavy fabrics usually need to be dry cleaned. If in doubt, dry cleaning is safest.

LINING

- Lined curtains hang better, provide more insulation and opacity and protect curtain fabric from sunlight. Identical linings display a uniform appearance outside a house.

SUGGESTED FABRICS FOR CURTAINS/ UPHOLSTERY

1. *Cotton*: Chintz, cretonne, blends. Cottons look fresh and crisp. They launder well but are inclined to shrink.
2. *Linen/linen unions*, suitable for loose covers. Expensive and crease readily. Blends such as repp and Moygashel are more suitable. All shrink considerably. Wash before making up, if possible.
3. *Velvet*: This cloth was originally made from silk, then cotton. Now most velvets are made from synthetics such as Dralon. They have a luxurious appearance when used on large expanses and drape well. While some velvets can be washed with care, dry cleaning is more successful.

4. *Wool*: Fine weaves and blends are suitable for curtaining. But since wool is very expensive it is less common today. It has good insulating properties and is dirt resistant but is liable to be attacked by moths. As it may shrink and felt when washed, dry cleaning is recommended. Tweed is a good upholstery fabric.

5. *Man-made/synthetic fibres*: Many have been especially developed for use as curtains. These have excellent draping qualities, are durable, resistant to fading, easy to wash and to drip dry. Examples: polyester, Dralon, glass fibre, blends with natural fibres.

6. *Curtain linings*: These are made from cotton such as cotton sateen and blends. Most are in shades of cream or beige to provide uniformity outside a house. They are available in various thicknesses or qualities, rising in price according to quality. Insulated lining has a plastic or metallic finish on one side and is best dry cleaned.

7. *Curtain interlining* is a thick flannelette-type fabric which gives curtains extra body and improves insulation.

PELMETS AND TRACKS

There has never been a wider range from which to choose. Tracks are available for attaching to the ceiling and for use with or without pelmets. Rods and poles made of wood or brass are also available.

Pelmets may be wooden structures, covered buckram, frilled or draped. Curtain headings may be: (a) simply gathered (standard); (b) pencil pleats (using deep 'regis' tape); (c) pinch pleats, using three-pronged hooks; or (d) scalloped.

A bedroom, using co-ordinated soft furnishings

MEASURING FOR CURTAINS

1. Fix and measure the length of the track.
2. The width of the curtaining should be 2 to 2½ times the width of the track, plus extra for turnings and seams — for example, if window track is two metres wide, curtaining should be at least four metres wide when ready to hang.
3. Measure the fall of the curtain, that is, from track to 25 mm from the floor (or to the sill). Add 150-200 mm for heading and hem, and extra for matching and shrinkage.

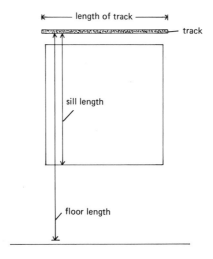

4. To calculate the amount of fabric: divide required width by width of fabric — furnishing fabrics are 122 cm wide. The answer is the number of lengths required. Multiply this by the fall of the curtain plus extra for hems etc. This gives the number of metres required.

BLINDS

These may be used as an alternative to curtains, to provide extra opacity or in recesses which are difficult to curtain.

1. *Roller blinds* can be made-to-measure or made at home from a kit. They roll up with the aid of a spring. They can be made from: (a) *Holland*, which is a specially-stiffened type of linen (difficult to clean); (b) *vinyl*: a wide range is available, and is easy to clean and stain resistant; (c) *fabric*, which is specially treated and often part of a co-ordinated range of soft furnishings.

Blinds are cleaned by wiping with a damp cloth, using a soft brush if necessary. Dry flat, then roll up before fully dry to keep them smooth. Unroll to finish drying.

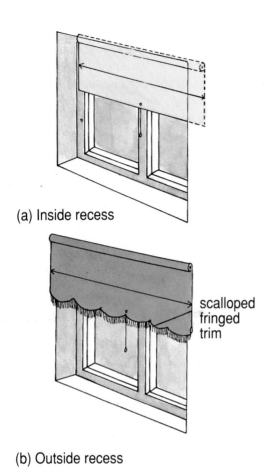

(a) Inside recess

(b) Outside recess

Placement of roller blinds

2. *Austrian or festoon blinds*: These are a type of draped curtain which can be raised or lowered by means of strings passing through rings at the back. Roman blinds are a similar arrangement which fold into horizontal pleats when raised.

3. *Venetian blinds* are slats of enamelled aluminium or plastic in a range of colours. They are useful in sunny rooms as they can be adjusted to limit the amount of light entering the room, protecting furniture etc.

Care of venetian blinds: They should be dusted regularly and cleaned with a damp cloth wrung out in warm water and detergent. They are difficult and time consuming to clean.

4. *Vertical blinds* are now available made from plastic-type fabric. These do not gather dust as easily as venetian blinds.

CUSHIONS

These add to the comfort and style of a room and there are many types available: tie-on chair cushions, scatter cushions, giant floor cushions and polystyrene filled 'bean bags' which are used as seating.

Almost any fabric may be used to cover a cushion provided it is closely woven and washable. Inner covers should have similar qualities — downproof fabric must be used when cushions are feather- or down-filled.

Fillings include: down and feathers (expensive), kapok, synthetic fibre fillings, e.g. polyester wadding and foam, which is available in varying sizes and thicknesses.

LOOSE COVERS

Loose covers protect upholstery from wear, damage and fading. They may be used to give worn, shabby upholstery a new lease of life.

Loose covers should be hardwearing, attractive, stain resistant and washable. Heavy-duty cotton, linen-type fabrics and synthetics may all be used. Cretonne and linen union are used to make traditional floral chair covers. Plain tailored covers are made from linens and repps.

► BED LINEN

SHEETS AND PILLOWCASES

These may be made from plain or brushed cotton, linen, polyester, nylon or mixtures. Fabrics should be closely woven, smooth, absorbent, easy to wash and drip dry, if possible. A wide range of colours and patterns are now available, many co-ordinating with duvet covers, curtains etc. Fitted sheets make bed-making easier but bottom sheets get worn out more quickly than top sheets as they cannot be changed around.

Sizes:

Single:	180 x 260 cm	£..........	each
Double:	230 x 260 cm	£..........	each
King size:	275 x 275 cm	£..........	each
Pillowcase:	50 x 75 cm	£..........	each

Note: These measurements relate to shrink-resistant fabrics — cotton sheets should be slightly larger.

Make sure sheets are sufficiently long, which should be about 90 cm longer than a bed to allow for tucking in and shrinkage. Man-made fibres are unlikely to shrink. Make use of the sales when buying bed linen as it is often considerably reduced in price.

NUMBER OF SHEETS REQUIRED

Two to three pairs of cotton or polyester sheets per bed. Three pillow cases per pillow: one in use, one in wash, one to spare.

BLANKETS

A loosely-woven light blanket provides more warmth than a thick one as it holds more air between the fibres. Blankets may have a plain weave or a cellular weave which has large air holes. Fibres used in blankets are:

scalloped fringed trim

1. *Wool*, which is warm and soft but expensive and liable to moth damage. Wool blankets must be washed with great care; i.e. cool wash, they will become hard and shrink if carelessly washed. Cost: about £.......... each (single), £.......... each (double).
2. *Wool mixtures*, e.g. wool and synthetic fibres, are cheaper and easier to wash than all-wool blankets.
3. *Synthetics* such as nylon, Acrilan and Courtelle are available in plain or cellular weaves. They are soft, warm, easy to wash and dry; are cheaper but prone to static electricity. Cost: £.......(single), £.......(double).

Blanket sizes: Single: 200 x 250 cm
                   Double: 280 x 250 cm
                   King size: 300 x 250 cm

DUVETS OR CONTINENTAL QUILTS

A *duvet* consists of a large fabric bag filled with down, feathers or polyester wadding. It has fabric channels, running the length of the quilt, to keep the filling in place so that it has an even thickness throughout — unlike an eiderdown which is thin in places. Duvets are a labour-saving and economical alternative to layers of blankets. Duvets:

- Should be large enough to hang over the bed a little at the sides and the end.
- Should be covered in downproof (in the case of down-filled duvets) or washable fabric.
- Should have a high *tog rating* which is a measurement of insulation provided. This is usually between 9 and 14 (max).

Duvet covers are made in a wide range of washable fabrics, usually fine cotton or cotton-polyester mixtures. Most duvet covers are part of a co-ordinated range of bed linen, including sheets, pillowcases and valances. They are easily removed for washing and usually drip dry.

Cost of duvet: £.......... (single),   £.......... (double).

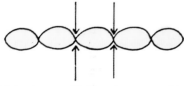

(a) Eiderdown: stitching leaves cold areas

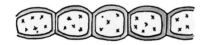

(b) Continental quilt: thick fabric channels, filled with down

Construction of (a) eiderdown, (b) duvet

ADVANTAGES OF DUVETS

1. Warm, light and cosy. Cool in summer, warm in winter.
2. They simplify bed-making and are ideal for bunk beds.
3. They eliminate much laundering, yet are easy to launder.
4. Polyester quilts are non-allergenic and are ideal for asthma sufferers.
5. A duvet is cheaper than several blankets.

BEDSPREADS

These cover the bedclothes and give an attractive finish to a bed. They should be almost large enough to touch the floor. Fabrics used should match or tone with the decor and be machine washable.

- Candlewick is tufted cotton. It is easy to launder and requires no ironing.
- Linen is durable but creases. Requires ironing.
- Cotton: Wide range of fabrics available and is easy to wash and iron.
- Polyester/nylon: Easy to wash, drip dry.

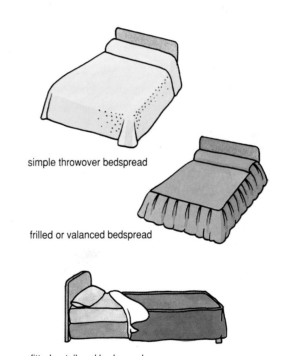

simple throwover bedspread

frilled or valanced bedspread

fitted or tailored bedspread

Bedspreads

ELECTRIC BLANKETS

There are two types of electric blanket: *underblankets* and *overblankets*. Both consist of a low voltage heating element enclosed in a wool/cotton/synthetic blanket.

Single and double blankets are available with one to three heat settings and an *indicator light* to show when it is on. Dual controls are available on some double blankets.

- *Underblankets* are used to preheat a bed. These should be turned off before getting into bed. *Cost: £..........*

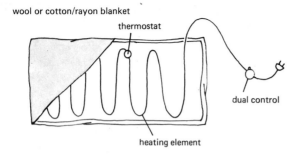

wool or cotton/rayon blanket

thermostat

dual control

heating element

■ *Overblankets* are used instead of conventional blankets. They should have a sheet beneath them, and a good insulating cover such as a thick blanket over them to keep the heat in. They may be left on after getting into bed. They are more expensive to run than an electric underblanket, as there is considerable heat loss upwards from them. They tend to break down more frequently than underblankets because they are handled and pulled during bed-making, whereas underblankets are left in place.

Cost: £.......... (single), £.......... (double).

■ Heated duvets are now available.

CHOICE AND USE OF ELECTRIC BLANKETS

1. Always buy a reliable make, electrically approved with cleaning/repair facilities available locally.
2. Avoid folding or creasing sharply as this may damage the wires.
3. Some models are machine washable.
4. All electric blankets should be cleaned and serviced by the manufacturer or an agent every 2-3 years.

Some simple experiments to identify fibres in furnishing fabrics		
	Burning	*Chemical*
Cotton	Burns quickly with a yellow flame; odour of burning paper; residue — light grey ash.	Shirlastain A: immerse well-washed, wetted article in a cold solution; result — lavender colour.
Wool	Smoulders in flame; odour of burning feathers; residue — inflated soft ash.	Millons test: boil a little fabric for 2 mins. in 1–2 ml of Millons reagent; a reddish brown colour indicates protein. *Note*: fumes are toxic; do not inhale. Shirlastain A: golden yellow
Linen	Flares up in a yellow flame; odour of burning paper; residue — large pale grey ash.	Shirlastain A: blueish purple
Rayon	Burns with a yellow flame; odour of burning paper; residue — after glow, then ash blackens.	Shirlastain A: pink
Acrylic (dralon)	Burns quickly with an erratic flame and dark smoke; odour — acrid and unpleasant; residue — uneven bead.	Shirlastain A: pinkish grey
Polyamide (nylon)	Melts first, then burns erratically; odour like celery; residue — hard grey bead.	Shirlastain A: dull yellow
Polyester (terylene)	Melts, then burns with a sooty flame; odour — characteristic; residue — hard brown smooth bead.	Shirlastain A: negative Shirlastain E: cream

Note:
1. *Burning*: Twist a few threads of the fabric together and ignite.
2. *Chemical tests*: Great care should be taken when using reagents and stains, as many are toxic if inhaled or swallowed and many are corrosive. Keep all chemicals away from heat, especially naked flame.
3. *Shirlastain tests*: These are stains specially developed to identify fibres. They may not work if fabrics are treated with dyes, finishes or fillers. Therefore the fabric must be washed or boiled several times before testing if these substances are thought to be present. To use: make up the solution. Immerse wet fabric and stir for one minute. Rinse, dry and compare. Further experiments are explained in *Simple Experiments in Textile Science* — A. Ridley, D. Williams (Heinemann).

For a note on furniture fire safety, please see Appendix C (page 369).

A well-planned room should:
1. Make full use of *available space*.
2. Be comfortable and visually *attractive*.
3. Take advantage of *good architectural features*.
4. Have adequate *storage*.
5. Have sufficient *furniture* for the purpose of the room.
6. Have a reliable source of *heating and ventilation*.
7. Have an efficient form of *lighting* to suit the purpose of the room.

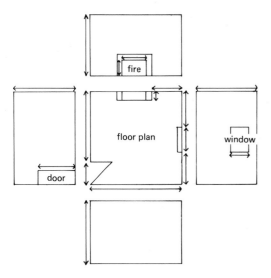

It is a good idea to draw a scale plan of each room — a floor plan and elevation of each wall as shown in the illustration. Show the length, breadth and height of the room. Show also to scale doors, windows, radiators, plumbing and electrical fixtures, power points, fireplace and built-in units or cupboards. These plans can be kept in a ring binder, together with paint charts, fabric and wallpaper swatches etc. The plans can then be brought to shops when purchasing various items.

CONSIDER:

■ *The layout of each room*: It should be flexible to allow for the activities which take place in it, such as eating, sleeping, cooking, studying, relaxing etc. Large rooms could be divided into areas in order to get the maximum use from them.

■ *Choice of furniture*, floor and wall coverings will depend on the purpose of each room and the amount of wear and tear the room gets. Heavy-duty furnishings are required in 'busy' areas such as the hall and living area.

■ *The stage of the family*: Small children will need somewhere to play under supervision. Students require a quiet study area and practical furnishings are necessary when children are around.

■ *Traffic patterns*: It is necessary to take these into account when planning a room and arranging furniture. There should be easy access to each area of the room — e.g. windows and fireplace — or accidents may occur.

■ *Heating, lighting, ventilation* and all electrical work: These must be noted early on in the planning stage as they may require structural alterations.

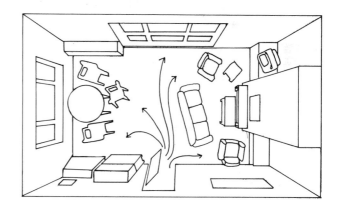

Traffic flow in a living room

PLANNING ROOM BY ROOM

HALL, STAIRS AND LANDING

The hall is the first place in which a visitor gets an impression of the home. It should be attractive and welcoming, yet practical and hardwearing. Hall, stairs and landing are usually treated as one for the purpose of decoration.

■ *The floor covering* in this area is subjected to considerable wear and tear. Choose practical, dark colours or patterned floor coverings. Heavy-duty fitted carpeting in an 80% wool/20% nylon blend would be ideal to cover hall, stairs and landings. Carpet tiles may also be used. Parquet wood flooring or vinyl tiles are attractive and hardwearing, but noisy and more difficult to maintain than carpeting. Use an outdoor and indoor mat for wet and dirty shoes.

- *Walls*: Choose a vinyl wallpaper in an attractive design. It can be washed regularly to keep it clean. Alternatively, vinyl emulsion paint may be used and touched up from time to time. A pale colour will make a small hall seem larger and mirrors will have a similar effect.
- Keep *furniture* to a minimum. Storage space is required for coats etc. and a cloakroom or coat-rack will provide this. A mirror, small table for a floral arrangement or plants and perhaps a telephone table and seat will complete the furnishing of the hall area.
- *Lighting and heating*: A ceiling light with an attractive shade, and a landing light which shines on the stairs and has a two-way switch at the top and bottom, will provide sufficient light. A porch light will guide visitors to the door. Central or storage heating will provide a background heat.

A hall should be welcoming

LIVING ROOM

The planning of this room will vary considerably, depending on the lifestyle and stage of the family. This is the room which receives the most wear and tear. It requires plenty of storage for the activities which take place there, e.g. hobbies etc., and comfortable seating.

This room, being a multi-purpose one, should be divided into areas for:

1. Conversation, requiring a grouping of comfortable chairs.
2. Reading and sewing, requiring one or two comfortable chairs with a suitable light placed behind the chairs.
3. Games and hobbies, requiring storage space.
4. Music centre (optional).
5. Desk for writing, accounts etc. (optional)

Comfortable seating

- *The floor* should be durable, comfortable, quiet, warm and attractive. It should be practical so that dirt and stains do not show, yet be easy to clean. A dark-coloured carpet in a mottled or patterned design fits these requirements. Avoid pale colours because they are impractical. Choose heavy domestic quality, like a wool/nylon mixture with a twist pile which does not show up furniture and foot marks.

  Fitted carpet is neat and attractive looking; carpet tiles or a carpet square may also be used. Wooden block floors or vinyl are suitable but not as comfortable as carpeting and may require considerable maintenance.
- *Walls*: A hardwearing vinyl wallpaper is durable and easy to clean. Vinyl emulsion is available in a vast range of colours and can be touched up in places when it gets soiled. Use gloss paint in matching or contrasting colours, e.g. white for doors and windows.
- *Furniture*: This will depend on the use to which the room is put. Comfortable, upholstered seating is required, like a three-piece suite or a selection of easy chairs which blend with the colour scheme and are easy to maintain. Unit seating, which assembles to form settees etc. is useful. A convertible sofa will provide a spare bed. Occasional tables near the main seating area are required, as well as some storage. A modular storage system is a good choice. It will hold all the paraphernalia which is used in the living room, such as books, hi-fi, TV, as well as providing a display area for ornaments, plants etc.

- *Soft furnishings*: Curtains are an important feature of the living room. They ensure privacy and provide texture and insulation against heat-loss. The fabric should be attractive, yet reasonably durable. If it matches the walls of a small room, it will make it seem larger. Co-ordinating wallpaper and curtains are also available. Suitable fabrics are: Dralon velvet, tweed, linen repp, linen union and cotton chintz. Lining and interlining provide extra insulation and protection against sun.

  Blinds provide extra privacy. Loose covers protect upholstered furniture and are easily laundered.
- *Heating*: An open fireplace is visually attractive and homely. A stove or solid fuel room heater is more efficient and a back boiler will provide hot water. Central heating is a labour-saving option, using warm air grilles or radiators.
- *Lighting*: There should be sufficient windows to provide plenty of natural light. Background lighting is required, e.g. wall lights or a ceiling fixture. Local lighting, using attractive shades, will provide extra light for reading, hobbies and other activities. Light fittings (e.g. up or down lighters) can be used to enhance the decor of the room and highlight good features.

DINING ROOM

If this is a much-used room, its general furnishing and decor will be similar to that of a living room. It should be situated within easy reach of the kitchen.

A traditional dining room

- *Floor*: This should be particularly easy to clean, stain resistant — vinyl, parquet and sealed cork floors are all suitable. Patterned carpet (not deep pile) is comfortable and can be vacuumed after meals. If the dining room is used daily, carpet is less practical.
- *Walls*: As these are unlikely to receive much wear and tear, a delicate finish is acceptable. In a busy room, use a washable vinyl paper or vinyl emulsion paint in calm, restful colours which will not upset one's digestion!
- *Furniture*: Choose an *expandable*, wooden table in a wipe-clean polyurethane finish. It should be placed in the centre of the eating area so that it is possible to walk behind the diners when serving. (See Chairs and tables, page 236.) A sideboard or dresser is useful for storing glass and china and acts also as a serving area. A trolley is also useful.
- *Heating*: Central heating is ideal as it provides an even heat. A convector heater is a useful alternative. It warms the air in the room evenly, unlike a radiant fire which might be uncomfortably hot for those nearest to it.
- *Lighting*: A rise-and-fall fitting fixed over the table shines light where it is needed — on the table, without dazzling the diners. Candle light is flattering and provides atmosphere for special occasions. A wall lamp or standard lamp near the serving area is important. Sockets will be required if items like percolators and hostess trolleys are used.

BEDROOMS

Today's bedrooms are not just used for sleeping but are also used for studying, reading, storage etc. Children's bedrooms double as playrooms and a study or living room can double as a guest room, if a convertible sofa is available. Bedrooms should, if possible, be at the back of a house to avoid noise from traffic. They should be warm yet well-ventilated, comfortable and restful.

- *Floor covering*: This should be quiet, comfortable and easy to clean. A fitted carpet is ideal. It is not necessary to use top-quality carpeting in a bedroom where there is little wear and tear. A sanded wooden floor, vinyl or sealed cork are less comfortable alternatives but scatter rugs can be used to provide warmth underfoot.
- *Walls*: Delicate finishes can be used here, such as cheaper wallpapers, emulsion paints — children's bedrooms may require a more durable finish, e.g. vinyl emulsion or vinyl wall-covering. Choose quiet, restful colours for bedrooms such as pastels.

  Attractive co-ordinating ranges of curtains, wall-coverings and bedclothes are available.
- *Furniture*: (Details of beds on page 236.) A bed should be placed in a suitable position for ease of bed-making.

A country-style bedroom

Avoid placing it in a draught, e.g. near a door or window. Storage drawers under beds provide storage for blankets, toys etc.

- *Storage*: Traditional suites such as wardrobe and dressing table are less common now as they take up a lot of space. Bedroom units save space — wardrobe, vanity unit, drawers etc. can be fitted along one wall. Mirrored doors can double the apparent size of a room. There should be sufficient hanging space for clothes. Drawers are required, as are shoe racks for shoes.

  A dressing table should have sufficient natural and artificial lighting for putting on make up and have a washable or glass-covered surface.

  A comfortable easy chair and/or dressing table chair are usually required. A wash basin or small bathroom en suite is a valuable investment and it takes the pressure off the main bathroom.

- *Soft furnishings* such as curtains and/or blinds are essential to provide privacy and insulation. Curtains should match the colour scheme of the room (co-ordinated ranges) and be sufficiently opaque to keep the room dark in the mornings. Bedspreads, cushions etc. are easily made and should also co-ordinate.

- *Heating*: It should be possible to switch off bedroom heating by day. Central heating is ideal; if not, convector heaters are good. Storage heaters are unsuitable as they would not supply heat when required.

- *Lighting*: A background light, e.g. on the ceiling, is essential. Extra lights are convenient: (a) a strip light over the dressing table; (b) bedside lights: (c) wardrobe lights. Sockets are required for hairdriers etc.

- *Children's bedrooms*: The emphasis is on safety and practicality. Heating and lighting should be safe and secure — central heating or an infra-red wall-mounted heater. A central light fitting is safest, with a desk light for older children. Keep furniture against the walls as far as possible, leaving space for play and other activities. Plenty of storage space is required. A desk is useful for studying.

  Vinyl paper or vinyl emulsion paint would be the most practical wall finishes. Vinyl flooring or a reasonably hard-wearing patterned carpet are suitable floor coverings.

BATHROOMS

The arrangement of a bathroom is restricted by the positioning of the plumbed fixtures such as bath, washbasin and lavatory. Have the lavatory in a separate room, if possible.

A bathroom in neutral colours.
Accessories provide the accent

In a bathroom it is necessary to use materials which cannot be damaged by steam or water. As there are lots of cold surfaces in this room, pattern and texture should be introduced, using accessories like curtains and towels. The room should be well-ventilated.

- *Floor*: This should be water-resistant, easy to clean, non-slip yet warm and comfortable. A vinyl floor, cushioned if wished, will provide the former qualities, while a nylon bathroom carpet will supply the latter, although it is not hygienic around the lavatory. Sealed cork tiles are also suitable.

- *Walls*: Use vinyl wallpaper (with an anti-fungal paste) or vinyl emulsion on the principal walls. A more impervious surface, such as ceramic tiles, should be used around wash-basin, bath and in the shower. A good-quality mirror is also required.
- *Bathroom fittings*: These are sold in suites and are available in a range of colours and designs. Remember: a coloured suite may go out of date and will restrict your choice of colour scheme. White suites are the cheapest.

Baths are made from vitreous enamelled cast iron, pressed steel, acrylic and fibre glass. The latter are cheaper but are damaged by heat and require special cleaning. Baths are usually boxed in. Grab bars, drop sides and non-slip bases are useful safety features, particularly for the elderly. A *shower fitting* or separate shower is useful and economical, as showers use less water. *Modern showers* have a thermostatic mixing valve. The cold water tank in the attic must be at a minimum height (usually one metre) above the shower, to provide sufficient water pressure for the shower to work efficiently. *Hand-basins, lavatory bowls and bidets* are made from glazed earthenware or vitreous china. They are non-porous and easy to clean. All should be securely fitted and any joinings with the walls should be well sealed.

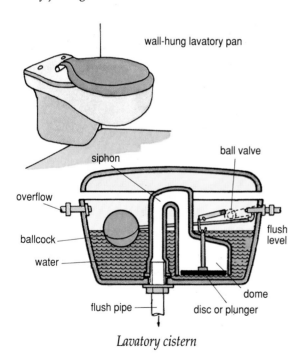

Lavatory cistern

Cost of bath: £..........;   shower: £..........;
washbasin: £..........;   lavatory: £..........;   bidet: £..........;

Lavatory bowls may be wall hung or attached to the floor. Flushing action is usually siphonic, which is a more efficient, quiet method than the wash-down principle which uses large amounts of water and is not as effective as the former.

- *Soft furnishings*: Use a washable blind or washable cotton curtains on the windows. Bath and lavatory mats should also be washable. Items like fluffy covers are unhygienic.
- *Heating*: A central heating radiator is ideal. A wall-mounted infra-red heater with a pull cord is another safe form of bathroom heating.

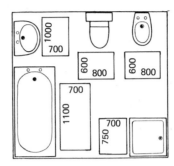

Space (mm) required to use bathroom equipment

- *Lighting*: A central fitting with a glass or plastic diffusing shade is easy to clean. Fluorescent strip lighting over the mirror, with a pull cord, provides light for shaving and make-up. A safety shaver socket is handy.
- *Ventilation*: If window ventilation is insufficient, an extractor may be required.

BATHROOM SAFETY

1. All electrical work must be carried out by a reliable electrician. *No* electrical sockets or switches are permitted in bathrooms, except pull cord lights and shaver sockets.
2. *No* electric heater or appliance should be within reach of the bath.
3. Gas heaters/geysers *must have* a balanced flue.
4. Medicines and other dangerous objects should be kept out of the reach of children. Safety locks are available for doors.
5. Avoid slippery surfaces. When wet, they are lethal. Use non-skid rubber backed mats and non-slip mats or strips in the bath.

KITCHENS

Since the kitchen is the work centre of the home, it should be very carefully measured up and planned to make work easier and more pleasant. The degree to which one can design or redesign the kitchen is mainly influenced by finance. In spite of this, it is essential to buy the best possible kitchen equipment and units, as they are more efficient and durable. Cheap kitchen units are false economy. Kitchens should be safe, easy to clean, well-ventilated with good lighting.

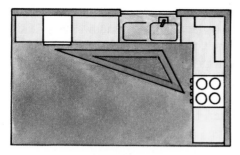

L-shaped kitchen

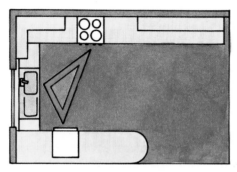

U-shaped kitchen

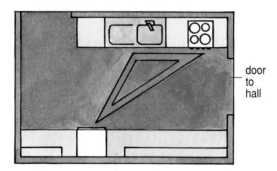

door to hall

Corridor (galley) kitchen

Three kitchen layouts, showing the work triangle

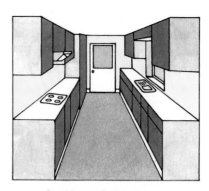

Corridor or Galley kitchen

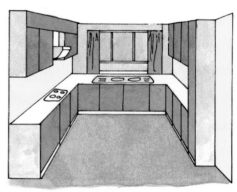

space here for dining area

L-shaped kitchen

U-shaped kitchen

PLANNING

The science of *ergonomics* relates to the efficiency of people in their workplaces. This is particularly important in the case of kitchen planning. In a kitchen, one walks constantly between the refrigerator, the cooker and the sink. These should therefore be close to each other and should form a triangle — called the *work triangle*. If these are far apart, or if there is a table or other obstacle in the way, it will involve much unnecessary walking as one goes about kitchen tasks.

There are three basic kitchen arrangements.

- *A galley kitchen* is long and narrow, with units on both sides.
- *An L-shaped kitchen*, equipment and units, form a right angle.
- *A U-shaped kitchen* has equipment and units on three walls. This is probably the most efficient arrangement.

Work sequence:

Preparing meals forms a natural sequence: *food storage; preparation; washing; cooking; serving.*

Arrange kitchen units in that order — for example, fridge/freezer; work top + cupboards; sink; work top + cupboards; cooker; serving work top.

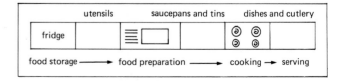

	utensils	saucepans and tins	dishes and cutlery
fridge			
food storage ⟶	food preparation ⟶	cooking ⟶	serving

Work sequence

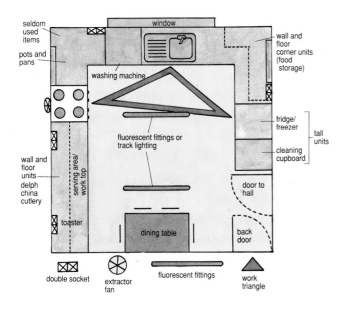

Kitchen plan

STEP-BY-STEP KITCHEN PLANNING

1. Decide on how much money can be spent and plan accordingly.
2. Draw up a kitchen plan, keeping in mind the work sequence.
3. Set down existing fixtures and fittings — for example, doors, radiator, water pipes and electric points — and plan around them.
4. The equipment used for each process should be stored in cupboards close to that area — for example, knives, chopping board etc. near preparation area; saucepans etc. near cooking area.
5. Make provision also for laundry equipment. For example, the washing machine should be near plumbing outlets.
6. Leave space, if possible, for subsequent additions of equipment.
7. There should be easy access from the kitchen to front and back doors and all areas of the house.

8. The sink should be near a window on an outside wall for ease of plumbing and so that it has efficient lighting and ventilation.
9. Provide hygienic refuse disposal.
10. All surfaces should be stain resistant i.e. resistant to acids, alkalis and fat and heat resistant, as well as being easy to clean.
11. A continuous work top is efficient, hygienic and has a neat appearance.
12. Install an efficient system of ventilation — for example, cooker hood or extractor fan.

KITCHEN STORAGE

- Make sure that there is sufficient storage for all present and future needs.
- Kitchen units should be well-designed and durable — buy the best that you can afford.
- Items used regularly should be stored near at hand, just over or under the work top (between 45 cm and 180 cm from the floor). Seldom used items can be stored in high cupboards.
- A standard floor unit is 915 mm from the floor, keeping it in line with other equipment, e.g. cookers. It is 600 mm deep (from front to back) and 500 mm wide. Most cupboards are sold in multiples of 500 mm.
- Floor units should have a recessed plinth at the base to allow space to stand comfortably. Cupboards and drawers are lined with a thin laminate and cupboard fronts and work tops with a heavy laminate, e.g. Formica.
- Wall-hung units are usually 350 mm deep x 550 mm high. They are sold, like floor units, in widths of 500 mm and multiples of this. Leave sufficient space between work top and wall units — about 330-350 mm. Otherwise they may cause bumped heads!
- Doors may hinge to the right or left. Sliding doors are less efficient but save space in a small kitchen.

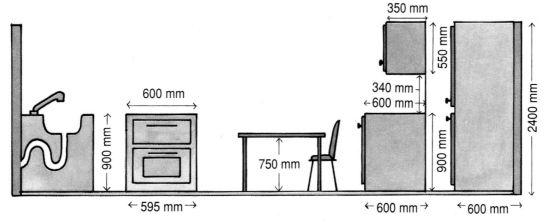

Dimensions of kitchen equipment

- Store food in wall cupboards to avoid infestation by vermin.
- Modern units include tall larder and cleaning cupboards; narrow vertical cupboards which may be fitted with towel rails to fill in non-standard spaces; adjustable shelves, carousels and corner units; fitted racks and baskets; fitted rubbish bins; deep drawers for saucepans, tins etc.; units which house ovens, refrigerators etc.; peninsular units. Self-assembly units are economical.

An easy-to-maintain kitchen, with treated wooden units and vinyl covering

- Work surfaces should be easy to clean, durable and heat resistant. Suitable materials: laminated plastic, e.g. Formica, Warerite. Wood is good for chopping. Marble is expensive but good for pastry. Ceramic tiles are hard-wearing but unhygienic work surfaces as bacteria and food particles may lodge in between them.
- A sink can be made of stainless steel, polypropelene or glazed earthenware. Mixer taps are practical and allow space for filling basins etc. A fitted sink and draining board is neat but must be carefully installed.
- *Floor*: Kitchen flooring should be non-slip when wet and dry, quiet, resilient, easy to clean, water-, grease- and stain-resistant, heat resistant, durable and attractive. Vinyl is the ideal floor covering in tile or sheet form, and it can be fixed to the floor with adhesive. Other suitable floorings are linoleum and sealed cork. Quarry and ceramic tiles are hard underfoot and objects break when dropped on them, but they are heat-, water- and stain-resistant, easy to maintain and virtually indestructible.

- *Walls*: Practical, hardwearing wall coverings are required which are easy to clean and maintain. Vinyl wall covering is a good choice in an attractive, patterned design. Ceramic tiles are useful around areas which are easily damaged and soiled — behind sink and cooker. Vinyl emulsion paint is washable and is easily touched up when grubby.
- *Heating*: Possible sources are: (a) solid fuel cooker or stove with a back boiler; (b) central heating; (c) wall mounted radiators, convector or infra-red heaters. Avoid portable heaters as trailing flexes are dangerous.
- *Lighting*: One or two central fluorescent fittings, depending on shape and size of kitchen. Strip lighting under wall units lights up work tops. Windows should be large enough to provide plenty of daylight and, when opened, to assist ventilation. An extractor fan or cooker hood (page 262) is required to deal with the condensation caused by cooking and laundry. Allow plenty of sockets: 3 or 4 double sockets would be a minimum requirement. Only use fused, earthed 3-pin plugs.
- *Waste disposal*: A kitchen bin should be placed in a convenient position. It should be emptied daily, kept absolutely clean and be disinfected regularly.

A *waste disposal unit* is a machine fitted beneath the sink which grinds away kitchen waste as it is emptied into the drain.

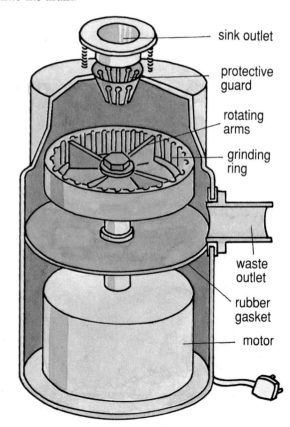

Construction of a waste disposal unit

This is washed away by a continuous flow of water. It consists of a cylindrical chamber inside which is a revolving disc with serrated outer edges. The food is ground between the disc and the outer wall. It is powered by a motor and can pulverise most kitchen waste such as small bones, peelings, etc. Fibrous matter should *not* be fed into the machine.

There are two types of waste disposal unit. The *batch feed*, which is the safer of the two, has a cover, is filled and then switched on. The *continuous feed* continues running as food is emptied in.

Advantages of waste disposal unit:
1. Convenient, labour saving and hygienic method of disposing of waste.
2. Reduces the necessity to have a bin *in* the kitchen.
3. Does not require cleaning.

Disadvantages of waste disposal unit: Noisy, expensive, some are dangerous for children.

KITCHEN SAFETY
1. Use non-slip floor covering.
2. Keep dangerous cleaners, chemicals and sharp objects out of the reach of children.
3. Avoid placing cooker and sink on opposite walls. One often moves from cooker with saucepans of hot liquid.
4. Do *not* leave saucepan handles sticking out.
5. Avoid curtains on windows near cooker and machines.
6. All gas and electrical work should be carried out by a skilled tradesman.
7. Have a fire blanket/fire extinguisher near the cooker.
8. All areas should be well lit.

➤ LARGE APPLIANCES

CHOOSING ELECTRICAL APPLIANCES

1. Buy from a reliable source which offers a wide choice, good value for money and an after-sales service.
2. Choose a recommended, reliable brand which carries a guarantee, is electrically safe and does its job properly.
3. Consider the size of the family and the amount of use the appliance will get when deciding on the size to buy.
4. Measure the space into which the appliance must fit and check this against the dimensions of the new appliance.
5. Appliances should be well-designed and easy to operate, giving a good selection of operations or programmes.
6. Consider proximity to existing plumbing/power points.
7. Arrange a demonstration, if possible, and read the instruction book carefully. Keep it in a safe place.
8. Consider the amount of money you can afford to spend.

COOKERS

Cookers may be run on gas, electricity, oil or solid fuel.

CONSTRUCTION

A cooker consists of a hob, an oven and usually, a grill. Cookers are generally made of enamelled steel, although many solid fuel heat-storage cookers are made from cast iron. They are well insulated with fibreglass to reduce heat loss.

Controls should be easy to read and manipulate, yet out of the reach of small children.

1. Hob

This generally consists of four hot-plates or burners. They should have variable controls and be quick to heat up.

- *Hot-plate elements* consist of nickel chromium wire, packed with magnesium oxide which conducts the heat but not the electricity.

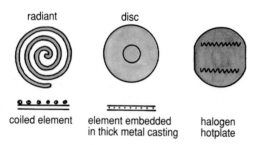

radiant   disc

coiled element   element embedded   halogen
in thick metal casting   hotplate

- *Sealed hot-plates* are clean. Otherwise a drip tray is necessary to cope with spills. Radiant (coiled) rings and disc (flat metal) rings are available.

- *Dual circuit rings* are economical as the inner part of the ring can be switched on alone when using small saucepans.
- *Simmerstat rings* contain a built-in heat-sensing device which maintains liquids at simmering point.
- *Ceramic hobs*: The hob surface is one continuous sheet of heat resistant glass such as Pyrosil. The elements are fixed beneath the glass, with circular markings to indicate their positions. Ceramic hobs are streamlined and easy to clean but may stain unless the recommended cleaner is used.
- *Halogen* rings consist of tungsten halogen lamps fixed beneath ceramic hobs. They light/heat up instantly. Combined gas/electric and conventional/halogen hobs are available.

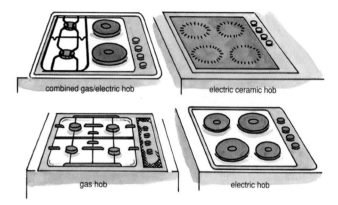

combined gas/electric hob   electric ceramic hob

gas hob   electric hob

2. Grills

These may be: (a) at eye level; (b) in a small grill compartment/oven; or (c) within the main oven.

- *Eye level grills* are convenient as they eliminate stooping, but they can be hot on the face and can dirty surrounding walls.
- *Enclosed grills* are neater and cleaner. The grill compartment of some cookers is a fully insulated second oven.
- *Main oven*: This is a bad arrangement as the oven cannot be successfully used when the grill is on and vice versa
- *Dual element grills* are economical. Just half the element can be switched on when grilling small amounts.

3. Ovens

The capacity of an oven is measured in litres and the standard oven is approximately 60 litres. Gas burners are situated at the back of the oven. Electric elements may be at the sides or on the base. Most ovens have a glass door and interior light.

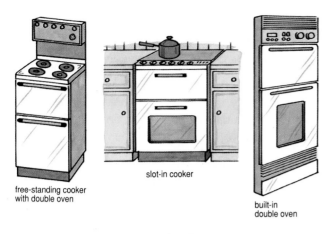

Types of cooker

Modern Features

- *Autotimers*: These consist of an electrically or battery operated clock which can be pre-set to switch the oven on and off automatically at given times. A minute-timing device may also be included. Moist dishes, such as casseroles, braised dishes and puddings cook well by this method. But those requiring a high temperature such as cakes and pastry are not as successful.
- *Double ovens*: Many modern cookers have a small oven which may also house the grill. This is used for cooking small items, while the full-sized oven is kept for large items. This arrangement saves fuel.
- *Fan ovens* (£. . . .): The element is fixed at the back of the oven with a fan behind it which blows the heated air all around the oven space. This gives an even temperature throughout the oven, unlike the conventional oven which is hotter at the top. Baking can be done on any shelf and the results will be identical, even when the oven is filled to capacity. It is ideal for 'batch baking' — for example, for the freezer. For this reason, four shelves are usually supplied.

  Fan ovens are easy to keep clean, since food is not as inclined to splash as in conventional ovens. They require less heating-up time and cook more quickly. For these reasons they are more economical to run.

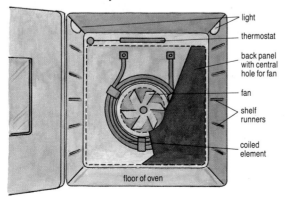

- light
- thermostat
- back panel with central hole for fan
- fan
- shelf runners
- coiled element

floor of oven

A fan oven

Rotisserie: This is a spit which is rotated by an electric motor. It may be fitted in the oven or on the grill. Some gas cookers may have a battery operated model. Poultry and meat joints can be roasted without basting, giving moist, evenly-roasted results.

Easy-to-clean ovens:

- Solid fuel ovens clean themselves by burning off splashes etc.
- Many standard cookers have enamelled, removable linings.
- Some have a coating of non-stick PTFE (polytetra-fluoroethylene).
- *Catalytic* or stay-clean oven linings contain a catalyst which oxidises splashes and spills when they occur.
- *Pyrolytic* or self-cleaning ovens which burn off splashes at high temperatures are very expensive to produce and run and are not readily available today. They have a safety lock which prevents the oven being opened while at cleaning temperature.

WHAT IS A PRINCIPLE?

The principle of an object is the basic idea/scientific reason behind it, or the basic theory on which it works. For example, the working of a refrigerator is based on the scientific principle of evaporation. The basic principle of detergents is that they reduce the surface tension of water thus making it easier for water really to wet an object and thus remove dirt.

WORKING PRINCIPLE OF COOKERS

Conduction, convection and radiation

- The hob heats cooking utensils such as saucepans by *conduction*.
- The food is subsequently cooked by *conduction* (frying) or *convection* (boiling, steaming, stewing).
- The grill cooks by *radiation*.
- The oven is heated when *convection* currents rise from the burner/element and circulate around the oven. The hot air heats the container and the food, which continues to cook by conduction.

COOKER TYPES/SIZES/COST

There are five basic cooker types:

- *Standard free-standing cooker* (£..........), with four burners or hot-plates, full width grill and one or two ovens.
- *Range-style cookers* (£..........): These are large, double-width cookers, usually run on solid fuel or oil, although some gas and electric models are available. Most have two ovens and a large hob. Solid fuel/oil versions such as Aga may incorporate a boiler which supplies hot water, and in some cases, central heating radiators.

- *Split-level cookers* (hob, £..........; oven, £..........): These are built-in cookers consisting of a hob which is fitted into a work unit, and an oven/grill which is separately housed in a tall kitchen unit. They are easy to clean and eliminate stooping. Split-level cookers may be fuelled by gas or electricity or by a combination of both. They are more expensive to buy and to fit than are standard cookers.
- *Table-top cookers* (£. . . .): These are small cookers for use when space is limited, as in bedsitters and caravans. They consist of two rings and a combined oven/grill. Most of them can be operated from a 13-amp socket, unlike standard cookers which require a directly wired cable to provide sufficient power.
- *Microwave cookers* (Chapter 4).

USE OF COOKERS

1. Most *electric cookers* must be connected directly to a powerful (35-amp) fuse. They produce heat without combustion and for this reason they are cleaner than others. They are efficient, easy to control, noiseless, odourless and have a wide range of modern features. Ovens retain heat well. Heavy machine-ground saucepans must be used on electric cookers. Halogen rings give instant heat.
2. *Gas cookers*: These burn a mixture of gas and air. Natural gas is now available in many cities. Gas cooks quickly and the flame is easy to see and to control. It is efficient, but fumes may soil kitchen surfaces.

    Combustion of gas creates condensation. Modern gas cookers have push button or spark ignition. All types of saucepan may be used.

Economy
Make full use of oven when it is on and do not light the main oven for one item. Turn off electric oven ten minutes before cooking is completed and the food will continue to cook in the retained heat. Turn rings to simmer once they have come to the boil. Never allow gas flames to rise up the sides of pans.

CARE OF COOKER

1. Wipe up spills as they occur. Turn off oven before cleaning.
2. Use oven cleaners with care, particularly caustic cleaners.
3. Avoid using harsh abrasives unless absolutely necessary.
4. Avoid dragging pots and pans over the hob, a ceramic one in particular.

SOLID FUEL COOKERS

Heat storage cookers are the most efficient form of solid fuel cooker. They are constructed from heavy cast iron, with a vitreous enamelled finish. They are very well insulated to prevent heat loss and have a very efficient draught control. They burn continuously using smokeless fuel. Some solid fuel cookers burn other fuels and household waste, but these are less efficient and pollute the air.

Boilers can be incorporated to supply hot water and central heating radiators.

Construction of solid fuel cookers
Solid fuel cookers consist of a well-insulated firebox with flues which carry heat to two or more ovens. They have two large, cast-iron hot-plates — one hot, one cool — and these are often covered by insulated lids. A balanced flue carries away smoke; an ashbox collects waste. Some have a fitted boiler. These cookers must be installed by a recognised fitter.

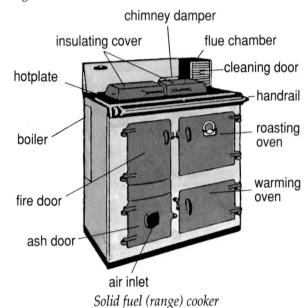

Solid fuel (range) cooker

Advantages	Disadvantages
Constantly ready for use Cheap to run	Expensive to buy Large: unsuitable for small kitchen
Warms kitchen Oven cleans itself	Flue required Fuel storage facilities required
Boiler provides hot water	Requires regular attention (e.g. fuelling, stoking, cleaning flues)
Can provide central heating	Difficult to regulate Machine-ground saucepans required
Can cope with large-scale cooking	Too warm in summer

► THE REFRIGERATOR

A refrigerator is a cold, well-insulated cupboard used to keep perishable food at a temperature sufficiently low to retard the growth of micro-organisms.

CONSTRUCTION OF REFRIGERATORS

Refrigerators are made from enamelled steel and are lined with polystyrene. Between these two layers is a thick layer of insulating material. The inside of the refrigerator is fitted with plastic coated shelves, vegetable drawers and moulded storage on the door. A thermostatically controlled dial, which is adjusted according to weather, controls refrigerator temperature. A magnetic catch and door seal ensure the temperature inside the refrigerator remains cold.

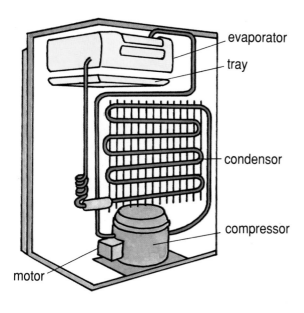

Construction of a refrigerator (compressor type)

WORKING PRINCIPLE OF REFRIGERATOR

During evaporation, heat is drawn from the surrounding area. In a refrigerator, a suitable liquid* is made to evaporate. This draws heat from the immediate area (the refrigerator cabinet), causing it to drop in temperature. This cold temperature (from 1° to 5°C) retards the growth of food spoilage micro-organisms.

Note: The recommended refrigerator temperature has been reduced to below 5°C due to the fact that certain food poisoning bacteria such as listeria can survive and multiply readily above this temperature.

There are two types of refrigerator:
(a) the compressor refrigerator; (b) the absorption refrigerator. As (a) is the most commonly used, it is described here.

COMPRESSOR REFRIGERATOR

1. A compressor, driven by a small electric motor, forces the gaseous refrigerant* into a condenser where it is cooled and changed to liquid.
2. The liquid refrigerant* passes into the evaporator (the coldest part of the refrigerator), where it evaporates, drawing heat from the refrigerator cabinet and thus cooling it.
3. The refrigerant, now gas again, is pumped into the compressor where the cycle begins again.
4. A thermostat disconnects electricity when temperature is cool enough and restarts it when the temperature rises.

   * Refrigerants: Liquid ammonia and Freon 12 convert readily from liquid to gas.

REFRIGERATOR SIZE

The capacity of a refrigerator is measured in litres. The average household 'fridge' is 115 litres. Sizes may vary between 28 and 350 litres.

Dimensions: Standard models have similar measurements to kitchen base units, i.e. 500 mm wide, 600 mm deep; 850 to 915 mm high. Large models and fridge/freezers which do not conform to these dimensions are usually placed at the end of a line of units.

STAR MARKING OF REFRIGERATORS

The temperature within a refrigerator varies between 1°C and 7°C, depending on thermostat setting.

The frozen food storage compartment of a refrigerator is star marked to indicate the length of time in which frozen food may be stored:

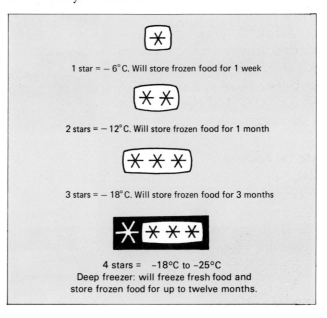

One star: * (-6°C or below), frozen food may be stored for one week.

Two stars: ** (-12°C or below), frozen food may be stored for one month.

Three stars: *** (-18°C or below), frozen food may be stored for three months.

Four stars: **** (-18°C, can be reduced to -25°C), indicate a *deep freeze cabinet* in which food may be stored for up to one year.

USE OF A REFRIGERATOR

1. Wrap or cover food before storing to prevent food from drying out.
2. *Never* put warm food in a fridge (because it causes a build-up of ice on the evaporator).
3. Allow free circulation of air. Do *not* overcrowd foods.
4. The shelf nearest the evaporator is the coldest part. Use it for storing the most perishable foods such as meat and fish.
5. Keep door closed. Avoid unnecessary opening of door.
6. Set thermostat according to conditions, e.g. low during warm weather.
7. Check contents daily. Use leftovers quickly.

CARE OF A REFRIGERATOR

1. Wipe shelves daily. Mop up spills at once.
2. Clean and defrost regularly (unless automatically defrosted).
3. Clean with a soft cloth wrung out in a little warm water, containing bread soda.

Cover food to prevent it drying out

4. *Never* place near a heat source such as a cooker or heater, as this wastes fuel.
5. Allow space for air to circulate behind the refrigerator so that heat can escape.

DEFROSTING A REFRIGERATOR

This is necessary to remove the build-up of ice on the evaporator. Failure to defrost regularly wastes electricity and causes the fridge to run inefficiently.

Manual defrosting: Set controls to 'off' or 'defrost'. When defrosted, reset dial to required temperature.

Push button defrosting: Refrigerator stops working until all ice is melted, then restarts itself.

Automatic defrosting: This takes place continuously. The compressor stops for 10-15 minutes every couple of hours to allow ice to melt.

FOOD FREEZERS

CONSTRUCTION

There are three types of freezers.

- *Chest freezers* have a horizontal layout with a top-opening lid. They are cheaper to run but take up more floor space than an upright freezer
- *Upright freezers* take up less floor space but are more expensive to buy and to run. They require defrosting more often and store less food per litre. The contents, which are stored in shelved baskets, are more accessible and the freezer can be fitted under a worktop.
- *Fridge/freezers* are upright combined refrigerators and freezers. They have separate motors, compartments and doors. They are convenient and save space and are cheaper than a separate fridge and freezer.

   All these freezers consist of an outer layer of enamelled steel with an inner lining of stainless steel or other material between which is a thick (10 cm) insulating layer. All should have a four-star marking. Frozen food storage compartments of fridges are not suitable for freezing fresh food.

CONTROLS

These consist of a thermostatically controlled dial and three indicator lights, usually:

- Green, to indicate that freezer is running normally.
- Red, to indicate that the temperature is too high.
- Yellow/orange comes on when the fast freeze switch is used to override the thermostat.

WORKING PRINCIPLE OF A FREEZER

This principle is the same as that for refrigerators (page 255), except that the temperature is lower. Most freezers are worked by the compressor system. The condenser may be external or internal, where it is embedded within the freezer walls.

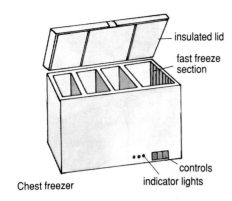

Chest freezer

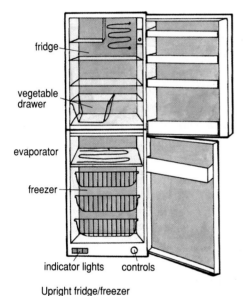

Upright fridge/freezer

Chest freezer and upright fridge freezer

CAPACITY/SIZE

Measured in litres. Sizes range from 100 to 510 litres.
Freezing capacity: The amount of fresh food which can be frozen in 24 hours. Usually one-tenth of the freezer capacity.

SITUATION

Place freezers in a cool, dry, well-ventilated area. Do *not* place near a heat source, e.g. cooker, boiler, as this would increase running costs and decrease efficiency. Allow 3 cm ventilation space at the back of freezer.

RUNNING COST

This depends on size, situation, amount of use, number of times door is opened and prevailing temperature. On average, each 15 litres uses one unit of electricity per week.

USE OF FREEZER

1. Cool foods before placing in freezer.
2. Open door as little as possible.
3. Label all foods. Store similar-type foods together.
4. Use foods in rotation, before their time limit is up.
5. It is more economical to keep freezer as full as possible.
6. Keep freezer shut during power cuts. Food should be safe for 12 hours.

CARE OF FREEZER

1. Place in a cool, dry, well-ventilated place, away from heat sources.
2. Defrost once or twice a year, when there is little food in the freezer. Remove frozen food and store in a cold, well-insulated place, e.g. another freezer or refrigerator. Disconnect electricity. Place one or two bowls of hot water in freezer and close door. Use a plastic or wooden spatula (*never* metal) to scrape frost from freezer interior. Collect frost and wipe up melted ice with an absorbent cloth.
3. Cleaning: Wash freezer interior with a clean cloth wrung out of warm water, containing bread soda. Dry thoroughly and bring freezer to –18°C before returning frozen food.
4. Wash outside of freezer occasionally with hot soapy water. Rinse and dry. Polish with a little silicone polish.

WASHING MACHINES AND DRYERS

WASHING MACHINES

Many types of washing machine are available.
- *Single tub* with a top opening lid and agitator action.
- *Twin tubs*, which have a separate, centrifugal spinner.
- *Automatic front loading machines*. As these are the most popular and labour saving, they are dealt with in detail.

CONSTRUCTION OF WASHING MACHINE

The *outer casing* consists of enamelled steel. Within this is a *watertight drum* which holds the water for washing. A perforated, horizontal *stainless steel drum* revolves within the outer drum, washing the clothes by tumbling action.

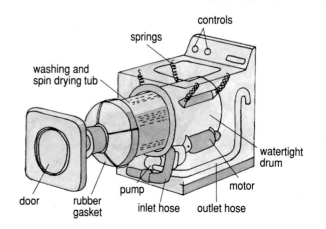

Structure of a washing machine

A *detergent dispenser* releases detergent and fabric conditioners at the appropriate time within the wash cycle. An *electric motor* drives the machine and a *pump* fills and empties it. A 2500 watt *heater* is fitted at the base of the machine.

Controls may include an on/off button, a programme selector dial and a heater dial. Some models have an economy button which uses half the amount of water for small wash loads.

INSTALLATION OF WASHING MACHINE

The machine should be level and plumbed in. Attaching hoses to taps is awkward and inconvenient. It may be connected to hot or cold water supply — the latter is more economical and convenient. A 13-16 amp socket is required.

WORKING PRINCIPLE OF WASHING MACHINE

A washing machine cleans clothes by tumbling or agitating them in hot water and detergent which loosens dirt. Detergent removes soil by lowering the surface tension of water. It then rinses clothes several times and spins or tumble dries them. Washing action is brought about by an electric motor.

filling a twin tub using a hose

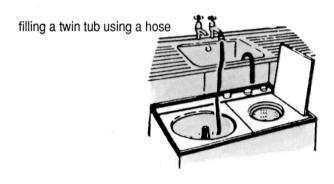

Twin-tub washing machine

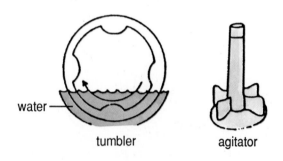

water — tumbler   agitator

Machine washing action

WASHING CYCLE

Automatic machines carry out a preselected programme which progresses without attention. Programmes correspond to the wash care labels on clothes and detergent packets.

Programmes may include:
1. Biological wash/soak for very soiled clothes. During washing, the drum rotates gently one way, then another.
2. Rinse, spin and hold.
3. Main wash is for varying lengths of time and temperatures, according to fabric.
4. Rinse and spins. Clothes are rinsed 2-3 times in fresh water with a short spin (400 rpm)* after each. After final rinse, clothes may be left floating in water to prevent creasing. This is known as a spin delay.
5. Long spin. Drum rotates at high speed (800 rpm),* throwing clothes against the perforated sides of the drum. Water is removed from clothes by centrifugal force. Rinse and/or spin programmes may be used alone, as when hand-washing clothes.

* Revolutions per minute

CAPACITY/SIZE OF WASHING MACHINE

Most washing machines hold 3-4 kg dry clothes. The dimensions correspond to base units — that is, 600 mm deep, 600 mm wide, 800-913 mm high.

USE OF WASHING MACHINE

1. Follow manufacturer's instructions.
2. Use recommended detergent. Low-foaming powders should be used. The amount will depend on the size and type of wash load, degree of soiling and hardness of water.
3. Check wash care labels and sort accordingly. Make sure colours are fast.
4. Select suitable programme and heat setting according to care label — long, hot programmes for cottons, linens; short, cooler programme for synthetics.
5. Programme proceeds with a minimum of attention.
6. Remove clothes after suitable spinning time and line or tumble dry.

CARE OF WASHING MACHINE

1. Do not exceed the recommended load. This strains the machine and gives poor washing results.
2. Empty pockets before washing as coins etc. could damage the machine.
3. Leave door open after wash to dry out machine.
4. Clean filter occasionally if necessary.
5. Many washing machines are fitted with safety locks. These will not open for 1-2 minutes after programme is completed. Avoid forcing such locks.

259

Textile/Machine Code			Handwash Instructions	Examples of Application
Old	New	Machine		
1/95, 9/95	95	Maximum Wash in Cotton Cycle	Hand Hot (50°C) or Boil Spin or Wring	White Cotton and Linen articles without special finishes
2/60, 3/60	60	Maximum Wash in Cotton Cycle	Hand Hot (50°C) Spin or Wring	Cotton, Linen or Viscose articles without special finishes where colours are fast at 60°C
4/50	50	Medium Wash in Synthetics Cycle	Hand Hot – Cold Rinse, Short Spin or Drip Dry	Polyester/cotton mixtures, nylon, polyester, cotton and viscose articles with special finishes, Cotton/Acrylic mixtures
5/40	40	Maximum Wash in Cotton Cycle	Warm Spin or Wring	Cotton, Linen or Viscose where colours are fast at 40°C but not at 60°C
6/40	40	Medium Wash in Synthetics Cycle	Warm, Cold Rinse, Short Spin. Do not hand wring	Acrylics, Acetate or Triacetate; including mixtures with wool; polyester/wool blends
7/40	40	Minimum Wash in Wool Cycle	Warm, Do not rub Spin – Do not hand wring	Wool, wool mixed with other fibres; Silk
8/30	30	Articles labelled 8/30 or 30 should be washed in the appropriate Medium or Minimum cycle or handwashed		
(hand)	(hand)		Handwash only See garment label	N.B. The terms 'Minimum, Medium and Maximum Wash' refer to the washing time and agitation levels
(no wash)	(no wash)		Do not Machine or Handwash	

Economy
- Wash a full load unless machine has an economy programme.
- Avoid high temperature settings unless necessary.

CLOTHES DRYERS

■ SPIN DRYERS
These may be part of a washing machine or an independent piece of equipment. Spin dryers remove excess water from clothes by *centrifugal force*. The dryer rotates at such a high speed that the clothes are thrown against the sides of the drum and water is forced out of them.

Advantages
They are cheap to buy and run. They speed up line drying by removing surplus water from clothes.

Disadvantage
They do not dry clothes fully.

■ TUMBLE DRYERS
These are an expensive method of drying clothes.
Construction
These consist of an enamelled steel cabinet into which is fitted a stainless steel perforated revolving drum. This is

perforated drum rotates at high speed

water is forced from clothes by centrifugal force

Spin dryer action

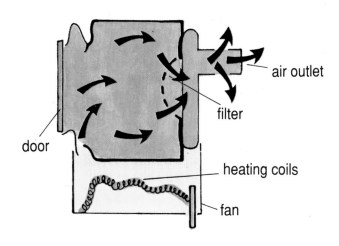

air outlet

filter

door

heating coils

fan

Construction of tumble drier

Working principle

Air is warmed by heating elements and then blown into the drum by a fan. As the drum rotates, the clothes are tumbled around in the warm air. Their moisture evaporates and the steam-laden air passes through a filter and leaves the machine through a ventilating duct. Some driers condense this moisture; they therefore do not have such a duct.

Size

Large models will dry 4 kg clothes; small models 3 kg.
Note: Tumble dryers are expensive to run.

USE OF DRYER

1. Spin clothes first. Very wet clothes waste electricity as they take a long time to dry. They are also more prone to shrinkage.
2. Check care label that garment is suitable for tumble drying.
3. Select correct heat setting — usually a choice of 1-4.
4. Select correct time. This will depend on whether clothes are to be left bone dry or damp dry.
5. Fabric conditioners soften clothes and prevent static electricity.
6. The heater switches off for final 5 to 10 minutes of drying time to cool clothes and reduce wrinkling. Remove clothes at once.
7. If carefully folded, many fabrics do not need ironing.

CARE OF DRYER

1. Clean filter after use.
2. Ensure that the air vent is not blocked as this would cause overheating.
3. Do not overload as it causes wrinkling and may damage the machine.

ridged to assist the tumbling action of the machine. A heating element warms the air and a fan blows it into the machine. Damp air is removed from the machine by an air venting hose.

▶ DISHWASHERS

A dishwasher is an efficient, hygienic and labour-saving way of washing a large number of dishes. Most are front-loading and can be fitted beneath a work top.

CONSTRUCTION

Dishwashers are generally made from enamelled steel and lined with stainless steel, which is hardwearing and rust resistant. They usually have the following components:
1. A thermostatically controlled *heating element* at the base.
2. A *water softener*, filled at intervals with salt.
3. A *motor* and *pump* which force water from the base of the machine into the spray arms or impeller.
4. A central column and *spray arms* which rotate at speed.
5. Two plastic coated racks designed to hold dishes and cutlery.

6. *Detergent dispenser* } Often on door
7. *Rinse aid dispenser*
8. *Filter* to prevent particles of food blocking the spray arms.
9. *Drain pump* which drains away soiled water.
10. A *laminated work top*.
11. *Controls*: An on/off switch and a programme dial.

WORKING PRINCIPLE OF DISHWASHER

An electrically-driven pump drives water through a rotating spray arm at high speed, forcing food particles from the dishes. This action is assisted by the use of very hot water, strong detergents and rinse aids. Dishwashers run from a 13 amp earthed socket.

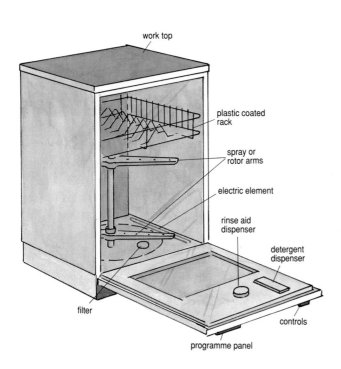

Construction of a dishwasher

SIZE/CAPACITY

Dimensions generally conform to those of a standard base unit — 600 mm deep, 600 mm wide, 850-900 mm high. Capacity is usually measured in terms of place settings which can be washed at one time. Standard machines hold 10-12 place settings — a day's washing up for a family of four.

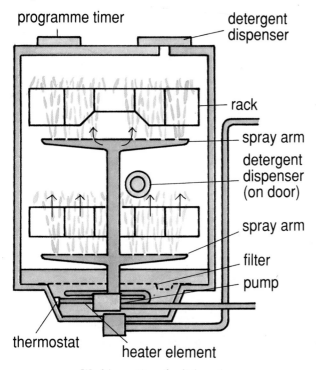

Washing action of a dishwasher

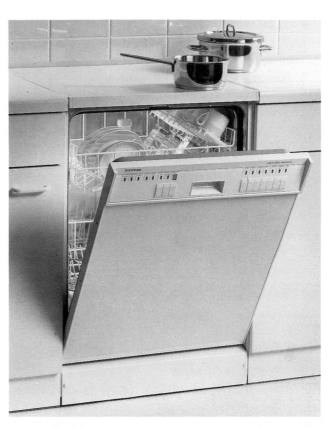

PROGRAMMES

Most dishwashers are fully automatic. Once the machine has been loaded and switched on, it will carry out the wash programme from beginning to end.

1. *Biological wash*: For badly-soiled dishes.
2. *Pre-rinse*: Removes loose particles and softens dried-on food. Useful to prevent food drying before main evening wash.
3. *Heating*: The machine refills with clean water, heats it to 65°C (hotter than hands can bear). While heating, pressure spraying removes some stains such as protein.
4. *Washing cycle*: Hot water and detergent (which is dispensed automatically) are sprayed at high speed by rotating arms and remove all the food from dishes.
5. *Rinsing cycle*: Dishes are rinsed with warm, then hot water. Rinse aid is added during the final rinsing to prevent streaking of dishes.
6. *Drying cycle*: May be carried out by residual heat from rinsing or by heating the washing chamber.

DETERGENTS

Dishwater detergents contain tripolyphosphates (which soften water), bleach and metasilicates to remove grease. *Rinse aid* helps to prevent streaking by reducing the surface tension of water. It is released automatically into the final rinsing water.

USE OF DISHWASHER

1. Scrape plates thoroughly, empty cups etc.
2. Load according to instruction booklet. Cups and other containers should face downwards.
3. Silver and stainless steel cutlery must be kept apart to prevent electrolytic staining.
4. Store dishes from each meal in the dishwasher until it is full. A rinse and hold cycle will prevent food drying onto dishes.
5. Avoid overloading as dishes will not be properly washed.
6. It is safer to avoid washing the following in a dishwasher: lead crystal; handpainted or very fine china; wood; non-heat-resistant plastics or utensils trimmed with these. Bone handled cutlery; narrow necked vases; non-stick items, unless stated on label.

CARE OF DISHWASHER

1. Follow manufacturer's instructions.
2. Clean filter(s) regularly.
3. Fill water softener/rinse-aid container, when necessary.
4. Wash door edges and other dirt traps at least weekly.
5. Wipe outside with a damp cloth, using silicone polish occasionally.
6. It is uneconomical to use machine when half full. Use shorter programme when dishes are not heavily soiled.

► EXTRACTOR FANS

These are electrically driven fans which draw stale air and steam from a room.

CONSTRUCTION OF FANS

The fan is made from aluminium or strong plastic. Rotating blades, powered by an electric motor are fitted into a strong frame. Fans vary in size (15 cm, 25 cm, 30 cm diameter). Many fans have two speeds and operate by a switch or pull cord. This opens the shutters of the fan and starts the motor.

WORKING PRINCIPLE OF FAN

The rotating blades, working at high speed, create suction which draws the stale air from the room. Some can be reversed to blow in cool air in summer.

USE OF FAN

1. The fan should be fitted to a wall or window by a qualified electrician.
2. Size should relate to the size of the room.

3. The position of fan is important. It should be fairly high up in the room, near both cooker and sink, which are the main sources of steam. It should be as far as possible from the door leading into the house to draw fumes away from this area and to prevent odours passing into the house.
4. A fused, earthed 13-amp socket is required.

CARE OF FAN

1. Wash occasionally with hot soapy water. Rinse well and dry.
2. It should always be disconnected before washing or before being handled in any way.

COOKER HOODS

CONSTRUCTION

A cooker hood is a fireproof canopy made from enamelled or stainless steel or copper. It contains a filter to remove grease and a fan, which draws air into the unit. There are two types:

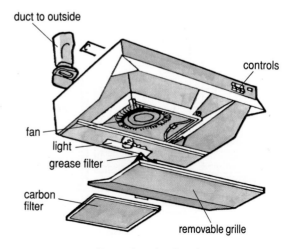

Ducted cooker hood

- The *ducted hood* which is the most efficient. It has a metal grease filter and a duct which opens outside the house so that stale air is completely removed from the room.
- The *ductless hood* has both a metal and activated charcoal or fibre filter which absorbs odours. Grease and odours are filtered from the air which is then recirculated into the kitchen.

  The charcoal/fibre filter must be replaced every 6-12 months, depending on use. Failure to do this could cause a fire. The ductless hood is simple to install as no structural work is involved.

Working principle
Hot, greasy, humid air is removed from (ducted) or filtered and recirculated (ductless) into the room by a high speed fan. Steam etc. from cooking is collected by the hood-shaped unit.

FITTING A HOOD
1. A 13-amp socket is required.
2. It should be placed 60-90 cm above the hob or 40-60 cm above an eye-level grill.
3. Most hoods run at two speeds and have a light which illuminates the cooking area.

CARE OF COOKER HOOD
1. Clean metal filter regularly in hot soapy water as it becomes very greasy.
2. Outside of unit should be washed occasionally in hot, soapy water.
3. Replace charcoal/fibre filter when necessary.
   Note: Kitchens in use need a complete air change 10-20 times per hour, depending on amount of cooking, washing etc. taking place.

VACUUM CLEANERS
Construction
Vacuum cleaners are made from tough, lightweight plastic and metal. There are two types:
   The upright model
- This has a hinged *handle* to which is attached the dust bag.
- Within the cleaner is a *rotating brush* attached to a fan by the fan belt.
- A *flexible hose* is attached to the cleaner for various jobs to which are fitted various attachments.
- The cleaner has *four wheels* on the base which makes it easy to move.
- A *light* shows up dark corners and it has a foot-operated *on/off switch*.

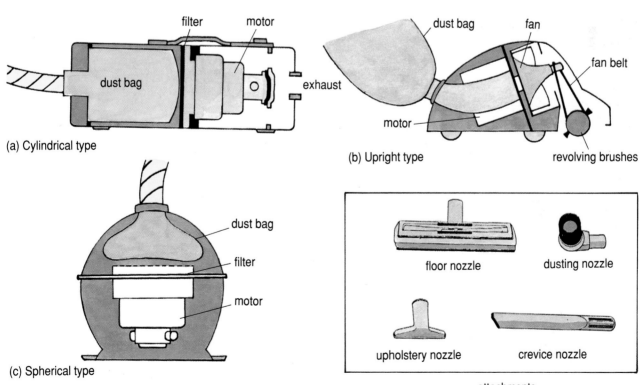

Different kinds of vacuum cleaners

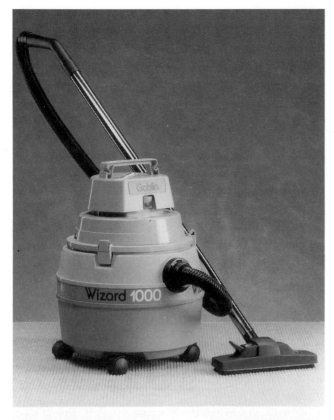

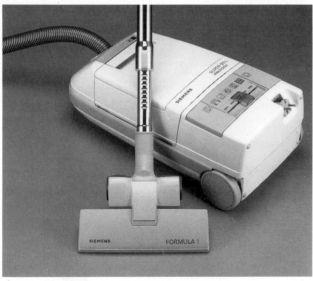

Advantages

- The upright cleaner cleans more thoroughly than others, as it cleans by suction and friction (brushes).
- It is less tiring to use as it moves easily.
- It is cheaper to run, as a less powerful motor is used than in other cleaners.

Disadvantages

- It is not very stable on stairs etc.
- It is not as efficient as others on hard/smooth floors.
- It tends to wear out carpets more quickly, due to friction from brushes.

THE CYLINDRICAL VACUUM CLEANER

- This type of cleaner may be round or cylinder shaped.
- It cleans by suction only and may have two speeds.
- A disposable bag is fixed within the machine.
- Most cylinder machines move fairly readily on wheels with a pull of the hose, which is attached to the machine.
- It is useful for homes where there is a combination of hard floor coverings and carpets.
- It works well on stairs and long piled carpets.

Disadvantages

- It is more tiring to use than the upright type.
- It is more expensive to run, as it requires a more powerful motor than the upright model.

WORKING PRINCIPLE

An electric motor drives a high speed fan which draws dirt, dust etc. from the floor by suction (and friction caused by brushes in the case of the upright cleaners). The dirt is sucked into a disposable dust bag which is emptied when full.

USE OF VACUUM CLEANERS

1. A 13-amp socket is required.
2. Follow manufacturer's instructions.
3. Do *not* handle roughly. Rubber bumpers prevent machine damaging furniture etc.
4. Empty bag regularly. Do *not* wait until it becomes too full as this reduces the efficiency of the machine.

CARE OF VACUUM CLEANERS

1. Rewind flex loosely to avoid straining or damaging it.
2. *Never* allow metal objects such as pins or large objects such as stones or fibrous objects like twine to enter the machine.
3. If such an object becomes lodged in the machine, switch it off at once, unplug and carefully attempt to remove it.
4. Have machine serviced regularly. Spare parts are available from recognised suppliers.
5. *Never* wash bag as it has been treated with a special finish to prevent dust escaping.

MODERN FEATURES

- Indicator to show when bag is full.
- Variable suction control.
- Hinged flex holder for quick release and a quick rewind button.
- Suction opening at side for cleaning carpet edges.
- Some models shampoo carpets.

ATTACHMENTS

- Flat nozzle for carpet edges and difficult corners.
- Flat perforated nozzle for cleaning radiators
- Soft brush for cleaning curtains and upholstery.

SMALL APPLIANCES USING A MOTOR

The following appliances are powered by a small electric motor positioned inside the appliance. All require a three-pin 13-amp socket and are largely constructed from plastic with stainless steel moving parts, as for example, with electric carving knives.

FOOD MIXER

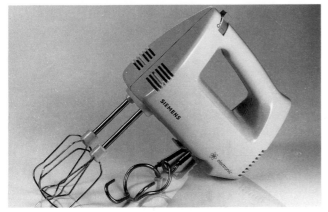
Hand-held mixer

WORKING PRINCIPLE
An electric motor drives rotating beaters or whisks which blend ingredients together and incorporate air.

Types of food mixers	
Handheld	*Large Mixers*
■ Small motor (150 watts)	■ Larger, powerful motor (400 watts)
■ Up to 3 speeds	■ Wide range of speeds
■ Cheap	■ Expensive
■ May be used in any container	■ Must be used with special bowl
■ Usually held in hand. May have special stand and bowl	■ Can be left to mix without much attention
	■ Wide range of attachments
Attachments for mixers	*Use beaters for*
■ Liquidiser (see over)	■ Creaming fat and sugar: icings and fillings
■ Mincer	*Use hook for*
■ Juice extractor	■ Pastry, bread, heavy cakes
■ Can opener	*Use whisk for*
■ Coffee grinder	■ Meringues, whipped cream, batters, sponges, soufflés, mousses, milk shakes
■ Potato peeler	

LIQUIDISER
This cuts food preparation time to a minimum. It can be used for:
- Blending: soups, sauces, milkshakes
- Grinding: coffee, nuts, sugar
- Chopping: nuts, raw vegetables, herbs
- Mixing: batters, mayonnaise
- Puréeing: raw and cooked fruits, fools, pâté, baby foods
- Making breadcrumbs and stuffings

Liquidiser attachment

WORKING PRINCIPLE
Four/six stainless steel rotating knives within a covered glass/perspex goblet are driven at high speed by a motor. This blends or grinds the food. The motor may be that of a large food mixer, or the liquidiser may be a free-standing machine with its own motor.

SIZE
Liquidisers vary in capacity between 1 and 1¾ litres. Many give a range of speeds.

FOOD PROCESSORS
These are multi-purpose food preparation machines consisting of a base containing the motor, a mixing bowl which fits over a spindle, a lid and blade or chopping

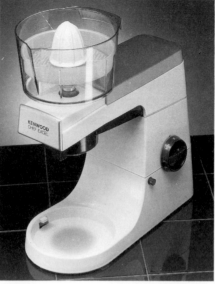
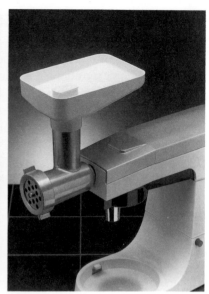

Full-sized mixer with (a) juice extractor and (b) mincer attachments

discs. They chop, slice, grate and purée foods. They make cakes, dough and pastry and many other products. All are done in one bowl, using one of three or four attachments.

WORKING PRINCIPLE
A motor drives a rotating blade which chops or purées food in the bowl. Slicing/shredding discs may be attached. The food to be processed is pushed through a funnel against the blades, to be sliced or shredded into the bowl. Most models have three speeds — a slow and high speed and a pulsating switch which is used for chopping foods. Chopping blades are used for:

- Chopping breadcrumbs, parsley, vegetables etc.
- Puréeing soups, sauces, fruit, pâté; making batters
- Mincing raw and cooked meat (be careful not to over-process)
- Making mayonnaise and other sauces
- Making pastry, bread and other doughs and cakes

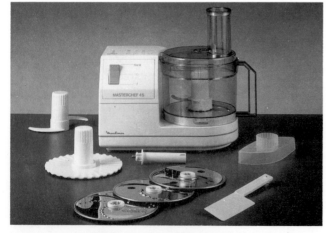

Food processor with accessories

Use slicing/grating discs for: finely or thickly slicing or shredding vegetables as for coleslaw. Grating carrots, cucumber, cheese etc. Making chips.

SIZE /CAPACITY
Standard capacity is 2 litres, but it must not be filled to capacity. Larger and smaller models are available.

USE OF MIXERS/PROCESSORS
- Follow instruction booklet.
- Use correct beater and speed for process.
- Warm beaters and bowl before creaming fat etc.
- Do not overload the machine with mixture or liquid.
- Stop machine to scrape down sides. Never stir while machine is on.
- Make sure that all parts are positioned correctly before machine is switched on.

CARE/CLEANING OF MIXERS AND PROCESSORS
1. Avoid overrunning the machine. Stop it now and then to cool it down.
2. Clean after use. First remove plug from socket.
3. Wash beater/blades and bowl in hot, soapy water.
4. Wipe over machine with a cloth wrung out of hot, soapy water. Do not use abrasives. Rinse and dry.
5. Never immerse machine in water or handle with wet hands.
6. Store machine with fittings loose and lid off to allow circulation of air. Cover loosely.

ELECTRIC CARVING KNIVES

WORKING PRINCIPLE
Two blades, which clip together, are moved backward and forward by the motor. It is possible to carve meat more thinly and evenly with an electric knife. Control is in the form of a button which is pressed to turn knives on.

CARE AND USE

1. Take great care when using these machines, as they are quite dangerous.
2. Always cut away from worker, using a carving fork with a protective guard.
3. Avoid cutting through bone, as this blunts the blades.
4. Use a wooden board for carving as it is less slippery.
5. Remove blades and wash in hot, soapy water. Never place machine in water and never use abrasives.

APPLIANCES USING A HEATING ELEMENT

These appliances are usually more economical than heating liquids/foods by traditional methods as they heat them more directly. Any appliance with a heating element has a higher wattage than one with a motor.

WORKING PRINCIPLE

Electricity flows into element where it meets resistance which causes it to heat up. The element in turn heats the liquid/food by conduction (sandwich maker, slow cooker, iron) convection (kettle, deep fat fryer), or radiation (toaster, infra-red grill).

A thermostat maintains the required temperature and, in the case of automatic appliances, switches them off. Handles, knobs and attachments of heating appliances must be heat resistant.

KETTLE

CONSTRUCTION

- The standard electric kettle is made of copper, chrome, stainless steel or tough plastic. An element within the base must be covered with water before switching on.
- Automatic kettles have a bi-metal thermostat which switches off the kettle when it boils.

Automatic chrome and jug kettles

Kettles should be easy to grip, with a secure lid and a stable base. They should pour well. Handles should be heat resistant.

Size

Kettles may hold between 1 and 2 litres. Those with a low element such as jug kettles can boil very small amounts of water.

Always unplug kettles before filling.

DEEP FAT FRYERS

These can deal successfully and safely with large amounts of fried food.

CONSTRUCTION

Deep fat fryers consist of a large pot, aluminium or stainless steel on the inside, enamelled steel on the outside. Around the base of the fryer, between these layers and well insulated, is an electric element. In some models a hinged lid prevents splashing and reduces fire risk. A washable filter on the lid reduces emission of grease, smoke and odours.

Most fryers are thermostatically controlled with three heat settings (between 100-200°C), a safety cut-out in case of overheating and a light to show when temperature is reached. A wire basket can be raised and lowered on a lever. Oil level up to 2 litres is marked with an arrow. If strained, oil can be used several times.

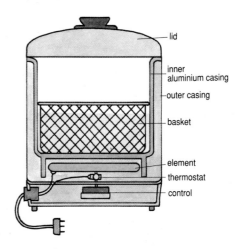

Deep fat fryer

MULTI-COOKERS

These are sometimes called electric frying pans. They consist of a deep vessel covered with a domed, vented lid. They may be made from stainless steel or aluminium; many have a non-stick interior. A thermostatically controlled heating element is connected to the base of the 'cooker'. Controls, usually on the handle, provide a selection of heat settings. Cooking pan can be removed for serving and for cleaning. As the cooker stands on four legs, it can be used safely on a work surface.

Multi-cookers can be used for steaming, stewing, braising, frying, roasting, boiling and even baking cakes. They are particularly useful in situations where space for a normal cooker is restricted, as in a bedsitter.
Capacity: up to 4 litres

SLOW COOKERS

Most slow cookers consist of a removable heat-resistant casserole set in an insulated outer casing. An electric element with two heat settings is fitted at the base of the casing. The cooker requires a very low wattage (about the same as that for a light bulb — 170 W), making it very economical to use.

Slow cookers are used for dishes requiring long, slow cooking such as soups and stews. The stewing is started in the usual way, using a high setting (to kill all micro-organisms). After a required time the heat is reduced to the lower setting (86°C) for several hours. It can be left on safely all day so that a hot meal is ready in the evening. They are very economical, and make meat very tender, while still retaining the flavour. Little evaporation takes place. The lid should not be removed during cooking time or it will take longer.
Note: Failure to bring food to a high temperature at the start of the recipe may allow micro-organisms, which may be present in the food, to multiply and cause food poisoning.
Capacity: 2.5 - 3.5 litres.

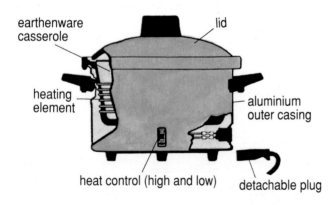

A slow cooker

earthenware casserole
lid
heating element
aluminium outer casing
heat control (high and low)
detachable plug

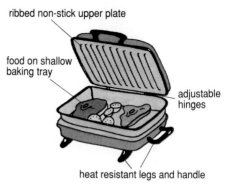

ribbed non-stick upper plate
food on shallow baking tray
adjustable hinges
heat resistant legs and handle

A contact grill

CONTACT GRILLS/SANDWICH TOASTERS

These consist of two ridged, aluminium heating plates coated with a non-stick material called PTFE. A thermostatically-controlled element behind the plate heats them evenly. The food is sandwiched between the plates so that it is in direct contact with the heat. The food cooks rapidly by conduction. Infra-red radiant grills emit heat rays of a longer length than normal grills. They penetrate food to a depth of 1 cm. Some have a selection of heat settings. Sizes 18 x 20 to 30 x 30 cm. Loading 1-3 kw.

Food such as steak, chops, fish, sausages and bacon can be grilled or dry-fried in these grills. Grills can also be used to make toasted sandwiches. Foods should be of uniform thickness.

The plates can be detached for washing. Alternative plates for items such as waffles are available. Drain off surplus fat during prolonged cooking.

IRONS

There are two basic types of hand iron: (a) dry iron; (b) steam iron.

DRY IRONS

A shiny sole plate, made from aluminium or stainless steel, has an element fitted directly over it. This heats the sole plate evenly. A thermostat, controlled by a heat control dial, turns the current off when the correct temperature is reached. An indicator light shows when thermostat is on or off.

The upper part of the iron is made from strong, heat-resisting plastic. Insulating material over the element directs the heat downwards.

STEAM IRONS

These are constructed in a similar way to the dry iron, but the larger body of the steam iron contains a small water tank which is filled through a hole in the handle. This drips water onto the hot sole plate which converts it to steam. This is released through steam holes in the sole plate. The control dial has settings which correspond to

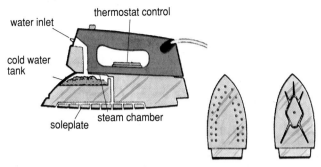

A steam iron

soleplate holes and grooves
for supplying steam

Standard heat setting

Hot	(210°C) ***	Cotton, linen, rayon
Warm	(160°C) **	Polyester, wool
Cool	(120°C) *	Acrylic, nylon, acetate, polyester

CORDLESS APPLIANCES

These are powered by in-built batteries. The appliance is fitted into electric recharging units either between use (vacuum cleaners, mixers, carving knives) or during use (kettles, irons).

Advantages:

- Safer — no direct electric connection when in use
- No cord to get in the way
- Useful for left-handed people
- Vacuum is more mobile and useful for awkward places, cars etc.

USING SMALL APPLIANCES SAFELY

1. Follow manufacturer's instructions, particularly in relation to heat settings, pre-heating and timing.
2. Only buy appliances which are electrically safe — usually well-known brands.
3. They should be sturdy, have a stable base and heat resistant handles.
4. Make sure plugs are wired correctly to a fused plug (see below).
5. Flexes should be firmly fixed by cord grip. Avoid trailing flexes
6. Use correct fuse. Up to 720 w, use a 3 amp fuse; over 720 w, use a 13 amp fuse.
7. Never use near water. Unplug when filling.
8. When cleaning, disconnect from electricity and wash according to instructions. Never immerse heating base in water. Wipe over outside with damp cloth.

fabric requirements. This can be set to 'steam', when required, which opens a valve releasing the water. Steam is only produced when the iron is horizontal. Steam irons may also be used as dry irons. Expensive models contain sprays and steam boosters for extra-dry clothes.

Note: Distilled water should be used and the tank emptied after use.

KITCHENWARE AND TABLEWARE

Well-designed equipment and utensils should:
1. Serve their purpose efficiently.
2. Be reasonably strong and durable.
3. Be of sound construction and well-balanced.
4. Be comfortable and easy to handle.
5. Be safe.
6. Be stain resistant, yet easy to clean.
7. Look attractive.

Pots and pans, as well as complying with the above points:

- Should conduct heat evenly and well to save fuel.
- Should have a thick, flat base, especially for electric and solid fuel stoves which require a machine-ground base.
- Lids should fit snugly, but not too tightly.

- Handles should be securely fixed, heat-resistant and designed so that they can be grasped without burning fingers.
- Large saucepans need a handle on each side.
- Materials used should not rust.
- Curved interiors are easily cleaned.
- Should match the size of the hot plate.

MATERIALS

Aluminium: Heavy gauge is best. Light aluminium buckles and burns easily. *Never* use soda on aluminium as it causes pitting.

   Cast iron is heavy, but holds heat well. It is breakable and it also rusts.

Enamelled cast iron is more attractive and hygienic and does not rust (e.g. Le Creuset pots).

Stainless steel is a poor conductor of heat. A base of another metal such as copper which conducts heat well must be inserted and this makes it expensive. It is stain-resistant and non-toxic.

Copper is an excellent heat conductor, but is toxic unless lined. It is difficult to maintain. Reduces vitamin C. Is expensive.

Tin is used for baking tins and many kitchen utensils. It is cheap, but rusts and is not very strong.

NON-STICK FINISHES

These are applied to the interior of pots, pans, tins etc. Most consist of a layer of polytetrafluoroethylene (PTFE). It consists of millions of atoms of carbon and fluorine bonded tightly together, making it resistant to almost every substance. Brand name: Teflon.

The utensil is first roughened to provide a key, then enamelled (fritting) before a first coat of PTFE is sprayed on and fired at 240°C. A second layer of PTFE is fired at 440°C, providing a smooth surface.

CARE OF NON-STICK PANS

- *Never* stack non-stick pots or pans.
- *Never* use metal utensils to turn or stir foods: use plastic or PTFE coated utensils.
- *Never* use abrasives.
- Wash in hot soapy water, rinse well and dry.
- *Never* heat an empty pan as this damages the surface.
- Follow exactly instructions for use.

CERAMIC AND GLASS COOKWARE

Casseroles and other dishes for oven use may be made from:

1. *Stoneware*: This is made from clay and fired at a very high temperature. When glazed, it is non-porous. It does not absorb flavours. It is stain resistant and easy to clean.
2. *Earthenware*: Is not as strong as stoneware. It is made from earth or red clay. It is porous and absorbs odours and flavours, unless glazed.
3. *Glassware*: Is made from sand, borax and silica etc. Glass is made heat resistant by tempering it (successively heating and cooling it). Such glass, e.g. Pyrex, may be heat resistant but will not withstand extreme changes of temperature. It may *not* be placed on direct heat.

   Pyroceram is an exceptionally tough glass, originally used for rockets to withstand the huge change in temperature when re-entering the earth's atmosphere. It can be taken from the freezer and placed on the hob without damage. It is attractive enough to be then used as a serving dish. It is used on ceramic hobs.

CARE OF HEAT-RESISTANT GLASS

1. *Avoid* sudden changes in temperature (exception: Pyroceram).
2. *Never* use a wet cloth to remove hot Pyrex from an oven.
3. *Never* place a hot dish on a cold surface.
4. *Steep* after cooling to facilitate stain removal.
5. *Never* place on a hot plate (exception, Pyroceram).

TABLEWARE

CHOICE

1. Tableware should be well designed, stable and attractive.
2. Handles should be securely fixed, yet comfortable to use.
3. Choose a well-established design and pattern, which will be unlikely to be discontinued.
4. Tableware should be easy to clean — preferably by dishwasher.

- *Ceramic ware*: Bone china/porcelain is translucent and delicate, yet strong.
  Earthenware is for everyday use. It may be glazed or unglazed. It is cheap and reasonably strong.
  Stoneware is similar to earthenware but heavier due to flint content.
- *Glass* is made from sand, silica and lime. These are melted in a furnace, then blown, pressed, moulded or rolled (sheets of glass). Lead crystal is usually blown, then decorated by cutting or engraving.
  Glass does not absorb flavours. It is cheap and hygienic but is very brittle and has little heat resistance.
- *Plastic* is used for kitchen utensils, buckets etc. (thermoplastic) and for cups, saucers, laminated plastic, handles of saucepans (thermosetting). Plastic is cheap, lightweight, washable, resistant to breaking but may be damaged by heat, certain acids, alkalis, sharp objects and may give a flavour to food.

CUTLERY

CHOICE

1. Buy good-quality cutlery. Stainless steel is cheap and strong.
2. Handles should be moulded all-in-one; otherwise they should be fixed securely. Handle materials include wood, bone and plastic.
3. Handle each item of cutlery before buying. It should balance well in the hand and on the table. Bad design features: Knives which do not cut; forks which do not hold food; spoons which are too shallow.
4. Be sure to buy sufficient cutlery, particularly if you own a dishwasher.
5. Type should suit place settings and style of table etc.

MATERIALS

1. Solid silver is expensive and needs lots of maintenance.
2. EPNS (electroplated nickel silver) is a cheap metal such as iron which is coated with an alloy (mixture) of nickel silver. Cheap cutlery has a thin coating. Thicker, good-quality coatings should last 25 years.

    Both solid silver and EPNS tarnish easily. They should be cleaned with silver polish or Dip, then washed, rinsed and dried.
3. Stainless steel varies in quality. High chromium content makes good-quality stainless steel. It is stain *resistant* rather than stain*less* and is easy to care for. It cannot be washed with silver in a dishwater, as the metals react with one another, causing staining.

CUTLERY REQUIREMENTS

Average place settings include:

- One dinner knife and fork
- One dessert knife, fork and spoon
- One teaspoon, one soup spoon
- Two tablespoons per 6 table settings

KITCHEN KNIVES

A sharp knife is probably the most essential kitchen utensil. Carbon steel knives take the sharpest edge, although stainless steel knives are easier to care for. The handle should be firmly riveted to the blade.

Requirements: 1 cook's knife; 1 filleting knife; 1 paring knife; 1 breadknife; 1 palette knife; carving knife and fork; knife sharpener.

16 ORGANISATION OF WORK AND CLEANING

A well-thought-out weekly work plan will ensure that a house is clean and well organised. When small children are around, not all plans can work like clockwork.

Children should help around the house, sharing household chores and keeping their own rooms tidy. All members of a family have responsibilities as well as rights. A parent should not become a slave to the family.

▶ ORGANISING A WORK PLAN

1. List the jobs which must be done daily, weekly and occasionally.
2. Place the daily jobs in logical order in a time plan which suits your lifestyle.
3. Fit one or two weekly jobs into each day.
4. Try out the weekly work plan once, and alter it if necessary.
5. Allocate specific jobs to each member of the family.
6. The most important priorities are children and meals. Most other jobs can wait, if necessary.

SAMPLE WORK PLAN (FOR FULL-TIME HOMEMAKER)

7.00 Get up, wash and dress. Help small children wash and dress, if necessary.
7.30 Prepare breakfast*, set table*, pack lunches*.
8.00 Breakfast. Wash up afterwards*.
8.30 Spouse and children may leave for work/school.
8.35 Make beds*, tidy bedrooms* and bathroom. Older children should do their own.
9.00 Clean out sitting room, hall etc.
9.30 Daily washing. Finish cleaning kitchen.
10.00 Tea or coffee.
10.15 At this time do one or more weekly jobs, for example:

Monday:	Change bed linen. Weekly wash.
Tuesday:	Clean one or two bedrooms and the bathroom thoroughly.
Wednesday:	Clean/vacuum hall, stairs, landing. Ironing, if applicable.
Thursday:	Clean kitchen thoroughly. Clean cooker and refrigerator thoroughly on alternate weeks.
Friday:	Clean sitting room and dining room.
Saturday:	Shopping and/or baking and cook-ahead meals.

12.00 Prepare lunch and/or do some extra cooking.
12.45 Lunch: Children back to school or rest.
1.45 Advance preparation for dinner.
2.00 Personal time†: Used for hobbies, relaxation, visiting, grooming, hairdresser, gardening, sport.
5.00 Prepare dinner.
6.00 Dinner.
6.30 Spouse/children wash up and tidy kitchen*.
7.00 Young children prepared for bed.

* These jobs should be allocated to family members.
† Parents of young children should arrange a rota with other young parents or have a baby sitter to mind the children so that at least one or two weekdays are free for personal activities.

Adapt this time plan to suit a person with a career outside the home. Remember:

- Couples who both work will not always have a perfect home but good organisation helps.
- Learn to think ahead. Make lists. Plan work. Avoid wasting time doing unnecessary chores.
- If you can afford it, employ a home help. At least buy as many labour-saving devices as possible such as dishwasher, automatic cooker, freezer, microwave oven, tumble dryer and food processor.
- Use paper towels for spills. Oven-to-tableware saves time dishing and washing up. Use non-stick utensils.
- Have house and furniture as easy to maintain as possible. For example, have vinyl wallpaper, easy-clean floors such as vinyl or fitted carpets, laminated plastic in the kitchen. Drip dry clothes and bed linen. Use duvets instead of bed clothes.
- Train the family to do all the household chores, to keep their rooms tidy and put things away. Regular jobs should be shared, regardless of gender. It is amazing how much extra work can be done by getting up an hour earlier.

FATIGUE AND STRESS

Good organisation and proper planning help to get the work done more efficiently and quickly. Take a breather now and then for a 'cuppa' and a rest. The males in the house can do the more strenuous jobs, including window washing and cleaning floors. They are physically stronger!

(Fill in price and brand name in the space provided)
Cleaning Agents

Type/Cost	Composition	Action	Use
1. Abrasives, e.g. powder, steel wool, paste, liquid £........	Abrasive, e.g. sand, soda bleach, detergent	Grinds stain/tarnish from surface. Bleach and detergent remove dirt.	Metals and other strong scratch resistant surfaces
2. Absorbent cleaners £........	French chalk, fuller's earth	Absorbs grease; is then brushed or vacuumed off.	On non-washable surfaces, e.g. upholstery, hats
3. Acids, e.g. £........	Lemon juice, vinegar	Remove tarnish. Dissolve stains.	Metals, brick and marble (rinse well)
4. Alkalis: many cleaning agents contain alkaline substances, e.g. drain cleaners; detergents £........	Bread soda, ammonia, sodium carbonate (washing soda)	(a) Soften water (b) Dissolve grease (c) Clears blocked drains	Most surfaces, except aluminium, which is damaged by strong alkalis
5. Bleaches £........	■ Sodium perborate ■ Sodium hypochlorite ■ Hydrogen peroxide	(a) Oxidise stains (b) Disinfect by killing micro-organisms (c) Whiten clothes (d) Remove odours *Poison*	Drains: glazed surfaces, e.g. baths etc. *Never* use with lavatory cleaners. They create chlorine gas. White cotton, linen
6. General purpose cleaners. Liquid, paste or powder form £........	Detergent + bleach or ammonia	Detergent cleans and removes stains. Dissolve powders in water. Rinse after use.	Many surfaces, e.g. enamelled surfaces, walls, paint work
7. Grease solvents £........	Volatile substances, e.g. carbon tetrachloride, benzine	Used to spot and dry clean. They dissolve grease, then evaporate quickly. Highly inflammable. *Toxic*. Use in well ventilated place. Air after use.	Fabric Upholstery
8. Lavatory cleaners £........	Crystalline powders containing detergents	Clean and disinfect lavatories	Do *not* use with bleach
9. Metal cleaners £........	■ Fine abrasive + alkalis or other grease solvents, e.g. acids ■ Impregnated wadding ■ Metal dips (for forks, etc.)	Abrasives and acids remove tarnish. Solvent dissolves grease.	Metals: use appropriate cleaner for each. Apply to metal with soft cloth, rub to remove tarnish. Polish off. Rinse and dry cutlery or food containers.
10. Oven cleaners £........	Based on strong alkalis, e.g. caustic soda, sodium hypochlorite	Dissolves burnt-in dirt and food	Oven interior only. Use with great care. Wash off splashes at once. Use rubber gloves.
11. Polish: Liquid, cream or wax £........	Natural or synthetic wax dissolved in solvent, e.g white spirit. Some contain silicones.	Wax shines and protects surface. Solvent helps it to spread. Silicones make it waterproof and easier to apply.	Furniture Floors
12. Emulsion polishes £........	Waxes and resins emulsified in water	Easily spread on with cloth. Water evaporates, leaving a hard shiny surface and a high gloss.	Floors, e.g. vinyl. Build-up becomes sticky and must be removed occasionally with special solvent.

Use the correct cleaning equipment for each job and keep equipment in good working order.

Mental fatigue and stress are often caused by a negative attitude to housework. The repetition and monotony become too much to bear. Get the worst jobs over quickly — the most strenuous in the morning when energy output is highest. Wear comfortable old clothes and footwear when working. Sit or stand in a comfortable position.

Simplify work by arranging equipment and furniture in logical order (see Kitchen Planning, page 248).

CLEANING ROUTINES

Rooms which are used daily must be cleaned and tidied daily. The following is the most logical order by which to clean a room.

Air, tidy, sweep, dust, vacuum, wash, polish. Use the correct cleaning equipment for each job and keep equipment in good working order.

Clean methodically and thoroughly. Collect everything you need before you start. Jobs which create dirt, such as cleaning out a fire, should be done before cleaning a room. Sweeping raises dust, therefore, dust *after* sweeping. When dusting, use a *very* slightly damp, soft cloth and carefully wipe over all surfaces. Do *not* flick dusters around: this only spreads dust.

Most cleaning is done from the top downwards — ceiling first, then walls, then furniture — otherwise dust will fall on clean surfaces. Plan work so that each room is cleaned in turn down through the house. This saves unnecessary walking. Use labour-saving cleaning appliances and agents. (See chart on Cleaning Agents.)

Adapt the following work plan to suit each room:

DAILY CLEAN OF A LIVING ROOM

1. Open windows.
2. Put away newspapers, toys, hobbies (better still, train each person to put away his/her own!)
3. Empty ashtrays, collect rubbish in waste bin and empty.
4. Clean out and reset fire.
5. Vacuum carpet.
6. Dust furniture. Water flowers and plants.
7. Wipe/wash over paint work, sills and fire surround.
8. Polish woodwork with a soft cloth, if necessary.

WEEKLY CLEAN

1. Same as above, giving a thorough clean.
2. Before vacuuming, dust ceiling, walls, high light-fittings.
3. Tidy out some shelves and/or drawers each week.
4. Clean windows, polish furniture, mirrors, metals e.g. brass and silver lamps.
5. Thoroughly vacuum rooms in rotation, moving all furniture.

SEASONAL CLEANING OR SPRING CLEANING

1. Tidy all cupboards, drawers etc., discarding unused items and storing seasonal items such as clothes and bedding.
2. Vacuum curtains, furniture, beds once or twice a year.
3. Dry-clean or wash curtains.
4. Clean ceiling, walls and furniture thoroughly.
5. Clean all small items thoroughly — ornaments, picture frames, books etc.
6. Clean floors, removing old polish, shampooing carpets if necessary.
7. Clean windows.

► SAFETY IN THE HOME

ACCIDENT PREVENTION

CHILDREN

1. Fix children securely in prams, high chairs etc.
2. Keep dangerous objects such as poisons, knives, matches, plastic bags and beads out of their reach.
3. Never leave young children to play without supervision.
4. Buy flameproof nightwear.
5. Avoid using a pillow in a child's cot. Put them sleeping on their stomachs.
6. Use a cooker rail. Turn handles inward when small children are about.

FIRES

The most frequent causes of house fires in Ireland are:
- Children playing with matches
- Smouldering cigarette ends
- Unprotected coal fires
- Chip pan fires
- Faulty electric wiring
- Chimney fires

1. Place a fireguard around fires. Never place a mirror over a fireplace.
2. Have a fire extinguisher — which works — in an accessible place and a fire blanket in the kitchen.
3. Do not leave lighted cigarettes unattended. Never smoke in bed.
4. Close all inside doors at night to prevent spread of fire.
5. Avoid use of inflammable furnishings or those that give off toxic fumes such as upholstery foam.
6. Clean chimneys regularly (once or twice a year).
7. Do not place clothes to dry over heaters.
8. Avoid curtains etc. near cookers.

FALLS
1. Avoid overpolishing floors. Do not polish under rugs.
2. Have worn floor coverings mended, particularly on the stairs.
3. Never leave objects such as toys on the stairs.
4. Use non-slip floor coverings, particularly in bathroom and kitchen.
5. Light stairs and steps well.
6. Use a sturdy set of steps or step ladder to reach high places.

POISONING
1. Keep medicines out of reach in a child-proof cabinet.
2. Keep poisons such as medicines and weedkillers in bottles clearly marked 'Poison' and out of reach. Never transfer poisons to harmless bottles such as lemonade bottles.
3. Make sure rooms containing gas appliances are well ventilated.

ELECTRICITY
1. Water and electricity are a dangerous combination. Never touch electrical appliances with wet hands.
2. Unplug electrical appliances when handling, repairing or filling.
3. Never take electrical appliances into a bathroom. Bathroom switches should be outside the room with only a pull cord inside.
4. Unplug TV and other appliances before going to bed.
5. Make sure electrical appliances are properly earthed. Use modern 3-pin shuttered sockets.
6. Do not use faulty appliances. Replace frayed flexes. Get a qualified electrician to do any electrical repair work.
7. Never run flexes or wiring under carpets.
8. Have electric blankets serviced every 2-3 years.

FIRE FIGHTING
1. Check with local fire station or fire prevention council for fire prevention advice.
2. Have a fire practice occasionally with all the family so that everyone knows what to do if a fire breaks out.
3. Make sure that everyone knows where fire fighting equipment is kept.
4. Use flame-retarding materials or finishes in the home.
5. Remember that double-glazed windows are very difficult to break. Every room should have a window that opens easily. Security window keys should be kept near the window.
6. Install a smoke detector. Many have lights that switch on in case of fire so that the way out is illuminated.
7. Remember that in a fire, the air nearest the floor is freshest. To get out, crawl along the floor.

IF A FIRE CANNOT BE PUT OUT EASILY
- Make sure everyone leaves the house, closing doors and windows after them. Prearrange a meeting place outside. *Do not re-enter the house.*
- Call the fire brigade.
- While waiting, attempt to extinguish the fire if that presents no immediate danger.

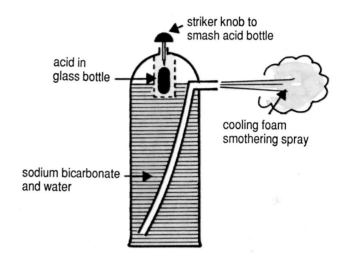

A water-based fire extinguisher

METHODS OF EXTINGUISHING
Fires can be put out by removing one of the conditions they require for burning — for example oxygen — or by cooling it, as with a hose or bucket of water. (Never pour water on fires involving electricity or oil — oil floats on water.)

Water-based fire extinguishers work as follows. The container is filled with a solution of bicarbonate of soda in water. A container of acid is positioned at the top of the container. When this is broken by pressing the knob at the top of the extinguisher, the acid mixes with the alkali, producing violent fizzing. The water squirts out of the hose, which should be aimed at the fire.

Other extinguishers use:
- Foam based on urea, which cools and quenches the fire.
- Carbon dioxide, which engulfs and smothers the fire.
- Dry bicarbonate of soda, which changes to CO_2 on the fire.
- Fibreglass fireblankets deprive fire of oxygen.

SOCIETY

Sociology is the scientific study of society. It includes the study of relationships, attitudes, behaviour patterns, customs, social groupings and social problems. Because of its scientific nature, it has its own specialised terminology which must be understood before proceeding with the subject (see Glossary below).

Since sociology deals with human behaviour in a scientific way, it is essential that any observations are based on available facts and reliable statistics rather than on simple opinions and value judgments (see below) which may be influenced by many factors such as upbringing, political persuasion, religious beliefs, prejudice and personal preferences.

GLOSSARY

Anthropology: A social science concerned with the evolution and adaptation of humankind to its environment.

Class: A form of economic and social stratification, ranking people into broad groups or strata. Factors used to determine social class are: occupation, wealth or income, status, power, education, family background, attitudes and norms, lifestyles and life chances. The main criterion is occupation.

Community: A group of people within a limited geographical area who have a sense of belonging and identification with one another.

Concept: An idea or notion concerning the qualities of the subject being analysed.

Conformity: Behaviour acceptable to a group as a whole.

Culture: The way of life of a society, with the language, knowledge, music, folklore, behaviour patterns and laws common to it. It is a learned system of established practices that are traditional in a society and transmitted through its generations.

Custom: An accepted way of behaviour that has existed in a society for a considerable time.

Delinquency: Law-breaking by those below the legal age of adult responsibility.

Democracy: A government chosen by the people and which involves the sharing of power.

Demography: The study of the size and structure of human populations.

Deviant: One who fails to conform to the norms of society.

Folk-ways: Simple customs or ways of behaviour that are generally practised in a society but which are not as important as customs. They include rules of etiquette, such as shaking hands.

Group: A social unit or collection of people who are linked by a common interest or purpose.

A family: a primary group

An audience at a pop concert: a secondary group

(a) *Primary groups* are small, intimate groups whose members have frequent contact with one another — for example, families, close friends. Primary groups are more permanent than. . .

(b) *Secondary groups* which are larger and more impersonal — for example, political parties, trade unions, religious or ethnic groups.

Institution (social): An important and established social pattern or custom such as marriage which is the approved and expected way of behaviour.

Kinship: Ties based on blood relationship.

Migration: The movement of persons or groups from one home to another.
  (a) *Emigration*: Movement of people to another country.
  (b) *Immigration*: Arrival of people to set up home in a country of which they are not natives.

Mobility (social): The ability to move up and down through social classes.

Mores: Customs of a society that are highly valued and considered important for the well-being of society — for example honesty, loyalty, fidelity. Some mores such as moral standards may be enforced by social pressure; more important mores may be enforced by law. Crimes such as murder and robbery are deviations from social mores.

Norms: Normal or expected patterns of behaviour such as living in a family, going to school etc. Society approves when we conform to accepted norms and shows disapproval when we fail to do so.

Peer group: A primary social group composed of people with one or more characteristics in common, such as age, interest and attitudes. Examples: a group of friends, workmates.

Prejudice: Preconceived opinion or bias usually unfavourable and often without considering the full evidence. (Latin *pre judicium* - before sentence or judgment.)

Pressure group: An organised social group that works together to implement certain policies, often by attempting to influence the government or the media.

Reference group: The group with which we compare ourselves.

Role (social): The pattern of behaviour considered appropriate for an individual.

Sex role: The pattern of behaviour expected of a person because of her or his gender.

Siblings: Offspring of the same parent, that is brothers and sisters.

Social change: Alterations or changes within society due to reform or to upheavals such as war or famine which bring about new attitudes and values.

Social control: Methods whereby society restrains individuals in order to achieve social order. These include laws, mores, norms and values.

Social problem: A situation considered undesirable by society or by important groups within society.

Socialisation: The lifelong process by which a person learns to fit into society. Language, behaviour patterns, attitudes etc. are all transmitted and absorbed in the socialisation process.
  (a) *Primary socialisation* occurs during childhood, mainly in the family.
  (b) *Secondary socialisation* takes place outside the home, for example at school, or due to outside influences such as television.
  (c) *Informal socialisation* occurs at home, at work and with friends.
  (d) *Formal socialisation* takes place in training situations, such as school and college.

Society: A group of individuals who share a common life style and between whom there is constant interaction and some form of social order, for example rules.

*Building workers form
a pressure group against unemployment*

Secondary socialisation: at school

An expensive car: a status symbol?

Status (social): The position of an individual in the social structure of society. *Ascribed status* is inherited and more or less unalterab¹e — for example, race, sex, position in family. *Achieved status* is a position earned by personal effort.

Stereotype: Oversimplified ideas about characteristics of members of a group — for example, that all women are weak or gentle, that all men are tough and aggressive.

Stratification: The ranking of people in society according to social differences such as wealth, power or privilege.

Urbanisation: The movement of a population into towns and cities, usually due to industrialisation.

Values: Beliefs and attitudes held by society as to what is right and wrong. They are often associated with religious beliefs.

Value judgment: A non-objective (subjective) interpretation of a quality or value.

A more detailed explanation of the terms above is found in *Home and Community*, Chapter 15 (Madden).

HUMAN RIGHTS

Each individual is unique, with an individuality and a value all of his or her own. This natural human dignity is inherent in every single human — man or woman, young or old, rich or poor, healthy or handicapped. To realise one's full potential as a person, each individual must be given sufficient freedom and opportunity. This is impossible if one lacks such necessities of life as food, clothing and shelter.

The United Nations has specified the rights of the individual. Here are some of the more important ones:

1. All human beings are *born free and equal* in dignity and rights.
2. Everyone has a *right to life, liberty, and security* of person.
3. *No-one should be held in slavery* or servitude.
4. *No-one should be subjected to torture*, cruelty, inhuman or degrading treatment or punishment.
5. Everyone has the *right to recognition as a person* before the law.
6. Everyone charged with a penal offence has the right *to be presumed innocent until proved guilty.*
7. *No-one should be subjected to arbitrary arrest*, detention or exile.
8. *No-one should be subjected to arbitrary interference* with his or her privacy, family, home or correspondence.
9. *Everyone is entitled to all these rights* without distinction such as race, colour, sex, language, religion, political or other opinion, national or social origin, property, birth or other status.

AGENCIES THAT PROTECT HUMAN RIGHTS

- *Amnesty International* works for the release of prisoners of conscience, for fair and early trial of all political prisoners, and the abolition of the death penalty and torture.

- The *Irish Council for Civil Liberties* defends and promotes human rights and civil liberties, e.g. the rights of travellers, psychiatric patients, prisoners, children.
- The *Irish Commission for Justice and Peace* is a research and educational body of the Catholic Church that promotes peace and human rights.
- The *AIM Group for Family Law Reform* is a pressure group that campaigns for family law reform, provides a legal information and referral service for those with marital problems, and defends women's rights.

18 THE FAMILY

Our family is the first and most important influence in our lives. It is the family — whether a one-parent family or a large, extended family — that first sends us on the path to adulthood. Most experts believe that the preschool years spent at home in the family are of vital importance in the development of well-adjusted individuals.

Our *family of origin* is the family in which we grow up. When we marry and have children, we form a *'family of procreation'*.

THE FAMILY

THE BASIC UNIT OF SOCIETY

The family is the most important primary group in society. As it forms an integral part of almost every society in the world, it is said to be a *universal institution*.

The family could be described as *a relatively small group of kinsfolk or blood relations who share the same name, home, culture and traditions, as well as legal, economic and emotional ties.*

Families traditionally set up home near other families. The neighbourhood thus formed provides a background, companionship and protection for all the families living within it.

THE FUNCTIONS OF THE FAMILY

1. REPRODUCTIVE FUNCTION

- The basic biological function of the family is to propagate the species — to produce children for society.
- The family also serves to regulate sexual behaviour in society, providing a legitimate and acceptable form of sexual access.

2. NURTURING OR REARING

One of the most important functions of the family is the care and rearing of children.

- The family provides a suitable social setting for the bearing and nurturing of children. The human child is dependent on its parents for physical needs such as shelter and protection for a long time.
- The family also takes care of the psychological and emotional needs of children. A secure background which provides love and care helps a child to develop a well-adjusted personality and prepares it for coping with personal relationships. (Children from unhappy homes often find it difficult to form relationships.)
- The family helps to form the character of its offspring. This is greatly influenced by the behaviour and personalities of other family members, particularly the parents, who act as role models.

3. CULTURAL OR SOCIAL FUNCTION

- The family is the primary agent of *socialisation* — the passing on of norms and values considered important in that society. Language, customs, traditions, religion etc. are passed on from parent to child, not necessarily in a formal way, but informally, as children imitate the behaviour of their parents. In this way children learn to behave in a manner considered appropriate by society. They learn how to co-operate with others and to differentiate between right and wrong. In some societies, religion plays an important part and may influence legislation. As a result of changing values, this is not the case in more secular, pluralist societies.
- The family acts as an agent of *social control* by disciplining its members, teaching them to conform to certain codes of behaviour and to obey the laws that society imposes for the general good of the community.

4. INTELLECTUAL FUNCTION

In the past, the home was the primary centre for learning. Children learned the skills they would require as adults in their society, including farming and hunting.

Because industrial society is more complex, few parents have the resources to educate their children to a sufficiently high standard, so they are sent to school at an early age and stay there from eleven to fourteen years.

The influence of the home still plays an important part in the educational achievement of a child. A good learning environment at home e.g. provision of books and other learning materials, encouragement and praise for achievements all help to broaden educational and cultural horizons. Parents have a duty to see that their children get the best possible education.

5. ECONOMIC FUNCTION

Most families function as an economic unit. In primitive societies this is an important function, with members of the family working to produce food and other family needs. This function is less clear-cut in modern society, where members go out to work and earn money to buy the needs of the family. Some members are dependent — full-time wives, children and the unemployed, who are dependent on the state.

6. PROTECTIVE FUNCTION

The family looks after its more vulnerable members — children, the handicapped, those who are ill and the aged.

Summary	
Essential functions	*Functions partly taken over by other bodies*
1. Reproduction of the species. 2. Nurturing — provision of a secure environment and caring for emotional needs of members. 3. Socialisation of the young. 4. Economic function	1. Intellectual function, education and preparation for work largely provided by educational system, e.g. schools. 2. Protection of less able members, assisted by social and health services.

FAMILY STRUCTURE

THE EXTENDED FAMILY

The *traditional family* consists of many kinsfolk — grandparents, parents, children, uncles, aunts and cousins, all living together or in close proximity. It is found mainly in societies based on agriculture and which experience little social change, such as those of undeveloped countries. It is still found in some urban societies where tradition is considered important, such as Japan, and in strongly working-class areas, such as the East End of London where married daughters often set up home with their parents or live close by.

Members of the extended family have fixed, segregated roles. The eldest male is usually the head of the family. The females fill traditional roles such as caring for children and the home as well as doing some of the farming work in rural societies.

All members of the extended family, including children, work together as a co-operative unit. Because of this, a large family is an economic advantage as it provides a work-force to perform essential tasks. The elderly are held in high regard as they are a source of knowledge in primitive societies, teaching skills and passing on the various aspects of culture to the young.

THE NUCLEAR FAMILY

In modern industrialised society a typical family, consisting of father, mother and their children, is known as a *nuclear family* as it is the nucleus or central core on which the wider family and society is based.

The nuclear family is economically and financially independent of the wider, extended family. Efficient family planning has led to a reduction in family size, as it is no longer economically as necessary to have large families.

A modern nuclear family

PATTERNS OF FAMILY LIFE

RURAL V URBAN

Stereotyped images of 'how the other half lives'

A traditional extended family	A Modern Nuclear Family
1. Large, with lots of children	1. Small in size
2. Durable: long-lasting, unchanging	2. Shortlived: only lasting the lifetime of the parents
3. Settled: economy based on stable occupations, such as agriculture or traditional crafts	3. Geographically mobile; families readily move to other areas in search of work
4. Relatives usually live locally	4. Family may be widely dispersed
5. Rigid class divisions: most power lies with wealthy; extreme poverty common	5. Socially mobile: education and training enable members to achieve a good job by effort
6. Authoritarian and patriarchal,* i.e. husband makes important decisions	6. Independent and democratic; decision-making shared; emphasis on companionship
7. Segregated conjugal roles: women considered to be inferior; their 'place is in the home'	7. Egalitarian roles: wife often works outside the home and contributes financially
8. Husband controls family spending	8. Budgeting and financial responsibilities shared
9. Leisure frequently taken separately	9. Leisure time shared; children often included
10. More family support available in time of need. Other members take over roles, e.g. that of a parent, and look after the weaker members.	10. Isolated, therefore vulnerable when tragedy strikes, e.g. death of parent, unemployment (although more state support today)
11. Strict discipline for children; corporal punishment acceptable	11. Family life more informal; physical punishment less acceptable
12. Repressive: lacking in emotional expression	12. Greater emotional expression
13. Aged are highly regarded as a source of knowledge and authority	13. Aged have less importance and lower status.
14. Little social change	14. Rapid social change in values, technology
15. Tradition is important; stronger religious influence	15. More tolerant and permissive society

* Patriarchal control: The family is dominated by the eldest male, usually the father or grandfather. Matriarchal families, i.e. those ruled by women, are rare. They occurred in Japan and in ancient Chinese and Polynesian societies.

There is far less difference today between family life in rural and urban areas than was the case in the past. This is probably due to:

1. The influence of television and other mass media.
2. Development of transport: People visit other countries and see different cultures. City-dwellers visit the country more often and country people the city.
3. Change in attitudes: Individuals are less inclined to have stereotyped images of 'how the other half lives'.

FAMILY LIFE IN RURAL AREAS BEFORE INDUSTRIALISATION

The traditional rural family in Ireland was large, although many children died at birth or in infancy. The father was an authoritarian figure, keeping wife and children in subordinate roles. Women were submissive and considered inferior to men. Marriages were arranged, often without taking the wishes of the female into consideration.

The woman's life revolved around the home — cleaning, cooking, bearing and caring for children — although she often kept hens (a source of personal income) and helped with seasonal tasks such as saving hay and milking cows, perhaps making butter and cheese as well. Her husband was unlikely to help with her 'female' household tasks as this would be considered unmasculine.

The general standard of living was low, barely at subsistence level at times. For this reason the number of marriages was also low because a man would not ask a woman to marry him unless he could support her. Upon marriage, the young couple usually moved into the husband's family farm. On the death of his father, the eldest son would take over. Other siblings often emigrated.

The *modern farming family* has an urban lifestyle. Farm labour today is highly mechanised, particularly on large farms, leaving the farmer more time for leisure. Such farms are run as businesses, often specialising in one branch of agriculture rather than remaining mixed farms. Farm workers are employed rather than using the family as workers.

The life of the small farmer has seen less change, and the standard of living is much lower. Many small farmers cannot make a living from the farm and receive social assistance to supplement their incomes.

The position of women has improved considerably, and many women run their own farms; others are run by a husband and wife partnership. Rural children, like urban children, are better educated. Many go on to third level education and large numbers move out of the countryside and seek work in towns and cities where they eventually settle.

THE URBAN FAMILY

The typical urban family is a nuclear family — father, mother and children (in many cases, single parents and children) living together. The nuclear family is more likely than is the extended family to move house in search of a better lifestyle.

Authority is democratic. Important family decisions such as those relating to education and finances are made jointly after discussion. In some cases, the children are included in the decision making.

Roles are less clearly defined. The women may work outside the home and the husband is more likely to share the household chores. Men are more involved in the up-bringing of their children. Boys and girls are more likely to be treated equally in the home and given equal educational opportunities, although this is not always the case.

Many family functions, such as the educational and protective functions, are now assisted by the state. Greater emphasis is therefore placed on the other functions of a family such as companionship, sexual and nurturing functions.

The modern urban family is very much a part of the 'consumer society', enjoying a relatively high standard of living and more leisure time. It is influenced greatly by technology, the media and advertising.

As societies in western countries become more secularised, *religion* has less influence on their lives and they have become more permissive in their mores. In Ireland, the Catholic Church is still influential, particularly in areas relating to the family, such as those of marriage, divorce and contraception.

Education has become more specialised, moving largely out of the family. Yet many parents are keenly aware of the importance of home influence in the educational achievement of their children.

Life in today's society is changing so rapidly that *older people* are considered by many to be out of touch with modern developments. For this reason they are pensioned off. The aged have little status in the modern family and are often seen as burdens.

The state helps to care for the less-able-bodied members of society such as the ill, the handicapped, the unemployed and the elderly.

FAMILY AND SOCIAL CHANGES WHICH HAVE OCCURRED IN THE 20TH CENTURY

- Decrease in size of families (see below)
- More one parent families
- Increase in marital breakdown
- Improvement in the status of women (see below). They no longer see marriage as their only goal. More equality in work, home
- People live longer. There are more elderly to be cared for
- Reduction in family functions — many taken over by the state
- Outside influences such as the mass media are affecting the roles and expectations of family members
- Infant mortality reduced — most childhood diseases under control

- Legislation protecting children from work, exploitation etc. — for example Childrens Act
- Compulsory education; free access to all
- Improved housing, standard of living, hygiene etc.
- Improved social and health services

CHANGE IN FAMILY SIZE

Probably the greatest change that the family in developed countries has experienced in the last half century has been the reduction in the average number of children born to families. There are several possible reasons for this.

1. BIRTH CONTROL

Family planning has become more acceptable and birth control more reliable. Parents can now decide on the number of children they wish to have. The medical profession encourages the spacing of children, two years being the recommended minimum time between children. This enables the mother to cope physically, emotionally and financially with one child before having another.

2. ECONOMIC CONDITIONS

Unlike primitive societies where children are an economic asset, children in modern society demand a considerable outlay of time and money. Education is expensive and books, uniforms, sports equipment etc. are required. Working-class families sometimes have to do without the income of a child who stays on in school, as well as paying for educational necessities. Some parents prefer a better standard of living and more creature comforts to having a large family.

Do you think that this is sensible or selfish?

3. FREEDOM OF WOMEN

Most women have taken control of their own lives. They are more independent. Many are not content to bear child after child for the duration of their reproductive years. Many want to work outside the home, and for this reason have small families.

4. SOCIAL PRESSURE

In undeveloped countries, and sometimes in traditional urban or rural families, there is pressure on young parents to have large families. In modern society, the opposite is often the case, where social pressure may be placed on couples to have few children. Two of the most frequent reasons put forward for this are the world food shortage and the 'population explosion'.

WOMEN TODAY

The last century has seen enormous changes in the role and status of women. These in turn have been a factor in social change, particularly that relating to the family and children. One hundred years ago, women were politically, legally, socially and economically second-class citizens. They received little or no education. The only career open to them was marriage, when they spent most of their life either pregnant or recovering from pregnancy. They had few legal rights and were in effect the property of their husbands.

Since the 'sixties, women have shed the inferior role delegated to them and have achieved equality in most spheres, backed up by legislation, including The Employment Equality Act 1977 and the Anti-Discrimination (Pay) Act 1974. However, as traditional patriarchal attitudes are slow to change, social and economic inequalities still exist. (Further reading - *Home and Community* - Madden)

THE FULL-TIME HOUSEWIFE

Housework is in most cases the most unproductive, the most barbarous and the most arduous work a woman can do. Lenin

Traditionally, the majority of married women did not work outside the home and farm. The traditional division of labour was the breadwinning father and the home-making mother. The problem is that homemaking, while an exacting job, is unpaid and has a very low status in a world where money to a large extent determines status. The full-time housewife has to rely on the goodwill of her husband to supply her with money to feed and clothe herself and their children.

The Irish Constitution (Article 41) states that 'by her life in the home, the woman gives to the state a support without which the common good cannot be achieved. The state shall therefore endeavour to ensure that mothers will not be obliged by economic necessity to engage in labour to the neglect of her duties in the home'.

Perhaps if the state took itself seriously, it would pay mothers an allowance to stay at home and rear children or at least give tax allowances for home help/child minders to mothers who go out to work.

PROBLEMS FACED BY FULL-TIME HOUSEWIVES

- Little or *no training* for her role as mother and home-maker.
- She *gives up her independence* and becomes fully dependent on her spouse.
- *Isolation*: Many young mothers are socially and geographically isolated in suburban housing estates, far from facilities, families and friends.
- *Feelings of inadequacy*: Many feel guilty or inadequate because their work has little status.
- *Dissatisfaction*: Many find the work boring and monotonous which contrasts with the domestic bliss portrayed in the media and advertising.
- *Lack of income*: The housewife is totally dependent on her spouse for money.

DUAL-CAREER FAMILIES

In many families today, the wife has a job outside the home. There are economic and social reasons for this.

Women with a career and a home to run often have a double work load

ECONOMIC REASONS

1. To provide the only income of the family — for example if the husband is unemployed or if it is a single-parent family.
2. To supplement the income of the family. One income may be insufficient for necessities.
3. To improve the standard of living of the family — for example to provide holidays etc.

SOCIAL REASONS

1. Change in attitudes: Today, society accepts married women working.
2. Work provides company; one makes friends.
3. It helps prevent loneliness — common in housebound housewives.
4. Work provides status — housework has little standing in our society.
5. It provides fulfilment.
6. It makes use of training. A woman who has spent time and money gaining qualifications may not wish to waste them.
7. It provides independence.

PROBLEMS FACED BY DUAL-CAREER WIVES

- *Conflicting demands of job and home*: Many such women are experiencing considerable stress and exhaustion trying to manage both. It is essential that both parents share house and child care duties.
- *Cost*: With high taxes and additional costs such as transport and child minders, it may not be worthwhile working if one is on a low or average income.
- *No tax allowance* for child minding.

- *Guilt*: A wife may feel she is not giving enough time and attention to her family — more so if her husband is not supportive.
- *Lack of suitable jobs*: A mother of a young family may not find a job that suits her child-minding commitments.
- *Lack of support* from husband and family.
- *Child minding problems*: Lack of creches, particularly those subsidised by state or industry.

Studies show that children of a mother who works outside the home show few ill effects. Many actually become more self-confident and independent. As long as the mother provides satisfactory substitute care, the child's development is unlikely to suffer. While some say that children of mothers who work outside the home are likely to become delinquents, this is not borne out in fact. Research indicates that it is the amount of supervision and type of discipline in the home, as well as the quality of parental care, that relates to the incidence of delinquency, rather than whether a mother is at home all day or not.

19 MARRIAGE AND FAMILY LIFE

► MARRIAGE

Marriage is an important social institution because it is central to the family system. Marriage could be described as *a socially or legally acceptable union between a man and a woman that regulates their sexual and reproductive functions and provides companionship and economic cooperation.*

Marriage confers certain rights and duties on the partners. There are various cultural and legal obligations within marriage which differ from one society to another. Some of these are discussed below.

A wedding: start of a life together

1. NUMBER OF PARTNERS
(a) *Monogamy* permits each spouse to have one partner only. In western society, marriage is based on Christian teaching: 'What God hath joined together, let no man put asunder' (Matthew, 19:6).

   Each union is expected to last for life. Those who marry a second partner during the lifetime of the first one without obtaining a divorce are guilty of *bigamy*.

(b) *Polygamy*: This allows one spouse to have more than one partner — either *polyandry*, where one woman may have more than one husband, or *polygyny*, where one man may have two or more wives, often several (permitted under Muslim law).

   Two other interpretations of marriage are seen today:

(c) *Serial polygamy*: Used to describe repeated divorce and remarriage, such as often occurs in 'show business' relationships.

(d) *Common-law marriage*: This describes a couple living together ('cohabiting') without a legal marriage contract.

2. RESTRICTIONS ON PARTNERS
In every society there are specific regulations regarding whom one may marry. Certain tribes, religions or classes may be encouraged or forbidden. (In India, for example, it was not permitted to marry outside one's 'caste'.) The only universal taboo is *incest*, that is, sexual relations or marriage between parent and child or between brother and sister.

In our society there are also legal restrictions forbidding marriage between several relations:
(a) *Consanguinity* (blood relationship): You may not marry your father, brother, son, uncle or grandfather (or female equivalents).
(b) *Affinity* (relationship by marriage): You may not marry your stepfather or husband's uncle; yet you are permitted to marry your deceased husband's brother! (or female equivalents).

3. MINIMUM AGE FOR MARRIAGE
While in some societies very young people are betrothed and even married before the age of 10, in our society young men and women must be at least 16 years of age before they can marry, and they they must have their parents' permission. Without parents' consent, one must wait until one reaches 21 years of age.* Three months' notice is required to ensure that couples have adequate time to prepare for marriage.

* Statistics show that very young marriages carry a high risk of breakdown.

4. RESIDENCE
In the past, most newly-married couples went to live with the husband's parents. This pattern of residence is called *patrilocal*. When the couple moved in with the wife's parents, they established *matrilocal* residence.

The general pattern in western society is for couples to set up home on their own, thus establishing *neolocal* residence. This enables the couple: (a) to have more privacy; (b) to avoid interference by relations; and (c) to make their own decisions. This provides a better start to a marriage, but may be a cause of loneliness and isolation.

5. PROPERTY LINEAGE
When property and title pass through the male line, for example from father to son, it is known as patrilineal. When these pass through the female line it is known as matrilineal. Nowadays property, farms etc. may be passed to both sons and daughters. This is a *bi-lineal* system.

Control of families uses similar terminology. When the father is the 'boss' as was the case in Victorian society, this is known as a *patriarchal* system. In China a female was often the head of the family. This was a *matriarchal* system.

LAWS RELATING TO MARRIAGE

Apart from the customs and restrictions mentioned above, there are legal conditions that must be fulfilled in order to make a marriage legal and valid:

1. Partners must be of the opposite sex.
2. Neither partner must already be married.
3. The partners must not be too closely related.
4. Without parents' consent, they must be 21 years of age or over.
5. They must give three months' notice of intention to marry.
6. The marriage must be voluntary (no shotguns!).
7. Religious ceremonies must take place in a certified place of worship, with civil ceremonies being performed in a recognised registry office.
8. The marriage must be registered by the registrar or celebrant immediately after the service.

RIGHTS AND OBLIGATIONS OF PARENTS

1. The right of each to the company of the other.
2. Duty to cohabit or live together.
3. Conjugal (sexual) rights and obligations (non-consummated marriages are null and void).
4. Loyalty and fidelity are important factors in a marriage.
5. Right to maintenance: The Maintenance of Spouses and Children Act stipulates that a dependent spouse has a right to maintenance. If a reasonable amount of money is not contributed towards the upkeep of the family, a spouse can claim maintenance in the courts.
6. Children: Parents are joint guardians of any child born within wedlock. This involves rights of custody and decisions relating to the religious upbringing and education of the children.
7. Parents are legally obliged to provide food, shelter and care, and to see that children get an education. Failure to do this may result in the children being taken into care.
8. Inheritance: Each spouse has a legal right to all (or half, if there are children) of the estate when a partner dies.

    Illegitimacy: In the past, a mother was the sole guardian of a child born out of wedlock. Under new laws, both parents are joint guardians of the child. Such children have equal rights to succession and maintenance, *once paternity has been established*. But the legal concept of illegitimacy remains, and also, until attitudes change, so does the social stigma.

Coping alone with parenting

SINGLE-PARENT FAMILIES

Most families consist of two parents and their children. One or both of the parents may earn a living, and one of them may opt to stay at home to take care of the children. Each parent acts as a role model for their children. Ideally, they support each other in the care and upbringing of the children.

Single parents, on the other hand, have to take over the role of both parents. They may include: unmarried mothers, deserted wives or husbands, widows, widowers, separated or divorced parents, or families with one parent in prison.

PROBLEMS FACED BY SINGLE-PARENT FAMILIES

1. The problem of combining the role of wage earner and parent. It is not easy to find well paid employment with flexible working hours which will leave sufficient time to care for children.
2. Coping alone with parenting: Being mother and father to a child and providing the same amount of care and attention are difficult tasks. One may possibly become too wrapped up in the child, which is good for neither parent nor child.
3. If a single parent opts to stay at home, state aid (Single Parent's or Deserted Wife's Benefit) is inadequate. It is likely that financial problems will occur.
4. Lack of day care facilities, particularly those subsidised by the state (although most state-subsidised child care facilities give preference to single and other disadvantaged parents).
5. Inadequate housing: Many landlords refuse to let accommodation to those with young children. Finances limit the choice of living accommodation available to most single parents. Local authorities generally allocate a number of houses or flats to single-parent families.
6. Social isolation: Single parents are rarely in a position to get out to meet people. Lack of money and difficulty in finding child-minders are partly responsible for this. The parent may feel stigmatised in our couple-

oriented society and have difficulty in forming new relationships.

7. Parents who are alone because of death, imprisonment or desertion of a spouse not only have to adapt their own life to the loss of a partner. They also have to help children to cope with the loss of a parent.

8. Deserted wives or husbands: Desertion leaves the remaining spouse in a very difficult situation. It is often unexpected: it is not known whether the spouse will return or when. She/he may return and desert again, leaving spouse and children feeling even more vulnerable and insecure.

Financially, there are particular difficulties. The state will not pay deserted wives/husbands any allowance until the spouse has been gone for three months — without paying maintenance. Social benefit is payable on either the husband's or wife's social insurance. Social assistance is only given subject to a means test. If, as is often the case, the deserted partner is in need, he/she may claim supplementary allowance from the Health Board.

ORGANISATIONS THAT PROVIDE ASSISTANCE FOR SINGLE-PARENTS

- *Ally* provides counselling and accommodation such as family placement for single, pregnant women. It campaigns for improvements in services for single mothers.
- *Cherish* provides counselling and practical assistance for single, pregnant women. It campaigns for social acceptance of single parents.
- *Cura*, a Catholic body organised on a diocesan basis, counsels and assists single, pregnant women. It offers sheltered accommodation, medical care, confinement facilities, adoption and post-abortion counselling.
- *Gingerbread Ireland* provides encouragement and advice, organising holidays and social activities for one-parent families.
- *The Federation of Services for Unmarried Parents and their Children* publishes a directory of services for unmarried parents.

► THE LIFE CYCLE OF A MARRIAGE

Most marriages go through a predictable series of stages. The move from one stage to another is often a period of stress, causing disruption in family life. Unless adjustments are made at these transitional stages, problems may occur.

1. EARLY MARRIAGE

This is known as the honeymoon stage. It is during this period that couples should have time to get to know one another and adjust to the day-to-day intimacy of living together. It is a time for learning how to balance the needs, desires and role expectations of one's partner with one's own. During this stage, couples have time together to establish a secure and satisfying relationship.

Premarital or very early pregnancy can reduce this 'getting to know you' stage to the minimum, and plunge a couple immediately into stage two.

2. CHILD-REARING STAGE

The arrival of the first child brings about a major change in the life of the couple. A great deal of adjustment must be made as partners learn to suppress many of their wishes in order to cater to the needs of their children. Sacrifices have to be made, of a financial, social and personal nature: husbands may feel left out; both partners find that they cannot get out together as often as they did before.

A couple enters the childrearing stage

3. LAUNCHING STAGE

During this stage, teenage children are loosening their ties with home. They become more independent, leave school, learn a trade or go to work or college. They have developed important relationships outside the family, and eventually they may get married. Some parents may find it difficult to 'let go', to allow the children to make their own mistakes, grow up and make their way in the world.

4. PRE-RETIREMENT STAGE

Often called the 'empty nest' stage. The children are now adults and most have left home. The relationship reverts back to a twosome. This can be difficult to cope with after years of caring for and worrying about the children. A mother whose whole life revolved around her children may feel that she is not needed any more. Her husband is still kept busy with work, but she may succumb to loneliness and depression. This is a good time for her to get involved in voluntary work, take up some adult education classes, or find a part-time or full-time job.

5. RETIREMENT STAGE

Husbands are those chiefly affected at this stage. If they have been compulsorily retired, they may feel rejected and useless. They may find that days are long, that they are under their wives' feet at home. Those who have been too wrapped up in their jobs may have few hobbies or interests to occupy their time. Pre-retirement courses help

The retirement stage

to prepare working people to fill the leisure time that now becomes available to them.

As couples grow older, they become more dependent on others. Death ends the relationship, leaving one partner to cope alone.

MARITAL STABILITY

Most marriages in Western society take place as a result of two people falling in love. In our culture, marriage is seen as the ultimate step in a loving relationship. Yet, romantic love alone is a weak basis for marriage (read *The Road Less Travelled* by M. Scott Peck). Romance can distract couples from the seriousness and responsibilities that come with marriage. More important criteria in selecting a partner would be mutual respect and compatible personalities.

Couples enter marriage with different expectations

The glamorous image of marriage portrayed by the media places an ideal before us which is far removed from real life. It gives us unrealistic expectations of marriage which are impossible to live up to, with the result that many are disillusioned and disappointed when their marriage turns out to be less exciting than they had expected.

In societies where there is little social change, where traditional norms and values remain unaltered year after year, marriage and family life tend to be stable. Marriages are frequently economic arrangements whereby each partner knows his and her role and fulfills the tasks within marriage without question. In Ireland in the past, marriages were commonly arranged by matchmakers. Such marriages were based on mutual suitability, had more realistic expectations and as a result had a better chance of survival.

The aims and goals of modern marriage are less clear cut.

FACTORS WHICH INCREASE THE CHANCES OF A STABLE MARRIAGE

1. *Family background*: A happy, secure home background will produce a well-adjusted person, capable of giving and receiving affection. An individual who comes from a repressed home will have difficulty in forming relationships and will be unlikely to make a satisfactory marriage partner.
2. *Positive personality characteristics*: Traits such as kindness, consideration, sympathy, honesty, flexibility and

unselfishness are most common in emotionally stable people. Such people make the best marriage partners.

Those showing negative traits, who are selfish, critical, unyielding, dominating or 'loners' who lack self-worth are harder to live with as they are likely to be emotionally unstable.

3. *Responsible attitudes*: Marriage brings with it many responsibilities. Parenthood is a major undertaking. It demands a great deal of maturity, co-operation and a sense of responsibility from each partner. Individuals must be responsible for their finances when setting up home — budgeting, tax, social insurance, mortgage or rent payments and regular large bills must be dealt with together. Housing problems, poverty and unemployment, when combined with inexperience and immaturity, can create pressures and problems which may be insurmountable.

4. *Maturity*: The age at which a couple marry tends to have a bearing on the success of a marriage. Statistics indicate that when both partners are under 20 at the age of marriage, it runs a greater risk of failure.

While many young couples are financially independent and physically mature when they marry, often they have not reached emotional maturity. A young person's personality may not have fully developed. As maturity brings further changes, characteristics may appear that are very different from the original person.

5. *Similar cultural background*: Those from similar backgrounds, with the same nationality, race, creed and socio-economic group tend to identify more readily with one another as there are fewer areas in which friction and misunderstanding can occur.

6. *Shared interests*: Similarly, if couples have many things in common — shared interests, similar intellectual ability and so on — they have a stronger foundation on which to build a relationship.

7. *Correct reasons for marrying*: While there are many reasons for marrying, some young people marry for all the wrong reasons, such as premarital pregnancy, to escape from an unhappy home, or simply because everyone else is getting married.

THINKING OF GETTING MARRIED? CONSIDER:

- Do you get on well together?
- Do you respect each other as individuals?
- Have you areas of common interests as well as separate interests?
- Have you similar attitudes to things you both consider to be important such as religion and family planning?
- Can you talk openly about them?
- What are your *role expectations* — what are your attitudes to which (if any) are the male and female tasks in a home or marriage?
- Do you *like* your partner? Remember that love is blind.

MARRIAGE PREPARATION

AT HOME

The real preparation for marriage begins in a child's home. A child who lives a normal, happy family life with two caring, well-adjusted parents will probably have little difficulty forming relationships, and the chances are that he or she will have a good marriage. A child's mother and father will be the models used for husband-wife and parent-child relationships in his or her own marriage.

A person who has had an unhappy childhood will find it difficult to trust and love. If subjected to violence and abuse, these may be the outlets taken when problems arise in adulthood and marriage.

AT SCHOOL

A society such as our own that makes little or no provision for the breakdown of marriage has a duty to prepare its young people for adult life and marriage. It is unfortunate that marriage and parenthood, with their inherent responsibilities, are the only careers for which there is no proper training.

The obvious channel through which young people can be prepared for marriage is the educational system. Boys and girls should be able to participate in a programme that prepares them for relationships and marriage.

The changing status of women leads to role confusion. The greater emphasis on emotional and sexual gratification puts greater pressures on marital relationships than ever before.

In today's society, when marriage, the family and society are undergoing rapid and profound changes, there is more need than ever for a specialised programme of marriage preparation at school level. This may be done as part of a religious education, health education, life skills or home economics programme.

PRE-MARRIAGE COURSES

Much time and money is often spent on preparing for the wedding day, yet little is spent on preparing for marriage itself. It is now accepted that couples who are about to be married should take part in a course that prepares them for their new way of life.

Marriage preparation courses are organised in centres around the country by: (a) the Catholic Marriage Advisory Council, organised by Roman Catholic clergy; and (b) the Marriage Counselling Service, a non-denominational organisation.

Most courses run one night a week for five or six weeks; alternatively, weekend courses are available. They cover practical subjects such as budgeting, setting up home, the legal aspects of marriage, love and sexual relations in marriage, family planning, parenthood and problems such as alcoholism, a significant problem in Irish marriages. Lectures are generally followed by open discussion and questions.

Lecturers are carefully selected and trained. As well as marriage counsellors, they include doctors, nurses, solicitors and home economists.

ADVANTAGES OF PRE-MARRIAGE COURSES

1. They encourage communication between couples so that their feelings about marriage, their attitudes towards family planning, children, sex roles etc. are aired before they actually get married.
2. Couples are made aware of practical problems such as housing, finance and parenthood.
3. They help couples to cope with the ups and downs of a marriage, help them to recognise problems in time and advise them on how to deal with them.
4. Positive qualities in their personal relationships are stressed and encouraged, such as kindness, sympathy, unselfishness and real sharing. Negative factors that can undermine a marriage are pointed out, such as taking one another for granted, lack of communication, selfishness, possessiveness and laziness.

5. Pre-marriage courses have particular significance in the case of very young couples, because teenage marriages have a high failure rate.

ENGAGEMENT

The engagement is traditionally a testing period during which couples get to know one another better before making the permanent commitment of marriage. During courtship, many couples never advance beyond the superficial level of dates and entertainment. They fail to consider the changes marriage will bring about in their lives and to discuss their values and attitudes to important aspects of marriage.

Some think marriage will bring them independence and freedom, when in reality it brings far more responsibilities such as housing and budgeting, particularly when children come along. Some who experience problems during courtship such as violence, excessive drinking or drug taking think that things will improve after marriage. Unfortunately, the opposite is often the case.

MARITAL INSTABILITY

Some of the possible causes of marital instability have already been discussed:
1. Very young marriages
2. Pre-marital pregnancy
3. Emotional immaturity
4. Irresponsibility
Other problems include:
5. Sexual problems
6. Mixed marriages: Marriage between individuals of different race, creed or colour may create problems, not only from within, but also due to prejudicial attitudes of parents and other members of society
7. Change in status of women: Women are expecting more from their marriages. They are less likely to accept a second-class role than in the past. They are no longer prepared to put up with an unhappy marital situation which involves circumstances such as violence and alcoholism

Some of the following problems are discussed in the next chapter.
8. Marital violence
9. Alcoholism
10. Unemployment
11. Housing problems
12. Gambling

EFFECTS OF MARITAL INSTABILITY AND BREAKDOWN

EFFECTS ON SPOUSES

- Marriage problems can result in emotional upset, bitterness and a great deal of suffering.
- Resentment may lead to mounting tension, hostility and aggression — even physical violence.
- Difficulty in coping with life.
- One partner may suffer rejection or mental illness such as depression, leading, in severe cases, to suicide.
- There is a sense of loss or guilt because the marriage has failed.
- Loneliness for adult company in the home.
- Financial stress: There may be two households to maintain — one or both partners may have to depend on social security.
- It may be necessary to move house, to a more modest dwelling, away from the support of friends and neighbours.
- The state makes inadequate legal provision for those affected by marital breakdown.

EFFECTS ON CHILDREN

- Insecurity: Their sense of security is destroyed as they see the two people they love most grow to despise one another.

- Their positive image of family life and of their parents is distorted by the emotional bitterness.
- They may be involved in violent physical or verbal exchanges between parents. They are torn between loyalty to each parent.
- Children may be used either in a form of emotional blackmail to 'get at' the other parent, or as a kind of confidant. Often the child is too emotionally involved and immature to cope with this burden.
- Mental stress, which often leads to psychosomatic symptoms such as headaches, loss of appetite and bedwetting, and anti-social behaviour such as stealing.
- If the breakdown leads to the separation of parents, the child will suffer the loss of a father or a mother.
- If the child has to move to another home, there will be even more stress in his or her life with, perhaps, loss of friends and change of school at a time when stability is of vital importance.

Research on marital breakdown indicates the following effects.

1. The age of children at the time of breakdown is crucial. Those least affected are very young children who are too young to be aware of what is happening, and older teenagers who are mature enough to understand why their parents can no longer live together. The children in between experience an emotional upheaval which may affect personal relationships and school work.
2. Children from broken homes are more likely to suffer personality defects and psychiatric illness, experiencing symptoms of anxiety such as insomnia.
3. Their own marriages are less likely to be a success.
4. Great importance is given to the attitudes of parents, both before and after a separation. If they put the children first, act in a mature and civilised way, air their disagreements in private and refrain from passing the antagonistic feelings they may have for one another on to their children and give a positive attitude towards the other parent rather than the reverse, the trauma of separation will be far less damaging.

EFFECTS ON SOCIETY

- Marital instability undermines the family and in turn society.
- It increases the number of one-parent families with their attendant problems.
- It places financial strains on the state with costs of legal aid, assistance for deserted wives etc.
- In certain cases, there may be an increase in delinquency and crime due to an unstable home environment.
- Absenteeism from work may occur due to mental stress etc.

- A person whose marriage has broken down may enter a second union which has no legal backing and which may result in children.

MARRIAGE COUNSELLING

Marital problems that are allowed to continue over a long time can build up to an intolerable level. At this stage, a couple may decide that the only course open to them is separation or, in other countries, divorce.

The reason why so many marriages break down irretrievably lies in the failure of many couples to seek help when the problems first arise. Professionals involved with marital breakdown, such as social workers, psychiatrists and counsellors, stress the importance of procedures that encourage reconciliation such as marriage counselling.

Marriage counselling helps those whose marriage has run into problems

Marriage counselling is a service provided by: (a) the Catholic Marriage Advisory Council; (b) the Marriage Counselling Service; and (c) the Family Mediation Scheme (under the Department of Justice) which deals with counselling those in the process of separation.

Marriage counselling is also available as part of family therapy and family counselling programmes that are generally associated with psychiatric hospitals.

The main function of marriage counselling is to assist couples whose marriages have run into difficulties. Carefully selected and trained counsellors listen sympathetically and help couples to talk through their problems, unravelling their practical and emotional difficulties. They may give advice and assistance, often referring couples to specialists, if necessary, on sexual, medical, alcoholic or legal problems. Counsellors may work with individuals, but effective therapy is generally only possible if both spouses attend together. Counselling is usually free and is confidential.

FAMILY LAW

The Constitution of Ireland protects marriage and the family (Articles 41 and 42). While few couples entering marriage contemplate the legal aspects of their union, it is in their interests to know their rights and the methods of protection available under family law.

Family law deals with the legal aspects of marriage: the family home, custody and guardianship of children, adoption, legitimacy and marital breakdown. Family law cases may be heard in the District Court or High Court, and are heard *in camera* (privately).

THE FAMILY HOME PROTECTION ACT, 1976

This act encourages joint ownership of houses. It prevents either spouse mortgaging or disposing of the family home without the consent of the other party. Neither may a spouse withhold mortgage repayments, if the house is already mortgaged, or have essential services such as water or electricity cut off.

THE FAMILY LAW (MAINTENANCE OF SPOUSES AND CHILDREN) ACT, 1976

This enables a dependent spouse, for example the wife, to claim maintenance for herself and the children of the marriage. This act is usually used in cases of marriage or separation, although even in cases where a couple are living together, a spouse may be bound by the court to hand over a set amount and may have an *attachment of earnings* order enforced on him — maintenance payments may be deducted from wages at source — and given to the district council clerk who in turn gives it to the spouse.

THE FAMILY LAW ACT, 1976, SECTION 22: BARRING ORDERS

In cases of physical or mental cruelty, the District Court is empowered to make an order barring a spouse from the family home for specific periods — for example three months or one year. As there may be a delay in processing this, an interim *protection order* may be obtained on the spot in cases of danger to spouse and/or children. A wife may also take out an ordinary summons for assault against her husband in cases of violence.

LEGAL AID

Under the scheme for civil legal aid, either spouse may be granted free legal aid or advice, subject to a means test. Due to lack of funds, only those on very limited means are eligible. There is a long waiting list.

LAWS RELATING TO BREAK-UP OF A MARRIAGE

LEGAL SEPARATION

A separation agreement can be drawn up by solicitors acting for each partner. This makes provision for:
1. Maintenance and custody of the children. Younger children usually stay with the mother.
2. Maintenance of dependent spouse.
3. Division of matrimonial property (the wife and children generally remain in the family home).
4. Releasing spouses from duty of cohabiting.
Note: A legal separation does not free couples to remarry.

THE JUDICIAL SEPARATION ACT, 1989

In cases where only one partner wants a separation, or where they cannot agree on the terms of their separation, one partner can apply to the courts for a judicial separation. Grounds for judicial separation include: adultery; unreasonable behaviour; desertion for a continuous period of one year; where the couple have lived apart for one year and both agree to a separation; where the couple have lived apart for three years even though one spouse does not want the separation; and finally lack of a normal marital relationship for one year.

Solicitors involved must encourage reconciliation. If this is ruled out, they must then suggest a mediated separation agreement, using qualified mediators (see below) in order to avoid a court hearing. If this is ruled out, the case is heard in the District or High Court when the court will make orders regarding custody, maintenance etc. Succession rights remain unless the right to the spouse's estate is extinguished by the court.

All family law cases are held in private and are less formal than normal court proceedings.

FAMILY MEDIATION SERVICE

This is a free service operated by the state which helps a couple to work out the terms of their separation — for example custody, maintenance, property division etc. It is not a marriage counselling service. It is for couples who have decided to separate and where reconciliation has been ruled out. Its main function is to enable couples to part with dignity and to come to terms with the new type of relationship which will exist between themselves and their children.

LEGAL NULLITY

A legal decree of nullity declares that a marriage never existed. This is extremely rare. Grounds for obtaining nullity are few: for example one partner was: (a) already married; (b) married under fear or duress; or (c) was under the influence of drink or drugs or insane at the time of the marriage; and (d) non-consummation of the marriage.

Note: Roman Catholic annulments are given after the history of the marriage has been examined by a marriage tribunal and it is shown that it was not a marriage in the eyes of the church. As this has no legal standing, many cases occur where a couple obtain a church annulment but may not legally remarry as they are still married in the eyes of the state and, on remarriage, would be legally guilty of bigamy.

DIVORCE

This is the legal termination of a marriage which frees couples to remarry. The Irish Constitution does not permit divorce. In other countries, divorce laws make provision for maintenance of spouse and children, and custody of children of the previous marriage or marriages.

Many marriages are of very young couples!

CHANGING TRENDS IN IRISH MARRIAGE

1. Marriage is still very popular. The number of marriages per year rose from 16,946 in 1965 to a peak of 21,113 in 1975; in 1985, there were 18,552.
2. Many marriages are of very young couples.
3. The average number of children per family is reducing.
4. In spite of smaller families, the population continues to grow due to: (a) younger marriages; (b) greater number of marriages; (c) improved ante-natal care; and (d) decline in infant mortality.
5. The economic situation affects marriage rates. When the economy is in a healthy state, more couples get married. For example, the nineteen-sixties was the period of great economic growth, during which the number of marriages rose noticeably. Today the marriage rate is decreasing.
6. There is a trend towards more egalitarian roles and relationships within marriage.
7. The number of marriages breaking down has increased.

► FAMILY ROLES

A family is made up of a network of roles and relationships

Each member of a family has a particular role and status, according to his or her position in the family — father, mother, child, eldest, youngest, and so on.

Each member performs one or more roles within the home, and other roles in the wider society in which they live.

WOMEN'S ROLES

In the past, women's roles were likely to be bound up with the biological function of childbirth and nursing children. Today, their roles are far less restricted and women fulfil as many roles as do men.

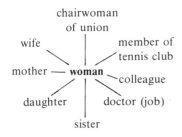

Female roles: (a) mother; (b) wife; (c) daughter; (d) home-maker; (e) career woman; (f) club member.

Balancing these roles can be difficult and tiring, but can be greatly facilitated if the partners adapt their traditional roles and provide assistance and support in the parenting and home-making functions.

The number of women in the work-force — particularly married women — has greatly increased. Women's equality is backed by laws such as the *Employment Equality Act, 1977*.

Woman pilot: in the past this was a male-only occupation

MEN'S ROLES

A man's role was also restricted in the past. He was expected to be, first and foremost, the provider — the breadwinner and protector of his family. Today, these roles generally remain an important part of a man's life, but not always. Unemployment may remove his bread-winning function; if his wife has a career, she will share this function.

Modern husbands interpret their role as father more broadly than did those of the past, when their parenting role was one of disciplinarian. Today, more husbands share the nurturing elements of parenting and the physical work involved in caring for a child and a household — more so, if the wife works outside the home.

Male roles: (a) husband; (b) provider; (c) home-maker; (d) member of outside groups.

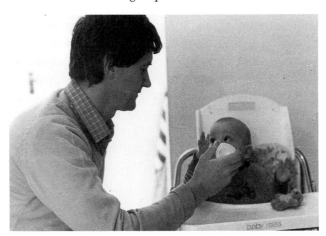

Modern husbands enjoy the nurturing role

CHILDREN'S ROLES

The roles of children are simpler, with fewer demands and complications, although during adolescence they may cause tension as children begin to prepare for adult roles by asserting themselves, questioning parental authority, and becoming more independent.

Children's roles: (a) son/daughter; (b) pupil; (c) member of class group; (d) member of team, club etc.

Role conflict occurs when the demands of one role interfere with another, such as the case of an adult with a demanding parent who may be torn between loyalty to parent and spouse, or a manager who is friendly with her employees yet must discipline them if necessary.

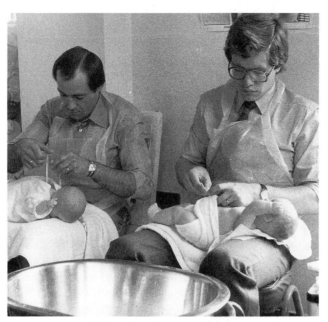
Fathers learn to cope with baby

SEGREGATED CONJUGAL ROLES

This describes marriages in which husbands and wives carry out most of their daily jobs independently of one another. They have separate friends, usually of their own sex, and separate leisure activities, and rarely perform tasks normally performed by their partner.

This situation is usually found in extended families, in societies where tradition plays an important part and social change is slow, e.g. rural and undeveloped areas.

Joint conjugal roles are found in marriages where equality plays an important part, where husband and wife share many of their activities and household tasks, and both share friends and leisure activities.

The modern nuclear family is more likely to experience joint conjugal roles.

SOCIAL GROUPS AND THEIR RELATIONSHIPS

Humans are social beings. They have a strong need for interaction with others. In order to achieve this, they tend to form groups of various kinds — the family, a group of friends, a team.

Social relationships exist between members of all groups in society. *Secondary relationships* occur between people who meet on a superficial level from day to day, e.g. the postman or, occasionally, uncles and aunts. Such relationships are usually brief and less involved.

Primary relationships are close and intimate and are usually long lasting. These occur between members of a family or between close friends.

Bonds of love, affection and personal obligation are an integral part of a healthy family structure. It is the family that lays the foundation for all social relationships between members of society. When relationships between family members are normal and well adjusted, it is likely that these individuals will have no problems forming relationships with others. When there are poor relationships within a family, it can lead to problems both within the family and in society.

Relationships within families, particularly the nuclear family, are extremely intimate. Members of a family live in close proximity. They see each other at their worst (and, hopefully, at their best). They often take one another for granted, yet such relationships are usually very close and are likely to last a lifetime — even if family members separate and move far away.

Relationships within the extended family are generally less intense. More people are involved. They may be very close to one or two members, but not the whole clan.

Relationships outside the family group are more impersonal still (except for close friends) and are rarely as long-lasting. Feelings may change, or people may move away from friends and neighbours.

HUSBAND-WIFE RELATIONSHIP

This is the most intimate of human relationships, taking in love, a sexual relationship, companionship, sharing and responsibility.

Loyalty, fidelity, trust and honesty are important qualities in a marital relationship. An ability to communicate is necessary if the relationship is to develop and grow. It is essential that each partner allow the other space for personal growth. Otherwise the marriage can become a restrictive, claustrophobic relationship where neither partner can develop his or her own identity. Individuality, independence, privacy and freedom of choice are essential. Couples should avoid the dangerous practice of trying to change their partners, making them lose the very qualities that drew them together in the first place.

Modern couples often form a *symmetrical* relationship (based on the study *The Symmetrical Family* by Young and Willmott) in which each partner is equal but different. Each takes on the roles most suited to his or her needs, temperament and capabilities. Many of these might be segregated activities — for example wife minding children or the husband going out to work — but all are of equal status. Decision-making and responsibilities such as budgeting are shared. Leisure is taken both separately and jointly.

CHILD-PARENT RELATIONSHIP

The first and most intense relationship a child experiences is with his or her mother. The infant is utterly dependent on others for the first few years of life — for physical needs such as food, warmth, clothing and for the equally vital emotional needs of love and security. In meeting

A father provides a model for masculine behaviour

Siblings have a very close relationship

these needs, both parents should develop a warm and affectionate relationship with the child. If a child is made to feel loved and wanted, he or she will develop a good self image and will in turn be able to form good relationships with others. If, on the other hand, a child experiences neglect, is ignored or abused verbally or physically, a negative self image will be established which will have a detrimental effect on its relationships for the rest of its life.

If a child lives with criticism, he learns to condemn.
If a child lives with hostility, he learns to fight.
If a child lives with ridicule, he learns to be shy.
If a child lives with shame, he learns to feel guilty.
If a child lives with tolerance, he learns to be patient.
If a child lives with encouragement, he learns to have
  confidence.
If a child lives with praise, he learns to appreciate.
If a child lives with fairness, he learns justice.
If a child lives with security, he learns to have faith.
If a child lives with approval, he learns to like himself.
If a child lives with acceptance and friendship, he learns to find
  love in the world.

SIBLING RELATIONSHIPS

Relationships between siblings are usually, but not always, close. Their ages can make a difference. For example, relationships between children who are close in age will be different from those between older siblings with the younger children. In the latter case, the relationship may be similar to that of parent to child. This is because they often have to look after younger children, particularly in the case of large and/or one-parent families. Eldest children are often serious and over-responsible as adults.

The relationships between siblings prepare them for relationships outside the home. Siblings of all ages fight with one another, then learn to make up. This enables them to cope with similar difficulties in other relationships. In most cases, siblings are fiercely loyal to one another and to their parents.

GRANDPARENT-GRANDCHILD RELATIONSHIPS

It is common for grandparents to have a particularly good relationship with their grandchildren. This is good for both parties. The elderly are often made to feel unwanted by society, yet they can offer a great deal of practical help and assistance to the young. They usually have more time to devote to the children, and the relationship is less fraught with rules and regulations than that between parent and child.

Grandparents and grandchildren have a special bond

As problems may arise when a grandparent lives with the family, this relationship demands patience and tact. Grandparents may interfere in the upbringing of grand-children, causing resentment on all sides. It should be made clear from the beginning where each person's responsibilities begin and end, which part of the house is shared, which is private and so on. If members of the family are firm yet understanding and do not allow themselves to be readily provoked, there will be fewer problems.

CHANGING RELATIONSHIPS WITHIN THE FAMILY

Relationships are rarely static. Within the family is a group of people who, although sharing one home, may vary considerably in personality, attitudes and age.

As we saw in the previous chapter, there are various stages in a marriage. During these stages, relationships may go through periods of change and stress. As people grow and mature, relationships, particularly those between parents and children, undergo change. For example, a father with little interest in babies may develop a close relationship with his children as they grow older, and both are able to share hobbies and interests. A mother and her child must grow apart if the child is to become independent.

A young married *couple* experience a profound change when the first baby arrives. This is an important period of adjustment in a marriage as they take on the responsible role of parenthood. The extra work and responsibility mean that a wife has less time to devote to her husband. He may feel left out, even jealous. She may feel that he does not give her sufficient help. They may have to forego outings and social occasions in order to cope physically and financially with the new member of the family.

The relationship of *fathers* with their children has changed considerably. They are more involved now than ever before in parenting and family life.

The most difficult adjustment of the *adolescent* is the effort to free himself or herself from parental authority and family ties in an attempt to grow up.

The greatest change in family relationships in the past century has been the increased emphasis on *love and affection* within the family, where in the past, relationships were strict and formal.

During times of change or *stress* in a family, open *communication* is extremely important. Ignoring a problem or pretending it isn't there will cause a build-up of tension and resentment which can have serious repercussions on relationships in later life.

COMMUNICATION AND GROWTH

A relationship cannot thrive without communication — really talking to the other person. A close, personal relationship needs deep emotional commitment to the other partner if it is to grow. It should be an honest, open relationship of peers based on equal identity and freedom of the other partner. If either partner is over-dependent or domineering, if they feel that they must go everywhere as a couple, or if one or both becomes complacent so that their relationship slips into a rut, there is a real danger that communication will break down and the relationship will cease to grow.

"Plant a flower in a pot and its growth is limited to the size of the container; in fact the container may stunt the growth of the flower. But plant it in a field and something different happens. Open to the sunlight and the air, with space to expand it can grow to the extent of its inherent capacity for growth." (Open Marriage, *Nena and George O'Neill*)

INFLUENCE OF FAMILY ON EMOTIONAL HEALTH

The family is often blamed for many personal and social problems which occur today. There is no doubt that our family background has a major influence on our emotional well being. Negative attitudes within the family lead to feelings of anger, resentment and worthlessness which may find expression in later life in anti-social behaviour such as violence, alcoholism and drug addiction.

Damaging Family Systems which: Lower self-worth	Healthy Family Systems which: Build up self-worth
• No talking; feelings internalised	• Open expression of feelings: conversation encouraged
• Entangled relationships; little respect	• Respect for individuals
• Manipulation and control	• Freedom highly valued
• Chaotic value system, e.g. discipline and rules constantly changing	• Consistent value system: minimum rules
• Rigid attitudes	• Open mindedness
• Past traditions revered	• New traditions encouraged
• Grim atmosphere — silences	• Pleasant atmosphere
• Frequent chronic illness	• Healthy people
• Dependent relationships	• Independence and growth
• Jealousy and suspicion	• Trust and love

RIGHTS AND OBLIGATIONS WITHIN THE FAMILY

1. THE RIGHTS OF THE CHILD: UN DECLARATION (PARAPHRASED)

- The child should be able to develop physically, mentally, morally, spiritually and socially, in a healthy and normal manner, in conditions of freedom and dignity.
- A child needs love and understanding, growing up within the care and protection of the family.
- A child is entitled to free education.
- A child should be protected against all forms of neglect and cruelty and protected from racial, religious or other forms of discrimination.
- Handicapped children shall receive special care and treatment.

The *basic needs of a child* in a family are: *food*, *clothing*, *warmth*, *shelter*, *love* and *security*. Parents have an obligation to provide these needs.

2. THE RIGHTS OF MARRIED PEOPLE

(see Chapter 19).

FRIENDSHIPS

Humans are social animals. Interaction with siblings, peers and many others influence personality and social development. A wide variety of relationships helps a child to develop a well-rounded personality, providing the child with a great number of experiences. A child's self-image is largely built up from inferences drawn from the social groups with which he or she mixes.

Relationships outside the family group are less charged with emotion than those within. As a child mixes with others, he or she becomes less self-centred, learns to share, to cope with a wider range of situations than would be found in the home. This prepares the child for the diverse problems of adult life, teaches it to co-operate, fend for itself and become more independent.

PEER GROUPS

The influence of the peer group on children is very strong. Classmates or close friends of similar age, ability and social background tend to talk, work and take their leisure together. They *identify* with one another.

The trend towards the nuclear family has given the peer group an added importance in the life of today's teenager. With fewer adults (and children) at home, the child is drawn towards this exclusive circle of friends, shutting out adults and often rejecting adult standards such as discipline, school work, 'acceptable' clothes etc.

Friendship teaches children to share

Teenagers 'identify' with one another

The group has its own values and means of identification — often a style of dress, hairstyle, behaviour or language. Adolescents, like children, have a strong need to be accepted by others. In order to do this, they must conform to the group and, in doing so, many lose their individuality. As young people mature, the influence of the peer group is less important.

GANGS

While the vast majority of young children conform to the more important standards set by society, many become alienated and form gangs which may indulge in delinquent behaviour such as vandalism and petty crime. These are more common in socially deprived areas, where unemployment, bad housing etc. lead to frustration and resentment. The gang provides the status denied to its members by society.

BOY-GIRL RELATIONSHIPS

Like most other important personal characteristics, our attitudes towards the opposite sex are formed in the home. Our first relationship with a member of the opposite sex is with one of our parents. Relationships between mother and father and between parent and child help to determine our attitudes to all relationships in later life, including sexual relationships.

Positive or negative attitudes to our bodies and bodily functions, sex roles and sexual behaviour are picked up in the family through the process of socialisation. As children grow older and begin to ask questions on these topics, the onus is on parents to answer them truthfully and honestly. Many parents fall short when it comes to discussing what are euphemistically called the 'facts of life', with the result that many boys and girls reach adulthood with a very sketchy knowledge of sexual matters. This can lead to serious risk-taking.

In school, the biological aspects of sex are taught, with little emphasis on the wider aspects of the sexual relationship, where qualities such as respect, responsibility, patience and restraint should be emphasised in an attempt to counteract the emphasis placed by the media on promiscuity, e.g. in television 'soap operas'.

Segregated schooling does little to foster normal, friendly relationships between the sexes. Members of the opposite sex are seen as sex objects. Girls feel that they must have a boy-friend because all their friends have one.

Boys often exploit girls, using them to gratify sexual desires. A double standard still exists whereby men feel free to indulge themselves sexually, while sisters and wives must be above reproach.

Love and sex are often confused. Young couples, unable to communicate with one another in any other way, may try to satisfy their social and emotional needs with sex: 'love-making' is easier than talking! The result has been an increase in the number of teenage pregnancies, abortions and young marriages.

CHARACTERISTICS OF MATURE RELATIONSHIPS

The characteristics of an immature personality are all typical of selfish or childish behaviour: sulking, over-emotionalism, an inferiority complex, rebelliousness, boasting, bullying, negative thinking, worrying about what others think of us.

Characteristics of a mature personality are an ability to get on with others, to empathise (put oneself in another's place emotionally), to be tactful and discreet, to be flexible, adaptable and emotionally stable. Mature people should:

- Be able to make their own decisions, based on available evidence, and take full responsibility for them.
- Be honest, open and trusting.
- Be able to accept their emotions — love, anger etc. — yet keep them under reasonable control.
- Be able to face criticism without feeling upset.
- Be able to face up to problems and unpleasant situations without fear or anxiety.
- Be able to relate well to others, to make friends.
- Be able to conform to the norms and laws of the society in which we live.
- Have the ability to adapt their will to the needs of others when necessary — that is, flexibility.

EIGHT BASIC EMOTIONAL NEEDS
- To give love
- To receive love
- To feel wanted
- To feel needed
- To have deep friendships
- To share
- To be creative
- To forgive

FAMILY PROBLEMS

"All happy families are happy in the same way — each unhappy family is unhappy in a different way."
— Anna Karenina, *Leo Tolstoy*

One of the main reasons why we study society is to learn more about its problems and how they can be alleviated or removed.

In the past (and today, where the extended family system is the norm), roles were clear-cut. Each family member knew what was expected of him or her, and usually conformed. Modern society is not as straight-forward. Norms and values have changed, causing people to feel less secure in their various roles.

Within the complex structure of modern society, a wide range of problems that affect the family has been identified. Many of these are wider social problems, outside the control of the family, such as poverty and unemployment. Yet these can cause severe hardship and seriously affect the functioning of a family.

Most of the problems, however, occur within the family. They can cause tension and stress, which in severe cases can lead to a crisis or even the breakdown of the family.

The following are some common family problems.
- Death of a close relative
- Child abuse
- Marital violence
- Alcoholism
- Drug abuse
- Gambling problems
- Delinquency
- Crime
- Imprisonment
- Housing problems

DEATH

Probably the greatest crisis to affect a family is the death of one of its members. When death occurs in the *extended family*, many others are at hand to support and to take over the role of the deceased. The impact of death on such a family is less traumatic as its members provide the practical and emotional support necessary. They will take over the education and care of the children and support the bereaved spouse. The period of mourning and funeral ceremonies are considered to be an important means by which the bereaved can express grief and come to accept a death.

As the *nuclear family* is more isolated and vulnerable than the extended one, a bereavement is likely to cause upheaval. The death of a breadwinner can result in severe poverty. Relatives today are less likely to feel obliged to provide more than the minimum of help. There is often social pressure on the bereaved not to react emotionally, yet weeping is one of nature's ways of coping with shock and is often the beginning of the emotional healing process. People react differently to grief. Many like to talk about the past, when the deceased was alive. Others react like Queen Victoria and immerse themselves in a prolonged period of mourning, shutting themselves off from friends and neighbours. Others bottle up feelings or use tranquillising drugs to help get them over the crisis. In this case, the bereaved are only delaying the reaction to grief which, more than likely, will erupt at a later date.

Death: a major family crisis

STAGES OF MOURNING

1. Avoidance — shock, disbelief, numbness, inability to accept the situation.
2. Anger, realisation of what has really happened, pain, guilt.
3. Acceptance — recollection of old memories.
4. Building a new life — relief from pain and negative feelings. Reorganisation.

EFFECTS OF DEATH ON THE SPOUSE

1. Loss of a spouse causes deep personal suffering and grief.
2. There is a sense of loss and loneliness, with perhaps depression.
3. The spouse may experience guilt for not being a better partner.
4. The spouse may have to learn how to cope with unfamiliar tasks. For example, widows may have to learn how to budget or how to earn a living. Widowers must learn to cook, to housekeep and to care for children.
5. In the event of insufficient insurance cover, there may be financial problems.

EFFECTS OF DEATH ON CHILDREN

1. Death of parent causes great emotional upset to a child.
2. It may increase its insecurity.
3. It may be difficult for the child to accept the finality: children need a great deal of help and understanding at this time.
4. Children often worry about the future of the family, financial and otherwise.
5. The loss of a father- or mother-figure can affect personality development.

HELP AVAILABLE

- The National Association of Widows in Ireland
- The Bereaved Parents' Association
- Special counselling is available for the bereaved from Bethany Support Group and the Bereavement Counselling Service.

▶ CHILD ABUSE

The increase in the media coverage of child abuse is probably due to its being more acceptable to talk about the subject instead of keeping it hidden, as has occurred in the past.

In many Irish homes, *physical violence* is considered to be a normal and effective form of discipline. Parents are believed by some to have a right to chastise their children. Yet most experts in child care consider that corporal punishment is cruel, emotionally damaging, and in fact less effective than more positive methods of discipline such as regular routines, gentle firmness, good example and praise practised with consistency. Parents (or others)

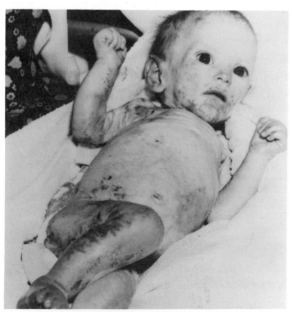

A child victim of neglect and abuse

who use physical punishment show *by example* that violence is an acceptable and normal part of everyday behaviour.

The number of reports of non-accidental injury to children has increased sharply. Hospitals and social workers now keep a lookout for suspected cases. Bruising, burns, head injuries and fractures are common, although cases of blindness, poisoning, brain damage, sexual assault and death due to violence also occur. Babies are those most at risk, particularly premature and mentally retarded babies, as these are inclined to cry a lot. Parents in these cases tend to make up excuses for the injuries, yet appear to be genuinely concerned and remorseful when confronted.

What causes parents to react so violently? Often it is a build-up of unfortunate circumstances that eventually reach a crisis in uncontrollable rage. Usually it is the parent who has the main role of looking after the children who abuses them, such as an unemployed father or a mother with a non-supportive husband. Both parents are likely to be mentally or emotionally immature and suffer from lack of self-worth or feelings of inadequacy. The marriage is often in a state of collapse. Violent parents are likely to have come from violent homes. Violence affects generations of unfortunate children unless the authorities step in or the couple get help.

Violence to children is not confined to one class, but it is less common in higher socio-economic groups which are generally in better financial circumstances. Their day-to-day living is less stressful, and they are more likely to be able to get relief from child care duties from time to time, e.g. in crèches, play schools etc.

EMOTIONAL VIOLENCE

Violence such as verbal abuse, hostility, neglect and rejection is also extremely damaging to the physical and mental well-being of children. (See page 327.)

SEXUAL ABUSE

In recent years the subject of child sexual abuse has come out into the open. Incest and other forms of sexual abuse appear to be far more common than had been previously suspected. Children may be blackmailed by the abusing relative so that they do not report them. When they do report such abuse, it is often not believed, yet it is the opinion of experts in such matters that children do not make up these stories. Incest and child sexual abuse are indictable crimes (see page 312).

A sexually abused child feels guilty and withdrawn

EFFECTS OF VIOLENCE ON CHILDREN

1. Retarded physical development, due to lack of food and physical care. Statistics shows that abused children fail to thrive.
2. Retarded intellectual development: Children who are abused or neglected have lower than average intelligence, and their development of language is retarded.
3. Retarded and emotional development: They lack trust and are dependent and clinging, finding it difficult to show affection and to form healthy relationships.
4. Abuse leaves emotional scars which are slow to heal. Child victims become abnormally withdrawn, as if they were afraid to draw attention to themselves. They are afraid to report the abuser for fear of further violence. Unable to trust adults, they have no one to whom they can turn.
5. They view violence as normal behaviour.

EFFECTS OF VIOLENCE ON THE FAMILY

1. Violence breeds violence. A violent child tends to become a violent parent. A pattern of violence is set up.
2. Violence makes for family insecurity and unrest and, in severe cases, family breakdown.
3. Unhappiness and bitterness result within the family.

EFFECTS OF VIOLENCE ON SOCIETY

1. Acceptance of violence at any level leads to a more violent society.
2. An increasing number of children who have been affected by violence are being released into society, unable to cope. Eventually, they may become a burden on society, for example as criminals or alcoholics.
3. Violence leads to instability in marriage and other relationships.

HELP AVAILABLE FOR CHILD VIOLENCE

- Aid for Parents under Stress: Provides a service for parents who are concerned about their feelings of aggression or rejection towards their children.
- The Incest Crisis Service: Individual group counselling for victims of incest and their families.
- Childline: A phone-in listening and referral agency for abused children.
- The Sexual Assault Treatment Unit in Dublin provides support for child victims of rape and incest, with medical and emotional counselling.
- The Irish Society for the Prevention of Cruelty to Children (ISPCC). (See page 331.)
- Local health board or clinic: Reported cases are investigated and the child may be taken into care for his or her own good.

MARITAL VIOLENCE

Marital violence has causes and effects which are similar to those in violence towards children. Two patterns emerge from existing studies on violence.

1. There is a connection between violence and alcohol.
2. Violence is learned (rather than inherited) behaviour. Children who are constantly exposed to it see it as normal and natural. They are likely to resort to it in their own relationships, both as children and as adults.

Violence is more common among individuals of low educational achievement. When confronted with an unpleasant situation, they cannot express their feelings and they hit out instead of speaking about their problems. Individuals who have low self-worth, feelings of inadequacy, or difficulty in forming relationships are more likely to resort to aggression and brutality.

Violence generally occurs as a result of stress. Unemployment, poverty and other social problems such as bad housing and drinking aggravate the situation, with the result that the highest level of violence is among those most socially disadvantaged.

Statistics on marital violence are difficult to find due to the reluctance of partners to admit it. Increased media coverage has highlighted the problem and, as a result, more and more victims are seeking help.

The effect of violence in the mass media, especially television and videos, is coming increasingly under scrutiny. It is thought to be particularly damaging to children.

EFFECTS OF MARITAL VIOLENCE ON INDIVIDUALS (FOR EXAMPLE BATTERED SPOUSE)
- Physical pain and suffering
- Emotional damage to children
- Emotional damage to spouse, who frequently becomes withdrawn and finds it increasingly difficult to cope with everyday living.
- Loss of self-worth, confidence

EFFECTS OF MARITAL VIOLENCE ON FAMILY
- Instability, resulting in the possibility of having to break up the family to protect it from the constant violence.
- Unhappiness
- Insecurity
- Children grow into dysfunctional and/or violent adults.

HELP AVAILABLE
- Under the Family Home Protection Act, 1976, a spouse can have his or her partner barred from the family home if there is evidence that family members are in danger. A summons for common assault may also be issued.
- Family Aid (formerly Women's Aid): This is a voluntary group founded originally by Erin Pizzey in London which provides a refuge for women (and their children) who have to leave home because of their partners' violence. It provides them with shelter and support to rebuild their lives. Adapt and Cuanlee are similar organisations in Limerick and Cork, respectively.

▶ DRUG ADDICTION

Addiction to a substance, e.g. a drug, has four characteristics:
1. An uncontrollable desire or *craving*
2. Physical or psychological *dependence*
3. Increasing *tolerance*, so that more and more of the drug becomes necessary to produce the same effects
4. *Harmful effects* on the individual and on society

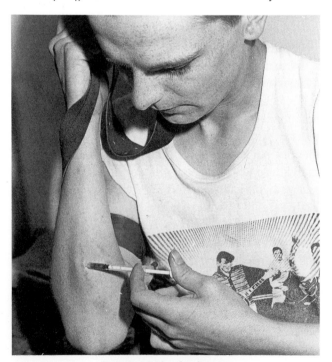

Drugs: a recipe for disaster

Dependence occurs because the body's chemistry changes to accommodate the drug, and when it is no longer taken, unpleasant 'withdrawal' symptoms occur.

The craving is often so great that addicts will resort to crime, e.g. larceny, prostitution, to feed their habit.

WHAT IS A DRUG?
A drug can be defined as *a substance other than food that by its chemical nature affects the structure or function of a living organism.*

Drugs range from *proprietary medicines* found in supermarkets, through *socially accepted drugs,* such as alcohol and tobacco, to *drugs forbidden by law* unless used under a doctor's prescription.

Drug abuse is the compulsive use of drugs by people who have no medical reason for taking them but who want to experience the effects the drug can produce. Drug abusers intend the drug to improve the quality of their lives, but it never does.

POSSIBLE REASONS FOR STARTING DRUG-TAKING
1. Many start off by taking drugs, e.g. tranquillisers or sleeping pills, on doctors' prescriptions to treat depression or sleeplessness or to tide them over a bad period in their lives, such as a bereavement. Before long they become accustomed to the drug and cannot do without it. Valium, a tranquilliser, is one of the most commonly prescribed drugs today.

2. Many young people start because they are curious. They want to see how a drug will affect them.

3. Others want to be 'part of the crowd'.

4. *Homes where drug-taking is acceptable* and freely practised, e.g. heavy alcohol intake and cigarette consumption, or where pills are taken for every minor pain and problem, are more likely to produce a drug addict in the family.

5. Drug abuse is more widespread in areas where community bonds are weak and society is undergoing rapid social change.

In Ireland, as elsewhere, serious drug abuse is more common among the *underprivileged,* who are school and social drop-outs, those with low self-esteem, unhappy family background etc.

DRUG DEPENDENCE

This can take the form of:

1. *Social dependence,* where a person depends on a drug in order to conform to the standards of his or her particular community. For example, a self-conscious, inhibited individual may take drugs, e.g. alcohol, to release his or her inhibitions and boost self-confidence.

2. *Physical dependence,* when the body needs the drug for its normal functioning. If one stops taking the drug, unpleasant 'withdrawal' symptoms occur. These include trembling, depression, severe anxiety, cramps, sweating, nausea, convulsions and intense craving.

These symptoms are usually so unbearable that the addict returns to the drug to alleviate them.

3. *Psychological dependence,* when a person uses a drug to provide enjoyment, to deal with relationships or to get over a problem — in other words as a prop which prevents the addict from coming to terms with life.

Note: Investigations on Dublin drug-takers have noted the following points:

1. Most come from homes where the father is a semi-skilled or unskilled worker.

2. They have a poor school or work record.

3. Many have withdrawn from their families; often they have left home.

4. Many reject the values of society and are disillusioned with their parents, school or religion.

5. Drugs were readily available in their homes, e.g. alcohol, pills, with a history of family illness and use of drugs.

6. There was a high level of psychiatric treatment (26%) before attending a drug centre.

7. The drug most commonly taken is cannabis.

8. The main reason for starting is given as curiosity.

9. The main reason for continuing is given as liking the effects.

10. The age range is predominantly 15-21 years.

Those who habitually abuse drugs belong to a close-knit group who approve of drug-taking, accepting it as normal behaviour. Drug usage confers status on group members.

The paradox remains that if young people attempt to demonstrate their independence or freedom from social restriction by taking drugs, the drugs themselves can rob them of the very freedom they are seeking.

Drug Dependence,
Dr A.J. Wood, Bristol Social Service Council.

LAWS RELATING TO DRUGS

The Misuse of Drugs Act, 1977, controls and regulates the storage, sale, dispensing and transport of drugs by manufacturers, doctors, chemists and veterinary surgeons. It stipulates the method of recording the sale of controlled drugs from chemists' shops. It lists penalties for unlawful possession of drugs, making it an offence to illicitly manufacture, supply, sell, export or import such drugs or to allow such drugs to be used on any premises.

The Garda Drug Squad was set up in 1968 to implement the laws relating to drugs. Members of the squad are trained to deal with drug abusers, usually giving a first offender a warning rather than prosecuting.

EFFECTS OF DRUG ABUSE ON INDIVIDUALS

(See also chart: Effects)

- Change in personality: Addicts become withdrawn, secretive, elated, then depressed.
- Schoolwork suffers, loss of job.
- Breakdown in relationships with non-addicts, for example family.
- Physical health suffers. Addicts lose interest in themselves. They fail to eat properly. They usually live in unhygienic accommodation and run a high risk of infection from unsterilised needles. AIDS (acquired immune deficiency syndrome) is common among drug-takers.
- Mental health suffers. Increasing psychological dependence makes it difficult to cope with living without the drug. Suicide is common among addicts.
- Accidental overdosing occurs, resulting in death.

EFFECTS OF DRUG ABUSE ON THE FAMILY

- Anxiety by parents and other family members.
- Drug-taker may abandon family. If the addict is a parent, this could cause its breakup.
- Lack of trust; family rows, secrecy.
- Physical neglect and emotional damage to children of addicts.

Summary of Drugs

Category	Example	Nickname	Source	Dependence	Effects	Withdrawal symptoms
Sedatives or depressants	Ethyl alcohol, barbiturates (sleeping pills)	Downers, Sleepers	Synthetic	Some physical, some social	Disorientation, slurred speech, drunken behaviour leading to coma	Tension, tremor, weakness, anxiety dizziness, nausea, insomnia, death
Stimulants	Amphetamines	Pep pills, Sweets	Synthetic	Marked psychic marked social, no physical	Euphoria, excitement, insomnia leading to agitation, convulsions	Extreme depression (encouraging further dose), dangerous degree of fatigue
	Cocaine	Coke, Snow	Coca plant	Strong psychic, minimal social minimal physical	Increased alertness, euphoria	Usually none
	Caffeine, nicotine		Tea, coffee cigarettes			
Analgesics/ opiates (pain-killers)	Heroin	'H', Horse, Smack	Manufactured from opium, which is obtained from a type of poppy	Intense, prolonged psychic (often life-long), severe physical (most addicts die before their early thirties)	Sleepiness, shallow breathing, euphoria, leading to nausea, convulsions, coma	Restlessness, perspiration, fever, nausea, vomiting, cramps, dehydration, deterioration of health, collapse. (Babies of addicts suffer withdrawal symptoms during the first few days of life.)
	Pethidine		Synthetic			
Hallucinogens (drugs that cause changes in perception)	Cannabis (marijuana, hemp)	Grass, Pot, Weed	Hemp plant (*Cannabis sativa*)	No physical, strong social, strong psychic	Relaxation, euphoria, disorientation leading to nausea, convulsions, coma	Disappointment, resentment, hyperactivity
	LSD	Sugar	Manufactured from ergot fungus	Strong psychic, minimal social, virtually no physical	Hallucination, perception of reality, e.g. distance altered, leading to possible brain damage, death	None known; if contaminated can cause brain damage
	Inhalants		Glue, solvents	Social, psychic	Hallucination, perception of reality, e.g. distance altered, leading to possible brain damage, death	Nausea, coma, death

Note: Narcotic: a sleep-inducing drug
'Hard drugs': heroin, cocaine and other opiates
'Soft drugs': all others

EFFECTS OF DRUG ABUSE ON SOCIETY

- Increase in crime, including robbery and prostitution, because of the addicts' need to feed their habit.
- Increase in drug-taking as addicts become 'pushers' to make money for their own addiction.
- Absenteeism, when addicts fail to turn up for work.
- Danger of spread of diseases such as hepatitis and AIDS to users and non-users.

TREATMENT AVAILABLE TO DRUG ABUSERS

1. Drug Treatment Centre Board, Trinity Court, Pearse Street, Dublin 2: Runs daily clinics staffed by doctors, nurses and psychiatric social workers. Offers a phone-in advisory service — office hours.
2. Beaumont Hospital, Dublin: Runs an in-patient drug detoxification unit as well as an analysis service for poisons and drugs.

3. Coolmine Therapeutic Community, Clonsilla, Co. Dublin: Offers drug abusers the opportunity to learn through self-help to live without drugs. It provides individual counselling, encounter groups and re-entry programmes. The residents run the entire house themselves, including administration and discipline.
4. Psychiatric hospitals: Drug addicts can be detoxified in any psychiatric hospital. Some provide rehabilitation courses which usually last for between six and eight months and during which they are prepared for re-entering society without drugs.
5. The National Drugs Advisory Board was set up by the government to gather and assess information on drugs. It advises the government on precautions, testing, manufacture etc. and disseminates information on drugs, principally to the medical and pharmaceutical professions.

ALCOHOL

Ethyl alcohol, which is present in all alcoholic drinks, is also a drug — probably the most abused drug in western civilisation. It is a sedative drug which can lead to physical, social and psychological addiction.

Ireland has a name for being a nation of heavy drinkers, and statistics bear this out. While in most other countries drinking to excess is not acceptable, in Ireland it is sometimes seen as a sign of manliness and 'fun' and drunkenness is widely tolerated.

Alcohol oils the wheels of business; it is present in plenty at christenings, marriages and deaths. The government itself makes hundreds of millions of pounds from the duty levied on alcohol.

In Ireland, drinking is very much a social activity. Seventy-five per cent takes place outside the home, in pubs and hotels and at social gatherings. The Irish spend a higher proportion of their incomes (13 per cent) on alcohol than any other nation recorded — well over £1 million a day! As we also have a high proportion of tee-totallers, this means that such spending is concentrated in a small proportion of the population: approximately one-third of the adult population are drinking too much. Of our estimated 1.5 million alcohol drinkers, about 75,000 are thought to be alcoholics.

DRINKING AMONG YOUNG PEOPLE

Under-age drinking (that is, under the age of 18) is an increasing social problem. The temptation to drink has never been more compelling. Pressure from peer groups and advertisers makes it difficult to say no. Young people see parents drinking, often to excess. Others may have experienced directly the trauma of living with an alcoholic. Statistics show that many young alcoholics were brought up in an alcoholic home.

"We are, in truth, more than half what we are by imitation."
Lord Chesterfield, 1750

It is illegal to serve alcohol to a person under 18 years of age in a public house, yet this law is not properly enforced. It is also illegal for those under 18 to buy alcohol in off licenses. 'Cider parties' are frequent occurrences among children as young as 10 years of age. Those who start drinking early run a far greater risk of developing a drinking problem.

The importance of setting a good example and promoting sound attitudes to drinking cannot be over-stressed. It is probably better that young people should take their first drinks in a family atmosphere, preferably with a meal. If drinking is treated as a crime and never discussed at home, young people have no guidance. The pub takes on an attractive aura; they may drink in secret, or give in to peer group pressure and drink to excess or mix drinks for a rapid 'high'. Parents need to show responsibility by setting limits on the places young people go and the time they should be home. Drinking to excess should not be tolerated.

Drinking is usually a social activity

DRINKING GUIDELINES

1. Drink moderately. Do not exceed the recommended limits, that is 2 units* per day (women), 3 units per day (men). (Royal College of Psychiatrists 1986)
   (* A unit is one glass of wine, a half pint glass of beer, or 1 small measure of spirits.)
2. Drink only when you are relaxed and not as a method of easing tension.
3. Try to eat before, and while, drinking.
4. Sip slowly and never gulp.
5. Do not mix alcohol with other drugs. Do not mix 'the grape with the grain' — wine with whiskey or beer.
6. Do not look upon alcohol as proof of adulthood or popularity.

7. Respect the rights of those who wish to abstain, and never worry about feeling conspicuous with a soft drink.
8. Reject drunkenness as unacceptable.
9. Set a limit to the amount of drink you have and do not be persuaded to exceed this.
10. Try to drink only on social occasions — never alone.
11. Discourage the 'rounds' system.
12. Never drink when driving (or using machinery).
13. Avoid drinking in the daytime.
14. Respect alcohol. In small amounts it can be enjoyable — excess causes trouble.
15. Do not let alcohol become an important part of your life.

ALCOHOLISM

An alcoholic is anybody who is dependent on alcohol and whose drinking causes harm to himself and/or others.

Alcoholism is a disease that causes certain people to become addicted to the drug ethyl alcohol. There is no single reason why certain drinkers become alcoholics. It is known that excessive drinking over a period of time, together with certain personality traits such as emotional immaturity or an inability to relate to others, may lead to alcoholism given the right circumstances. The stereotyped image of the down-and-out in the gutter is not typical of alcoholics. Most are ordinary social drinkers who gradually reach a point when they can no longer control their drinking and become addicted to alcohol.

The down-and-out is not the typical alcoholic

Alcoholism is a *progressive* (gradually gets worse), *chronic* (cannot be cured) disease which often leads to death. *Denial* is a feature of alcoholism. Most addicts refuse to believe that they have a problem. Yet they will go to considerable lengths to conceal the extent of their drinking by deception, lying, blaming others, hostility or refusing to talk about it.

EFFECTS OF ALCOHOL

Contrary to popular opinion, alcohol is not a stimulant but a depressant. It slows down brain activity so that the drinker becomes relaxed and uninhibited. The effects are shown here in stages.

Stage 1 Skin flushes. Greater sociability, lessening of inhibitions.
Stage 2 Slow judgment, deterioration of speech, lack of co-ordination.
Stage 3 Blurred vision, considerably slowed reactions, nausea, dizziness.
Stage 4 Loss of balance, double vision.
Stage 5 Unconsciousness; in severe cases, death.

Heavy drinking contributes to alcoholic hepatitis, cirrhosis of the liver, dementia (loss of mental functioning), delirium tremens, cancer of the liver and gullet, heart disease, ulcers, obesity, gout and malnutrition. The death rate for alcoholics is twice the average; their suicide rate is six times the average.

Children born to mothers who are heavy drinkers may be retarded. Pregnant women should abstain from alcohol consumption.

Note: Alcohol tolerance is lower in women than in men. Because they have a lower level of water in their bodies in proportion to men, women absorb alcohol into the bloodstream at a faster rate than men so that the alcohol in the blood becomes more concentrated and more damaging. Also because they are usually smaller and lighter, it takes less drink to have the same effects.

EFFECTS OF ALCOHOLISM ON THE INDIVIDUAL
- Physical effects (see above).
- Loss of self-respect.
- Unhappiness, depression.
- Guilt for hardship caused to the family.
- Job loss and/or severe financial problems.
- Social stigma.
- Prosecution for drink-related offences.

EFFECTS OF ALCOHOLISM ON THE FAMILY
- Tension in the home, leading to marital problems.
- Family violence as a result of excessive drinking.
- Complete disruption of family life.
- Poverty and hardship.
- Mental illness in spouse, for example depression. Disturbed children, for example, teenage alcoholics and drug addicts.
- Unwanted pregnancies; increased risk of miscarriage in the case of pregnant alcoholics.
- Social stigma; shame if prosecuted for drink-related crimes.

EFFECTS OF ALCOHOLISM ON SOCIETY

- Crime, particularly crimes of violence.
- National problem of alcoholism wastes money and resources that would be better put to other uses*.
- Absenteeism from work due to heavy drinking; many thousands of days are lost through drink-related absenteeism.
- Loss of production, faulty workmanship etc.
- Drunken driving, threatening the lives of the innocent; at least half of all road accidents are drink-related.

* £500 million per annum

TOUGH LOVE — HELPING AN ALCOHOLIC

An alcoholic is never really cured. The term 'recovery' is used to describe abstinence from alcohol.

Those who live with a problem drinker may unknowingly act in such a way that they shield the drinker from the harmful consequences of his/her drinking. This may be out of kindness or in an effort to hide the problem from others. This is the worst possible thing — it supports and enables the drinker to continue drinking and avoids the crises that might bring him to see the problem. Sympathy can destroy the alcoholic.

Today it is accepted that *intervention* is the best way of breaking down the drinker's defences: that is confronting them with the reality of the situation. This usually occurs after a crisis and with professional help.

The alcoholic can be detoxified and rehabilitated in one of many centres around the country, many of which are attached to psychiatric hospitals.

Detoxification may include the use of drugs that react unpleasantly with alcohol. Counselling during treatment and after is effective, particularly when family is involved. Long-term sobriety depends on the individual's abstaining from alcohol indefinitely 'one day at a time'.

STATISTICS ON ALCOHOL

- Alcohol abuse costs the country £500 million per annum.
- State revenue from taxes on alcohol is £390 million per annum.
- £12 million per annum is spent on advertising alcohol.
- One in four admissions to psychiatric hospitals are for alcohol abuse (7,000 per annum).
- Teenagers who drink four or five pints regularly, starting at age 17 or 18, can suffer brain damage and memory loss by 25 to 30.
- The risk of alcoholism increases, the younger the drinker begins to abuse alcohol.
- The number of under 25s being treated for alcoholism has increased by almost 400 per cent in fifteen years.
- Alcohol is the main cause of death in the coroners court. (Dublin county coroner)

GROUPS TO CONTACT

- The Irish National Council on Alcoholism encourages research, education and training, and promotes measures to prevent alcoholism. It provides a free referral service.
- Alcoholics Anonymous (AA). Founded in the 1930s in the United States, AA helps alcoholics maintain sobriety through personal support and group meetings.
- Adult children of alcoholics (ACOA): Self-help courses and group support for adults affected by parental alcoholism.
- Al-Anon: Assists the families of alcoholics through group meetings and mutual support.
- Alateen helps teenage children affected by alcoholism.
  Membership of the fellowships of Al-Anon or Alateen brings understanding, comfort and hope to anybody affected by alcoholism. Members learn how to help themselves and, indirectly, how to help the alcoholic. By removing their preoccupation with the drinker's behaviour, they are able to focus on their own development and sense of identity. These changed attitudes can result in the problem drinker seeking help.
- Cuan Mhuire (Athy) is a centre for alcoholics run by Sister Consilio.
- The Rutland Centre, Knocklyon, Co. Dublin: Treatment and therapy for all addicts.
- Belmont Park Hospital, Waterford, and many other psychiatric hospitals such as St John of God offer alcoholism treatment.

> ### Finding help: the cycle of emotional damage
> Most emotionally damaging family problems such as alcoholism, violence and sexual abuse are learned systems of behaviour which are passed on to damage generation after generation.
>
> In order to break the cycle, it is important that those affected (and *all* are emotionally damaged by such behaviour) seek help. This is available in the form of counselling and psychotherapy — for example the Rape Crisis Centre, Rutland Centre, and also through membership of self help groups such as AA, Al-Anon etc.

GAMBLING

Gambling is also an addiction. While not a substance addiction, as with drugs or alcohol, it is a craving for excitement, the adrenaline-producing 'high' that comes from taking risks.

One can gamble on cards, horses, dogs and other sporting fixtures, and many do so without coming to much harm.

The problem arises when gambling gets out of control. The type of person who becomes addicted to gambling is

Slot machine gambling has become a serious social problem

similar to the type who becomes addicted to drink or drugs: he or she is likely to have little self-esteem and an immature personality, unable to accept reality. She/he wants a good lifestyle without having to work for it.

EFFECTS OF GAMBLING ON THE INDIVIDUAL

1. Financial problems such as borrowing and spending large sums of money.
2. Trouble at work, perhaps due to absenteeism or dishonesty, with possible loss of a job.
3. Lowering of values: Lying, stealing, cheating become acceptable.
4. Loss of interest in relationships, for example family and friends.
5. Change in personality: Preoccupation with gambling.
6. Worry and guilts.

EFFECTS OF GAMBLING ON THE FAMILY

1. Financial problems, having insufficient money for the basics of life. Loss of a job and possible loss of home.
2. Tension and stress, leading sometimes to mental breakdown.
3. Mental disturbance in spouse (for example depression), and anxiety in children.

EFFECTS OF GAMBLING ON SOCIETY

1. Possible absenteeism.
2. Taxes on gambling provide large sums for the state.
3. Acceptance of gambling (for example lotteries) encourages irresponsibility. May result in social welfare payments being gambled away.

HELP AVAILABLE FOR GAMBLERS

1. Gamblers Anonymous organises group therapy to help the gambler to overcome or to control his or her addiction. It offers advice, support etc.
2. Gam-Anon provides help and support to families of compulsive gamblers.
3. The Rutland Centre provides counselling and treatment for those addicted to gambling.

► CRIME AND DELINQUENCY

Individuals who ignore or persistently break important rules of society, for example laws, are considered to be deviants and are likely to be penalised. Such behaviour is seen as a social problem in society, even though the person who 'misbehaves' often fails to see that such behaviour is wrong — for example, the poor person who steals from a wealthy home.

CRIME

Crime is behaviour that breaks criminal laws. There are two types of crime:

1. *Indictable offences:* These are serious offences which must be brought to court by the Garda Siochana and, on conviction, are punishable by imprisonment or fines.
2. *Non-indictable offences:* These are less serious than indictable ones and include motoring offences, damage to property etc. Most crimes are of this type.

JUVENILE DELINQUENCY

This is law-breaking by a person between the ages of 7 and 17. (Below the age of 7, one is deemed to be incapable of committing a crime.) The most common offences of which juveniles are convicted are theft, including car theft, shoplifting and burglary.

SOCIAL FACTORS THAT CONTRIBUTE TO DELINQUENCY AND CRIME

1. Anti-social behaviour is learned behaviour. Many juveniles who come before the law come from homes where there are problems such as violence, abuse or alcoholism. Parents may be involved in crime themselves. Parental discipline tends to be either too firm or too lax. While some delinquents come from broken homes, it is the relationship with parents which is more important. Rejection by parents is common. Delinquents tend to be hostile or else indifferent and apathetic towards parents.

2. Delinquents tend to have low self-esteem and to have strong feelings of rejection and inadequacy. They are often emotionally damaged, defiant, angry, resentful and suspicious of authority, impulsive and lacking in self-control.

A protest march turns to violence

3. While crime and delinquency are committed by all social classes, many juvenile delinquents come from an underprivileged, working-class background, living in over-crowded, substandard housing conditions where there are many social problems.

4. Homelessness is common. Many delinquents have run away or have been thrown out of their home. They may be sleeping rough or in squats.

5. Crime appears to be more common in urban areas: the very nature of urban life offers more opportunity for crime.

6. Peer pressure: Misfits, dropouts and teenagers simply looking for friends tend to congregate in gangs, where they have a sense of identification and belonging and where they can show off and learn new ways to break the law.

7. Juvenile delinquents usually show low educational achievement. They are rejected by and in turn reject the middle-class education system and drop out as soon as possible.

8. As a result, they tend to be unemployed, or work in unskilled jobs. Boredom leads them to search for excitement in crimes such as joy-riding or burglary.

9. Drug addiction has led to an increase in crime as addicts steal to get the money for drugs.

10. Many suggest: (a) the decline in the influence of family and religion; and (b) the influence of violence on television and videos as reasons for the increase in irrational teenage violence and vandalism.

11. While the vast majority of juvenile delinquents and criminals are male, an increasing number of females are being convicted of serious offences.

EFFECTS OF DELINQUENCY AND CRIME ON THE INDIVIDUAL

- Emotional disturbance.
- Criminal record may hamper an individual when looking for a job later.
- Prison sentences or fines.
- Rejection by large sections of society.

EFFECTS OF DELINQUENCY AND CRIME ON THE FAMILY

- Tension and strain are experienced by most families, particularly those who have done their best to give their child a good upbringing, yet see their offspring turn to crime.
- The family home may have to be subjected to Garda searches etc.
- Bad example to younger family members.

EFFECTS OF DELINQUENCY AND CRIME ON SOCIETY

- Crime has a destabilising influence on society.
- It causes anxiety in law-abiding citizens who have to guard against muggings, assault, rape, housebreaking etc.
- There are feelings of hopelessness and powerlessness, particularly when lenient sentences are passed for serious crimes.

Football hooliganism is now a frequent form of violence

AVOIDING DELINQUENCY

It is important to note that responsible parents who care about their children, setting standards of law-abiding and responsible behaviour while also encouraging self-reliance and independence, are far less likely to raise delinquent teenagers than parents who are over-permissive, authoritarian, or who reject — or simply neglect — their children.

Many juvenile delinquents settle down when they get married, and only the hardened few continue in a life of crime.

It is sometimes said that the needs of teenagers are not being adequately met, and that a greater allocation of funds to education, housing, youth employment etc., would reduce the risk of many turning to crime.

HELP AVAILABLE FOR DELINQUENCY AND CRIME

- *The School Attendance Service*: School attendance officers are employed to ensure that young people attend school regularly.
- *The Child Guidance Service* is available for children with psychological difficulties. Special centres provide counselling and treatment for children and their families. Specialists include child psychiatrists, educational psychologists and social workers.
- *Family therapy*: The whole family is involved in group discussions with a psychologist in order to unravel the problems of an individual, for example an adolescent, within the family.
- *Children in care*: Health boards are empowered to take children into care for many reasons — for example, if they are under the age of 14 and have committed an offence, or if the courts decide that the parents cannot control the child. Such children may be fostered out, placed in residential homes or in special schools.
- *Juvenile liaison officers*: These are plain-clothes members of the Garda Siochana, both male and female. They are specially chosen to work with children who have committed minor offences or are likely to become involved in crime. It is hoped that this service helps to prevent crime.
- *The Probation Service*: The courts may make an order for a child who is charged and found guilty of a crime to be discharged on condition that he or she formally agrees to be of good behaviour for a specified time. During this time, the offender must be under the supervision of a probation officer.

  Probation officers assist and advise those committed to their care. They assist in finding employment, if necessary. They investigate family circumstances and report progress to the court.
- *Remand homes* are places of detention for juvenile offenders where they are medically and psychologically assessed while awaiting trial.

- *Special schools* are secure places of detention for juveniles convicted of offences and committed to care by the court. They are staffed by specially trained personnel, including teachers. At present there is only one secure unit — Trinity House — for boys detained for offences. There is no such facility for girls.
- *Youth Encounter Projects*: These are family support projects that provide an alternative to residential special schooling for minor delinquents, persistent truants etc. After suitable assessment, children are enrolled in a supervised project in small groups of boys and girls aged between 10 and 16. Each project has some full-time staff, but there is a large contribution of voluntary work. Projects include both educational and out-of-school programmes. The objectives are:
  1. To enable children at risk to remain in the community, while receiving skilled help aimed at lessening their personal and social problems.
  2. To mobilise neighbourhood potential to meet the needs of young people.
  3. To develop strategies to guide social workers and voluntary groups in their work with similar children.

IMPRISONMENT

When society punishes an individual by imprisonment, the family of the prisoner also suffers. When an offender leaves prison having completed the appropriate sentence, many people fail to accept that he or she has paid for the crime and continue to discriminate against the ex-prisoner. Many are involved in a cycle of arrest, court appearance, prison release and re-arrest.

EFFECT OF IMPRISONMENT ON THE INDIVIDUAL

- Sense of shame.
- Loss of freedom: Prisoners are separated from loved ones.
- Difficulty in obtaining work when one has a criminal record.
- Prisons can be 'schools of crime' where those imprisoned for relatively minor offences learn how to carry out more serious crimes.

EFFECTS OF IMPRISONMENT ON THE FAMILY

- Reduction in income.
- Loss of parent or spouse.
- Possible gossip or scandal from neighbours and relatives.
- Embarrassment to children; teasing; emotional damage.

EFFECTS OF IMPRISONMENT ON SOCIETY

- It protects society from dangerous criminals.
- The upkeep of the prison service costs the state a large amount of money.
- It acts as a deterrent in certain cases.

HELP AVAILABLE

- Families of prisoners are entitled to social assistance, subject to a means test.
- The Prisoners' Rights Organisation keeps the public informed about the prison system; aims for prison reform; encourages the rehabilitation of prisoners; provides vocational training and after care.
- Prisoners' Aid through Community Effort (PACE) helps to rehabilitate ex-prisoners; provides accommodation in a hostel, training workshops etc.

HOUSING

Bad housing is one of the most destructive social problems in relation to family life. Some of the problems related to housing are:

Substandard housing puts families at risk

Inner city slums:
no place for children

1. Shortage of housing: This is particularly bad in large urban areas. Severe shortage leads to overcrowding and substandard dwellings. Because the demand for houses generally exceeds supply, a waiting list based on a system of points is used by most local authorities. Points are awarded for unfit housing, health circumstances, overcrowding, lack of amenities, sharing facilities with another family and so on. Dwellings are allocated on the principle that those with the highest number of points are housed first. Details of such schemes are available from the local authorities.

2. Substandard housing: As a result of the shortage of houses, many people live in appalling conditions. Damp, vermin, dry rot, inadequate plumbing, no indoor lavatory or a shared bathroom are common in poor-quality dwellings. Young children and the elderly are particularly at risk in such substandard accommodation.

3. Expense: Rent or mortgage repayments take a considerable percentage of family income. Those in receipt of social welfare benefits are entitled to reduced rent under the differential rents scheme.

4. Lack of services and amenities in new housing estates: Community facilities such as health centres, play groups and clubs for the elderly contribute to the comfort, health and happiness of residents. Shops and schools are essential. A community centre is a focal point for an area that is often lacking in recreational and other basic amenities.

5. Loneliness and isolation are experienced by many young mothers in the vast housing estates at the edge of cities. Many are far from relatives and childhood friends and are isolated by inadequate transport or insufficient funds to avail of it.

6. Segregation: Most housing areas are segregated along class lines, reinforcing social and economic differences. When large local authority estates are built they often house large numbers of unemployed people. Bored youngsters frequently form gangs, terrorising and vandalising the estate and giving it a bad name. When this happens, it is often difficult for residents to get a job, as employers form a bias against an area solely on the bad publicity it receives.

HIGH-RISE LIVING ACCOMMODATION

High-rise flats are now known to be unsuited to the needs of the people for whom they were intended: namely, young families.

- They soon become uninhabitable due to vandalism, violence and neglect.
- The open space around the blocks is public property. No one feels responsible for it, so it is often defaced with litter and graffiti.
- Small children need enclosed play space where they can play under supervision. This is not possible in high-rise blocks.

Faulty towers? Problems at Ballymun include loneliness and vandalism

- The busy mother in a tower block finds it simpler to remain indoors than to bring children out-of-doors.
- There is constant fear of children falling from balconies.
- Lifts are frequently out of order due to vandalism. When this occurs, prams, buggies and shopping trolleys must be hauled up several storeys.
- Children frequently run amok, forming gangs and terrorising helpless residents. Ground floor tenants are particularly vulnerable to harassment.
- Loneliness and neuroses such as agoraphobia are common, and suicide an all-too-frequent occurrence.
- There is a high turnover of occupants, with little sense of belonging to the community and little interest in the immediate environment.
- Social problems such as drugs become endemic as more and more disadvantaged people are crowded into unsuitable accommodation.

EFFECTS OF BAD HOUSING ON THE INDIVIDUAL

- Mental strain such as stress, tension, depression.
- Inability to cope with the housekeeping, children etc.
- Tendency to stay out of the home — for example in the pub — with little family life.
- Ill health due to lack of hygiene, dampness etc.

EFFECTS OF BAD HOUSING ON THE FAMILY

- Cause of stress and tension, leading to family rows.
- Difficult for children to cope with homework etc. Due to overcrowding, such children tend to fall behind in school.
- Health risks due to damp, cold, unsanitary conditions and infestation by vermin.

EFFECTS OF BAD HOUSING ON SOCIETY

- Bad housing breeds many other social problems. Residents often stay away from home to drink in the pub. Young people form gangs and sometimes turn to drugs.
- Vagrancy; homeless people sleeping rough.
- Lack of civic pride.

HOUSING ESTATES

Good housing is a social need which can be provided by the state or the citizen. Local authority housing is subsidised by the government, and mortgage interest on purchased homes can be offset against income tax liabilities.

Local authority planning regulations and by-laws see to it that houses and housing estates are well planned, safe, and provided with the necessary amenities and services such as public lighting and refuse collection.

In the past, estates were badly planned. They were often in a grid formation, with as many houses as possible packed into the designated area. Today, developers and town planners are more conscious of the total environment: curved roads, mature trees and open spaces are retained.

Modern town houses are more suitable for families

Planning permission for large-scale housing is only granted on certain conditions — for example, that a certain proportion of the total area will remain an open space amenity. Restrictions are imposed regarding height and line of houses. Variation in house design is encouraged, although the estates should have an attractive visual unity. Experiments have been made on traffic-free estates, such as Darndale in Coolock, Dublin. There is a swing towards 'town houses' and small apartment blocks suitable for single people and elderly couples.

New towns are being built on the perimeter of cities. They are provided with shopping centres, community facilities, schools, play areas and green space. Employment is available nearby in industrial estates and offices, and transport to the city centre is provided.

Ballymun: a dense housing development at the perimeter of the city

HELP AVAILABLE FOR HOUSING

- Housing welfare officers: Some local authorities employ housing welfare officers to assist tenants who need help in coping with problems relating to housing, budgeting, rent, social welfare benefits etc. They advise on making the best use of accommodation and put tenants in touch with suitable voluntary organisations such as the following.
- The Association of Combined Residents' Associations (ACRA) fosters development of residents' associations. It assists residents in fighting for rights of householders — for example, against imposition of rates and ground rents.
- House a Marriage (HAM) helps couples to save for a house by providing a flat at a reasonable rent.
- The Housing Centre provides information for voluntary housing organisations.
- Threshold is a national voluntary housing advisory and research service which attempts to tackle the problem of homelessness, the lack of a secure place to live.
- Hope helps young homeless people who sleep rough.

LAWS AND AGENCIES CONCERNED WITH HOUSING

- The Housing Acts (1966 etc.) control legislation relating to acquisition of land, provision and management of dwellings, overcrowded and unfit houses, loans, grants, demolition and squatting.
- The Department of the Environment is responsible for national housing policy. It supervises social, financial and technical aspects of local authority and private housing.
- The National Building Agency plans development and helps to meet housing needs by providing about one-third of public housing output.
- Local authority housing, (Chapter 10).

HOMELESSNESS

A person or family that is without a home and must live and sleep on the streets is defined as homeless. It does not take into account those living in overcrowded or substandard conditions. Often called vagrants or down-and-outs, the homeless are easily identified by their obvious poverty, shabby clothing and lack of possessions. Homelessness is not simply lack of a regular place to sleep. It is a lack of the familiar comforts associated with a home, lack of people who care about you, lack of a family and friends. Many homeless sleep rough — out-of-doors, in cars or in derelict houses in inner city areas. Some stay a night or two in a hostel before they are moved on.

Hundreds of people sleep rough every night

CHARACTERISTICS OF A TYPICALLY HOMELESS PERSON

Usually single or separated (up to 80%)	May feel personally and socially inadequate.
Majority are male (90%)	Dependant on social welfare payments.
Unemployed (95%)	May suffer physical or mental illness — often
Unskilled	an addict, e.g. alcoholic.
Unkempt appearance	Lives in chronic state of poverty/deprivation.

FACTORS WHICH LEAD TO HOMELESSNESS

1. Disturbed home background: neglect by parents, violence, abuse, alcoholism.
2. Anti-social behaviour such as mental illness, drug or alcohol abuse may have caused the individual to be thrown out of home.
3. Many homeless were brought up in care, having no experience of family life, no experience of controlling their own lives or coping with day-to-day living such as handling money and other life skills.
4. Many have a history of illness — both physical and mental.
5. Their way of life brings some into frequent contact with the law — often resorting to begging, petty crime and drunkenness. (Vagrancy Act, which is still on the statute books, makes homelessness itself a crime!) Some are frequently in and out of prison for minor offences.

YOUNG HOMELESS

1. Most lack education, having dropped out of school. They are unskilled, therefore find it difficult to find regular work.
2. They cannot get a job without an address and cannot rent accommodation without money — a vicious circle.
3. Because they have no money, they resort to petty crime.
4. Their age leaves them open to exploitation and abuse, such as prostitution and drugs.
5. Until the Childrens Act, 19 _ _, those between the ages of 16 and 18 were not the responsibility of any statutory agency.
6. Under 18s are not entitled to welfare allowances or housing.
7. Residential homes/special schools in which many were in care provide no aftercare in spite of such a recommendation made as far back as 1969 in the Kennedy Report on Childcare.

EFFECTS OF HOMELESSNESS ON THE INDIVIDUAL

1. Lack of self-worth, no sense of identity, security or self determination.
2. Isolation from family, friends and community.
3. Negative attitudes and prejudice (they are called 'dossers' or 'winos') from housed community.
4. Deterioration in health due to lifestyle and lack of health care. Although they are entitled to medical cards, many homeless use hospital casualty units for treatment instead.
5. Lack of dignity, privacy: Nowhere to wash self and clothing.
6. Nowhere to store belongings: they must be carried everywhere, for example 'bag ladies'.

PROBLEMS AND POLICIES

- Lack of proper legislation to deal with the problem.
- Lack of government finance to set up hostels, daycare centres and rehabilitation units.
- Most work in this area is done by voluntary agencies — taking the onus away from government departments.
- Health boards are required (Health Act, Sect. 43) to provide institutional assistance to persons unable to provide shelter or maintenance for themselves or their dependants. This is not done — particularly since most county homes, which used to house such people, have now closed. Psychiatric hospitals, due to cutbacks, can only admit more seriously ill patients.
- New Childrens Act, 19 _ _, makes health boards responsible for the welfare of 16-18 year olds.

HOSTELS

About 2,000 beds are occupied by the homeless of Ireland each night and these numbers are insufficient for those needing them. Only a small number of hostels provide for women. The average city hostel holds 80 people, mostly in dormitories. Those drunk or disorderly are not usually admitted. Those staying must be in by 7-8 pm and must leave the hostel by 9 am. Due to the absence of day centres, such people are left each day to walk the streets, regardless of weather, until the evening. While the hostels are clean and adequate, they are impersonal and they lack privacy.

HELP AVAILABLE

Organisations which provide shelter for the homeless usually receive grants from the Department of Health. Most are run by religious groups and voluntary organisations.

- Salvation Army ⎫ Hostels, meals, assistance.
- Legion of Mary ⎭
- St Vincent de Paul Society: Clothing, financial assistance.
- Simon Community: Provides night shelters, hot meals, organises 'soup runs'.
- Trust: Provides socio-medical service for single homeless.
- Focus Point: Sister Stanislaus established this 'drop-in' centre which runs a low cost restaurant, provides assistance and support for the homeless and teaches them how to cope on their own.

One of the reasons that people remain homeless is that they are unable to use their own resources and to fend for themselves.

"No man is an island, entire of itself; every man is a piece of the continent, a part of the main."   John Donne

Due to our natural tendency to form groups, families usually set up home near other families, thus forming a neighbourhood. Some neighbourhoods consist of a well-balanced mixture of people — people of differing occupations, young and old, rich and poor. Others are more socially segregated, including wealthy suburban areas and blocks of inner-city local authority flats. Some rural villages have a predominantly elderly population due to urbanisation and emigration.

The existence of a neighbourhood does not necessarily mean the existence of a community. It depends on the degree to which people identify with one another. Community spirit is strong where there is a common set of values, attitudes and lifestyles, where there is considerable interaction between neighbours, where people are helpful and co-operative, and where they rally round in times of trouble. Community ties tend to be weak: (a) in newly built areas because people have not got to know one another and because there are often no facilities where neighbours can meet — parks, community centres, health centres; (b) in places with a floating population, as in an area consisting of small flats and bedsits, particularly high-rise dwellings; (c) in affluent suburbs; (d) where the geographical area of the neighbourhood is large.

Some members of a community will be better off than others; they may have had a better education, more opportunities, fewer setbacks in life. Others will have been handicapped from the start. They may have been born into a poor family, living in unhealthy, overcrowded surroundings with not enough to eat, their life chances hampered by too many of life's hard knocks.

In every community there are people who need help, and many who can afford to give it; not merely material help but also support, assistance and at time just a shoulder to cry on. A community's concern for the welfare of its members will depend on the active concern shown by individuals and groups within that community. The needs of the weaker sections of the community, such as the aged, the handicapped and the poor, can often be met more successfully from community resources, that is voluntary groups, rather than depending solely on more impersonal government agencies. Yet the government must not shirk its responsibility to the more vulnerable members of society.

Modern urban society has the effect of isolating the individual and the family: this is the cause of many of our social problems. A caring community can be effective in reducing or ridding society of many of these problems.

► COMMUNITY DEVELOPMENT

In the past few years, increasing interest has been shown by local people within a community to organise their own affairs. Citizens get together in residents' associations, community councils etc., often enlisting the services of voluntary organisations and state services in order to improve the social and economic life of their area.

It is clear that community co-operation improves the quality of life in a community — people get to know one another and they feel less isolated. Community events such as festivals, community weeks, summer projects etc. bring the community together and at the same time provide useful services, education and entertainment for local people.

COMMUNITY COUNCILS

A community council is a confederation of voluntary groups in a particular area. It should be apolitical and inter-denominational. It would normally consist of representatives of:

- the *local community* such as business people, teachers, residents, clergymen or women.
- *voluntary groups* such as credit unions, sports associations.
- *statutory agencies* such as health boards.

The basic function of these councils is to assess community needs in the area and to find out which services and facilities would be most beneficial to the community. They may attempt long- or short-term projects such as cleaning up towns, parks and other amenity areas (for example, local schoolchildren could be involved in an anti-litter campaign), providing swimming pools, youth clubs and community centres. They organise fund-raising and social services such as Meals on Wheels, home helps and laundry service, and may assist and visit the elderly or the infirm. A local youth group could help to redecorate the homes of elderly people.

Community councils should avail of any resources from government, local authorities and voluntary agencies. Local authorities are empowered to assist and co-operate with any community council set up by local people that furthers their social and economic interests. Grants and other forms of assistance are available from local authorities and health boards.

ADVANTAGES OF COMMUNITY COUNCILS
1. They enable people to participate in their local affairs.
2. Important decisions affecting the community are taken by the community instead of by outside agencies.
3. They can pressurise official bodies, such as local authorities and government departments, to provide an important service or amenity or to prevent an unwanted development.

NATIONAL SOCIAL SERVICE BOARD
This board co-ordinates the activities of public and voluntary agencies that work in social service. It assists the development of social services and publicises such services so that members of the public are aware of their entitlements. It provides training courses and advice on the setting up and running of social service and community councils and community information centres. It publishes a directory of social service organisations and many other helpful booklets such as *Relate: Entitlements for the Elderly/Unemployed*.

COMMUNITY INFORMATION CENTRES
Much of the information any member of a community might require is available in their local public library and in *community information centres*. These are centres, serviced by volunteers, which are situated in the heart of a local community, as in a town community centre. They provide information on various government and local authority services such as social welfare, housing, health services, employment, labour and family law, consumer rights etc.

Their chief aim is to make people aware of their entitlements and to direct them to agencies that will advise or assist them. Centres are funded by government and local funds. There are about eighty such centres registered with the NSSB.

Social service councils represent the various voluntary organisations in a particular area. Their aim is to work together in the provision of social services, to co-ordinate services (to avoid overlapping) and to identify needs in the area and try to ensure that they are met. Many employ a full-time social worker. They also provide information on local events.

Community development officers are employed by the local authority to assist in the development of the community by co-ordinating community activities and providing general guidance. They will assist in the setting up of new services and projects, community councils etc.

NEIGHBOURHOOD WATCH
This is a crime prevention programme that enlists the voluntary help of the community in co-operation with the Garda Siochána.

The community's part in the project is to observe and to report criminal activity in its own locality — before crime takes place. With the gardai and community working together, the opportunity for crime is reduced. The gardai assist in the formation of area groups and instruct their members in crime prevention techniques and other safety measures.

► VOLUNTARY ORGANISATIONS

No matter how comprehensive the services provided by the state, there will always be a place for voluntary services. Voluntary work complements the work of statutory (government-backed) agencies. Without it, many areas would be ignored.

In the past, most voluntary services were provided by churches and religious organisations such as the Salvation Army and the Society of St Vincent de Paul. In the last few years there has been a great increase in the involvement of secular groups which provide a wide range of services for the community. Many of them work in close co-operation with government agencies, as with the community care programme. This helps to avoid overlapping of valuable resources.

Voluntary service has three functions:

1. It provides a service that supplements or complements those of the state.
2. It saves large sums of money, as services are provided free.
3. It develops those in receipt of the services and those who offer them.

ADVANTAGES OF VOLUNTARY WORK

1. Voluntary work can be a rewarding, maturing experience.
2. It encourages the building of relationships, the emphasis being on working *with* people rather than *for* them.
3. It teaches people to make decisions. It helps people to help themselves, rather than depend on hand-outs.

ADVANTAGES OF VOLUNTARY ORGANISATIONS

1. They complement and supplement the work of statutory agencies.
2. Volunteers give their services free, which keeps costs low.
3. They eliminate much bureaucratic paperwork, often providing more direct services and more quickly.
4. They place important emphasis on preventive work, whereas the state must usually wait for a specific incident before it can act.
5. Volunteers often have more time to sit and listen to a problem than an overworked doctor or social worker.

6. They provide a more personal service and are often better able to deal with a local problem.
7. They often pioneer social reform, acting as pressure groups (see below) for changes in policy.
8. Many are recognised as experts in their fields so that their opinions are sought when new policies are being implemented.

PRESSURE GROUPS

A group of people who band together to lobby (apply pressure on government or statutory bodies) in the hope of bringing about a desired change is known as a pressure group. Many voluntary organisations are, at least in part, pressure groups.

The group attempts to change public opinion by advertising, by writing to the press or by using any form of media coverage to highlight their cause. Demonstrations, marches, fasts and pickets may be used to draw attention to the issue. Pressure groups are of two kinds.

1. *Protective groups* act to defend or protect the interests of their members if they are threatened. Examples of protective groups are trade unions, An Taisce and SPUC (The Society for The Protection of the Unborn Child).

2. *Promotional groups* seek to promote or amend legislation that they feel will benefit a particular group, the whole of society, or just themselves. Examples of promotional groups are AIM which is concerned with family law reform and the Divorce Action Group.

► THE PROBLEM OF THE AGED

"Dishonour not the old; we shall all be numbered among them."   Ecclesiastes 8:6

Age in itself is not a problem, but there are certain difficulties particularly associated with the elderly that we will discuss here. Some are unavoidable, but a great number could be prevented or alleviated by suitable preparation and by care from family and community.

The number of people over 65 in Ireland has more than doubled since the turn of the century. This has been due to improvements in standards of living, hygiene, diet and medical knowledge. But there is little use in increasing the *quantity* of life if the *quality* of those extra years leaves much to be desired. One of the main aims of those working for old people is to improve the quality of the remainder of their lives.

1. PHYSICAL AGEING

This is characterised by losses in structure and function of various organs of the body. Skin becomes less elastic and more wrinkled, muscles less strong, bones more brittle. There is a weakening (or loss) of particular senses such as sight or hearing. Brain cells die and are not replaced, and this leads to loss of memory and mental confusion. Old people are physically less agile. They suffer painful complaints such as rheumatism and arthritis. Incontinence is not uncommon. A stroke may result in partial or permanent disablement. These and many other physical problems make old people extremely dependent on others.

Many old people suffer physical disabilities

2. HYPOTHERMIA

Control of body temperature often becomes defective in old age, so that in cold weather it may reach dangerously low levels (below 35°C). When this occurs, the body systems cannot function properly. The heartbeat is reduced, creating a shortage of oxygen supply to the brain, and if this is undetected the patient may lapse into a coma and die. This is a particular problem for the immobile, the bed-ridden and the disabled.

To prevent hypothermia, ensure that heating and clothing are adequate. It may be wise to allow an old person to sleep in a heated living-room for the winter months. As it is difficult to meet the high cost of fuel from old-age pensions, the state provides fuel vouchers and electricity or gas allowances for the elderly.

3. INADEQUATE DIET

It is important that the elderly eat a healthy diet, but as many old people have a very limited income this can pose problems. Anaemia, scurvy, brittle bones and lack of energy are conditions frequently found in elderly people, and all can be caused by poor diet.

Old people who live alone often become apathetic and lose interest in cooking and eating, living on bread and jam or a few convenience foods. Cooking processes can be difficult for those crippled with arthritis or failing sight. Many old people are afraid to go shopping for fear of being robbed. For these reasons, 'Meals on Wheels' operations have been implemented all over the country. Food is cooked at a central kitchen, possibly in a local hospital, and distributed to the elderly by voluntary workers. Government grants help offset costs.

Individual neighbourly acts, such as doing some cooking for elderly neighbours, is a practical and caring service.

4. REDUCED INCOME

Many people refuse to accept the fact that they will get old. As a result, they fail to provide for old age by contributing to some form of pension fund. Such an arrangement leaves one secure and independent so that one neither needs to depend on the state for its small pension, or on relations, for the necessities of life.

Elderly people on fixed incomes are the first to suffer in times of economic recession or inflation. In spite of the rise in the cost of living, their pensions remain static. For this reason it is essential to ensure that any pensions or investments are index-linked, that is linked to the cost of living index.

5. HOUSING

Housing the elderly must have top priority in any housing programme. Most old people wish to spend their last years in the neighbourhood in which they lived all their lives, where they have friends and are part of the community. Too often they are rehoused far from friends and familiar surroundings. Accommodation provided by the state includes:

1. *Sheltered housing units*: These are purpose-built, self-contained flatlets or bungalows grouped on a single site and often connected by an alarm system to the living quarters of a resident warden.
2. *Flats for the elderly*: Provided by local authority or voluntary groups.
3. *Institutional care*: Large numbers of elderly people are accommodated in local authority or private homes for the elderly, for example in welfare homes, nursing homes. Others remain in psychiatric or general hospitals, although now the emphasis is on returning patients as soon as possible to their own homes.

Institutional care:
an opportunity for friendship or . . .

. . . an invasion of privacy?

PROBLEMS OF INSTITUTIONAL CARE FOR THE ELDERLY

- Cost — takes up almost all their pension.
- Some patients dislike communal living.
- There is a lack of privacy, individuality and independence
- Many are afraid of being 'put away' and that they will never come out.
- Some institutions are felt to be too authoritarian, treating patients with a condescending attitude.

ACCOMMODATION FOR THE ELDERLY

Accommodation for the elderly should include the following features.

- It should be easily accessible, on one level if possible, with ramps and as few steps as possible.
- Not too large, with a pleasant aspect and garden.
- Doors and corridors wide enough for wheelchairs.
- Handrails near steps, bath and lavatory.
- Sockets set high in the wall to avoid stooping.
- A telephone is an important facility (telephone rental is free to pensioners).
- Avoidance of slippery floors, loose or frayed rugs or carpets, poor lighting, trailing flexes. Fires should be protected with a secure fireguard.

6. LIVING WITH THE FAMILY

It is sometimes possible for an elderly relative to live with a son or daughter (or in-laws). This can have its advantages, as the elderly relative has company and can baby-sit and help with the chores. But it is frequently a source of problems, such as extra work, interference and communication problems.

In order to avoid conflict, certain 'rules' must be made clear at the beginning, particularly:

- That the parents and not grandparents are totally responsible for the upbringing and disciplining of the children.
- Which areas of the house may be used by the elderly parent, if this is necessary. A 'granny flat' or bed-sitter with its own kitchenette and bathroom is ideal. This allows each generation to have its privacy and independence, yet be available when help is needed.

7. LONELINESS

Many elderly people remain alone by choice. Some withdraw from society and avoid visitors. Others are simply left alone, as visits from family and friends become a rarity.

Loneliness leads to apathy, self-neglect and eventually loss of self respect. An added worry to the old person is the increase in violent crimes against the elderly. Robbery with violence is a frequent occurrence. Extra security precautions must be taken such as door chains, strong bolts on doors and windows.

8. ATTITUDES TOWARDS THE OLD

In simple societies, the elders in the community have a high status and are valued for their knowledge and wisdom. They are the ones who pass on traditions and living skills to the younger generations.

Modern society is changing so rapidly that it is inclined to devalue old age and place great emphasis on youth. Old people in our society are often treated like children, and a patronising attitude is adopted towards them in hospitals, homes etc. State pensions are not particularly generous and perhaps are a reflection of our attitude towards the old.

COMMUNITY CARE

Many old people are at risk because of physical disabilities, mental confusion and self-neglect. The community care system ensures that public health nurses and social workers visit those over the age of 65 who may be at risk (a register of such citizens is kept up to date).

There is increasing emphasis on preventive medicine when dealing with elderly people. Those with relatively minor problems are treated at home, as this is cheaper and socially more desirable. Prolonged hospitalisation is discouraged as it takes away the independence of the elderly.

Geriatric medicine deals with the special health problems of the old. Day hospitals have been established where patients can receive daily nursing care, physiotherapy, speech therapy, chiropody and rehabilitation, as is necessary after strokes. This reduces the number of hospital beds occupied, provides company, relieves the strain on the family who look after the patient and saves the health service considerable sums of money.

Geriatric assessment units specialise in the investigation of elderly people so that the most appropriate accommodation can be arranged — for example, for short-term treatment or long-term care.

Long stay geriatric hospitals are available for those who need continuous nursing care or who are mentally disturbed.

LOCAL COMMUNITY ASSISTANCE

Neighbours can be of enormous help and support to the elderly.

- By acts of neighbourliness — for example, dropping in for a chat, inviting them in for a meal, lighting a fire, doing some cooking or housework.
- Those dealing with the elderly should avoid a condescending attitude. Old people are very proud. Respect their privacy.
- Help with some spring cleaning, repairing or redecorating.
- Do not start unless you mean to continue. Be reliable. Maintain the continuity of visits and, if it is not possible to keep an appointment, let them know.

SERVICES PROVIDED FOR THE ELDERLY

1. PUBLIC SERVICES
- Health service/community care: Many old people qualify for a medical card, whereby they are entitled to dental, optical and aural services, and special appliances such as a walking frame.
- Nursing service: Visits by public health nurses are free to over 65s.
- Long-stay nursing homes: State and private (fees — tax deductible).
- Home help service: Home helps are paid by the health board to give assistance to the elderly in their homes (see page 335).

2. VOLUNTARY ORGANISATIONS
- *Meals on Wheels* are available in many urban areas. A nominal charge is made and it is grant-funded.
- *Day centres*: Rooms are often set aside in places such as community centres as social centres for the elderly. Here they can meet in warmth and comfort and have a cup of tea and a chat, or attend occasional functions.
- *Old people's clubs or associations*: These also provide day centres and organise activities and holidays for old people. They arrange a voluntary rota of visitors for those with few relatives.
- *Voluntary visiting schemes* are particularly beneficial to those confined to homes and institutions.
- *Alone* was founded by Dublin fireman Willie Bermingham to give practical help, to publicise problems and to improve the living conditions of the elderly. Many old people are extremely poor and live in squalid, unsanitary conditions, often with no light, heat, furniture or sanitary arrangements.
- AOSTA: The Association of Services for the Aged co-ordinates voluntary and statutory work.

STATE SERVICES FOR THE ELDERLY
(see NSSB booklet, Entitlements for the over 60s.)
It is important to *apply* for these benefits.
- Retirement pension
- Contributory widow's pension
- Non-contributory widow's pension*
- Living alone allowance
- Blind pension
- Death grant
- Allowance for elderly single woman*
- Free electricity or bottled gas allowance*
- Free travel by bus and train
- Free telephone rental*
- Free black-and-white television licence*
- National fuel scheme (October-April). Most of those who are in receipt of long-term social welfare payment can obtain a book of fuel vouchers, cashable at a post office.

* These are means-tested.

RETIREMENT

Most workers must retire at 65. They should prepare for retirement both financially and socially.

1. PENSIONS

- A contributory old-age pension is paid to insured persons with a yearly average of between 20 (for minimum pension) and 48 (for maximum benefit) contributions.
- A non-contributory old-age pension is available to those not entitled to a contributory pension, and is subject to a means test.
- Private pensions are voluntary schemes that may be arranged through one's employer or privately with insurance companies. Premiums are deducted from one's salary over the years, and a pension is provided after a certain number of years' service.

2. SOCIAL PREPARATION FOR RETIREMENT

- Do not consider retirement as the end of one's useful life, but rather as an opportunity to get involved in new experiences.
- Those who were totally wrapped up in their jobs may have a difficult transition into a life of leisure.
- At first one may feel discontented, redundant, bored and frustrated. This is less likely if one prepares for retirement.
- Income will be reduced considerably, particularly if no provision such as a pension or savings have been made for retirement.
- Pre-retirement courses offer advice on subjects of interest such as health, finance, occupation and welfare services.

Note: The Retirement Planning Council of Ireland publicises the problems of retirement. They publish a booklet on retirement and provide courses on retirement preparation.

► PROBLEMS OF THE HANDICAPPED

A handicap may be defined as any limitation, congenital (from birth) or acquired, of a person's mental or physical ability that affects daily activity and work by reducing one's social contribution, employment prospects or ability to use public services.

The *physically handicapped* are those who are without one or more specific senses, such as sight or hearing, who are without the use of limbs, for example paraplegics, or who may have a combination of handicaps — a spastic, for example, may have a speech handicap and also lack physical co-ordination.

Mental handicap is defined as arrested or incomplete development of the mind. Mentally handicapped individuals may be mildly, moderately or severely handicapped.

AIM

The principal aim in dealing with the handicapped should be to help them to overcome their disability, to assist them to develop their potential and to integrate them into community life.

PREVENTION OF HANDICAP

Improved antenatal care has reduced the number of handicapped children born. Intensive medical tests soon after birth, and vaccination of young girls against rubella ('German measles'), can reduce such instances even further. Women over 40 who become pregnant run a greatly increased risk of having a child with Down's Syndrome. Smoking, drinking and taking any drugs during pregnancy also increase the risk of bearing a handicapped child.

SCHOOLING FOR THE HANDICAPPED

If the handicap is not severe, it is preferable that the child go to the local school and mix with other children. Many first attend play groups or nursery schools. Special schools are available for those whose disability cannot be catered for within the normal school system. Such schools include those for the blind, the deaf and the mentally handicapped. These schools have specially trained teachers and modern equipment designed to overcome the difficulties in learning. There are small numbers in each class, so that pupils get a great deal of individual attention. Ideally, children should remain at home with their families and attend such schools during the daytime only. However, children from rural areas may have to stay as boarders and return home at weekends or holiday time.

The Department of Education provides funds for the operation of such schools, assisted by grants from the European Social Fund.

THE NATIONAL REHABILITATION BOARD

This is the statutory agency responsible for providing services for the handicapped. It is under the control of the Department of Health and it advises that department on all aspects of handicap and rehabilitation.

The board provides a wide range of services for the handicapped and works with other agencies, such as voluntary groups, to provide further services.

- It arranges for the assessment, treatment and placement of disabled persons.
- It provides career guidance for handicapped school-leavers.
- It provides an educational advisory service.
- It runs a placement service for disabled adults.
- It runs a training and rehabilitation centre at Shannon for the mentally handicapped.

WORK FOR THE HANDICAPPED

Like everyone else, most handicapped people want to work. Work gives the disabled a sense of independence so that they do not feel they are a burden on their families and the state. Most prefer to *earn* their money rather than receive a handout such as the disability allowance.

Positive discrimination is necessary to help overcome handicaps. This includes special training centres for the handicapped, special conditions of employment, reserved places and sheltered workshops.

Sheltered workshops cater for those whose disability prevents them from working in open employment. Such workshops include those providing simple sorting and packing jobs, as well as more skilled operations such as shoemaking, gardening, carpentry and light engineering. Grants are provided by health boards for each disabled person in training or employed in a sheltered workshop.

INTEGRATION OF THE HANDICAPPED IN SOCIETY

In the past it was difficult for many of the disabled to lead a normal life as so many facilities such as buildings, buses, trains etc. were inaccessible to them. Since the International Year of the Disabled in 1981, many public buildings such as schools, churches, shops and offices have installed ramps, lifts, wide doors and toilet facilities for the disabled. It is now compulsory that all newly-built public buildings be accessible by wheelchair. Footpaths have been lowered at crossing points. Many pedestrian crossings have bleepers so that they may be safely used by the blind.

"It's not the handicapped people who need rehabilitating but the rest of the world. Don't pat on the head, offer to help, talk to handicapped people out of pity. Talk to them because you like them. Otherwise, don't bother."

David: a physically handicapped teenager

Many disabled people are not given the opportunity to do things for themselves. Another problem when attempting to include disabled people in everyday activities is the difficulty that the able-bodied seem to have in communicating with the disabled. The more they are integrated into the community, for example in local schools, the less of a problem this becomes.

In the past, disabled people were shut away in homes and kept out of the public eye. Now that they are able to get out and about, they have become very much a part of the community.

Integration has two-way benefits. Young and old alike are being encouraged to mix with, and do voluntary work with, the disabled. Many young disabled join youth clubs and are involved in a wide range of activities, including table tennis, archery, snooker, swimming and dancing. Special Olympics are held to encourage the handicapped to become involved in sport.

Many voluntary organisations organise summer camps and holidays for the disabled. Ask what you can do to help.

VOLUNTARY ORGANISATIONS CONCERNED WITH THE DISABLED

1. The Rehabilitation Institute: Established in 1951 to provide after-care for polio victims, it has since widened its range of activities to include physiotherapy, occupational therapy, schools and social centres for the handicapped, and sheltered workshops. It is also involved in research into the causes of handicap. It is financed almost entirely by fund-raising activities.
2. The Polio Fellowship of Ireland: This is an organisation with aims and objectives similar to that above. It provides schools, training and sheltered workshops for the physically and mildly mentally handicapped.
3. The Central Remedial Clinic: Similar to above.
4. The Cheshire Foundation in Ireland: This provides residential accommodation for chronically ill and permanently disabled persons.
5. The Irish Wheelchair Association: This aims for social and economic integration of wheelchair users into community activities. Services include social work, occupational therapy, holidays, sports and social activities.
6. Breakaway: This is a scheme that provides a holiday for mentally handicapped people so that their families are also free to take a holiday away from the responsibilities of caring for them.
7. The National Association for the Mentally Handicapped in Ireland.

8. L'Arche Community, Co. Kilkenny: An international federation of communities where mentally handicapped and those caring for them live and work. Founder: Jean Vanier.
9. The Irish Association for the Blind/Deaf.

The government assists the disabled in the following ways:
- Disability (Sickness) Benefit
- Invalidity Pension (permanently incapable of work)
- Disablement Benefit
- Disabled Persons Maintenance Allowance (DPMA)
- Handicapped Child Allowance
- Blind Pension/Welfare Allowance

Those receiving DPMA may also be entitled to one or more of the following:
- Free electricity allowance
- Free TV licence (black and white)
- Free telephone rental
- National Fuel Scheme

Other benefits for disabled are at discretion of health board, subject to a means test. There are also grants for converting cars and other car-driver benefits, including exemptions from parking fees/restrictions. Medical and surgical aids such as wheelchairs are free to medical card holders.

More information in the NSSB booklet: *Entitlements for the Disabled*.

DEPRIVED CHILDREN

Children in any society are totally dependent on adults for their wants and needs. When a society fails to provide these requirements, the children suffer deprivation.

Children all over the world are frequently exploited, neglected, assaulted and abused. The social problems that cause the greatest outcry are often those relating to children. When the problems are considered to be too damaging, the children may be taken into care.

FORMS OF DEPRIVATION

1. CHILDREN IN FAMILIES UNDER STRESS
The Care Memorandum on deprived children listed the types of family most likely to suffer stress:
- Families where one or both parents are not sufficiently mature or adequately adjusted to fill the role of parent well.
- Families living in demeaning or inadequate housing.
- Families where the father is continuously unemployed and where there is not an adequate income.
- Families where the father or mother has deserted.
- Families where there is a problem of alcoholism or chronic illness.
- Single-parent families often find it difficult to cope. The Status of Children Act has improved the situation for children born out of wedlock, but has not abolished the concept of illegitimacy. Such children have no succession rights (unless paternity has been established).

2. POVERTY
Child deprivation is frequently associated with poverty (see above). A family without the basic necessities of life — that is food, clothing and proper housing — experiences deprivation. Malnutrition and unsanitary conditions are common, often leading to illness and hospitalisation. Such conditions often affect educational performance.

Studies show that the children in the lowest socio-economic groups are the most likely to suffer deprivation, to be taken into care, and to get into trouble with the law.

3. EMOTIONALLY DEPRIVED CHILDREN
A child need not be poor in order to be deprived. A common form of deprivation is emotional deprivation. A child who is brought up in a home where there is little love and affection, where he or she is neglected, ignored, or subjected to mental cruelty such as sarcasm or constant teasing, will have little sense of security and may suffer emotional scars that last a lifetime. Juvenile delinquency is frequently a symptom of emotional disturbance.

4. CHILD ABUSE AND CRUELTY
See page 304.

5. ILL-HEALTH AND HANDICAP
Children born with a disability, or those who suffer from chronic illness, are deprived in that their chance of leading a normal life is impaired.

The state attempts to make up for these handicaps by providing grants, special schools etc. Those with many chronic illnesses are entitled to medical cards. Children who spend much time in hospital may become withdrawn and fall behind in schoolwork. The Association for the Welfare of Children in Hospital gives advice to parents of such children. Most children's hospitals allow unlimited visiting. Many provide overnight facilities for parents who wish to stay with their children to offset the emotional trauma of separation.

SERVICES FOR DEPRIVED CHILDREN

1. Preventive services such as pre-school play groups and day care centres. Grant-aided child care centres give preference to children of families experiencing stress.
2. Health services include social work services, child guidance services and voluntary services such as the ISPCC.
3. Children in care: Health boards are empowered to take children into care if they are orphans, abandoned or deserted, or if they are the children of parents who cannot provide for them. The courts may also commit children to care for reasons such as crime or begging, when their parents cannot control them, or are not exercising proper guardianship. Some children are put into care temporarily due to a bereavement or parental illness.

ACCOMMODATION IN CARE

1. Residential homes (called 'orphanages' in the past): Most are now small units such as family group houses which are under the charge of a caring adult — for example a social worker or a member of a religious order.
2. Special schools: Children convicted of offences and committed to care by the courts are placed in secure special schools (called 'reformatories' in the past). These are staffed by teachers and other specially trained personnel such as wardens.
3. Foster homes: The majority of children in care are placed with foster parents as it is now known that care provided in a normal family environment has the most stabilising effect on children who are emotionally vulnerable.

FOSTERING

Fostering can be short-term or long-term.

- *Short-term fostering* provides for the temporary care of children during a family crisis. It is also used for children about to be placed for adoption.
- *Long-term foster care* involves caring for children who may be from broken homes and emotionally disturbed, from a period of a few months to several years.

WHY CHILDREN MAY BE PUT IN FOSTER CARE

- Desertion of parent, particularly the mother.
- Parents are incapable of looking after children due to illness, addiction, inadequacy, bereavement etc.
- Children abandoned by parents (children cannot at present be adopted without consent of parent(s)).
- Single mothers who cannot cope but are not willing to give up child for adoption.
- Children who have been removed by the courts from parent(s) who cannot support them, have neglected or ill-treated them or who have committed offences against them.

ARRANGEMENTS FOR FOSTERING

Fostering is arranged by the health boards. Foster parents are recruited by advertising and at open meetings. They are interviewed by a social worker who subsequently visits the family in their home. It is essential that all the family agree to the fostering. When approved, they undertake to foster on behalf of the health board. A social worker will visit them regularly during the fostering period to offer assistance both to the foster parents and the foster children.

Fostering differs from adoption in that the foster parents do not take over the legal rights of parents. The foster child keeps his or her own name and the parents are encouraged to keep in touch. The foster child will never belong to the family and it is impossible to guarantee how long the child will stay. Foster parents must accept the fact that the child will eventually return to his/her own parents.

WHO MAY FOSTER?

Health boards usually prefer married couples of 25 years or older who have been married for at least three years, preferably with children of their own. Foster parents receive a regular allowance from the health board, as well as a medical card for the child and help towards expenses such as school books. Responsibility for the child rests jointly with the real parent or parents, the foster parents and the health board.

► YOUTH

Adolescence is the period of greatest change when an individual makes the transition from childhood to adult life. While the status of the adult and the child in society is clear-cut, the adolescent has no clearly defined role. While teenagers may aspire to the status of adults, they are often treated like children. They are physically mature, yet emotionally are often immature. The interval between sexual maturity and adult status is considerable.

Many young people attending third-level education are financially dependent until well into their twenties.

This may create conflict as they question traditional values and perhaps reject the values set by their parents. They often demand freedom, yet are restrained by their families. Rigid attitudes by parents who allow the adolescent no independence or responsibility may lead to rebellion and the so-called 'generation gap'.

Adolescents have no clearly defined role

The rebellious teenager dissociates from society by choosing fashions and music unacceptable to the older generation. He or she might experiment with alcohol and drugs and may 'drop out' of society.

For many teenagers, however, the transition from child to adult is less stormy. They gradually learn to make their own decisions, to take on responsibility and to 'do their own thing' without too much interference from parents or damage to themselves.

YOUTH CULTURE

The concept of the 'teenager' was developed in the 1950s to the background of 'rock 'n roll' music. This phenomenon has been largely created by the media and commercial interests, aware of growing capital in the hands of young consumers. It promotes materialism and, through advertising and technology, encourages young people (who have more money than their parents ever had) to spend this on themselves — on stereos, tapes, records, drinks, cosmetics and clothes.

Youth culture has its own music, fashion and cult figures such as pop stars and its own problems such as

Pop concert hysteria is a teenage phenomenon

drugs and delinquency. Drugs and delinquency sometimes give teenagers a separate identity which protects them by excluding parents and other adults from their world.

POSSIBLE PROBLEMS FACED BY TEENAGERS

1. Physical changes: Changes that occur during puberty bring about emotional and sexual feelings that may be difficult to deal with. Marriage is often postponed for several years until the young person is financially independent.

2. Relationships: Many young people find difficulty in dealing with relationships. These become more complex as they mature. Relationships with parents and teachers may become strained while relationships with the opposite sex are fraught with anxiety and despair. Those with a sense of self-worth find relationships less of a problem than those with low self esteem.

3. Peer pressure: This is never more influential than at this time. Young people identify with one another and imitate one another's behaviours, attitudes, dress and habits. Acceptance by the group is vitally important. They will go to any lengths to conform to its standards in order to avoid rejection.

4. Gangs: Young people, particularly in socially disadvantaged areas, get together in gangs and may be involved in vandalism, violence, drug-taking and other law-breaking behaviour in order to conform to peer pressure.

5. Urge for independence and freedom, constrained by financial and emotional dependence on family.

6. No clear status — neither adult nor child.

7. Need to develop a personal value system. Adolescents who, as children, never questioned moral standards now see themselves surrounded by conflicting messages. The media seems to advocate sexual promiscuity, while family and church promotes restraint. 'Thou shalt not steal' is commanded, yet parents help themselves to office stationery without qualms. Young adults must develop their own code of behaviour. The importance of example cannot be overstressed.

8. Major decisions must be made during this period which will affect the rest of their lives. Subject and career choices, whether to continue studying or to find a job are difficult decisions in an increasingly complicated and competitive world.

9. Pressures from commercial interests to spend money on records, concerts, discos and fashion when many teenagers have a limited amount of money may put pressure on young people to obtain money by illegal means such as stealing.

10. Drugs, page 306 and Alcohol, page 309.

YOUTH WORK

Youth organisations provide young people with a means of fulfilling themselves and playing a meaningful role in the community. They aim to develop the unique qualities and abilities that are inherent in every individual, and to assist the young person to realise his or her own special value, both for the good of the individual concerned and for the benefit of the community. Youth work is therefore concerned with the role of the young person in the community and in society. The youth worker can be a paid professional such as a social worker or teacher, or a voluntary, unpaid person who gives up his or her leisure time to work with young people.

ADVANTAGES OF YOUTH WORK

- It supplements the work of parents and schools in developing young people.
- It provides additional programmes for recreation.
- It provides opportunities for self-expression and communication.
- It keeps young people busy and interested, so that they avoid boredom.
- It helps young people to relate to one another in a meaningful way.
- It helps to educate children from deprived backgrounds.
- It equips young people with the basic skills necessary to enable them to participate in society.

FINANCIAL RESOURCES

Most youth organisations receive government grants, for example from the departments of Education and Labour. The remainder of the money needed is raised through fundraising activities such as flag days, or from parish funds.

SETTING UP A YOUTH CLUB

Development of youth services costs money, but failure to do so can cost the state more in the long run. If energetic young people have no means of channelling their energies into constructive projects, they may find negative, destructive ways of doing so, as through vandalism, violence and crime.

The main problems to be overcome when setting up a youth club are:

1. *Finance*: Money can be raised through government grants, from local (for example parish) funds and through fundraising.
2. *Finding premises*: Some clubs have obtained derelict premises cheaply and refurbished them themselves.
3. Finding suitable *youth leaders* to organise the running of the club.

4. *Publicising* the club and encouraging new membership.

Over a quarter of a million young people are involved in various youth groups. Joining a youth club offers:

1. A chance to mix with people of similar age and interests.
2. A chance to take part in a wide range of activities.
3. An opportunity for personal development.
4. A chance to learn a new skill or train as a youth leader.

Youth clubs are run along democratic lines. Youth leaders are trained to help the young people to run the clubs. Clubs run various educational courses, including personal development programmes, which teach young people how to cope with a wide range of experiences. Many organise summer projects and sports fixtures for young people. Most provide information on a range of topics of interest to the young. Entertainments such as discos are also provided.

A new development in services for youth is the youth *information centre*. This provides a wide range of information of interest to young people, such as that relating to education, apprenticeship, employment, leisure activities, emigration and problems such as drug and alcohol abuse.

Most of the large towns and cities in Ireland now have such a centre run by young people themselves, where youngsters can drop in during normal office hours.

Young people have much to offer society

LEADERSHIP

Everyone has potential for leadership. Group-centred leadership allows for the sharing of responsibility and talent and calls for co-operation and good communication within an organisation.

A true leader:

- Understands others and is sensitive to their needs.
- Represents the wishes and needs of the group.
- Has the ability to communicate readily with others.

- Is enthusiastic, with a sense of humour.
- Never underestimates the importance of participation and lets everyone give an opinion.
- Is relaxed about leadership and does not take it too seriously.
- A youth leader must have a natural liking, respect for and acceptance of youth — and be able to help them to help themselves.

VOLUNTARY ORGANISATIONS YOU CAN JOIN

There is a wide range of voluntary organisations that cater for almost every need and interest group. Here are some of them, grouped according to their interest or motivation. Further information is contained in the *Directory of National Voluntary Organisations*, published by the National Social Service Board.

ALCOHOLISM
- AA, Al Anon, Alateen (page 311)

CHILDREN
- Barnado's: Provides services for children and young people in need; adoption advice service; community projects; day foster care service and social work services for single parents.
- The Irish Society for the Prevention of Cruelty to Children (ISPCC): Professional case work service for families with children under 17; voluntary support service; operates specialist projects such as family centres and pre-school groups and volunteer community services such as play groups, baby-sitting service; help with handicapped children; children's outings etc. Its primary aim was to help children who had experienced suffering or neglect. Today, the ISPCC places stronger emphasis on preventing cruelty by dealing with its causes, by providing services for disadvantaged mothers and their children and by research. Pressure group: Action for Children.
- Care: The campaign for the care of deprived children. Seeks improvements in legislation and services for children.
- The Association for the Welfare of Children in Hospital.
- Children First: Rights of children; special area: adoption and fostering.
- HOPE helps homeless children and young people; runs a hostel.
- The United Nations Children's Fund (UNICEF) promotes children's welfare throughout the world.

COMMUNICATION AND COUNSELLING
- The Samaritans befriend the lonely, despairing and suicidal; provide a 24-hour phone-in service.
- CMAC (see Family Problems).

- Daybreak helps the lonely and isolated; group activities; meetings; outings etc.
- GROW (see Family Problems).

COMMUNITY
- Local community council (see page 319)
- Community games
- Community Information Centres
- Residents' associations
- Civil Defence (Department of Defence) trains volunteers for rescue, casualty etc.

DRUGS
- Coolmine Therapeutic Community
- Tranx Release: Self-help group for those addicted to tranquillisers and sleeping pills.
- NAR ANON: Provides support for those addicted to drugs.

An Taisce

ENVIRONMENT
- An Taisce (the National Trust for Ireland) promotes conservation of the natural and man-made environment through research, education; campaigns to protect architectural and cultural heritage; anti-pollution campaigns.
- The Irish Environmental Conservation Organisation for Youth (ECO): A voluntary youth (under 26) movement that works in association with An Taisce to improve the environment.
- The Irish Wildlife Federation promotes conservation awareness.
- The Irish Wildbird Conservancy deals with wildlife and habitat protection as they relate to birds.
- HOPE (Help Organise Peaceful Energy), Bantry, Co. Cork, encourages the use of renewable energy sources; against nuclear energy; for disarmament.
- The Green Alliance aims to raise the level of awareness of the environment through participation in the political process, anti-nuclear campaigns etc.

FAMILY PROBLEMS
- Adapt (Limerick) provides support and shelter for battered wives and children.
- The AIM Group for Family Law Reform campaigns for family law reform, operates a legal information and referral centre for those with marital problems, educates women on their legal rights.
- Aid for Parents Under Stress.

- The Catholic Marriage Advisory Council: Diocesan-based services; counselling for marriage problems.
- Family Aid provides a refuge for battered wives and their children.
- The Family Law Reform Group seeks changes in family law, equal treatment for men and women in court, improved family courts system.
- The Rape Crisis Centre offer counselling and therapy for individuals who have been sexually assaulted or raped recently or in the past.
- GROW: Community mental health movement; weekly group meetings which emphasise a self-help and mutual help approach to mental health; helps people to avoid and recover from mental breakdown; anonymous.
- The Irish Cancer Society raises funds for cancer research; provides information, etc.
- The Irish Heart Foundation aims at preventing heart disease.
- The St John Ambulance Brigade.

HANDICAPPED
See page 326.

HOMELESS
- The Simon Community cares for homeless people; runs night shelters, soup runs, community houses and other services for the homeless.
- Shelter Referral: Rehabilitation programme for alcoholics.

INTERNATIONAL RELIEF
- Christian aid: Relief and development agency of the Irish Council of Churches.
- Concern: Fund-raising; education and recruitment of volunteers to work for the relief of hunger and suffering in the Third World.
- The Irish Red Cross Society aims to improve health and to alleviate suffering throughout the world; provides training in first aid etc.
- Oxfam campaigns for world development; raises funds for relief and development projects in the Third World.

LEGAL AID
- Free legal advice centres are available to those unable to afford a solicitor; campaigns for a comprehensive scheme of legal aid.
- The Legal Aid Board: Set up by the state to run the scheme of civil legal aid and advice on a means-tested basis. There are several full-time law centres and part-time legal aid clinics.

OLD PEOPLE
See page 324.

POOR
- Salvation Army.
- The Society of St Vincent de Paul: Catholic voluntary group that works for the alleviation of need. They supply necessities to the poor, arrange visits to people in their homes, holidays and housing for the homeless.
- The National Council for the Travelling People aims to assist travelling people; helps with settlement or obtaining halts; education work; youth work.
- Minceir Misli (Travellers' Movement) promotes self-determination, better conditions and human rights for travellers. Provides support and advice to all travellers, settled and unsettled.
- The Simon Community (see Homeless).
- The Dublin Central Mission gives care and advice; provides accommodation for the elderly; rehabilitation for ex-prisoners, alcoholics etc; day facilities; second-hand clothes shop.

RURAL INTEREST
- Macra na Feirme caters for young adults in rural areas; aims to promote agriculture by assisting development and education of rural youth.
- Foróige (formerly Macra na Tuaithe) aims to develop a youth educational programme complementary to home, school and work; mainly, but not exclusively, operational in rural areas; develops and services clubs, trains leaders; publishes news sheets etc.
- Muintir na Tire: National movement that aims to promote welfare of Irish people through community development (interdenominational); involved in community councils.

SINGLE PARENTS
All are involved in promoting the interests of single parents. Some arrange accommodation and counselling for pregnant, unmarried women.
- Cherish
- Cura
- Gingerbread
- Adapt (deserted spouses)

SPORTS

A wide range of sports clubs and associations are available (see *Stepping Out*, Wolfhound Press). The following are some of the largest:

- Community Games
- The GAA
- Ireland Special Olympics (for the handicapped)
- Cospoir (the National Sports Council) is an advisory body to the Minister for Education; promotes and encourages sport and physical recreation.

WOMEN'S INTERESTS

- The Council for the Status of Women has about forty-two affiliated organisations; liaises between government departments and women's organisations; promotes educational programmes for women; examines cases of discrimination against women; runs an information centre; holds seminars, assertiveness courses; researches and publishes booklets on women, for example *Women at Home, Women in Rural Ireland*.
- The Irish Countrywomen's Association (ICA) aims to develop and improve the conditions of rural life in Ireland; holds meetings, lectures, courses, demonstrations, competitions; organises work parties, study groups, outings etc., many at their headquarters at An Grianan, Termonfeckin, Co. Louth.
- The Irish Housewives' Association aims to unite housewives so that they can play a part in all spheres of planning for the community; concerned with consumer affairs and mother-and-child issues.
- The Employment Equality Agency is a statutory body that promotes equality of opportunity between men and women in employment, investigates and initiates proceedings when necessary in cases of discriminatory policies and advertisements; undertakes research and publishes informative booklets etc.

YOUTH

Most of the organisations below receive government grants.

- The National Youth Council of Ireland is the co-ordinating body of youth organisations in Ireland; provides a general information service; library; promotes interests of youth. Most of the organisations listed are affiliated to the council.
- The National Federation of Youth Clubs is the co-ordinating and training body for the majority of Ireland's youth clubs (outside the cities of Dublin and Cork); provides leadership training, information and guidance to clubs, courses and conferences, a youth employment programme, youth exchanges, national competitions, a community work programme and international contacts.
- The Irish Girl Guides
- Boy Scouts
- The Catholic Youth Council is a youth work service organisation within the Dublin diocese; organises training courses.
- An Óige (the Irish Youth Hostel Association) aims to help all, particularly the young, to appreciate and to preserve the countryside and our heritage; provides basic hostel accommodation throughout the country. Members can use similar hostels in over fifty countries.
- Foróige (see Rural Interest, page 332).
- An Chomhairle le Leas Óige: Under the Dublin VEC; aims to help adults and young people to develop effective, worthwhile programmes and activities through youth clubs; provides grants to clubs.
- Junior Chamber Ireland (youth section of Chamber of Commerce).
- YMCA, YWCA, CYMS
- Young Ireland promotes the purchase of Irish goods.

Child health services help keep children fit and healthy

Social and welfare services may be statutory (state-run) or voluntary. In the past, such services were totally the responsibility of the family. Today, both the state and voluntary bodies help to implement them.

The social services provided by the state include:

- Health services
- Welfare services such as social insurance and assistance
- Education
- Housing

► HEALTH

The state ensures that each person, regardless of income, has access to medical care. There is, in effect, a tiered system which is subject to a means test.

CATEGORY I (40%) — MEDICAL CARD HOLDERS

To qualify for a medical card, people must earn less than a certain income which is laid down each year. They are entitled to a wide range of services free of charge. These include choice of doctor, prescribed drugs, dental, eye and ear services, out-patient treatment, maintenance and treatment in hospital.

CATEGORY II (45%) — HOSPITAL SERVICES CARD HOLDERS

These people must have an income less than a prescribed limit. They are not eligible for a medical card but get free treatment in a public ward subject to a daily maintenance charge (see below). Out-patient charges are free.

CATEGORY III (15%)

Those who earn over the Category II prescribed income are in this category. They get maintenance in a public ward subject to the daily charge. They must pay consultants fees, both as in-patients and out-patients.

HOSPITAL CHARGES

1. In-patient maintenance in a public ward. Currently £10 (_ _ _) per day up to a limit of £100 per year.
2. Out-patient currently £10 (_ _ _) on first visit (subsequent visits relating to the same illness/accident are free of charge).
3. Private/semi-private patients — people in all categories must pay full maintenance and treatment charges.

HEALTH CONTRIBUTIONS

The majority of the population pay a health contribution of 1.25 per cent of their income, up to the maximum annual income limit for Category II services. Exceptions include medical card holders, those in receipt of deserted wife's allowance, unmarried mothers or prisoner's wives' allowance.

The contribution is deducted at source by one's employer as part of the Pay-Related Social Insurance (PRSI) contribution. The self-employed pay their contribution annually to the Revenue Commissioners.

Guide to income limits (more detailed information from Health Board)				
	1990		Current	
	Weekly	Yearly	Weekly	Yearly
Single person (living alone)	£75	£3,900		
Married couple	£108	£5,616		
Allowance for child under 16. Other outgoings may be considered (higher income limits for those over 66 years)	£12.50	£650		
Annual Prescribed limit Category I - under		£5,616		
Category II - under		£16,700		
Category III - over		£16,700		

ORGANISATION OF THE HEALTH SERVICES

Health services are administered by eight regional health boards.

- Eastern
- North-Eastern
- South-Eastern
- Midland
- Southern
- Mid-Western
- Western
- North-Western

Each health board consists of about thirty members. They include representatives of the pharmaceutical, medical, nursing and dental professions, as well as three nominees of the Minister for Health. Half the board consists of elected councillors.

Health boards are financed mainly from government funds. The remainder comes from the health contributions of employees.

COMMUNITY CARE

Each health board is subdivided into a number of community care areas, each of which has a community care team led by a director. Indirectly involved are general practitioners and voluntary organisations such as Meals on Wheels.

The aim of a community care programme is to provide as many services as possible within the community care area. It includes all health services in which care is provided outside hospitals and institutions (most are provided through health centres).

SERVICES PROVIDED BY COMMUNITY CARE TEAMS

1. Medical services, including general practitioners, treatment of infectious diseases, vaccination and other preventive services.
2. Community Welfare Services provided by welfare officers, and assistance officers who are involved in providing cash payments.
3. Dental service.
   - To medical card holders and their dependants.
   - To children under 6 and pupils of national schools.
4. Child health services
   - Medical screening of the development of all children between the ages of 1 and 2. Those with diseases or defects are referred to appropriate care.
   - Free examination of all children under 6.
   - Regular examination, free of charge, to pupils attending national schools, together with free dental, aural, ophthalmic (spectacles) treatment.
5. Home help service
   Health boards can assist in the maintenance at home of the following:
   - Sick or infirm persons or their dependants.
   - Women availing of surgical or midwifery services etc.
   - Persons who, without such services, would have to go to a home — for example the elderly, who are the main beneficiaries of this scheme.

Home help service is usually confined to Category I patients. Home helps may be full- or part-time and are employed by the health board.

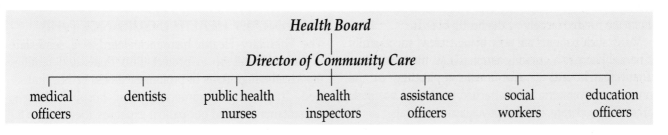

Health Board
|
Director of Community Care
|

medical officers | dentists | public health nurses | health inspectors | assistance officers | social workers | education officers

6. Public health nurse
The duties of the nurse include:
• Midwifery • Care of the Aged • Nursing of the chronically ill • Child welfare • After-care of patients discharged from hospitals
7. Social worker
These workers are: (a) community-based, liaising with doctors and voluntary organisations; or (b) medical or psychiatric, providing social services for those in hospital or outside.
8. Children's officers
These officers are public health nurses or social workers with special responsibility for children in their area, offering support to families of children at risk. They organise adoption, fostering and the placing of children in care.

GENERAL HOSPITAL PROGRAMME

This programme covers the treatment of patients in medical, surgical or maternity hospitals, including treatment in out-patient clinics. Hospitals are financed mainly (90%) by the health boards.

St Vincent's, Elm Park, Dublin: a general hospital

SPECIAL HOSPITAL PROGRAMME

This covers services for the mentally ill, e.g. treatment by consultant psychiatrists, both in and out of hospital. The mentally handicapped are cared for mainly in institutions and schools run by voluntary and religious organisations which are funded largely by the health boards.

Many such patients are now being treated successfully at home. There is a growing emphasis on the integration of psychiatric and general medicine, leading to the concept of psychiatric units attached to general hospitals rather than separate, isolated psychiatric hospitals.

HEALTH SERVICES AVAILABLE TO EVERYONE

- Maintenance in public wards (subject to a daily charge).
- Infectious diseases: Immunisation and hospital services.
- Refund on drugs scheme: Anyone who spends more than £28 (1990) on prescribed drugs and medicines in one calendar month is entitled to a refund of the balance from the health board.
- Free drugs for certain long-term illnesses, including mental handicap, cystic fibrosis, diabetes, epilepsy, multiple sclerosis, Parkinsonism, acute leukaemia in children and some other diseases.
- Children under 16 are entitled to free in-patient and out-patient treatment of many long-term diseases.

MEDICAL CARD HOLDERS MAY ALSO BE ENTITLED TO:

- Home nursing services
- Walking aids and wheelchairs
- Chiropody service
- Assistance in travelling to and from hospitals and health centres

HEALTH BOARD CASH PAYMENTS

- Maternity grant (£8) is payable to those on medical cards (separate from the maternity benefit from social insurance).
- Disabled person's maintenance allowance.
- Allowance for care of physically or mentally handicapped children.
- Blind welfare allowance.
- Supplementary welfare allowance: Administered by health boards under the supervision of the Department of Social Welfare. This is a flexible, speedy local service to provide a basic income for those with insufficient means and who are not provided for under the usual social welfare schemes. Application is made to the community welfare officer at the health centre. Urgent cases are dealt with on the spot.

HEALTH SERVICES IN THE EC

Insured persons and their dependants staying temporarily in an EC country are entitled to urgent medical treatment on the same basis as insured citizens of that country. Those receiving a social security pension from another EC country are entitled to a medical card here.

VOLUNTARY HEALTH INSURANCE (VHI)

The Voluntary Health Insurance Board is a semi-state organisation set up to protect individuals and families against the high costs of prolonged illness or hospitalisation. It provides insurance against hospital charges, consultants' fees and out-patient expenses. (See chapter 8.)

SOCIAL WELFARE

Most governments take money from the better-off in the form of tax in order to give those with little or no income enough to provide the basics of life.

Most employees in Ireland also pay a proportion of their earnings, up to an annual limit of £17,300 (1990) in pay-related social insurance (PRSI) contributions. The employer pays the remainder. These contributions help to pay for social welfare benefits.

During a recession there are more claims for unemployment benefit

SOCIAL INSURANCE BENEFITS

CONDITIONS

- Payable only if the insured has made a certain number of contributions (if unemployed, these will be credited) currently 39 weeks in the year prior to the claim.
- Duration of benefit varies, as does procedure for making claims.
- Additional amounts are payable for dependants such as a wife and children.
 (For further details see *Summary of Social Insurance and Social Assistance Services*, Department of Social Welfare.)

BENEFITS

Most of these benefits are 'pay-related': contributions and benefits are worked out as a percentage of salary.

1. Unemployment benefit (not paid during strikes).
2. Disability benefit, paid during periods when one is incapacitated or ill.
3. Maternity benefit, which is paid for approximately seven weeks before and seven weeks after delivery.
4. Invalidity pension for those who are permanently incapable of work.
5. Contributory widow's pension.
6. Contributory orphan's allowance, paid to children of insured workers up to the age of 18 (or 21, if one is in full-time education).

7. Deserted wife's benefit, paid on wife's or husband's insurance; only paid after three months' desertion has elapsed. (Supplementary allowance may be claimed during this time.)
8. Contributory old-age pension, payable at the age of 66.
9. Treatment benefit, paid to insured persons who are eligible for dental and optical benefit and to their spouses.

SOCIAL ASSISTANCE

This may be claimed by those not covered by PRSI or those who have reached the limit of their entitlement. It is non-contributory. Rates of payment are lower and claimants are subject to a means test. It includes:

1. Unemployment assistance
2. Non-contributory widow's pension
3. Non-contributory orphan's allowance
4. Non-contributory old age pension (over 66)
5. Deserted wife's allowance (see Deserted wife's benefit, above)
6. Prisoner's wife's allowance
7. Unmarried mother's allowance (increases with each child)
8. Single woman's allowance: Paid to women between the ages of 58 and 66 who have stayed at home to care for aged parents.
9. Blind person's pension

OTHER SERVICES AVAILABLE TO THE NEEDY

- *Rent allowance.*
- *Family income supplement*: This is to ensure that low-paid workers are not worse off than those on social welfare. It may be granted to a family where the earner is in a low-paid job and there is at least one child. It varies according to the number of children in the family.
- *Supplementary welfare allowances* paid by community welfare officer at health centre: This is a payment to people on low incomes, for example, unemployment assistance which brings their total income up to a basic minimum income.
 An exceptional needs payment may be made to meet a particular problem such as rent arrears or funeral expenses to those in receipt of the supplementary allowance.
 Emergency payments may also be made in urgent cases, for example after a house fire.
- *School meals*: Provided to pupils of national schools in deprived areas.
- *Free footwear* to children under 15 whose parents receive supplementary welfare. Vouchers are issued for use in shops.

Those in receipt of certain disability and old-age pensions and who are living alone, or with a dependant, may be entitled to:

- Free electricity allowance
- Free licence for black and white television
- Free telephone rental allowance
- Free fuel scheme

OTHER BENEFITS

- All citizens over the age of 66 are allowed free travel at off-peak times.
- Child Benefit (formerly called Children's Allowance) is a monthly sum (1990 = £15.80) paid in respect of each child under 16 (or up to 18 if in full-time education).

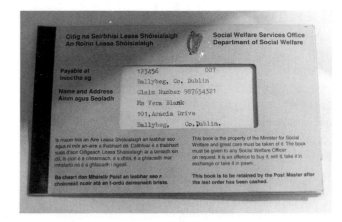

Child Benefit Book

24 CHILD DEVELOPMENT AND EDUCATION

A child grows and develops in various ways during its formative years. Much of the responsibility for optimum growth and development lies with its parents.

CHILD DEVELOPMENT

1. PHYSICAL DEVELOPMENT

The child grows, increasing in size. Optimum growth and good health are more likely if the child eats a well-balanced diet and receives sufficient rest, sleep, fresh air and exercise. Unhealthy living conditions can interfere with the health and development of growing children.

A healthy diet gives a baby a good start

2. MOTOR DEVELOPMENT

This is learning to control and to co-ordinate movement: learning to grasp, sit, walk, talk and develop various motor skills. Audio-visual stimulation and toys to touch and play with help development and manual dexterity.

3. EMOTIONAL OR PERSONALITY DEVELOPMENT

Personality is the distinct personal identity of an individual. It is the combination of characteristics that determine the way in which each person reacts to life in behaviour, feelings and relationships with other people.

The personality is based on a foundation of inherited temperament and is continuously being moulded and modified by our experiences as we go through life.

A new-born child has no real emotions — a baby cries because it is hungry or uncomfortable but it doesn't experience feelings such as love or anger. These are learned in time from his family and those around him.

Adult emotions are greatly influenced by childhood experiences. The family is the initial environment in which a child's personality develops. A child is completely dependent on its parents to meet its physical needs. It also has a strong need for love and security. If these needs are not met, the child may suffer lifelong feelings of insecurity and rejection. *Good parenting prevents many behavioural disorders.*

It is essential for a child to develop a sense of *identity* and *self-worth*. Parents and siblings greatly influence the image a child has of itself — its self-image. If a child is made to feel loved and wanted, given lots of affection, praise and encouragement, it is likely to develop a positive self-image. On the other hand, parents who neglect their children, who ignore their achievements and tease them or tell them they are stupid or good-for-nothing will give children a low opinion of themselves.

Factors that influence personality development
- Good parenting
- Relationships with family and friends
- School and teachers
- Social life
- Experience and responsibility
- Coping with life and its stresses

Qualities found in a well-balanced personality
1. Ability to form enduring relationships with others.
2. Ability to cope with life and to tolerate reasonable stress.
3. Ability to accept responsibility.
4. Ability to defer gratification, not to demand instant satisfaction.
5. Ability to satisfy basic drives (ambition, sexual) without harming others.

6. Willingness to submerge personal interests at times for those of others.

4. DEVELOPMENT OF INTELLIGENCE

Learning occurs in several ways: imitation, experience, association, identification and play. The two basic factors that influence our intelligence are heredity and environment.

■ *Heredity*

Intelligence is largely genetic, but experts fail to agree to what extent. It is generally accepted that 80 per cent of our intelligence is inherited; the remaining 20 per cent is influenced by environment. This means that nature has set a limit to our potential which cannot be altered.

■ *Environment*

Factors such as family life, housing, schooling, and emotional and social relationships can all have a favourable or unfavourable influence on our development. Environmental influence in the years from birth to the age of five is particularly profound (as shown by child psychologist Maria Montessori).

The world of the child is that created by its parents. When this is enriched by love, encouragement and appropriate stimulation, the child feels secure and has a greater opportunity to come close to its potential. When it is restricted and a child is ignored, scolded or undisciplined, or when family problems impinge on its life, the child grows up with a poor self-image and is unlikely to reach its full potential.

Enriched Environment	*Deprived Environment*
• Plenty of love; good family relationships	• Poor family relationships
• Frequent encouragement and praise	• Neglect, physical and mental
• Consistent parenting	• Inconsistency
• Regular routines	• Irregular, disordered life
• Generous, caring parents, who give good example	• Selfish parents, or those overwhelmed with problems
• Gentle discipline	• Too much or too little discipline
• Conversation encouraged	• Little conversation; child ignored
• Lots of activities, often shared by parents	• Boredom; too much television
• Lots of books in the home	• Little reading material
• Other children with whom to play	• Isolated; no-one to talk to
• Children gradually allowed freedom and independence	• Little freedom; too many restrictions

5. SOCIAL DEVELOPMENT

First a child develops a relationship with its parents, then its brothers and sisters and the wider circle of the family such as grandparents. This must be a gradual process as young children are often afraid of strangers. By the time it

Social development: learning to make friends

is three, the child is ready to make friends with other children. This is an important stage, as it is at this time that the child discovers it cannot always have it own way, but must recognise and respect the rights of others. This knowledge enables the child to mix and prepares it for a world away from its parents, as when it goes to school. Separation from parents, as during a stay at hospital, is quite traumatic for a young child. For this reason, mothers are allowed unlimited visiting and are even encouraged to stay in some hospitals.

Social development can be defined as a *progression of stages through which a child learns to relate to others*. Social life demands that children conform if they are to fit into the group to which they belong. If social development does not proceed normally, a child is likely to remain self-centred and demanding. Discipline and consideration for others are factors which assist social development.

DISCIPLINE

In order to fit into society, children must learn how to behave appropriately and to recognise the rights of others. This is achieved by imposing a certain amount of discipline on them. Parents need to set definite limits on what is and is not permitted. By doing this, children will know where they stand and this will make them feel more sure of themselves. When discipline is inconsistent, or totally lacking, the child is confused.

Discipline requires patience, firmness and understanding. The best form of discipline uses praise as a reward for good behaviour. Physical (or corporal) punishment gives children a model of violence that they will imitate, as well as engendering resistance and rebellion. Postponed punishment ('Wait till your father gets home') is not very effective.

Withdrawal of love must never be used as a threat when disciplining children. In fact, children need to be reminded that they are loved even though they are being punished for doing wrong.

Eventually, correct use of discipline brings about self-control, self-restraint and finally self-discipline — when the individual no longer requires control from outside sources to make him or her behave correctly.

CHILDREN REQUIRE DISCIPLINE

1. For their own safety.
2. So that they will be accepted by others.
3. Because they are not yet experienced or mature enough to make the wisest decisions in their own interests and in the best interests of society.

GOOD MANNERS

The basis of good manners is consideration for others. It is never too early to instil in a child habits of good manners. The child needs an awareness of the feelings of others (tact and consideration) and the ability to put oneself in the place of another (empathy). Good manners help to smooth the way for social interaction in an ever more unpredictable and complex world.

Bad manners are caused by ignorance, selfishness and an indifference to the feelings of others. Good manners display an interest in others and an awareness of their existence and dignity. Punctuality, respect for the old and infirm, gratitude, thoughtfulness and generosity cannot be learned from an etiquette book. Children need to see their parents and other adults putting these positive traits into practice if they are to develop a genuine caring for and sensitivity to, the feelings of those about them.

EDUCATION

"The State acknowledges that the primary and natural educator of the child is the Family and guarantees to respect the inalienable right and duty of parents to provide, according to their means, for the religious and moral, intellectual, physical and social education of their children"

Constitution of Ireland, 42:1

Education of children, like charity, should begin at home. In the past, the *only* education a child received was from the family. The last century has seen schools take over the job of educating the young. Yet from research, we now know that a child has developed much of his or her intellectual capacity *before* entering the schoolroom. The onus, therefore, is on parents to provide suitable stimulation and a good learning environment from birth if the child is to develop its full potential. Just as food, rest, fresh air and sunlight help a child to grow physically strong, mental abilities can be developed by stimulating the mind at home: by reading, talking to and playing with children, and giving them every opportunity to broaden their interests.

PRE-SCHOOL CARE

The growth in the numbers of working mothers has led to an increased demand for nurseries, day care centres and play schools. Pre-school care may be organised on a voluntary or community basis. It can be privately run or organised and subsidised by the state or its agencies.

1. DAY NURSERIES, DAY CARE CENTRES, CRÈCHES

These care for children from birth to school-going age. They generally have facilities for sleeping, washing, changing and play. Most are under the supervision of a nursery nurse or SRN. The Department of Health subsidises a number of day care centres, which must conform to certain standards to be eligible for grants. Preference in such centres is given to children who, for social or medical reasons, are most in need of their services, e.g. children of single parents or of parents who cannot cope. Private child-minders also take care of the children of working mothers for a fee.

2. PLAY GROUPS

These exist for the purpose of providing a stimulating environment in which young children, usually of three to four years of age, can play and mix socially with other children. Play groups may be set up privately, on a rota basis by parents, or run by a community that employs a play group leader. Play groups generally operate for about three hours each weekday morning. While they are not schools, a good play group will provide an environment that will stimulate learning potential and creativity, in which the child learns by doing rather than by being taught.

342

Play groups stimulate learning and creativity

3. NURSERY SCHOOLS
These are often run by teachers, e.g. Montessori-trained instructors, who encourage young children to learn through play. Special learning equipment is used and children learn at their own pace.

WHAT TO LOOK FOR IN PRE-SCHOOL CARE
1. Facilities: Premises should be sufficiently large, safe, clean, with plenty of ventilation and sufficient toilet facilities.
2. Equipment should be safe, with a good selection of art materials, construction toys and educational aids, e.g. water, sand.
3. Nursery nurse or leader should have a genuine liking for children — personal recommendation is the best indicator.
4. Avoid overcrowded nurseries, play schools etc.; children may not be sufficiently supervised.
5. Check insurance — fire, accident, personal and public liability.

ADVANTAGES OF PRE-SCHOOL CARE
1. Some form of pre-school child care is essential for working mothers with pre-school children.
2. They enable full-time mothers to get some relief from their child-minding routine.
3. Trained personnel can help to bring out the best in a young child, channelling its energies into constructive play and learning experiences.
4. Children learn independence and self-discipline.
5. Children learn to mix with others, to form relationships and to share, which is very important, especially for only children.

6. Pre-school groups and nurseries are particularly important in deprived areas where there are few facilities for play, and in order to counteract the social disadvantages experienced by children living in poor housing conditions.

THE EDUCATIONAL SYSTEM IN IRELAND
This is organised into a three-tier system:
- First-level or primary education
- Second-level or post-primary education
- Third-level education

Age	School/College	Stage
Years 2-5	Play groups/nursery schools	Pre-school
4-12	National; special schools (handicapped)	First level
12-18	Vocational/community/comprehensive/secondary/special	Second level
16 +	Apprenticeships/day-release courses/secretarial/agricultural colleges	Second level
17 +	Colleges of education; universities, RTC, NIHE, DIT	Third level
18 +	Vocational/community colleges/DIT/RTC/universities	Adult education

PRIMARY SCHOOLS
Most children receive their primary education in state-supported *national schools*. Attendance at school is compulsory for children between the ages of six and fifteen, although children may enrol once they reach their fourth birthday. Primary education is entirely free. Books and other extras must be provided by the parent, but there is a scheme that provides needy children with textbooks.

'I hear — I forget
I see — I remember
I do — I understand'

Most national schools are denominational, being under the patronage of Roman Catholic or Protestant parishes, although no child may be refused admission to the local national school because of religious beliefs. Government of national schools is the responsibility of a management board made up of parents, teachers and nominees of the religious body running the school.

A set curriculum is followed, which is more child-centred than in the past. There is a greater emphasis on art and practical work, e.g. nature study, as well as the core subjects such as English, Irish, mathematics, history and geography.

SPECIAL SCHOOLS

Special primary schools are available to children with mental or physical handicaps, for itinerant children and for emotionally disturbed children.

SECOND-LEVEL EDUCATION

Most second-level schools provide junior-cycle courses and Leaving Certificate courses, the main difference between the schools being in the system of ownership or management.

1. SECONDARY SCHOOLS

These are schools privately owned by various bodies. Over 90 per cent are non-fee-paying, although voluntary donations may be requested; the remainder charge a fee.

Most secondary schools are single-sex schools and denominational, but this is changing. Most concentrate on academic subjects. Some schools are selective, i.e. they use an entrance examination to determine which pupils they will take.

2. VOCATIONAL SCHOOLS/TECHNICAL SCHOOLS/COMMUNITY COLLEGES

Run by the local authority vocational educational committee (VEC), these are usually co-educational, non-denominational schools which provide academic subjects and which also concentrate on practical and technical subjects such as commerce, woodwork, metalwork and home economics. Vocational schools also prepare pupils for employment in trades, commerce and industry by providing apprenticeship courses, secretarial courses and day-release courses.

Vocational schools play a major part in adult education (see page 346).

Community college is the name given to new schools under the VECs.

3. COMPREHENSIVE SCHOOLS/COMMUNITY SCHOOLS

Comprehensive schools were established in areas that had neither a secondary nor a vocational school. Their

A co-educational second-level school

aim was to combine academic and technical subjects in a broad curriculum. There are fifteen comprehensive schools in Ireland and no more are planned. The emphasis has now shifted to community schools, which have a similar aim: to provide equal educational opportunity to all children of an area, regardless of ability, by providing free, comprehensive educational facilities in one school. They also make their facilities available for adult education, community projects and other uses. Costs are met by the state; management includes two parents, two religious and two VEC members.

THIRD-LEVEL EDUCATION

About 13 per cent of second-level students go on to third-level education. Third-level fees are heavily subsidised. Grants for fees and accommodation are available to those who satisfy a means test. Entrance to most of the colleges is achieved through a points system based on Leaving Certificate results and processed through the Central Applications Office (CAO). There are several types of third-level college:

1. UNIVERSITIES

There are seven university colleges in the Republic of Ireland.

- University colleges in Dublin, Cork and Galway } National
- St. Patrick's College, Maynooth } University of Ireland
- Dublin University (Trinity College)
- Dublin City University } formerly NIHE
- University of Limerick }

Universities offer some of the following courses, and many more, all leading to degrees.

- Arts
- Sciences (natural and social)
- Law
- Engineering
- Medicine
- Dentistry
- Veterinary science
- Agriculture
- Business studies

Former NIHE colleges specialise in technology and communications

Students leave UCD

2. REGIONAL TECHNICAL COLLEGES

Situated in cities and large towns such as Cork, Waterford, Sligo, Dundalk and Letterkenny, these offer degree and diploma courses in a wide field of subjects — some based on local industry or local needs. Financed by the Department of Education through the VEC, courses include business studies, art and design, science, engineering and other technological courses.

3. THE DUBLIN INSTITUTE OF TECHNOLOGY

Specialist colleges in Dublin are collectively known as the Dublin Institute of Technology (DIT) and are run by the Dublin VEC. They include:

- The College of Technology, Bolton Street, specialising in engineering and construction.
- The College of Technology, Kevin Street, specialising in electronics and chemistry.
- The College of Commerce, Rathmines, specialising in business, marketing, journalism.
- The College of Marketing and Design, Parnell Square.
- The Dublin College of Catering, Cathal Brugha Street.
- The Municipal College of Music, Chatham Street.

4. COLLEGES OF EDUCATION

These are affiliated to universities and offer degrees in education (B.Ed.). They include:

(a) Those which train primary school teachers, for example St. Patrick's, Drumcondra, Dublin.
(b) Thomond College, Limerick, specialising in physical education.
(c) Home economics colleges in Sligo and Blackrock, Dublin.
(d) The National College of Art and Design.
(e) Agricultural colleges.

Notes

- The National Council for Educational Awards (NCEA) validates and awards degrees and diplomas to most third-level students outside the university system.
- The Higher Education Authority (HEA) co-ordinates and advises on higher education, assesses their financial requirements and allocates grants to students who achieve sufficient points in their chosen subject areas and satisfy a means test relating to parents' income and family size. Those living outside commuting distance also get an accommodation grant.
- 72 per cent of entrants to third-level education come from the top four socio-economic groups. Children of unskilled and semi-skilled workers account for only 1 per cent of the number attending UCD.
- Third-level education is heavily subsidised. The amount spent on each third-level student is over six times that spent on each primary pupil.

THE PURPOSE OF EDUCATION

Education has three important functions.

1. It is a method of socialisation, transmitting the norms and values of society, preparing individuals to fit into society. It attempts to instil a national identity, as we learn how our country functions — its history, geography, language etc.
2. Education influences personality development by broadening the child's experiences. In school, a child learns to be independent, and to co-operate on projects and teams. Other qualities developed should include self-discipline, loyalty (to school), team spirit, honesty, obedience, responsibility, leadership and decision-making.
3. School assists social development in helping the child to relate to adults and to other children.

THE IMPORTANCE OF EDUCATION TO SOCIETY

1. It has a stabilising effect, helping to preserve the existing order of things without, it is hoped, being too conservative.

2. It has an economic function in preparing members of society for earning a living by providing a general education.

3. It has a social function, in that it teaches individuals how to deal with people and how to fit into normal society.

Educational achievement: young scientist meets elder statesman

FACTORS WHICH INFLUENCE EDUCATIONAL ACHIEVEMENT

1. *Parental attitudes*: Encouragement increases potential. Lack of interest or failure to encourage are significant factors in poor performance.

2. *Family size/situation*: Children in large families spend less time in conversation with adults. With limited vocabulary, they do less well in school.

3. *Educational level of parents*: Well-educated parents understand the system better. They have the interest and ability to help children with school work. Their homes have more books where reading is encouraged. All of these are factors which provide children with an educational advantage.

4. *Degree of parental care*: Children from a secure, loving environment are more likely to be healthy and miss fewer days from school. They tend to be brighter and less likely to be in trouble with the authorities than children from troubled homes.

5. *Local environment*: Children from socially deprived areas, where unemployment and delinquency are common, show poor performance in school. Their motivation and achievement are usually low.

6. *Educational environment*: Factors such as streaming, size of class or school, its reputation, teacher attitudes and skills, and the standing of the principal in the eyes of pupils all influence attainment. A high turnover of teachers has a bad effect, particularly at primary level.

7. *Peer group*: This influences attitudes to school and work. Children will raise or lower their standards of both school work and behaviour in order to conform to group pressure.

"Correction does much. Encouragement does more."
Wolfgang von Goethe

FEATURES OF CONTEMPORARY EDUCATION

- Primary education is more child-centred than it was in the past.
- Students spend longer at school than in the past. They may not leave until they are fifteen years of age.
- Free education has enabled those in the lower socio-economic groups to avail of education up to, and including, third-level courses.
- There is more parental and community involvement than in the past.
- *Streaming* is used in some schools. This involves separating children into classes purely on the basis of their intellectual ability. While it enables children of similar ability to be taught at the same pace, it tends to create an intellectual elite and, at the other extreme, low-status groups.
- *Examination stress* can be caused by competition for places and by parental pressure.
- There is increased emphasis on *technology*, for example the use of computers.
- *Remedial teachers* provide specialised help for slow learners.

Examinations are a common cause of stress in young people

- Some schools provide a *transition year*, away from the pressures of examinations, in which the wider aspects of education, living and work experience are explored.
- *Pre-employment courses* involve placing pupils in a selection of jobs for work experience and general training for work and living. These courses are aimed at those who are about to leave school.
- Introduction of new child-centred junior cycle syllabus. A single examination CSE (Certificate of Secondary Education) replaces the Group and Intermediate Certificate.

ADULT EDUCATION

Adult education facilitates those who are no longer in full-time education to study their choice of subjects at any stage in their lives. It is now regarded as an important section of our general educational system.

About 10 per cent of adults participate yearly in further education. Most of these are from the higher socio-economic groups.

An adult literacy class

THE IMPORTANCE OF ADULT EDUCATION

1. Many older adults have never progressed beyond primary education.
2. Some of those who completed their education can neither read nor write. They are therefore unable to cope with the normal functions of living that require these skills, including writing letters, filling out forms, reading notices, warnings and advertisements. *Literacy classes* are now available for such people in centres around the country.
3. Married women who have time on their hands when their children have grown up may regret their lack of qualifications and wish to take up learning again.
4. Higher qualifications increase one's chances of finding a job.
5. Changing technology may require adults to re-train in order to keep abreast of the times.

6. There is a growing respect for education, not just for the qualifications but for the personal fulfilment it brings.
7. Adult education enables people to meet others with similar interests.

Hobbies such as pottery may be studied at night

CENTRES FOR ADULT EDUCATION

The government has made available increased funds for adult education. Many vocational education committees have full-time adult education officers whose function is to improve and co-ordinate adult education in their region.

Aontas (the National Association of Adult Education) represents most of the voluntary agencies involved in adult education. It promotes the development of adult education, arranges courses and co-ordinates the work of the many bodies involved in adult education.

1. *Vocational education committees* provided the only sources of adult education for years. Today they are still in the forefront, providing both day and night classes in examination subjects, technical skills, hobbies and other courses of general interest such as psychology and child care.
2. *Comprehensive and community schools* provide similar courses today.
3. *Regional technical colleges* provide courses leading to technical and business qualifications.
4. *The Dublin Institute of Technology* provides second- and third-level courses for adults, as well as evening classes, leading to trade certificates (for example London City and Guilds).
5. *Dublin City University*, Glasnevin, Dublin, provides 'distance learning' courses, combining correspondence tuition, lectures and tutorials, supplemented by radio broadcasts, leading to certificates and diplomas. Open university courses are also being made available through DCU.

6. *Universities* provide extra-mural courses on a wide range of topics. Some evening and part-time degree courses are also available.

7. Certain centres such as the *Dublin Institute of Adult Education*, the College of Industrial Relations and the Irish Management Institute specialise in adult education courses.

8. *FÁS (the Industrial Training Authority)* provides training for trades and other job-related courses, including 'Run Your Own Business' courses.

9. Voluntary organisations such as Macra na Feirme and the ICA run regular courses.

25 MODERN SOCIETY

In every human society, each person makes a contribution, usually through his or her work. In simple societies, such work is directly associated with one's needs — tilling the soil, hunting, making food and clothing. In modern society, our labour is paid for in money which we use to buy what we need.

Money is the medium of exchange in western society and it is often the yardstick by which our *status* in society is measured. For example, if we are poor, we have little power and status; those who are rich are powerful and influential.

▶ THE GROWTH OF INDUSTRIALISATION

Before the Industrial Revolution, people worked mainly in agricultural occupations. During the nineteenth century they began to abandon their farms and move into factories, leading to the development of large towns and cities (*urbanisation*). The conditions in these early factories were often inhuman. They were badly designed, badly ventilated 'sweat shops'. Workers, including children, worked long hours in intolerable conditions. Work was dangerous, dirty and exhausting. Workers were exploited, working for very low wages with no breaks, no holidays and no benefits. It was no wonder that *trade unions* developed to protect the rights of their workers.

The twentieth century has seen enormous changes in the working conditions of employees.

- The working day and *working week* have been *reduced* — 40 hours or even fewer per week is the norm.
- *Work is less dangerous*. Machines are safer and easier to use, involving less labour. Legal safety standards are imposed.
- *Work conditions have improved*. Factories today are purpose-built, warm, well-lit and well-ventilated.
- *Job rotation* and team work in factories make assembly-line work less monotonous.
- The *social welfare of workers* is emphasised. Maternity and sick leave, paid holidays, insurance and pensions are standard benefits.
- *Labour legislation* sees to it that workers are no longer exploited. For example, there are strict conditions regarding children working, minimum holidays etc.
- *Worker participation and profit sharing* are common, leading to greater involvement in decision-making and improved efficiency of workers.

Research shows that such improvements make workers happy, increase output, reduce absenteeism and staff turnover. A job that gives no satisfaction, which is boring, with little chance of promotion, makes workers discontented. This leads to tensions and frustrations at work, as well as industrial unrest and strikes.

AUTOMATION

The term automation describes mass-production by machines, with minimum human supervision. One operator can now control the work formerly done by several workers. Computers and the microchip can, in seconds, do work that humans would take hours or even days to achieve.

An automated assembly plant

ADVANTAGES OF AUTOMATION

1. Automation makes industrial work cleaner, easier, safer and less strenuous.
2. The more tedious, repetitive jobs such as assembly-line work are taken over by machine, thus reducing job frustration.
3. Jobs are more interesting and responsible; controllers and operators are skilled workers.
4. Automation increases output.
5. Automation speeds up output. Computers can do in seconds what a human would take much longer to do.
6. Labour costs are reduced as fewer workers are needed.
7. Technology enables us to plan work more efficiently, providing us with more leisure to enjoy life.

DISADVANTAGES OF AUTOMATION

1. Increased automation leads to unemployment, particularly among unskilled workers.
2. There is little pride felt in such work as it is done by machine.
3. It is expensive to set up a fully-automated plant.
4. Services requiring personal attention are now done by machine, with less social interaction.
5. Women are often channelled into low-paid, repetitive work.

WORK

Work is a central feature of life in modern industrial society.

WHY DO WE WORK?

1. *Physical survival*: To satisfy our needs — for food, clothing, shelter — and our wants such as cars, holidays, entertainment etc.
2. Work and the money it earns provide *independence*, *security* and a reasonable *standard of living*.
3. Work *satisfies social and psychological needs*. It gives us *self-respect* and earns us the respect of others. It gives us a sense of satisfaction and personal worth.
4. Work confers *status*. It often determines our social status or class. Menial jobs, for example, may have low status, while responsible, well-paid jobs have high status. In industrial society, only paid work has status, hence the inferior position of housework and child care in many people's eyes, even though it is known to be responsible work.

5. It *satisfies a basic drive*. Most of us were brought up to believe that work is virtuous and that idleness is wrong. This is known as the *'work ethic'*. We are conditioned by our upbringing to go to work each day. Those who do not work may be called derogatory names such as 'dossers' or 'loafers'.
6. Work provides *interest* and is one of our deepest sources of achievement and pride. To some, work is a vocation, as with those who want to help others — doctors, nurses, religious, teachers.
7. We have a *right to work*.
   "Everyone has the right to work ... to protection against unemployment ... to equal pay for equal work."

   UN Declaration of Human Rights, Article 23.

ATTITUDES TO WORK

Our work is affected by many factors outside the workplace. Our goals, aims, aspirations and ambitions are influenced by our upbringing, education, family and friends.

1. HOME BACKGROUND

Our attitudes to work, like many other things, are formed in the home. A positive or negative attitude towards learning and the rewards of working hard is passed on from parent to child.

2. SOCIAL CLASS

We tend to accept the values set by members of our own background and social class. We may therefore consider certain jobs unsuitable because they are associated with people of a higher or lower class.

3. EDUCATION

Attitudes to education tend to be similar to our attitudes to work. Those who do not attach much importance to education leave school as soon as possible. They are generally satisfied (or will have to make do) with low-status, badly paid jobs. Those who are willing to continue working towards long-term goals, such as by denying themselves an income so that they can gain professional qualifications, will be more likely to be employed in responsible, rewarding or well-paid jobs.

A good craftsman gets satisfaction from his work

4. PEER GROUP

Attitudes towards school and work are influenced by peer groups, with close friends following similar careers. A boy who sees his friends leave school early will more than likely follow suit. A boy who attempts to enter a so-called 'female' trade such as fashion may be ridiculed by his friends. A female mechanic may be resented by her male colleagues. This, however, is becoming less common today as sex stereotyping decreases.

5. ECONOMIC FACTORS

Economic recession and widespread unemployment can affect the aspirations of young people. They may feel that it is pointless to work hard at school when they are unlikely to find a job. The result is that they fail examinations; without qualifications they are unlikely to find a job, and thus their fears are fulfilled.

Those from deprived areas, such as the inner cities or some rural areas, have fewer options: they may settle for a badly-paid or unpleasant job or join the dole queue. (See Government Response to Unemployment, page 352.)

CHANGING PATTERNS OF WORK

The past century has seen:
- Change from largely agricultural work to non-agricultural work, that is industrial or commercial work.
- Large increase in number of women working.
- Increase in incomes, resulting in a higher standard of living.

	Agriculture	Non-agriculture
1926	80%	20%
1978	22%	78%

- Greater influence of trade unions
- Greater job mobility
- More skilled workers, fewer unskilled workers employed, due to developing technology, including automation and computerisation
- Working conditions improved

TECHNOLOGICAL CHANGES: TRANSPORT

The transformation from rural to industrial life brings with it other changes such as urbanisation, mass communications and rapid transport. The development of high-speed transport has turned the world into a 'global village'. City people are no longer separated from their country cousins. Motor transport and high-speed trains have reduced the geographical and cultural differences between them. Workers commute from outlying areas; children are bused into schools in town.

Foreign travel is no longer the privilege of the rich. Package holidays have brought many places abroad within our price range. We have become cosmopolitan in our outlook, eating habits and tastes.

We have become both socially and geographically mobile, moving to where there are jobs, greater opportunities and, hopefully, a higher standard of living.

PROBLEMS OF INCREASED TRANSPORT

1. Traffic congestion
2. Pollution and noise
3. Increased use of fuel, depleting world resources
4. Damage to roads and buildings
5. Destruction of city communities

► UNEMPLOYMENT

Not everyone has a job. The four main groups who are not in paid employment are:

1. Children and young people in full-time education.
2. Housewives: women who stay at home to look after home and children.
3. Retired people.
4. The unemployed.

These people are provided for, to a large extent, by the working population. Ireland has a very high dependency rate (the ratio of dependants to paid workers). This is mainly due to our large proportion of young people — for every 100 workers there are 75 dependants. In 1989, there were about 230,000 unemployed people in Ireland.

Employment fluctuates with the economic situation. When times are good, as in the 1960s, there is little unemployment. During a recession, unemployment figures rise as factories close and workers are laid off. This leads to a reduction in the amount of disposable income being spent, causing further unemployment.

Ireland has the highest rate of unemployment (17.1%) in the EC (twice the average).

SOME CAUSES OF UNEMPLOYMENT

1. Economic recession: When there is a world-wide economic slump, this is reflected in the employment figures in most countries. This causes a drop in consumer spending which in turn causes further unemployment.

Unemployment brings about loss of self esteem

2. Technological advances such as automation lead to redundancy and unemployment.
3. Shortage of jobs in certain areas, for example rural areas.
4. Lack of skills: The largest number of unemployed are the unskilled workers.
5. Seasonal unemployment: Certain jobs such as tourism and construction are more plentiful at certain times of the year. Workers are laid off during the off-season.
6. High taxes and PRSI are disincentives to work, particularly for those who would be only marginally better off employed than on the dole, such as those with large families.

EFFECTS OF UNEMPLOYMENT

1. ON THE INDIVIDUAL

- Loss of income brings loss of status, loss of purpose, loss of social contacts.
- Worry and guilt for failing to provide for family.
- Loss of self esteem, feelings of inadequacy. Conditioning that work is an essential part of life leads people to believe that without a job, they are worthless. Society's attitude reinforces this.
- Anxiety and depression: The unemployed are more likely to suffer physical and mental illness.
- They run a greater risk of dying and are twice as likely to commit suicide as those who are employed.
- An unstructured lifestyle leads to boredom if one gives in to it. Alternatively, it gives an opportunity to try new things, if finance permits.

- Applying for jobs and unemployment benefit is demoralising.

2. ON THE FAMILY

- Unemployment is the single greatest cause of poverty in Ireland.
- Loss of income leads to a lowering of living standards for the family. In cases of prolonged unemployment, this leads to extreme hardship.
- Children may experience deprivation — no money for school books, uniforms, trips etc. They may have to leave school early to provide for the family.
- Anxiety on the part of children may interfere with school work.
- Family relationships become strained. Worry, unhappiness, resentment and violence may result unless the family is supportive. (This was well portrayed in TV series, 'The Boys from the Blackstuff'.)
- The tense atmosphere in the home may cause emotional disturbance in family members; they may turn to alcohol or tranquillisers. Family breakdown may occur.
- Statistics show a greater level of ill health in families of the unemployed.

3. ON SOCIETY

- Children of unemployed parents grow up with a pattern of unemployment. They are more likely to join the unemployed.
- High unemployment creates feelings of resentment and unrest in society, leading to anti-social behaviour such as vandalism, violence and crime.
- The state must pay out more in unemployment benefit/assistance. In order to do this, those who work are forced to pay even more tax.
- 'The Black economy': With high taxes and PRSI as disincentives, employers and workers collude to have those claiming unemployment benefit work illegally for a low wage, to their mutual benefit — but to the detriment of the economy.
- Emigration: See page 353.

UNEMPLOYMENT BENEFIT

This benefit cushions the most immediate effect of unemployment: the loss of income. Unemployment benefit is paid to unemployed persons:

1. Who are capable of work and are available for work.
2. Who satisfy the contribution conditions, that is have paid at least 39 contributions in the year prior to the claim.
3. Who are not disqualified from benefit. This may occur if a person leaves employment: (a) without just cause; (b) because of an industrial dispute; or (c) if one refuses a reasonable offer of employment.

Apart from the basic benefit (1990 = £.......... a week), additional amounts are payable if the claimant has adult and/or child dependants. A person who is not entitled to unemployment benefit may be entitled to unemployment assistance, but this is subject to a means test.

THE GOVERNMENT'S RESPONSE TO UNEMPLOYMENT

1. Job creation is the most obvious way to keep unemployment to a minimum. The IDA are involved in encouraging companies to set up new factories etc. An employment levy of 1% is imposed on all workers' wages.
2. Encouragement of school-based courses which help young people become more employable. These include:
   - Vocational preparation and training programme (VPTP) — a one-year course which includes subjects which are relevant to work such as woodwork, office skills and catering skills.
   - Mini companies in second-level schools which give young people experience in running a business.
   - Introduction of 'technology' as a subject of the new junior cycle course makes young people more employable.
   - Vocational training opportunities scheme — gives a number of unemployed the opportunity to study full time for examinations up to Leaving Certificate. Free travel is available. (Normally those in full-time study are not officially available for work, and are therefore not entitled to unemployed benefits.)
3. Teamwork: A temporary employment programme operated through the Department of Labour. It pays grants to community bodies to give temporary work to young unemployed on community based projects.
4. Training courses run by CERT (catering) and Teagasc (farming).
5. FÁS: FÁS is the government training and employment authority (it combines the former AnCO, Manpower Service and Youth Employment Agency). It has a network of over 70 offices nationwide. It provides practical advice, information and training aimed at helping the unemployed find work and at the same time helps employers recruit suitable employees.

FAS SERVICES

1. Training for apprentices in construction, electronics, engineering, furniture making, metalwork, mechanics and printing. Apprentices must be fifteen years or over and become apprenticed to a suitable employer. Training generally lasts four years. Apprentices receive a set rate of pay and are entitled to normal workers' conditions, such as holidays.
2. Training for adults: Unemployed workers can receive free retraining in many of the skills listed above, as well as clerical, computing, electronic and supervisory skills. 'Back to Work' and 'Start Your Own Business' courses are also available.
3. A job register of those looking for work: Jobs are advertised and displayed in FÁS offices around the country.
4. An employment incentive scheme: Employers are given a grant to take on extra employees. The grant lasts for nine months, but the employment must be permanent.
5. Enterprise allowance scheme ('Start Your Own Business'): Gives advice and assistance, including a weekly allowance to a person starting up a business after at least thirteen weeks' unemployment.

The NSSB publishes a booklet 'Entitlements for the Unemployed'.

► MIGRATION AND EMIGRATION

MIGRATION

Migration involves the movement of people from one area to another within a country. The main reason that this occurs is the search for employment. Rural areas in particular have few opportunities for employment.

Farms have become mechanised, so fewer people are required in agricultural work. The rural population is also becoming increasingly isolated. Transport services from outlying areas to large towns and cities have been cut back. Local hospitals and small schools have been closed.

Food is more expensive. In west Connemara, there has been a 50% drop in population in the past sixty years. The result is that there is large-scale movement from the countryside (*rural depopulation*) into the cities, or abroad as emigrants. The country villages are left with a predominantly elderly population who are isolated and vulnerable. The young people marry and settle in cities, which become overcrowded and sprawling as the agricultural land surrounding them is taken over for housing.

The government attempts to slow down this movement in various ways.
1. *Policy of decentralisation*: Moving government departments and large industries out of cities into the countryside.
2. *The Industrial Development Authority (IDA)* is involved in research and projects to develop employment in rural areas. It encourages new industries with grants.
3. *Forestry schemes* provide recreational amenities as well as employment. (Ireland has an ideal climate for forestry.)
4. Small, *local industries* are encouraged, particularly in the Gaeltacht.
5. *Tourism*, one of our biggest industries, is encouraged by Bord Fáilte.
6. The small farmer is assisted with *grants*, social assistance and low-interest house-purchase schemes.

EMIGRATION

Emigration is the movement of people across a national boundary with the intention of taking up residence there.

Like migration, the principal motivation behind emigration is a belief in better employment prospects and a higher standard of living. Emigration was a notable feature of Irish life from the Famine up to the 1960s. By this time, industrialisation had brought economic growth, and the flow of emigrants virtually ceased. Emigrants even began to return to take up employment. With the recession of the 1980s, a pattern of emigration is again establishing itself — many of the emigrants being highly-qualified graduates and skilled workers.

SOME REASONS FOR EMIGRATION
1. High level of unemployment.
2. Tax/PRSI rates particularly high, leaving a very low 'real' income to spend.
3. Ireland's ratio of young people is the highest in Europe. Many are graduates and/or highly skilled.
4. Shortage of young workers in UK, USA and EC due to preference for smaller families since the 1960s.
5. Poverty and isolation in rural areas are particularly unacceptable. The west cannot sustain its own population.
6. Natural urge of young people to travel and see the world.

URBANISATION

The movement of people from rural areas has resulted in an increased growth of cities. City life is characterised by a high density of people, noise, congestion, a rapid pace of life, impersonal relationships and a considerable number of social problems.

SOCIAL PROBLEMS THAT OCCUR IN CITIES
1. Housing problems such as shortages or poor-quality housing, particularly in inner city areas.
2. Violence, vandalism and crime.
3. Poverty and unemployment.
4. Stress from the rapid pace of life.
5. Pollution, noise and congestion.
6. Loneliness.

CIVIC PLANNING

The main purpose of civic planning is to achieve balanced development and a pleasant environment, to the benefit of all sections of the community. Without planning, there would be uncontrolled development. Builders could build what and where they liked. Planning ensures that there will be adequate water and sewerage facilities as well as essential services and amenities.

The *Department of the Environment* controls nationwide development through its enforcement of the Planning Acts and its regulations.

Under the Local Government (Planning and Development) Act, 1963, each planning authority is obliged to make a *development plan* which is revised every five years and which provides the framework for planning and development decisions taken in that area. The draft plan is open to public inspection. It shows:
- The land zoning (see below)
- Proposals for traffic
- Proposed redevelopment and renewal of run-down areas
- Proposals for preserving and improving amenities

Planning permission must be sought from local authorities for most kinds of development: building, demolition, or making any material change in the use of buildings or land. If refused, an appeal may be lodged with An Bord Pleanála, which is an independent body.

ZONING

The main method of controlling development is the system of land zoning. This states the purpose for which any particular piece of land may be used. There are often up to twenty types of zone, including those for agricultural, residential, commercial, industrial and recreational use. Zoning controls the density of developments and stipulates that a certain proportion of land is to be left as open space.

PLANNING PROBLEMS

1. Importance of keeping the *needs and wants of people* in mind. A town plan or housing scheme should serve the population rather than the developer.
2. *Lack of integration:* Buildings are often seen as separate units rather than in relation to the town, estate or street as a whole.
3. *Traffic congestion* is eased by restricting certain areas to pedestrians, improving public transport and building ring roads around towns and cities.

Tenements are demolished to make way for new housing

Traffic congestion is an effect of urbanisation

4. *The inner city:* Planners must take into account existing structures and communities when adapting a city to the demands of present-day living. That which is good, e.g. trees, parks, waterways, beautiful and historic street-scapes and buildings, should be preserved. *Problems of the inner city include:* Lack of permanent residents, most being from the lower socio-economic groups; large numbers of decaying tenements, which lack basic amenities, such as bathrooms; few facilities, e.g. play areas for children; overcrowding, traffic, pollution.
5. *Urban dispersal:* Residents of inner-city areas are often moved to outlying areas far from families and friends. Because this is socially undesirable, emphasis is now being placed on renewing city-centre housing, rebuilding small dwellings and re-creating communities in inner city areas.
6. *High-rise living:* Tower blocks are used to house underprivileged tenants, leading to a wide range of other social problems (page 316).

▶ POVERTY

"Society as a whole suffers and is weakened by the existence of poverty."

Sister Stanislaus Kennedy
(chairwoman, Combat Poverty)

One of the principal causes of poverty is the unequal division of wealth found in most capitalist societies. Much of the wealth of a country, i.e. houses, land, unearned income, is held by a minority of the population. One million people in Ireland are below the poverty line (at present £42 a week, single person).

Poverty is a relative concept. People are considered poor when they are so seriously below the average standard of living that they are *deprived of the opportunities, comforts and self-respect regarded as normal in the community to which they belong.* It is when we compare a family living in squalor with the average standards of those around us that we realise what poverty means.

The poor are not only affected by *economic hardship;* they are also likely to experience *social, educational* and *cultural deprivation.*

People are more likely to experience poverty at certain stages of the family life cycle: at *childhood, early parenthood* and *old age.*

The sections of the community most likely to be poor are:

- The unemployed
- The sick and disabled
- Large families
- One-parent families
- The elderly
- The homeless, including travellers
- Low-paid workers, including small farmers

An elderly, homeless man caught in the poverty trap

REASONS FOR POVERTY

There are many who believe that poverty is the fault of the individual, that the poor fail to take care of themselves or to get on in life because they are lazy or unambitious. This is rarely the case. The reasons for poverty are often beyond the control of the individual, who is trapped in a cycle of poverty from which it is difficult to escape.

1. THE POVERTY TRAP

Poverty is generally inherited. Parents may be unemployed or working in an unskilled, badly-paid job. The child of such a family is likely to suffer many deprivations and has little motivation to work.

Schools in poorer areas are often overcrowded, have greater discipline problems and a higher turnover of staff. Such young people tend to show little interest in school. They leave early and either take up unskilled jobs or fail to get employment. They get married young, to partners from a similar background. They cannot afford suitable accommodation, they have children quickly, change jobs frequently and tend to be regularly unemployed.

2. ECONOMIC RECESSION

Recession causes widespread unemployment and reduced living standards.

3. SOCIAL WELFARE BENEFITS

These benefits, although based on the minimum income necessary to provide basic needs of food, clothing and shelter, are generally inadequate. They become lower in real terms each year. As workers get cost-of-living increases, the poor, in effect, get poorer. Further allowances to help those on low incomes are Family Income Supplement, Supplementary Welfare Allowance and tax allowances for children of low-paid workers.

4. GOVERNMENT ASSISTANCE - UNCLAIMED

Many of those entitled to government assistance fail to claim their allowances because they are unaware of their rights. They may also find the claiming procedure difficult due to illiteracy or bureaucratic 'red tape'.

5. LOW-COST HOUSING

There is a shortage of low-cost housing and rented accommodation provided by local authorities. What is available (for example high-rise flats, slum dwellings) is unacceptable because of its unsuitability and the many problems encountered in these areas. There is a special need for accommodation for single people, especially single parents and the aged.

6. SOCIAL POLICY ON POVERTY

There has been little real planning or commitment by governments to developing a social policy on poverty. Efforts to alleviate the problem have been piecemeal, generally involving handouts instead of tackling the reasons for poverty. Members of the government and civil service tend to be from the middle classes and thus give low priority to the problem of poverty.

7. ADMINISTRATION AND POVERTY

The highly bureaucratic system of administration wastes much time, money and personnel resources on administration. Such money might be better spent on practical schemes to alleviate poverty.

ELIMINATION OF POVERTY: PRIORITIES

The total elimination of poverty requires basic social changes. These are difficult to achieve and slow to bring about, as they require changes in attitude and education as well as political and economic changes. These might include:

1. Public education about the extent and nature of poverty, injustice and inequality in the country.
2. Increased allocation of finance to those in genuine hardship — for example those with large families, the aged; income supplements, for example FIS, to families

whose income is not sufficient to make ends meet, that is, those in low-paid jobs.

3. Increased provision of low-cost accommodation for the underprivileged (see 5 above).

4. Positive discrimination in poverty pockets such as inner-city areas; extra amenities such as community centres and child care facilities.

5. Education: Reduction of pupil-teacher ratio in schools in these areas; greater provision of remedial teachers; job creation programmes. (Some of these provisions have already been implemented but more needs to be done.)

6. Greater research to find ways of preventing poverty (see below).

Deprived families need positive discrimination

SOME ATTEMPTS TO ALLEVIATE POVERTY

1. 'COMBAT POVERTY'

The National Committee on Pilot Schemes to Combat Poverty (NCPSCP) was established in 1974, funded under the EEC social action programme. Its objectives were to bring about practical intervention in areas of deprivation and to contribute to the evolution of effective long-term policies against poverty.

Four main pilot schemes were started:
- An urban resource scheme
- A supplementary allowance project
- A social service council scheme
- Community action research schemes

All projects were designed to initiate a process of self-help within communities and to involve the poor themselves in programmes that are being implemented for them.

Poverty . .

. . . and privilege

2. TRAVELLERS
- The Dublin Committee for Travelling People assists travellers in practical ways. It provides a day care centre and a night shelter, a residential home for boys and one for girls requiring full-time care. They initiate training and work programmes and are involved in education and youth work.
- The National Council for Travelling People assists travellers. It helps with settlement or obtaining halting sites. It is involved in youth work and education.

3. FOCUS POINT (page 318)

COMMUNICATIONS: THE MEDIA

One of the most striking features of modern society has been the growth of an elaborate communications network. Through radio and television, news is relayed to our living-rooms almost as soon as it happens.

Moon landings, assassinations and battles are seen live on our television screens. Electronic communication aids such as telephone, telex and satellites assist the dissemination of information. The world has become what has been called a 'global village'.

WHAT IS COMMUNICATION?

Communication is the method by which we pass information, ideas and attitudes from one person to another. We can communicate by signs (a glare, a smile), by words, by writing.

Mass communication is a means of communicating with large numbers of people in different places at the same time. The first mass medium was the printed page (but only a privileged few could read at that time). Books, newspapers and the radio followed. Today, we have television piped into our living rooms from all parts of the world.

THE PURPOSE OF THE MASS MEDIA

They provide:

- Information
- Education
- Entertainment

1. INFORMATION

News is relayed in an easily understood way. Political views may be put forward, portraying a wide range of opinions and attitudes. This assists the workings of democracy.

Information provided should be *truthful, accurate,* and *objective,* i.e. reporters must be impartial, giving both sides of the case. When the media are used by the powerful to indoctrinate or to tell people only that which a government wishes them to know, it is known as *propaganda.*

2. EDUCATION

The media, particularly television, are a powerful means of informal education in the world today. Videos and television are increasingly used as educational aids in schools and colleges. Broadcasting, either by radio or television, is one of the most effective ways of communicating with illiterate people and is extensively used in underdeveloped countries. Documentaries and current affairs programmes are both educational and informative.

3. ENTERTAINMENT

The media are among the most important outlets of the leisure industry — firstly through their function as entertainment media, and secondly because of their importance as a source of advertising (see page 359).

Much mass media entertainment is harmless and undemanding (many would say trivial). Cartoons, comedy programmes, quiz shows, drama and light entertainment such as singing, dancing are all provided. It is difficult to achieve a good balance. Programme planners have to appeal to a very mixed audience. Many argue that television lowers standards, that there is not enough worthwhile material. But who is to say what is worthwhile and what is not? This depends on one's background, education and culture.

THE PRESS

In its broadest sense, this includes newspapers, journals and magazines and books. The main purpose of newspapers is to transmit news, but as 'news' is now quickly out of date, due to television and radio coverage, the press concentrates on providing news information in greater depth, providing comment and criticism on current affairs. The press is also a source of local news and information.

Certain newspapers sell by appealing to the baser instincts of human nature, by sensationalising news, stressing its violent, shocking aspects. They probe into people's private lives to satisfy one's curiosity and, perhaps, self-righteousness. They exploit women by printing erotic photographs. Generally, people pick papers that reflect their social status.

Advertising keeps down costs and helps to sell newspapers and magazines. Because of this, articles may be influenced by the advertisers, so that a true picture may not be portrayed.

RADIO

This is a quick, cheap method of mass communication. It is an ideal news medium: a news bulletin can relay news within seconds of its occurrence. Radio also provides programmes on serious issues, e.g. current affairs, consumer issues, as well as music, drama and many other forms of entertainment. It is useful for educational broadcasts, particularly to the illiterate. One can continue working while listening to the radio and this is one of the reasons for its popularity with those at home during the day. It enables those who are tied to the home with young children to feel less isolated. They can keep up to date with news and current affairs, even though they have no time to read a newspaper. Many social issues have been aired, aimed at such an audience, including issues such as incest, rape and violence, which might be unsuitable for family viewing on television.

One of the main industries to develop from radio is the pop music and record industry. Many networks cater specifically for the tastes of the young.

TELEVISION AND VIDEO

Television is probably the most controversial, influential and commercially successful mass medium. For many, the 'telly' is their only leisure-time occupation. Household routines are organised around television schedules. And when two programmes coincide, it is now possible to see them both, thanks to the technology that brought us the video recorder.

Television is a marvellous educational medium. Through documentaries, current affairs and a wide variety of educational programmes, our horizons are broadened, and subjects that might have been thought boring in school come alive before our eyes. Culture and learning are thus brought to the mass of the people.

Like radio, television is an excellent news medium, visually bringing us the day's news from the four corners of the earth.

Television, however, is principally an entertainment medium, offering a wide variety of programmes from Sibelius to soap opera. For many, television relieves the boredom of a humdrum existence (or is it that television has that effect on their lives, making the viewer into a passive spectator who substitutes watching for living?).

THE INFLUENCE OF TELEVISION

While it is difficult to prove conclusively how influential television can be, it certainly has greater influence than any other mass medium. Its influence will depend on age, intelligence, social class and education. Those most likely to be influenced are children and less stable individuals. It must be remembered that it is not the only influence in our lives. Family, school and peer groups probably have a far greater influence on our children.

- Television has enormous cultural influence. Imported television programmes and series influence our life-styles, music, modes of speech and behaviour (witness the Americanisation of Japan).
- Many argue that it has a corrupting influence, portraying permissiveness, violence and brutality, and lowering our moral standards.
- Television portrays a very materialistic view of life: through soap operas such as 'Dallas'; in games shows where money is all-important; in advertising, where material objects and money are made so desirable; where we are bombarded with consumer goods ('If I buy the right car/drink/detergent, I'll have it made!')

- Children are particularly influenced by television, especially when busy mothers use it as a baby-sitter. It then becomes the principal socialising influence in the life of the child who gets its view of the world from the screen rather than from home and family. Children become passive, *watching* instead of *doing*. They become aggressive and irritable, particularly when their prop is removed from them. It may interfere with homework, and violent or frightening scenes may produce anxiety.
- It is difficult to prove the connection between violence portrayed in the media and real-life violence. Certainly, television violence produces greater tolerance of violence in the individual. Seeing a great deal of violence in the media may lead people to a tacit acceptance or even approval of violence (to the extent that it is glamourised by the media): *They might ... think first of violence as a means of problem-solving rather than of non-violent alternatives.* — REPORTS AND PAPERS ON MASS COMMUNICATION (UNESCO), No. 63.

Research in 1978 suggested that violence may reinforce aggressive tendencies among emotionally unstable adolescents. Also in 1978, Belson, in *TV Violence and the Adolescent*, suggested that television violence can lead to real-life violence among some with aggressive personalities, since it was often glamourised.

ADVANTAGES OF THE MEDIA

1. Source of information and opinion: We are better-informed now than in earlier times.
2. Source of entertainment.
3. Media can be used to mobilise public opinion and break down traditional prejudices and fears.
4. Social role: Media can highlight social problems, e.g. the famine in Ethiopia, and their relief, e.g. Live Aid.
5. Experiences formerly enjoyed only by a minority, e.g. drama, opera, are now available to all.

DISADVANTAGES OF THE MEDIA

1. Much influence is in the hands of a few individuals: studio heads, editors, programme controllers. It can be abused in the wrong hands.
2. Media present an artificial, mercenary life-style, particularly in advertising.
3. Media are influenced by commercial interests, e.g. whether a newspaper, film, etc. will sell or not.
4. Media can be used to manipulate an audience, e.g. disseminate propaganda, maintain the status quo.
5. People are conditioned by the media, encouraging conformity.
6. Certain papers or programmes may lower values and distort the moral standards of those who see them.

ADVERTISING

Advertising is a form of mass communication or mass persuasion. It is important to manufacturers, retailers and consumers. The manufacturer wants to sell a product to the consumer — advertisements tell the public that the product is available. Not all the public is interested in every product. The advertiser identifies a 'target group' — the teenager or the housewife — and aims the advertisement at this group.

Advertising takes a number of forms:
- Television and radio advertisements
- Cinema
- Billboards and hoardings
- Newspaper advertising
- Magazine advertising
- In-store promotions
- Packaging, carrier bags etc.
- Unsolicited: samples delivered to homes
- Sponsorship, e.g. of sporting events

Advertising agencies use many ploys to sell a product. They hire market researchers to find out what you like, then bombard you with psychological tactics such as greed, envy, pride or sex to persuade you that you must have their product.

While their tactics may work on the uninformed, and perhaps occasionally on those who are wise to them a product that is a bad buy will not sell a second time.

Advertisers have a *voluntary code of practice*, recommending that:
1. Advertisements should be legal, decent, honest and truthful.
2. All descriptions and claims must be true, e.g. 'leather' must be leather.
3. Advertisements must not be misleading.
4. They must not discredit other products.
5. Advertisements must not misuse scientific or medical terms, e.g. stating that a product contains nutrients if this is not so.

(How many advertisements can you name that break one or more of these codes?)

Advertisements pay for a large proportion of the production costs of other media. Newspapers, magazines and television would all be more expensive without the revenue gained from them.

ADVANTAGES OF ADVERTISING

1. The consumer is made aware of the availability of a product or service.
2. It creates a demand for consumer goods, stimulates the economy and encourages competition.
3. Governments and their agencies use advertising to inform us of grants, social welfare benefits and important changes.
4. The public depends on advertisements when looking for jobs, accommodation, houses and goods for sale.
5. Advertisements inform the public of the time and date of various forms of entertainment and sporting events.
6. Some advertisements are entertaining.

DISADVANTAGES OF ADVERTISING

1. The consumer may be exploited, misled and deceived by advertisements. Many advertisements mislead by implication or omission.
2. Insufficient information is provided about the product (EC directives have improved food labelling).
3. Advertisers exploit consumers by encouraging people to buy unnecessary goods, e.g. large sums of money are used to persuade young people to buy alcohol; others may be encouraged to buy on credit in order to have an item.
4. An unrealistic life-style is often portrayed, making consumers feel dissatisfied and inadequate and undermining their sense of values.
5. Advertising puts up the cost of a product.
6. It often gives the consumer, particularly women, little credit for intelligence. e.g. 'whiter than white' advertisements for detergents.

ADVERTISING AND YOUTH

The consumer society, with its emphasis on advertising and consumer goods, has to a large extent been responsible for the explosion of youth culture. Until the 1950s and 1960s, there was little mention of adolescence and its pop culture. With the economic boom of the 1960s, young people found that they had plenty of money to spend as they wished. Youth today has its own sub-culture with music, language and a way of dressing all its own. This is due to a large extent to advertising and the media.

► LEISURE

"Labour is doing what we must; leisure is doing what we like."
George Bernard Shaw

The stresses and strains of modern life and the monotonous nature of much of our work have created a greater need for leisure today than ever before. In the past, people worked long hours and had little time for leisure. Today, the working week has been reduced and is getting shorter; holidays are longer. Most of us have a far greater amount of leisure time to be filled.

The economic recession has resulted in a huge increase in unemployment. Many young people cannot get a job on leaving school or college. Such people have lots of time but little money to spend on leisure facilities and entertainment.

Aerobics: a current leisure craze

Leisure can be used for several purposes:
1. To provide physical relaxation and to improve health
2. To release pent-up energy, i.e. to unwind
3. To relieve monotony or boredom — a break from routine
4. To gratify the senses: taste, sight, hearing
5. To satisfy the intellect and to assist personal development

Leisure patterns vary between people of different ages, sex class and occupation, although the differences are becoming less marked. Children play chess; women watch and play football; boys enjoy cooking. Some leisure pursuits such as film-going and television are enjoyed by all types and ages, but the choice of programme may be influenced by class, background and education.

Occupation should influence the form of relaxation we take. Those with sedentary jobs should indulge in active hobbies such as sport and gardening. People whose work is strenuous would be more likely to choose passive restful hobbies such as reading and watching television.

THE LEISURE INDUSTRY

The increased availability of leisure time has resulted in the growth of a highly commercial leisure industry. More people can now afford to join sports clubs, indulge in expensive hobbies and travel abroad. Advertising is not slow to cash in, with elaborate campaigns to encourage us to buy that stereo, or to fly to far-away holiday resorts.

Tourism is now an important industry in many countries, particularly our own. *Entertainment* is big business. Pop groups, film stars and other cult figures command huge fees and audiences are prepared to pay to be entertained. Bingo, pool, race tracks, amusement arcades, video games, gambling casinos, pubs and discos cater for every taste. All help people to escape from the stresses of work or the worries of unemployment.

Disco dancing: a popular leisure activity with the young

SPORT

Physical exercise plays a useful part in leisure, developing powers of co-ordination while at the same time improving the health and efficiency of the body and mind. There is increasing interest in sport, both participant and spectator sports. Television provides coverage of important sporting fixtures. Yet, strangely enough, instead of turning us into a nation of passive spectators, it seems to be stimulating the interest of a wide range of people in active sports.

Doctors blame inactive life-styles for our lack of health and fitness. Health centres and sports clubs are opening

Leisure Pursuits of Different Age Groups

Teenagers	Young marrieds	35–45 years	45–64 years	Over 65
Much time spent outside the home with peer group; working class often have more spending money than middle class, who have less time for leisure due to school work and exam pressures. Spectator, competitive and individual sports. Considerable time may be spent on a particular hobby, e.g. stamp collecting, music, sport, motorbikes. Much time spent on boy-girl relationships. More money to spend on records, clothes and non-essentials. Danger period as unchannelled leisure time can lead to boredom and search for excitement and danger, e.g. drugs, alcohol, sex and crime	The majority are married by the age of 25. Most of the time is spent setting up home and coping with pregnancy and young children. Costly leisure pursuits curtailed by expenses involved in buying a home, car and furnishings. Do-it-yourself and home-centred hobbies such as dressmaking, gardening, painting, car maintenance provide interest and save money. Young wives have little time to spare, as child-minding tends to be a 24-hour commitment. Couples may spend much leisure time in pubs, reading, television, cinema.	Home ties decrease as children become more independent. More time is spent outside the home. Entertaining at home and visiting friends, dinners, cinema, television, pubs, voluntary activities, do-it-yourself. Holidays with the family in country, seaside or abroad. Jogging, squash and health clubs for the better off.	Most affluent age, as responsibilities for children are lessened (except for those with children in third-level education). Less physical energy, therefore fewer active leisure pursuits. More elaborate home entertainment. Golf, bridge, theatre (usually middle-class pursuits). Television, bingo, pubs, particularly those providing cabaret (often working-class activities). Holidays abroad (often without children).	Physical and mental decline. Less money to spend on leisure pursuits. Compulsory retirement brings almost unlimited leisure time: can be difficult to adjust. More leisure and less expensive pursuits: television, walking, reading, gardening, knitting, bridge, bingo.

up to cater for the growing number of keep-fit enthusiasts. Jogging and oriental techniques such as yoga, judo, and karate are being taken up by large numbers of people.

The government encourages sport by providing grants to build and maintain sporting and leisure facilities, such as parks, playing fields, swimming pools and leisure centres.

EDUCATION FOR LEISURE

If not channelled into positive pursuits, the boredom of too much leisure can result in social problems such as alcoholism, vandalism and delinquency. With leisure now occupying a greater share of our lives, it has become necessary to educate people to use their spare time wisely.

In the past, people had to make their own entertainment. Today, individuals are often at a loss to know what to do with their leisure time. The gap is frequently filled with passive television viewing.

Education for leisure begins *at home*, where positive thinking and worthwhile values and goals can be installed into young people.

At *school*, hobbies, sports and other interests such as music, art and drama can be taught and encouraged. Extracurricular activities such as school tours, sports tournaments, debates and drama can show children the possibilities.

Adult education has an important part to play in education for leisure. Not only are the classes themselves an interesting occupation, but they also teach a number of useful and creative activities which help people to fill their leisure time more constructively.

Those who are about to retire have leisure forced on them, and often find the transition from a life of work to one of leisure quite a problem. *Pre-retirement courses*, which help the elderly to prepare for retirement as well as encouraging them to develop new hobbies and interests, can help old people to enjoy their retirement and look upon the extra leisure as a bonus instead of a liability.

"The wise use of leisure, it must be conceded, is a product of civilisation and education. A man who has worked long hours all his life will be bored, if he suddenly becomes idle."

IN PRAISE OF IDLENESS, Bertrand Russell

APPENDIXES

APPENDIX A

► COMPOSITION OF FOODS

Food	Inedible waste %	Energy kcal	kJ	Protein g	Fat g	Carbohydrate (as monosaccharide) g	Water g	Calcium mg	Iron mg	Vitamin A (retinol equivalent) µg	Thiamin mg	Riboflavin mg	Nicotinic acid equivalent mg	Vitamin C mg	Vitamin D µg
Milk															
Cream, double	0	449	1,848	1.8	48.0	2.6	47	65	0	420	0.02	0.08	0.4	0	0.28
Milk, liquid, whole	0	65	274	3.3	3.8	4.8	88	120	0.1	44[1] 37[2]	0.04	0.15	0.9	1	0.05[1] 0.01[2]
Milk, condensed, whole, sweetened	0	322	1,361	8.2	9.2	55.1	28	290	0.2	112	0.10	0.37	2.0	3	0.09
Milk, dried, skimmed	0	352	1,498	36.0	0.9	53.3	5	1,260	0.5	4	0.30	1.73	9.7	10	0
Yogurt, low-fat, natural	0	53	224	5.0	1.0	6.4	86	180	0.1	10	0.05	0.26	1.3	0	0.02
Yogurt, low-fat, fruit	0	96	410	4.8	1.0	18.2	75	160	0.2	10	0.05	0.23	1.2	1	0.02
Cheese															
Cheese, Cheddar	0	412	1,708	25.4	34.5	0	37	810	0.6	420	0.04	0.50	5.2	0	0.35
Cheese, cottage	0	114	480	15.3	4.0	4.5	75	80	0.4	27	0.03	0.27	3.2	0	0.02
Meat															
Bacon, rashers, cooked	0	447	1,852	24.5	38.8	0	32	12	1.4	0	0.40	0.19	9.2	0	0
Beef, average	17	226	940	18.1	17.1	0	64	7	1.9	0	0.06	0.19	8.1	0	0
Chicken, roast	0	148	621	24.8	5.4	0	68	9	0.8	0	0.08	0.19	12.8	0	0
Ham, cooked	0	269	1,119	24.7	18.9	0	54	9	1.3	0	0.44	0.15	8.0	0	0
Kidney, average	11	89	375	16.2	2.7	0	79	9	6.0	300	0.39	1.90	10.7	12	0
Lamb, roast	0	291	1,209	23.0	22.1	0	54	9	2.1	0	0.10	0.25	9.2	0	0
Liver, fried	0	244	1,020	24.9	13.7	5.6	56	14	8.8	6,000	0.27	4.30	20.7	20	0.75
Luncheon meat	0	313	1,298	12.6	26.9	5.5	52	15	1.0	0	0.07	0.12	4.5	0	0
Pork, average	15	330	1,364	15.8	29.6	0	54	8	0.8	0	0.58	0.16	6.9	0	0
Sausage, pork	0	367	1,520	10.6	32.1	9.5	45	41	1.1	0	0.04	0.21	5.7	0	0
Steak and kidney pie, cooked	0	304	1,266	13.3	21.1	14.6	51	37	5.1	126	0.11	0.47	6.0	0	0.55
Fish															
Cod; haddock; white fish	40	76	321	17.4	0.7	0	82	16	0.3	0	0.08	0.07	4.8	0	0
Cod, fried in batter	0	199	834	19.6	10.3	7.5	61	80	0.5	0	0.04	0.10	6.7	0	0
Fish fingers	0	178	749	12.6	7.5	16.1	64	43	0.7	0	0.09	0.06	3.1	0	0
Herring	37	234	970	16.8	18.5	0	64	33	0.8	45	0	0.18	7.1	0	22.20
Salmon, canned	2	155	648	20.3	8.2	0	70	93	1.4	90	0.04	0.18	10.7	0	12.50
Sardines, canned in oil	0	217	906	23.7	13.6	0	58	550	2.9	30	0.04	0.36	12.4	0	7.50
Eggs															
Eggs, fresh	12	147	612	12.3	10.9	0	75	54	2.1	140	0.09	0.47	3.7	0	1.50
Fats															
Butter	0	731	3,006	0.5	81.0	0	16	15	0.2	995	0	0	0.1	0	1.25
Lard; cooking fat; dripping	0	894	3,674	0	99.3	0	1	0	0	0	0	0	0	0	0
Low-fat spread	0	365	1,500	0	40.5	0	57	0	0	900	0	0	0	0	8.00
Margarine	0	734	3,019	0.2	81.5	0	15	4	0.3	900[4]	0	0	0.1	0	8.00[4]
Oils, cooking and salad	0	899	3,696	0	99.9	0	0	0	0	0	0	0	0	0	0
Preserves, etc.															
Chocolate, milk	0	578	2,411	8.7	37.6	54.5	0	246	1.7	6.6	0.03	0.35	2.5	0	0
Honey	0	288	1,229	0.4	0	76.4	23	5	0.4	0	0	0.05	0.2	0	0
Jam	0	262	1,116	0.5	0	69.2	30	18	1.2	2.0	0	0	0	10	0
Sugar, white	0	394	1,680	0	0	105.0	0	1	0	0	0	0	0	0	0
Vegetables															
Beans, canned in tomato sauce	0	63	266	5.1	0.4	10.3	74	45	1.4	50	0.07	0.05	1.4	3	0
Beans, broad	75	69	293	7.2	0.5	9.5	77	30	1.1	22	0.28	0.05	5.0	30	0
Beans, runner	14	23	100	2.2	0	3.9	89	27	0.8	50	0.05	0.10	1.4	20	0
Beetroot, boiled	20	44	189	1.8	0	9.9	83	30	0.7	0	0.02	0.04	0.4	5	0
Brussels sprouts, boiled	0	17	75	2.8	0	1.7	92	25	0.5	67	0.06	0.10	1.0	41	0
Cabbage, green, raw	30	22	92	2.8	0	2.8	88	57	0.6	50	0.06	0.05	0.7	53	0
Cabbage, green, boiled	0	15	66	1.7	0	2.3	93	38	0.4	50	0.03	0.03	0.5	23	0

	Inedible waste %	Energy kcal	kJ	Protein g	Fat g	Carbohydrate (as monosaccharide) g	Water g	Calcium mg	Iron mg	Vitamin A (retinol equivalent) µg	Thiamin mg	Riboflavin mg	Nicotinic acid equivalent mg	Vitamin C mg	Vitamin D µg
Vegetables (continued)															
Carrots, old	4	23	98	0.7	0	5.4	90	48	0.6	2,000	0.06	0.05	0.7	6	0
Cauliflower	30	13	56	1.9	0	1.5	93	21	0.5	5	0.10	0.10	1.0	64	0
Celery	27	8	36	0.9	0	1.3	94	52	0.6	0	0.03	0.03	0.5	7	0
Crisps, potato	0	533	2,222	6.2	35.9	49.3	3	37	2.1	0	0.19	0.07	6.3	17	0
Cucumber	23	9	39	0.6	0	1.8	96	23	0.3	0	0.04	0.4	0.3	8	0
Lentils, dry	0	295	1,256	23.8	0	53.2	12	39	7.6	6	0.50	0.25	6.3	0	0
Lettuce	20	8	36	1.0	0	1.2	96	23	0.9	167	0.07	0.08	0.4	15	0
Mushrooms	25	7	31	1.8	0	0	92	3	10	0	0.10	0.40	4.5	3	0
Onions	3	23	98	0.9	0	5.2	93	31	0.3	0	0.03	0.05	0.4	10	0
Parsnips	26	49	210	1.7	0	11.3	83	55	0.6	0	0.10	0.09	1.3	15	0
Peas, fresh or frozen, boiled	0	49	208	5.0	0	7.7	80	13	1.2	50	0.25	0.11	2.3	15	0
Peas, canned, processed	0	76	325	6.2	0	13.7	72	27	1.5	67	0.10	0.04	1.4	0	0
Peppers, green	16	14	59	0.9	0.2	2.2	94	9	0.4	42	0.08	0.03	0.9	91	0
Potatoes, raw	27	76	324	2.1	0	18.0	78	8	0.7	0	0.11	0.04	1.8	8–30[5]	0
Potatoes, boiled	0	80	339	1.4	0	19.7	81	4	0.5	0	0.08	0.03	1.2	4–15[5]	0
Potato chips, fried	0	236	1,028	3.8	9.0	37.3	48	14	1.4	0	0.10	0.04	2.2	6–20[5]	0
Potatoes, roast	0	111	474	2.8	1.0	27.3	64	10	1.0	0	0.10	0.04	2.0	6–23[5]	0
Sweet corn, canned	0	79	336	2.9	0.8	16.1	73	3	0.1	35	0.05	0.08	0.3	4	0
Tomatoes, fresh	0	12	52	0.8	0	2.4	93	13	0.4	117	0.06	0.04	0.7	*	0
Turnips	16	18	74	0.8	0	3.8	93	59	0.4	0	0.04	0.05	0.8	25	0
Fruit															
Apples	20	46	197	0.3	0	12.0	84	4	0.3	5	0.04	0.02	0.1	5	0
Apricots, dried	0	182	776	4.8	0	43.4	15	92	4.1	600	0	0.20	3.4	0	0
Bananas	40	76	326	1.1	0	19.2	71	7	0.4	33	0.04	0.07	0.8	10	0
Blackcurrants	2	28	121	0.9	0	6.6	77	60	1.3	33	0.03	0.06	0.3	200	0
Gooseberries	1	27	116	0.9	0	6.3	87	22	0.4	30	0.04	0.03	0.4	40	0
Grapefruit	50	22	95	0.6	0	5.3	91	17	0.3	0	0.05	0.02	0.3	40	0
Lemons	60	7	31	0.3	0	1.6	91	8	0.1	0	0.02	0	0.1	50	0
Melon	40	23	97	0.8	0	5.2	94	16	0.4	160	0.05	0.03	0.5	25	0
Oranges	30	35	150	0.8	0	8.5	86	41	0.3	8	0.10	0.03	0.3	50	0
Orange juice canned unconcentrated	0	47	201	0.8	0	11.7	87	10	0.4	8	0.07	0.02	0.2	40	0
Peaches, fresh	13	36	156	0.6	0	9.1	86	5	0.4	83	0.02	0.05	1.1	8	0
Peaches, canned (incl. syrup)	0	88	373	0.4	0	22.9	74	4	1.9	41	0.01	0.02	0.6	4	0
Pears, fresh	25	41	175	0.3	0	10.6	83	8	0.2	2	0.03	0.3	3	0	
Pineapple canned (incl. syrup)	0	76	325	0.3	0	20.0	77	13	1.7	7	0.05	0.02	0.3	8	0
Plums	8	32	137	0.6	0	7.9	85	12	0.3	37	0.05	0.03	0.6	3	0
Prunes, dried	17	161	686	2.4	0	40.3	23	38	2.9	160	0.10	0.20	1.7	0	0
Raspberries	0	25	105	0.9	0	5.6	83	41	1.2	13	0.02	0.03	0.5	25	0
Rhubarb	33	6	26	0.6	0	1.0	94	103	0.4	10	0.01	0.07	0.3	10	0
Strawberries	3	26	109	0.6	0	6.2	89	22	0.7	5	0.02	0.03	0.5	60	0
Sultanas	0	249	1,064	1.7	0	64.7	18	52	1.8	0	0.10	0.30	0.6	0	0
Nuts															
Almonds	63	580	2,397	20.5	53.5	4.3	5	247	4.2	0	0.32	0.25	4.9	0	0
Coconut, desiccated	0	608	2,509	6.6	62.0	6.4	3	22	3.6	0	0.06	0.04	1.8	0	0
Peanuts, roasted	0	586	2,428	28.1	49.0	8.6	5	61	2.0	0	0.23	0.10	20.8	0	0
Cereals															
Barley, pearl, dry	0	360	1,531	7.7	1.7	83.6	11	10	0.7	0	0.12	0.08	2.2	0	0
Biscuits, chocolate	0	497	2,087	7.1	24.9	65.3	3	131	1.5	0	0.11	0.04	1.9	0	0
Biscuits, cream crackers	0	471	1,985	8.1	16.2	78.0	4	145	2.2	0	0.22	0.05	2.3	0	0
Biscuits, plain	0	431	1,819	7.4	13.2	75.3	3	126	1.8	0	0.17	0.06	2.0	0	0
Biscuits, rich, sweet	0	496	2,084	5.6	22.3	72.7	3	92	1.3	0	0.12	0.04	1.5	0	0
Bread, white	0	251	1,068	8.0	1.7	54.3	39	100	1.7	0	0.18	0.03	2.6	0	0
Bread, wholemeal	0	241	1,025	9.6	3.1	46.7	38	28	3.0	0	0.24	0.09	1.9	0	0
Cornflakes	0	354	1,507	7.4	0.4	85.4	2	5	0.3	0	1.13[3]	1.41[3]	10.6[3]	0	0
Crispbread, Ryvita	0	318	1,352	10.0	2.1	69.0	6	86	3.3	0	0.37	0.24	1.3	0	0
Flour, white	0	348	1,483	10.0	0.9	80.0	13	138	2.1	0	0.30	0.03	2.7	0	0
Oatmeal	0	400	1,692	12.1	8.7	72.8	9	55	4.1	0	0.50	0.10	2.8	0	0
Rice	0	359	1,531	6.2	1.0	86.8	12	4	0.4	0	0.08	0.03	1.5	0	0
Spaghetti	0	364	1,549	9.9	1.0	84.0	12	23	1.2	0	0.09	0.06	1.8	0	0
Beverages															
Chocolate, drinking	0	397	1,683	5.5	6.3	84.8	3	5	2.8	2	0.03	0.09	1.4	0	0
Coffee, ground	0	0	0	0	0	0	4	0	0	0	0	0.20[6]	10.0[6]	0	0
Cola drink	0	46	195	0	0	12.2	90	0	0	0	0	0	0	0	0
Squash, fruit, undiluted	0	122	521	0.1	0.1	32.2	63	16	0.2	0	0	0.01	0	1	0

APPENDIX B

► PROJECTS

Work on projects is now an essential part of the Home Economics curriculum. A project gives the student the opportunity, for a change, to find out facts instead of passively obtaining all information from teacher and textbook. It gives one experience in gathering and co-ordinating facts and in presenting finished work. Remember, the knowledge gained from your project is the most important reason for doing it.

HERE ARE SOME TIPS THAT MAY HELP YOU CREATE A BETTER PROJECT

1. *Choose the right subject.* It should interest you and be within your capabilities (i.e. not too ambitious). Choose a subject area about which you will be able to gather lots of information, samples etc., or an area of investigation that would increase general knowledge about a specific topic, e.g. the diet of adolescents or voluntary services in your area. Aim at a small, clearly defined area of research rather than a broad, vague one such as nutrition.
2. *Have a clearly defined aim.* Decide on a main theme, then break it into topics (see sample project).
3. *Allow sufficient time* to gather all the necessary information and to complete the project neatly. Remember there may be a visit to organise, business firms and factories to be contacted, interviews to be arranged and perhaps questionnaires to be worked out, completed and analysed.
4. *Display it attractively.* Decide whether you will mount your project as an exhibition — e.g. wall chart — or as a simple written record in a project file.
5. *Be original.* As well as the usual wall charts, graphs, scrapbooks etc., tape and video recordings can be used. On wall displays, use a colourful backing paper onto which written reports, illustrations, samples, charts etc., are securely attached. All writing should be neat and clear, using the same colour ink throughout. Use printing and/or Letraset for a neat display.
6. *Intersperse writing with illustrations.* Use these to draw attention to points in the text. Use pie charts and diagrams to bring apparently boring statistics to life. If you have a talent for drawing or photography, use this to advantage in your project. Cartoon-type drawings can make technical facts more fun. On the other hand, avoid too many pointless illustrations.
7. Staple or glue specimens, samples, etc., securely to thick card, and label them clearly.

GATHERING FACTS

- Use the telephone directory to find addresses. Government services are grouped together at the beginning of the directory. The Golden Pages supply countless useful sources of information, grouped according to type of service.
- The school and public libraries are excellent sources of information. Ask the librarian for assistance.
- Local knowledge can be obtained from local authorities, health centres, social service centres etc.
- Encyclopaedias, specialised books and magazines, newspapers and publicity material from manufacturers are all useful.
- Visit local manufacturers and other firms and supermarkets.
- Voluntary organisations are helpful. You might wish to work for one for a period as part of your project.
- Professional organisations, e.g. the Insurance Information Service, are pleased to provide information.
- Interview members of the public, using questionnaires.
- Interview experts and public representatives: TDs, local councillors, social workers, solicitors, dietitians etc. (a tape-recorded interview is helpful — but get permission).
- Use a camera to record the stages of your project or to illustrate aspects of your research. Take photographs of those you interview.
- Letters: When writing letters — for appointments, publicity material etc. — make sure they are neat and legible, with correct spelling and punctuation (have a teacher check them). Give the name and address of your school, and list clearly the specific information or items you need. Make sure to send a 'thank you' letter to any firm or individual who has been helpful.
- Avoid copying large sections of information from books — and *never* from your textbook! Just take what you need and leave the rest. An essay-type project copied from one source is not acceptable. It is more interesting and satisfying to gather your information from a variety of sources.

PROJECT FOLDER

Decide on an eye-catching front-page title. Inside have:
1. contents — a list of chapters
2. a list of major illustrations or samples
3. acknowledgments (thanking those who helped you)
4. bibliography — a list of books you have used
5. the project itself

► SAMPLE PROJECT

SETTING UP HOME

1. Aim: *To show the procedures involved in buying and furnishing a home.* As this is quite a wide subject area, read a good deal about it first. Then decide how best to display it: scrapbook, folder or a wall display (preferable if it is going on exhibition, e.g. for the school).
2. Divide the project into three sections: (a) Buying, (b) Decorating, (c) Furnishing.

(A) BUYING

Economics: Describe an imaginary family, their income etc., and work out how they would cope financially. Visit an estate agent (who might be able to give a talk to the class). Study the advantages and disadvantages of using an estate agent, surveyor and solicitor.

Visit a building society; get sample forms. Find out the maximum loan available to your imaginary family. List some house purchase terms and give definitions: mortgage, freehold, ground rent and so on.

List grants available and how to go about getting them. List all extra fees and expenses.

You might like to look over suitable properties in your area and choose one for your imaginary family. Make a scale plan of the house of your choice (measurements are often given with estate agents' details). Make a clear visual aid or chart of the step-by-step procedure involved in buying a house.

(B) DECORATING

Work out a budget; how much can your 'family' afford to spend in this area?

Make a decorating file. Get samples of wallpaper, paint charts, furnishing fabrics etc., with prices. Draw scale plans of at least one or two rooms on graph paper and give a detailed plan of work and decorating chart, showing materials to be used in each room.

(C) FURNISHING

Work out a furnishing budget for your family. List absolute essentials. Visit furniture shops, showrooms, show houses. Study interior design magazines, *Which*, etc. Decide on the basic furniture you would buy for your house — showing pictures, if possible, and listing prices. Show the layout of furniture in the rooms of your choice. Show the total cost.

Some sources of information for projects
(addresses in telephone directory):
Bord Iascaigh Mhara
National Social Service Board
Health Promotion Unit (Department of Health)

► RECORD OF PRACTICAL WORK

It is now compulsory for all students who sit Home Economics at Leaving Certificate level to keep a permanent record of their practical work. The following guidelines may offer some assistance.

- Use a hard-covered copybook (not a notebook), or a ring-binder.
- *Each entry* of practical work must be dated and signed by the *pupil*.
- A description of the practical class should be given, e.g. a recipe, with method or time plan of order of work done.
- Demonstrations should also be recorded, dated, signed and evaluated
- In the case of recipes, each dish should: (a) be costed; (b) have the nutritive value assessed; and (c) have an evaluation given.

► EVALUATION

Ask yourself the following questions, and state answers briefly (not all will apply to every lesson).
- Reasons for choice of dish (if choice was given)?
- Economic value of dish: expensive, medium-range, economical? Why?
- Use of new or labour-saving equipment, e.g. processor, garlic crusher? Was it helpful?
- Use of seasonal foods, e.g. vegetables?
- New skills learned: draining lasagne on cloth to prevent sticking?
- Length of time required: quick, time-consuming?
- Were you satisfied with your method of work?
- Were you satisfied with the result? Check — Appearance, colour: neat, good colour, too pale, over or undercooked? Flavour: bland, bitter, mild, sour, salty, spicy, greasy? Texture, consistency: creamy, firm, lumpy, moist, tender, tough?
- What mistakes did you make? How would you correct them?
- Garnish: Was yours attractive, adequate, careless, not good?
- Suggested accompaniments: wholemeal roll, green salad?
- Variations possible: other vegetables, whole-wheat pasta?
- Comments on dishes cooked by other students: Were they better or worse than yours?

COSTING

Ingredient	Amount	Price	Nutritive value (Use food tables, which are based on 100g)
Lasagne	(½ packet)		High in carbohydrate (84 g), protein (10 g).
Onions	(2)		All high in water, traces of protein — mushrooms are the best
Mushrooms	(225 g)		best source (1.8 g). Tomatoes have Vitamin A. All vegetables
Courgettes	(2)		contain vitamin C (reduced in cooking by 50%). None of
Tomatoes	(450 g)		these are a particularly good source of iron.
Milk	(300 ml)		Protein 10 g. Fat 11 g. Carbohydrate 14 g. Calcium 360 mg. Vitamin B.
Cheese	(100 g)		Protein 25.4 g. Fat 34.5 g. Calcium 810 mg. Vitamin A: good source.
Other ingredients: oil, margarine, flour, herbs, etc.			Complete dish: Adequate source of protein. Good source of carbohydrate and fat, therefore energy. Rich in calcium. Contains vitamins A, B, C and traces of D. Lacks iron, therefore should be served with a raw green salad. Wholewheat lasagne should be used to supply fibre.
	Total:		

SAMPLE RECORD

Title of lesson: Vegetarian Cookery		Dish chosen: Vegetarian Lasagne Date
Ingredients:	Sauce:	Cooking method:
8-10 sheets whole wheat lasagne 2 medium onions 2 tablespoon oil 1 crushed garlic clove 225 g mushrooms 2 medium courgettes 400 g tomatoes 2 level teaspoon oregano 1 dessertspoon tomato purée Salt and pepper 300 ml vegetable stock or water	25 g margarine 25 g flour 300 ml creamy milk 100 g Cheddar cheese (grated)	1. Peel and roughly chop onion. Heat 1 tablespoon oil in a separate saucepan, add onion and garlic, and sauté for 3–4 minutes. 2. Meanwhile wipe, trim and slice mushrooms and courgettes. Skin and chop tomatoes. 3. Add mushrooms and courgettes to the pan and cook until beginning to colour. Add tomatoes, oregano, purée and seasoning and stir in. Cover and cook gently for 10–15 minutes. 4. Sauce: Melt fat in a small saucepan, add flour and cook for 1 minute, stirring all the time. Gradually add milk and stir as it comes to the boil. Simmer for 3–4 minutes over a low heat, stirring occasionally. Stir in most of the cheese. 5. Grease a lasagne dish. Place a layer of the vegetable mixture with sheets of lasagne on the base. Cover with a thin layer of sauce. Repeat, then sprinkle with remaining cheese. 6. Bake in moderate oven, 180°C/350°F/Gas 4, for 30–40 minutes until heated through and bubbling.

APPENDIX C

FURNITURE FIRE SAFETY

It is unlawful to sell furniture unless the filling material complies with IS419.

It is unlawful to sell furniture (with certain exceptions) unless

- it has a permanent label
- it passes the cigarette test
- it has a display label
- the cover complies with the regulations.

(a) Filling and cover are fire resistant

(b) Cover fabric is non match resistant and must be used with a fire-resistant interliner

QUESTIONS

(a) FOOD

CHAPTER 1

1. Describe the structure of *proteins* and explain how protein may be denatured during food preparation.
   State why amino acids are important in the diet and name <u>four</u> amino acids essential to the human body.
   Describe a test you have carried out to establish the presence of protein in a foodstuff.   1986 (O)

2. Classify *lipids* and give an account of their chemical structure.
   What causes rancidity in fat and how may it be controlled?
   Discuss the importance of fat in the diet and comment on whether or not the optimum amount of fat in the diet can be exceeded.
   Describe a simple experiment to denote the presence of fat in a food.   1983 (H)

3. Name the <u>three</u> main classes of *carbohydrates* and give <u>two</u> examples of each class.
   Give an account of (i) the composition, (ii) the properties, (iii) the biological functions of carbohydrates.
   Describe an experiment you have carried out to establish the presence of carbohydrate in food.   1988 (H)

4. Name the *fat-soluble vitamins*. Give (i) the properties, (ii) the function, (iii) the effects of deficiency, (iv) the sources in the diet of any <u>two</u> of the vitamins you have named.
   State the possible ill-effects on the body of taking large amounts of fat-soluble vitamins over a long period.   1989 (O)

5. Name <u>two</u> *water-soluble vitamins* of importance in human nutrition. State (i) the properties, (ii) the functions, (iii) the sources in the diet of vitamins you have named.
   Explain how careful preparation, cooking and serving of food can ensure maximum retention of these vitamins.
   Describe a test to indicate the presence of a water-soluble vitamin in food.   1987 (H)

6. State the functions of *calcium* and list the main food sources of calcium in an average diet.
   Discuss the importance of an adequate intake of both calcium and cholecalciferol for the following groups of people: (a) babies and young children, (b) pregnant and nursing mothers, (c) the elderly.
   Explain why emphasis is now being placed on reducing the amount of *sodium* in the diet and say how this is best achieved.   1986 (H)

7. Discuss the various causes of *iron* deficiency in adolescents and indicate its consequences for the human body.
   List <u>six</u> sources of dietary iron and incorporate these foods into a set of menus for one day for a teenager.
   What factors affect iron absorption in the body?   1985 (O)

8. Classify the kinds of *additives* commonly used in foods and give <u>two</u> examples of <u>each</u> class.
   How does the use of additives in foods benefit the consumer?
   State how the consumer is protected from the indiscriminate use of food additives.
   Give a brief account of the additives present in cooking fats and oils.   1985 (H)

CHAPTER 2

9. Outline the dietary modifications necessary for each of the following conditions: (i) heart disease, (ii) obesity, (iii) acne, (iv) anaemia.

Select a hot main course luncheon dish suitable for a person with <u>one</u> of the above conditions.
Give clear directions for preparing, cooking and serving the selected dish.
Comment on the possible ill-effects of excessive *dieting*.   1989 (H)

10. Explain what is meant by dietary *fibre* and say how it affects the functioning of the body.
Comment on the possible effects of fibre-depleted diets and suggest some practical ways of
increasing the daily fibre intake of the average person.
Give clear directions for preparing and presenting a supper dish with a high-fibre content.   1984 (H)

11. With reference to *meal planning* in the home, set out points of information on each of any <u>two</u>
of the following:
(i) age and occupation of members of the family; (ii) arrangement and presentation of meals;
(iii) adaptation of the diet to meet the needs of a diabetic.
Set out in menu form <u>three</u> meals for one day, suitable for a child suffering from diabetes.   1979 (H)

12. Set out details of a project which you have completed in connection with *vegetarian cookery*.
Treat your answer under the following headings:
(i) types of vegetarians, (ii) difficulties in meal planning, (iii) prepared protein foods available
for vegetarians, (iv) adaptation of the diet to the digestive system.
Describe fully the method of preparing and serving any <u>one</u> substantial main course dish related
to the practical aspect of the project.   1975 (H)

CHAPTERS 3 AND 4

13. Assess the nutritive and economic value of *meat* in the diet.
Indicate the factors on which the tenderness and toughness of meat depend.
Explain how enzymes assist in the process of tenderising meat.
List the changes that meat undergoes during cooking and processing.   1985(H)   +
1987 (O) combined

14. Discuss the nutritive and dietetic value of *fish*.
Explain why fish (i) spoils more easily than other fresh foods, (ii) requires less cooking time
than meat.
Using fish steaks <u>or</u> fish cutlets, describe how you would prepare, cook and serve an appetising
main course dish for a family luncheon.   1986 (O)

15. Set out details of any research or study you have done in relation to *milk*. Treat your answer
under the following headings: (i) nutritive value, (ii) uses in cookery, (iii) regulations governing
the quality of milk, (iv) processing methods used to render milk safe.
Explain the chemical change that takes place when milk goes sour.   1974 (O)

16. Assuming that you have participated in a group project on *cheese*, report your findings under
the following headings: (a) classification, (b) nutritive and dietetic value, (c) effects of cooking.
Suggest <u>four</u> different uses of cheese in the menu and name a dish to illustrate <u>each</u> use.
Give instructions for preparing and serving a hot cheese dish suitable for an evening meal.   1984 (O)

17. State the nutritional and practical reasons for including *egg* dishes in the family menu.
Name <u>four</u> properties of *eggs* and select a dish to illustrate the use of <u>each</u> property.
Using eggs as the chief ingredient, give detailed directions for preparing, cooking and serving a
hot savoury dish for the main meal of the day.
Name the proteins present in eggs.   1987 (H)

18. Discuss the nutritive, dietetic and economic value of *fruit*.
What may account for discolouration in fruit during its preparation and how may it be
prevented?
Describe how you would prepare and present a fresh fruit soufflé or flan suitable for a party
meal.
Suggest some interesting ways of introducing dried fruit into the diet.   1983 (H)

19. From the wide range of *margarines and vegetable oils* marketed today, select a fat suitable for each of any <u>two</u> of the following: (a) rough puff pastry, (b) one-stage cake mix, (c) deep fat frying. State (i) the composition and (ii) the properties of the fat you have selected in <u>each</u> case.
Give directions for preparing, cooking and serving an appetising dish using rough puff <u>or</u> cheese pastry.

1986 (H)

20. Tabulate the various processes involved in the production of *sugar* and indicate the uses of sugar in cooking.
Give the method of preparing and serving any dessert dish that includes honey <u>or</u> golden syrup in its ingredients.
Write a short note on (a) saccharine <u>or</u> (b) cyclamate.

1981 (H)

21. List the physical and chemical changes that take place during the making of *yeast bread.* Explain in detail how yeast causes a bread mixture to rise.
Using fresh or dried yeast, give detailed directions for making and baking a loaf of bread <u>or</u> a batch of dinner buns.
Comment on the nutritional importance of bread in the diet.

1987 (O)

22. Compare basic *Madeira cake mixtures* using conventional and quick mixing methods with reference to: (a) time required for making, (b) appearance and texture, (c) flavour.
What physical and chemical changes take place during the baking of bread and cakes?
Describe how you would prepare any two icings suitable for decorating small cakes.

1984 (O)

23. Explain the working principle of a pressure cooker.
In relation to the use of a pressure cooker, state (a) the weights which represent different pressures, (b) results obtained when various pressures are applied to water that boils at 100° C.
Outline the method of using a pressure cooker for preserving fruit.

24. The use of *convenience foods* by housewives is widespread at present. Mention some of the factors that have contributed to this situation.
Classify the various convenience foods now available, and give a brief account of the method by which any <u>one</u> class is processed.
Discuss the value to the consumer of the 'economic use' of convenience foods.

1978 (O)

25. Describe in detail the working principle of a *microwave oven* and indicate the factors that influence successful results.
Suggest any points that should guide you when choosing this type of oven for an average household.
Comment on the advantages and disadvantages of microwave ovens.

1980 (H)

CHAPTERS 5 AND 6

See also 1988 (H)

26. Assuming that you have made a study of different types of *fungus*, give a detailed account of moulds and briefly indicate how mould spores contaminate food.
Describe any <u>one</u> test you carried out in relation to fungus growth.
Name at least <u>two</u> different kinds of moulds and use clear diagrams to indicate their sporing structures.

1979 (H)

27. Name <u>two</u> types of *food poisoning* and give an account of <u>each</u> one under the following headings: (a) method of infection, (b) foods involved, (c) symptoms of illness.
Draw up a set of rules for *food hygiene* to ensure the preparation and presentation of clean healthy food in the home.

1988 (O)

28. Give an account of microbial *spoilage of food* and describe how it affects the characteristics of food products.
List the foods which are the most usual vehicles of bacteria and explain why some foodstuffs are comparatively immune to bacterial invasion and spoilage.
What measures can be taken to ensure a high standard of *food hygiene* in the home?

1984 (H)

Note: The previous two questions are a good indication of the difference in style of questioning between ordinary (pass) and higher (honours) level papers. The standard of English is more difficult at honours level and it is not so easy to see what information is required.

29. Specify the methods which could be used to preserve a surplus of home-grown tomatoes <u>or</u> apples in order to provide variety in family meals during winter months.
State the principles governing each of any <u>two</u> methods of *home preservation*.
Give detailed directions for preserving 5kg (11lbs) of tomatoes <u>or</u> apples by a method of your choice. Comment briefly on the nutritive value of the preserve.   1985 (O)

30. Compare (i) the structure, (ii) the growth, (iii) the mode of nutrition of a *mould* and a *bacterium*.
What factors affect microbial growth in food?
Describe in detail <u>one</u> method of preserving a quantity of home-grown peas <u>or</u> beans.   1987 (H)

CHAPTER 7

31. Explain, with the aid of labelled diagrams, the structural differences between arteries, veins and capillaries.
Describe how the body may react to prevent blood loss when a *blood vessel* is cut or damaged.
How does the blood play a part in defending the body against infection?   1985 (O)

32. Explain what is meant by (a) internal and (b) external respiration.
Using diagrams where necessary, give a detailed account of the *pulmonary respiratory system*.
Write a brief note on oxygen and carbon dioxide transport in the body.   1980 (O)
Pancreas: See 1982 (H) paper which follows questions.

33. Describe the relationship between the liver, the gall bladder and the duodenum. Use a well-labelled diagram to supplement your answer.
Explain how the flow of bile into the *digestive tract* is controlled.
State the source and function of any <u>three</u> enzymes active in the digestive tract.   1986 (O)

34. Give an illustrated account of: (a) the structure of the *liver*, (b) the hepatic circulation.
Outline the role of the liver in protein metabolism.   1987 (H)

35. Enumerate the glands that constitute the *endocrine system* and indicate with the aid of a labelled diagram their position in the body.
To what extent do the endocrine glands control normal growth and health of the body?
What ill-effects may result from the malfunctioning of these glands?   1983 (H)

36. Enumerate the functions of the *kidneys*. Give an account of the renal circulation and use a clearly-labelled diagram to illustrate your answer.
State the changes which blood undergoes in passing through the kidneys.
Name <u>one</u> hormone associated with the kidneys and state how it affects their functioning.   1986 (H)

37. Give an account of the structure of *the skin* and use a well-labelled diagram to supplement your answer. Explain in detail how the skin acts as: (a) a protective organ, (b) a sensory organ, (c) an excretory organ, (d) regulator of body temperature.
Comment briefly on the skin's contribution to the satisfactory development and maintenance of bone tissue.   1985 (H)

38. Write an account of the autonomic *nervous system* and summarise its functions.
Explain how a nerve impulse is transmitted from its origin to the effector organ.
Differentiate between sensory and motor nerves.   1984 (H)

39. Give an account of (i) the position, (ii) the structure, (iii) the function of the *female reproductive organs*. Use well-labelled diagrams to illustrate your answer.
State what you understand by: (a) testosterone, (b) sperm.   1988 (H)

40. Give an informative account of (i) the structure and (ii) the function of *the male reproductive system*. Use labelled diagrams to illustrate your answer.
Explain what you understand by: (a) progesterone, (b) amniotic fluid, (c) placenta.   1989 (H)

(b) HOME

CHAPTERS 8 AND 9

41. A knowledge of *budgeting* is essential for a young person commencing work. Bearing this in mind, draw up a suitable weekly budget for a young girl who earns eighty pounds nett per week and lives away from home.
What deductions are made by an employer from an employee's gross salary?
Explain what is meant by PAYE.

1979 (H) amended

42. Facilities for *saving* are flexible and comprehensive. Elaborate on this statement. What forms of savings are state guaranteed?
Describe two different saving schemes that are offered to the depositor by: (a) The Post Office Savings Bank, (b) commercial banks.
Include reference to: (i) interest or bonus payable, (ii) withdrawal terms.

43. Describe the benefits to the consumer of (i) planned spending, (ii) planned saving.
What rights do you have as a *consumer*, (a) when buying goods for personal use, (b) when goods purchased prove faulty?
Write a brief note on: (i) credit cards, (ii) cheque cards, (iii) direct debit.

1989 (O)

44. State the advantages and disadvantages of (i) bulk buying, (ii) using a mail order service to select and purchase goods.
Give an account of any <u>two</u> *consumer laws* that protect the rights of the consumer.

1988 (O)

45. Write an informative account of any *consumer* association with which you are familiar.
Explain the importance of (a) consumer education, (b) consumer protection for the modern housewife.
Describe how guarantees protect the consumer.

1980 + 1985 (O)

CHAPTER 10

46. *Buying a house* is the biggest financial decision most individuals or families ever make. Show your understanding of the implications of house purchase by discussing: (i) the transitional costs that have to be met, (ii) two sources of mortgage finance and the conditions that apply, (iii) a suitable type of insurance cover for the investment.
Explain what is meant by (a) certificate of reasonable value, (b) stamp duty.

1983 (H)

47. Report the findings of a study which you have carried out in relation to *modern housing* in a rural or urban area. Refer to: (i) design and plan of houses, (ii) quality of materials used, (iii) workmanship in relation to finish, (iv) cost.
Comment of the communal amenities of present-day housing estates and suggest some extra features which would attract prospective occupiers.

1975 (H)

48. Write an informative account of the importance of good household ventilation.
Compare an extractor fan with a ductless cooker hood in relation to (i) construction, (ii) efficiency. Explain the working principle of <u>each</u> appliance.
What causes condensation to occur in the home?

1988 (H)

49. Enumerate the different causes of *dampness* in the home and explain how to combat the problem.
What are the effects of humidity on the human body?
Give an informative account of air-conditioning and say how it could create a comfortable and healthy atmosphere.

50. Many factors must be considered when purchasing a site and *building a house*. Show your understanding of the factors involved by setting out information on (i) location, (ii) site, (iii) house plan.
Comment on the construction and finish of modern houses.

1989 (H) + 1982 (O)
adapted

CHAPTER 11

51. Give an account of the dangers to health of a contaminated water supply.
Briefly describe how local authorities ensure a safe supply of piped water to rural and urban households.
Explain the chemical difference between hard and soft water. Describe any <u>one</u> method which may be employed to soften hard water and explain the reaction involved.   1986 (O)

52. Why is it important to health to have an efficient household drainage system?
Describe how water-borne waste is discharged from a house and explain what happens to it when it reaches the sewage treatment area.
State the function of the U-shaped pipe directly connected to a stainless steel sink.   1987 (H)

53. Using a well-labelled diagram to illustrate your answer, describe the hot and cold water circulatory system in a house, where solid fuel is used as a heat source and where radiators have been installed.
Explain the scientific principles that underline this system.
List some precautions that should be observed when installing this type of system in the home.   1980 (H)

CHAPTER 12

54. Set out the results of a study that you have carried out on oil and gas as domestic central heating fuels. Treat your answer under each of the following headings: (i) advantages, (ii) disadvantages, (iii) cost.
Describe two methods of insulating a house in order to reduce heat loss.
Explain the working principle of (a) a time switch, (b) a room thermostat.   1989 (H)

55. With the ever-increasing range of electrical appliances used in the home today, a study of electricity is an essential aspect of home management. Write a concise explanatory account of the ring-circuit electrical installation in a house.
Sketch a three-pin fused standard plug, and explain the purpose of each pin. Describe clearly how you would wire such a plug.
State the causes of electric shock, and write a brief note on the safety devices used to protect consumers of electricity from this type of accident.   1973 (H)

CHAPTER 13

56. Give an account of a study project which you have carried out on: (a) hard and semi-hard floor finishes <u>or</u>, (b) soft floor coverings.
Include reference to: (i) types, (ii) compositions, (iii) qualities and grades, (iv) suitability for use, (v) ease of cleaning and maintenance, (vi) tests carried out and results observed.
Explain the difference between spirit-based and water-based floor polishes. State where each type may be used.   1973 (O)

57. Summarise the basic points and the general information that will help to guide you when choosing colour schemes for the home.
In relation to colour, what do you understand by any three of the following terms: (a) hue, (b) harmony, (c) intensity, (d) tone.
Select two different types of wall covering suitable for a hallway and compare them in terms of: (i) ease of application, (ii) maintenance, (iii) cost.   1984 (H)

CHAPTER 14

58. Show your appreciation of (i) colour, (ii) texture, (iii) design, in a plan for decorating and furnishing a family television lounge <u>or</u> living room.
Select (a) lighting arrangements, (b) suitable types of seating for this room. Give reasons for your choice in <u>each</u> case.   1988 (H)

59. List some interesting and useful features of modern kitchen fittings.
Design a practical lay-out for a family kitchen in a newly built house.
Suggest a suitable lighting arrangement for the kitchen.
State what you understand by (i) refraction, (ii) reflection, (iii) diffusion of light rays. 1987 (H)

60. Enumerate some useful guidelines for the decoration of a bathroom in a modern house. Refer specifically to wall and ceiling finishes, floor coverings, lighting and heating.
Suggest suitable accessories both functional and decorative, which would add to the appearance and comfort of the room. 1980 (O)

CHAPTERS 15 AND 16

61. What factors should influence the choice and purchase of a dishwasher <u>or</u> a washing machine for a family of four?
In relation to one of the above appliances, describe (i) the construction, (ii) the working principle, and (iii) the wash programme.
Write a brief note on (a) the economy button on a washing machine, (b) the water softener in a dishwasher. 1989 (O)

62. Discuss modern trends in the development of food preparation appliances for the home.
Describe two electric food preparation appliances which you would recommend for a household kitchen. In each case refer to: (a) construction, (b) use, (c) initial and running costs.
Explain the principle on which one of the appliances work. 1985 (H)

63. Indicate how the cleaning and maintenance of a home has been influenced by the use of modern equipment and modern cleaning agents.
Explain the scientific principles underlying the cleansing action of any <u>three</u> of the following:
(i) chemical disinfectants, (ii) silicone furniture polishes, (iii) liquid metal polishes, (iv) enzyme detergent powders.

64. Give an account of a study you have undertaken on 'fire safety in the home' under the following headings: (i) common fire risks, (ii) fire preventive measures, (iii) plan of action when a fire is discovered.
Name three different fire extinguishing agents and state: (a) when to use each type, (b) how they are effective in quelling fire.

(c) SOCIETY

CHAPTERS 17, 18, 19 AND 20

65. Write an informative account of social pressure groups, with special reference to (i) protective groups, (ii) promotional groups.
Name any one above-related pressure group that operates in this country, and give detailed information regarding its formation, its role and its achievements. 1978 (O)

66. Outline some of the features of social change that have influenced the contemporary family in Ireland.
Enumerate the essential functions of the family and say how the state and voluntary organisations assist the family in fulfilling these functions. 1983 (H)

67. Discuss fully each of any two of the following: (i) the influential position of the mother in the home, (ii) the changing role of the father in the family structure, (iii) children's rights and obligations to their parents.
Write a brief note on the value of the family circle as a source of love and affection for young children. 1974 (O)

68. Marriage instability is the result of the interaction of several factors. Examine some of its causes and consequences.
What desirable qualities should marriage partners have?
Give your considered opinion of marriage counselling.

69. To what extent do relationships in the family and with neighbours affect the quality of people's lives?
Explain how young people's ability to form satisfactory relationships with others can be encouraged and developed within the school situation.
Indicate the personality traits which you consider important for the development of good relationships.   1985 (H)

CHAPTER 21

70. The battered wife and the battered child seem to be among the casualties of modern society. Discuss this statement, giving your critical assessment of the help available to them at present. Comment on the long-term effects of cruelty to children.   1978 (O)

71. 'Drug addicts are basically sick people who require treatment.' Discuss this statement, and outline: (i) the evil effects of drug addiction, (ii) the steps that are being taken to prevent drug abuse in Ireland, (iii) the points that should be considered when rehabilitating narcotic addicts. Suggest ways by which the young people of today could help prevent illegal drug-taking.   1975 (H)

72. Recent surveys have focussed attention on excessive alcohol consumption among young people. Discuss the factors responsible for this social problem.
Comment on alcohol-related absenteeism from work and outline the difficulties caused by this problem.   1989 (H)
State the function of (i) Alateen, (ii) Al-Anon.   See also 1986(O)

73. 'Emotional unhappiness is the most potent cause of juvenile delinquency.' Discuss this statement with particular reference to the importance of social and emotional development during the early years of childhood.
Mention some reforms in our legislation which in your opinion would benefit young offenders.

74. Give an informative account of any of the following: (a) the ill-effects of gambling addiction, (b) the causes and consequences of juvenile delinquency, (c) sex education is not only education in facts, but also in attitudes, (d) the problems of homelessness.   (a) and (b) 1989 (O)

CHAPTER 22

75. Community councils have been formed in many areas in this country in recent years. Write an informative note on any two of the following: (i) the forming of a community council, (ii) the reasons why these councils were considered necessary, (iii) community councils in relation to local authorities.
List some worthwhile projects that could be undertaken by community councils.   1975 (H)

76. 'Retirement is a time of change and upheaval.' Elaborate on this statement with reference to: (a) the emotional, (b) the functional, (c) the financial changes that retirement brings.
How can (i) education, (ii) employers, (iii) the employees themselves contribute to preparation for retirement?   1985 (O)

77. State how attitudes towards disadvantaged citizens have changed.
In relation to any two disadvantaged categories in our society indicate: (a) the special facilities that exist or are desirable in your area to help them maintain their independence and self respect, (b) some of the statutory services provided for them.
Comment on the difficulties which people with physical disability may experience in our society.   1985 (H)

78. Young people experience a number of needs in the course of their development to adulthood. Identify and elaborate on some of these needs.
To what extent does youth work and the provision of youth services meet the developmental needs   1983 (H)
of young people?   (Read also chapter 24)

79. How can voluntary workers co-operate with their housing estate or parish community in helping to organise services for the locality?
Describe the aims and activities of one voluntary group in your area that is involved with aged.
How do the workers themselves benefit from their experience?   1984 (H)

CHAPTER 23

80. Discuss fully each of any two of the following: (a) social security provides most of the requirements of those in need, (b) health services available to the mentally ill, (c) social assistance. Who benefits? (d) the community care system.   (a) 1978 (O)

CHAPTER 24

81. What are the particular effects which (i) praise, (ii) disapproving remarks, (iii) corporal punishment are likely to have on a young child?
State why children in the pre-school age group need to be disciplined and indicate how this discipline should be administered.
To what extent does a child's environment affect its behaviour?   1985 (H)

82. Explain how organised pre-school activities can assist (i) the social, (ii) the emotional, (iii) the physical, (iv) the mental development of young children.
Enumerate the guidelines you would use to assess the suitability of a nursery school.   1988 (H)

83. Discuss any two of the following:
    (a) education is an important part of socialisation,
    (b) school educates students for modern life,   1980 (H)
    (c) factors which influence educational achievement,   1982 (O)
    (d) free education — fact or fallacy?

CHAPTER 25

84. Specify some of the causes of unemployment in our society and state the effects of unemployment on (i) the individual, (ii) the family.
List some of the changes that have taken place in the working conditions of employees in this century.   1989 (O)

85. Define the term *poverty* and outline the main causes of poverty in modern Ireland.
What groups in our society are most affected by poverty?
State what can be done (i) to make society more aware of its responsibilities towards the poor,
(ii) to relieve the hardship of the poor.   1988 (H)

86. The mass media serve an important function in society. Give your opinion on this statement with special reference to the role of the media in (i) education, (ii) entertainment.
Briefly indicate how advertising campaigns influence the lifestyle of the consumer.   1987 (O)

87. Describe the changing patterns of leisure activities in the twentieth century and indicate the factors responsible for these changes.
Enumerate the leisure needs of young people and state how these needs are catered for by
(i) schools and colleges, (ii) voluntary youth organisations.   1987 (O)

88. Discuss any two of the following: (i) the role and effectiveness of pressure groups, (ii) the advantages and disadvantages of automation, (iii) the influence of television on attitudes and behaviour, (iv) the causes and consequences of the increase in our urban population.   1983 (O)

89. Discuss two of the following: (i) work is an important means of self fulfilment, (ii) the causes and effects of emigration, (iii) the problems of urbanisation, (iv) the aspirations and the problems of travelling people (itinerants).

LEAVING CERTIFICATE EXAMINATION 1982

HOME ECONOMICS (SCIENTIFIC AND SOCIAL) — ORDINARY LEVEL

WEDNESDAY, 16 JUNE — AFTERNOON, 2.00 to 4.45

(400 marks)

<u>Five</u> questions to be answered.
<u>One</u> question must be chosen from <u>each</u> section; other questions at choice of candidate.
All questions carry equal marks.

SECTION I — SCIENTIFIC

1. Give points of information regarding calcium and iron in the diet. In each case refer to food sources; functions; effects of deficiency; recommended daily allowance.
Discuss the factors that affect (a) the absorption of calcium and (b) the absorption of iron in the body.

2. Describe the structure of fish flesh and explain the changes that take place when fish is subjected to heat.
Using white fish, explain how you would prepare, cook and serve a fish dish suitable as the main course of an evening meal.
Comment on the economic and dietetic value of fish.

3. Enumerate the different methods of preserving fresh fruits at home and explain fully the principles governing each of any two methods.
Give clear directions for making and storing a small quantity of chutney or jam using a fruit of your choice.
Describe a test that establishes the pectin content of fruit.

4. Describe the position and the structure of the small intestine in the human body. Use a good explanatory diagram to illustrate your answer.
Give a detailed account of the digestion and absorption of food in the small intestine.

SECTION II — SOCIAL

5. Discuss each of any <u>two</u> of the following:
(i) factors which influence educational achievement;
(ii) the role of the stay-at-home wife and mother;
(iii) advantages of a pre-marriage course;
(iv) leisure activities of teenagers.

6. Name <u>three</u> organisations which work for the benefit of under privileged sections of the community in this country.
Write a short account of (a) the aims and (b) the work of any <u>two</u> of the organisations you have named.
Explain what is meant by social assistance and enumerate some of the benefits which are available under this scheme.

7. Suggest some useful guidelines on the selection of a split-level cooker for a modern kitchen.
Write an informative paragraph on any <u>two</u> of the following:
(a) a 'stay-clean' oven; (b) a simmerstat; (c) a fan oven.
List the safety precautions which should be considered when using electrical appliances in the home.

8. Assuming that you have visited a new housing estate in an urban area for the purpose of observation and study, report your findings under the following headings:
(i) construction and finish of houses;
(ii) plan of houses in relation to efficient work methods for the housewife.
Outline the features and the facilities in the housing estate that appealed particularly to you.

9. Give an account of <u>two</u> different types of floor coverings suitable for modern household requirements. Refer to: (a) composition; (b) properties; (c) uses; (d) cost.
State the advantages of carpet underlays.

LEAVING CERTIFICATE EXAMINATION, 1982

HOME ECONOMICS (SCIENTIFIC AND SOCIAL) — HIGHER LEVEL

WEDNESDAY, 16 JUNE — AFTERNOON, 2.00 to 4.45

(400 marks)

<u>Five</u> questions to be answered.
<u>Two</u> questions must be chosen from <u>each</u> Section; the other question at choice of candidate.
All questions carry equal marks.

SECTION I — SCIENTIFIC

1. State what you understand by (i) globular proteins and (ii) fibrous proteins.
   Explain how protein may be denatured during food preparation. List some of the properties of protein and substantiate your answer by describing a test you carried out to establish <u>one</u> of the properties you have listed.

2. Enumerate the factors that affect the daily energy requirements of the human body.
   Give some guidelines regarding meal planning for low income families so that a balanced diet may be provided.
   Using pasta <u>or</u> patna rice as one of the chief ingredients, describe how you would prepare and serve a substantial hot savoury dish suitable for a main meal.
   What do you understand by a low calorie diet?

3. Describe clearly the position, shape and structure of the pancreas in the human body. Use suitable diagrams to supplement your answer.
   Give the functions of the pancreas in the body and state the composition of pancreatic juice.
   Explain what you understand by hydrolysis.

4. Outline the processes involved in the manufacture of any type of table margarine which you have used during your course.
   Give the method of preparing, cooking and serving a dish of your choice using a rich pastry made from fresh ingredients.
   Explain the importance of temperature control in the baking of pastry.

SECTION II — SOCIAL

5. 'Work satisfies social and psychological needs.' Elaborate on this statement.
   List some factors which determine our attitudes to work and work attainment.
   Comment on the changes that have taken place in the working conditions of employees in the twentieth century.

6. Enumerate some of the qualities which are found in a well-balanced personality.
   Explain how social problems in modern society may lead to a build-up of stress in young people. Suggest ways in which the ill-effects of stress may be lessened or overcome.

7. Explain how the use of small pieces of electrical equipment in the home can effect economies in relation to time, energy and money.
   Name <u>any</u> two such pieces which you would recommend for the average household kitchen. Describe the working principle and state the approximate cost of <u>each</u> one.
   What points should influence the choice of cooking utensils for the home, considering the present day energy-saving compaign?

8. Give an informative account of any <u>two</u> consumer laws which are implemented by the Department of Health and which relate to the preparation or sale of food.
   From your experience of shopping, give some examples of the consumer information which manufacturers now provide on food packets.
   Write a note on the Institute of Industrial Research and Standards and include reference to the services it provides.

9. Describe with the aid of a clearly labelled sketch, the drainage system used in a modern house.
   Outline the principles involved in the treatment of waste when it reaches the sewage treatment area.
   Write a concise note on water pollution.

INDEX

cheese, 60-62
  storage of, 83
  (recipes), 100-101
cheese pastry (recipe), 103
cheese soufflé (recipe), 100
cheese straws (recipe), 103
chicken Marengo (recipe), 94
child abuse, 304-5
children
  and parents, 297-9
  and poverty, 327
  cruelty to, 331
  deprived, 327-8
  diet for, 33
  fostering of, 328
  health services for, 335
  in care, 328
  rights of, 301
  safety of, 274
  violence against, 305
chipboard, 233
chlorination (domestic water), 200
chocolate éclairs (recipes), 104
cholera, 117
cholesterol, 38
choux pastry (recipe), 104
chutneys, 127
circuits, electrical, 217
circulation (blood), 133-6
  in liver, 151
  in kidneys, 154
civic-planning, 353
class (social), 279, 349
cleaning, 274
cleaning agents, 273
  for drains, 205
  for floors, 229
  for lavatories, 205
clostridia, 113
Clostridium botulinum, 115,116
Clostridium welchii, 115, 116
clothes dryers, 259-60
clotting (blood), 137-8
cocci, 113
coeliac disease, 39
colleges
  community, 343
  of education, 344
  regional technical, 344
  university, 343-4
colour, 219
colour schemes, 220
colourings (food), 27-28
community, 279, 319-33
community care, 324, 335-6
community councils, 319-20
community development officers, 320

community information centres, 184, 320
community schools, 343
comprehensive schools, 343
condensation, 197, 207
condensed milk, 58
conditioning agents (food), 31
conduction, 206, 253, 267
conductors, electrical, 216
connective tissue, 132
'conservative' cooking, 86-7
consumer information, 180-82
Consumer Information Act (1978), 183
consumer protection, 183-4
Consumers' Association of Ireland, 184
contact grills, 268
contamination (food), 31, 114-18
continental quilts, 241
convection, 206, 253, 267
convenience foods, 79-81
conveyancing, 190
cooker hoods, 262-3
cookers, 252-4
  microwave, 88-90
  slow, 268
  solid-fuel, 254
cooking fats, 65
cooking methods, 85-7
cookware, 270
coronary arteries, 134
coronory thrombosis, 138
counselling, marriage, 294-5
covers, loose, 240
cream, 60
  storage of, 83
credit, 172-3
credit cards, 173
credit unions, 176
crime and delinquency, 312-15
  juvenile, 312
  factors contributing to, 313
cruelty to children, 331
cryogenic freezing, 129
culture, 279
current accounts, 175
curry, vegetable (recipe), 96
curtains, 237-9
  fabrics for, 238-9
  measuring and fitting of, 239
cushions, 240
custom, 279
cutlery, 270-71
cyanocobalamin (vitamin B_{12}), 19

D

dairy spreads, 59
damp-proof course, 193
date-stamping, 181
deamination, 8
death, 303-4
decoration, interior, 219-29
dehydrated milk, 58
dehydration: *see drying*
delinquency, 312-14
demography, 279
denaturation, 8
deposit accounts, 175
dermis, 152
detergents, dishwasher, 261-2
dextrin, 11
diabetes, 38-9, 141, 142
dietary problems, elderly, 34
diets
  macrobiotic, 42
  planning of, 32
  special, 35-42
  vegetarian, 41-2
diffusion (oxygen), 144
digestive system, 145-9
dining room
  lighting of, 232
  planning of, 245
disaccharides, 10
discipline, 340-41
diseases
  food-borne, 117
  respiratory, 145
dishwashers, 260-62
disinfection, 118
  of drains, 205
divorce, 296
double-glazing, 195
drainage, 204
drains, 204-5
  cleaning agents for, 205
draught-proofing, 194
drugs
  addition to, 306-9
  effects of, 307-8
  laws relating to, 307
drying (food), 128-9
Dublin Institute of Technology (DIT), 344
duodenal ulcers, 39
duodenum, 148
duvets, 241
dysentery, 117

strawberry jam, 126
streptococci, 113
stuffed peppers (recipe), 96
stuffings (recipes), 102
sublimation, 208
sugar, 75-6
    in jam, 125
sulphur dioxide (food preservative),
    130
superannuation, 167 (*see also* pensions)
supermarkets, 179
supplementary value (proteins), 7
sweat glands, 152
sympathetic nervous system, 157
synapse, 156

T

tables and chairs, 236
tableware, 269-71
tax-free allowances, 167
television, 358
temperature, measurement of, 208
tenant's rights, 186
term assurance, 177
testes, 142
textile care labelling, 181, 259
textured vegetable protein (TVP), 52-3
thermal expansion, 206
thermostats, 206
thiamine (vitamin B$_1$), 20
thickeners (food), 31
thrombocytes (blood platelets), 137
thrombosis, coronary, 138
thyroid gland, 142
tiles, floor, 228
tissue (human), 132-3
tocopherols (vitamin E), 19
tomato purée (recipe), 92
toxins, 113
trace elements, 22
trachea, 143
trading stamps, 180
travelling people, 332, 356
trustee savings banks, 175
tumble dryers, 259-60
typhoid, 117

U

ulcers (duodenal and gastric), 39
ultra-heat treatment (UHT), 58
underfloor heating, 214
unemployment, 350-52
universities, 343-4
urbanisation, 281, 348, 353-4
urine, 154-5

V

vacuum cleaners, 263-4
values, 281
vegetable and nut risotto (recipe), 96
vegetable curry (recipe), 96
vegetable oils, 65-6
vegetables, 67-9
    freezing of, 68
    (recipes), 96-7
vegetarianism, 41-2
    (recipes), 96-7
veins, 136
veneers, 233
venetian blinds, 240
ventilation, 195-8
violence
    against children, 304
    emotional, 305
    marital, 305-6
vitamins, 16-22
    and minerals, 25
    fat-soluble (A, D, E, K), 17
    water-soluble (B group, C), 19
vocational education committees, 343
vocational schools, 343
volts, 215
voluntary health insurance, 336
voluntary muscle, 133
voluntary organisations, 320-21

W

Waldorf salad (recipe), 97
wall units, 249
wallpaper, 223-5
walls
    construction, 193
    coverings, 223
    finishes, 221
washing machines, 257-9
washing symbols, 181, 259
waste disposal units, 250
waste, domestic, 204
water, 25-7
    body's requirement, 27
    pollution, 199
    supply, 199
    treatment, 200
water-soluble vitamins (B group, C), 19
watts, 215
wells, 199
wheat, 71-2, 74-5
white yeast bread (recipe), 106
wholemeal bread (recipe), 107
wholemeal flour, 74
wholemeal pastry (recipe), 102
wiring, 217-18
women
    organisations for, 333
    role in family of, 284-7
wood, in furniture, 233
work, 349-50
work plan (housework), 272
work surfaces, 250
working conditions, 348

X

xerophthalmia, 17

Y

yeast, 77-8
    bread (recipe), 106
    in baking, 78
yoghurt, 60
youth clubs, 330
youth culture, 329
youth encounter projects, 314
youth information centres, 330